Cell Behaviour: Shape, Adhesion and Motility

The cover illustration kindly provided by Drs Graham Dunn and Alistair Brown is a Jamin-Lebedeff interference microscope image of a chick heart fibroblast after digitization and pseudocolour enhancement. The colour sequence blue, green, yellow, red represents regions of increasing dry mass of the cell.

Cell Behaviour: Shape, Adhesion and Motility

The Second Abercrombie Conference

Proceedings of the
British Society for Cell Biology – The Company of Biologists Limited Symposium
Oxford, April 1987

Organized and edited by

Joan E. Heaysman
(University College, London)

C. Adam Middleton
(University of Leeds)

and

Fiona M. Watt
(Imperial Cancer Research Fund, London)

SUPPLEMENT 8 1987
JOURNAL OF CELL SCIENCE
Published by THE COMPANY OF BIOLOGISTS LIMITED, Cambridge

Typeset, Printed and Published by
THE COMPANY OF BIOLOGISTS LIMITED
Department of Zoology, University of Cambridge, Downing Street,
Cambridge CB2 3EJ

ISBN: 0 948601 12 4

JOURNAL OF CELL SCIENCE SUPPLEMENTS

This volume is the latest in a continuing series on important topics in cell and molecular biology. All supplements are available free to subscribers to *Journal of Cell Science* or may be purchased separately from The Biochemical Society Book Depot, PO Box 32, Commerce Way, Colchester CO2 8HP, UK.

1 (1984) Higher Order Structure in the Nucleus (US$23.00)
2 (1985) The Cell Surface in Plant Growth and Development (US$30.00)
3 (1985) Growth Factors: Structure and Function (US$30.00)
4 (1986) Prospects in Cell Biology (US$30.00)
5 (1986) The Cytoskeleton: Cell Function and Organization (US$30.00)
6 (1987) Molecular Biology of DNA Repair (US$70.00)
7 (1987) Virus Replication and Genome Interactions (US$70.00)
8 (1987) Cell Behaviour: Shape, Adhesion and Motility (US$60.00)

PREFACE

I am honoured to have been asked to write a Preface to this fine volume dedicated to the memory of Michael Abercrombie. During his fruitful research life Michael Abercrombie made a number of important contributions, but none more important than his studies of the contact relations of moving cells. Indeed, by subjecting cell movement to objective quantitative analysis, particularly in his papers with Joan E. M. Heaysman, he not only led us to the concept of contact inhibition but showed a way for all to follow. I shall not dwell on other aspects of the rich scientific and personal life of Michael Abercrombie, for there exist four excellent obituaries that say what we would wish to say about this remarkable man and say it very well.* I wish simply to add a personal note. I was among the many younger colleagues who profited from his warm encouragement, knowing full well that it came from someone with a keen critical understanding of what is known and not known of the subject at hand and where the field should be going. I am deeply grateful for this.

Now, to help perpetuate the Abercrombie spirit, I would like to indicate what I think are some of the significant recent advances in the general areas of cell motility and morphogenesis and then point to certain problems that in my opinion deserve special attention. Naturally, what I have to say will be strongly influenced by my own background. I will not attempt to summarize this excellent conference. That would be presumptuous; the summaries of the authors speak for themselves.

Thanks to the work of a number of laboratories, we can now give answers to several important familiar questions. Cells move in fundamentally the same way *in vivo* as *in vitro* and respond to changes in the form and composition of their substrata in similar ways. Moreover, invasive cancer cells and normal tissue cells move basically the same way *in vitro* (the only environment where we have detailed knowledge of the movement of living transformed cells). The main difference between the invasiveness of normal cells and cancer cells lies in their controls. This is not to say that different tissue cells and cancer cells do not differ in their detailed motile behaviour; it is just that these differences are less important than their similarities. We do not yet understand how these various cells undergo movement, but in recent years we have progressed considerably closer to such an understanding. Filopodia and lamellipodia are the commonest organs of locomotion. But, since they are interconvertible, the difference between them seems trivial for cell locomotion. Blebs also may lead cells along. In cells that move by means of lamellipodia, recent observation of the movement of lamellar fragments teaches that the main motor of cell movement is confined to this leading cytoplasm and does not reside in the

* Dunn, Graham (1979). *Nature, Lond.* **281**, 163.
Medawar, Peter (1980). *Biographical Memoires of Fellows of the Royal Society* **26**, 1.
Newth, David (1982). *Cell Behaviour* (ed. R. Bellairs, A. S. G. Curtis & G. Dunn), p. 1. Cambridge University Press.
Weston, James (1982). *Embryonic Development, Part B: Cellular Aspects*, p. 1. New York: Alan Liss.

impressive cytoplasmic flow that accompanies the movement of many cells. Nor are microtubules involved. Further, in both filo-lamellipodial and blebbing movement, protrusive activity is localized at a particular site on the exposed cell surface and tends to remain there, giving the cell a distinctive polarity, and often leads to persistence of movement in that direction. Oriented microtubules reinforce this polarity, at least in certain cells.

A number of factors involved in these protrusive activities of the cell surface have now been identified: local increase in osmotic pressure, polymerization of actin (probably to give structure), linkage of polymerized actin filaments to the cell surface with some of the linking molecules characterized, opening of Ca^{2+} channels for influx of Ca^{2+}, availability of extra cell surface locally (either from surface flow, exocytosis, stretching, or all three), reduction of tension of the cell surface, and, of course, a portion of the cell surface exposed to the medium and free of contact restraints. In addition, now, at last, we have sound evidence for the existence of adhesive molecules in and at the cell surface, a few of which have been identified and characterized and one of these has been shown to traverse the membrane and interact with the cytoskeleton. All of this knowledge and more have recently served as a basis for the construction of mathematical models of how cells move; some of these are testable, as well as stimulating.

There have also been advances in our understanding of morphogenetic cell movements. Early embryonic cells need to differentiate to a motile state before they can begin to move. In some instances, where cells must break away from other cells or extracellular matrix to which they are adhering, a decrease in adhesiveness of the cell surface seems to be involved. Then, during morphogenesis, the cells move directionally. Since contact inhibition and chemotaxis have recently been shown to operate *in vivo* as well as *in vitro*, they emerge as primary candidates for directing these movements. Galvanotaxis is also a viable candidate; embryonic cells move directionally in electric fields *in vitro* and they do it at voltages comparable to those found in embryos. These advances, coupled with recent intensive study of the movements of individual cells and cell clusters during embryogenesis, in particular cells of the neural crest, give reason to hope that we will soon have substantially more understanding of directional cell movements *in vivo*. Cells within cohesive epithelial sheets also show movement. They rearrange during the convolutions of epithelial layers during morphogenesis and thus provide a partial explanation for some of the mass changes in the form of embryos. Moreover, this rearrangement constitutes proof of the dynamic nature of cell junctions such as tight junctions and desmosomes, by which epithelial cells are tightly joined. Large mass cellular movements of other densely packed cell groups such as cell streams, can depend on small active motile activities of their individual constituent cells. Gross tissue rearrangements may also be passive, due to the strong tractional forces exerted by certain associated cells, like fibroblasts. A number of embryonic cells are programmed to start directional cell movement well before these movements actually begin; and other cells not so programmed will not move in previously established migratory pathways. Also, some partially or fully differentiated cells are programmed for their eventual position within the embryo, or even the adult, as in sponges. They assume a position because of their differentiation rather than differentiate according to their position.

These genuine advances and others, of which investigators in the field can be proud, have set the stage for new investigations. There is clearly a need for more effort in quantifying the responses of cells to each other, in the Abercrombie tradition. Also, how do cancer cells move *in vivo*? Like embryonic cells? Though apparently trivial for cell movement, the interconvertibility of filopodia and lamellipodia is of morphodynamic interest. Although in some instances environment plays a role, the actin-containing cytoskeleton is unquestionably always involved; but how? Why do growth cones, which are so much like the leading cytoplasm of fibroblasts, invariably terminate in filopodia, in contrast to some other cells that form filopodia only under certain circumstances? Also, we need a systematic study of how the orientation of actin filaments (or lack of it) relates to the stiffness and flexibility of filopodia. But cells also move by means of blebs, which apparently are unstructured; how does the motile machinery of these cells differ from that of cells with structured protrusions, like filo-lamellipodia?

Although we now have realistic and therefore useful theoretical models of cell protrusive activity, big questions remain. Is the spreading of a lamellipodium of a fibroblast and other tissue cells related quantitatively to the osmotic pressure of the medium, as is the extension of an acrosomal process of certain spermatozoa or the protrusive activities of certain epithelial cells? And what about actin polymerization? Can it provide protrusive force, as often postulated, or is its function purely to provide structure? Is utilization of the big reserve of unpolymerized actin in fibroblasts related to extension of their actin meshwork and thus to their protrusive activity? As genes for different actins are discovered and cloned, perhaps they will give us a new handle in the analysis of cell movement. And what about intermediate filaments? What is their function, particularly relative to cell motility? How is influx of Ca^{2+} actually involved in formation of protrusions and could this influx be the basis of the protrusive activity at the free exposed edge of a contact-inhibited cell? If not, what else in the ambient medium to which this surface is exposed could be crucial? Further, what determines that only a localized part of the exposed surface protrudes and once established tends to polarize the cell, leading to persistence in direction of movement? Retraction-induced spreading (RIS) has been proposed as an explanation of the persistence of fibroblasts moving *in vitro*. But what about other cells, such as blebbing cells? And, besides, we still do not understand the structural or molecular basis of RIS. Since tension at the cell surface is commonplace in a moving cell population and inhibits spreading of individual cells, its role in the social behaviour of motile cells must be great. It needs quantification of its relation to protrusive activity and exploration of its mechanism of action, especially its effect on cortical microfilaments, which it clearly orients, again relative to the mechanism of the formation of protrusions. The source(s) of the local increase in cell surface that accompanies formation of a protrusion is still not settled definitively. The difficulty seems to have been the sporadic attention given to this fascinating and seminal problem – a stab here and there. It is begging for concerted attention. Finally, now that there is good evidence that certain molecules at the cell surface really attach cells to each other, how does their location on the cell surface relate to the movement of cells, where some attachment to the substratum, but not too much, is necessary? The initial studies of integrin stand as encouraging steps towards a solution of this fundamental problem.

Analyses of the molecular changes beneath, in and at the cell surface that might lie at the basis of the programming of cell populations for morphogenetic movements have begun in certain laboratories. This is encouraging, for there is no more fundamental developmental concept than the old-fashioned principle of determination. Could it involve changes in surface adhesiveness or receptor-mediated endocytosis, common responses on the part of the cell population to an external signal, or response by some cells and communication to others by coupling? Since this programming often occurs in cells engaged in rapid cleavage, this brings us to the well-known antagonism between cytokinesis and cell movement. How is the motile machinery shifted from one to the other? Moving on to subsequent morphogenesis, the role of chemotaxis and contact inhibition in directional cell movement needs more attention; and, since galvanotaxis operates so well *in vitro*, its probable role *in vivo* needs confirmation and detailed study. May I suggest that a number of overlooked, but beautifully transparent, embryos and larvae are available for such studies. The discovery that cells rearrange during the morphogenetic convolutions of a variety of tightly joined epithelia presents an interesting problem in motility. How do they do it? And what are the coordinating factors that make these rearrangements so orderly?

And now, knowing this, in addition to the long-known capacity of differentiated cells to move about within heterotypic cell aggregates, what conceptual right do we possess for our common assumption that cells within differentiated tissues and organs remain forever each in its appointed place? Perhaps their demonstrated capacity to move is normally expressed to some degree and, accordingly, the integrity of each tissue and organ, so essential to the life of the organism, is more the result of a coordinated motile steady state, than of a static immobility. Sponge cells do it.

Finally, a number of techniques and probes have been introduced recently that add substantially to the arsenal and therefore the research power of the cell and developmental biologist interested in cell movement. I mention a few examples among several: vastly improved video microscopy, including image enhancement, fluorescein dextran, fluorescent monoclonal antibodies, new specific inhibitors, and computerized image analysis for following cells. When placed in the hands of concept-oriented investigators, technical advances like these are bound to advance the field. They have already.

In conclusion, it is clear that for many of us this has been, is and will continue to be, a very exciting and productive epoch. It is a privilege to be part of it.

Woods Hole
August 1987

J. P. Trinkaus
Yale University

CELL BEHAVIOUR: SHAPE, ADHESION AND MOTILITY

CONTENTS

MODELLING AND ANALYSING NORMAL AND MALIGNANT CELL BEHAVIOUR

CELL–SUBSTRATUM ADHESION MOLECULES

CELL SHAPE AND DIFFERENTIATION

Continued overleaf

Contents

CELL BEHAVIOUR DURING DEVELOPMENT

J. Cell Sci. Suppl. 8, 1–18 (1987)
Printed in Great Britain © *The Company of Biologists Limited 1987*

ACTIN CORTEX AND MICROTUBULAR SYSTEM IN MORPHOGENESIS: COOPERATION AND COMPETITION

J. M. VASILIEV
All-Union Cancer Research Center of the Academy of Medical Sciences of USSR and Moscow State University, Moscow, USSR 115478

SUMMARY

Actin cortex and microtubules determine two different types of morphological organization of the cytoplasm. Cooperation and competition between these two organizations may produce a diversity of final forms. Actin cortex alone, without the other cytoskeletal systems, is sufficient for the organization of vectorized pseudopod-forming cytoplasmatic units termed 'actinoplasts'. Reversible segregation of cytoplasm into actinoplasts and microtubule-rich stable domains ('tubuloplasts') is suggested to play an important role in many types of morphogenesis. Segregation of this type can be induced in fibroblasts of certain lines by the tumour promotor, tetradecanoyl phorbol-acetate (TPA). Self-organization of each actinoplast leads to the development of microfilament bundles associated with focal contacts. Analysis of the evolution of these bundle-contact structures during spreading of mouse fibroblasts suggests that their patterns are determined by the degree of centripetal tension within the actin cortex; the microtubular system stabilizes these patterns. Pseudopodial activity of the edges of the actinoplasts can be controlled by environmental factors. One particular type of control, i.e. the effect of cell–cell contact, is discussed. Actin cortex and microtubules seem to have alternative effects on the distribution of vimentin-containing intermediate filaments.

INTRODUCTION

Any alteration in the shape or position of a cultured cell involves cytoskeletal reorganization. What is more, it is based on this reorganization (see previous reviews on this subject: Abercrombie, 1980; Vasiliev & Gelfand, 1981; Vasiliev, 1985; Bray *et al.* 1986). Most cells contain three types of cytoskeletal structure. However, even the cells that contain only one type of functioning cytoskeletal structure, the actin cortex, are still able to acquire a certain morphological organization. A colchicine-treated cultured fibroblast is apparently an example of such a cell: its microtubules are depolymerized, while vimentin-containing intermediate filaments are collapsed near the nucleus. Nevertheless, these cells extend, attach and contract pseudopodia at the peripheral edges; attached pseudopods exert centripetal tension on the substratum; unattached pseudopods move towards the centre as ruffles; membrane receptors crosslinked by corresponding ligands move directionally along the surface from the periphery towards the centre. Thus, the presence of the actin cortex alone, without other cytoskeletal structures, seems to be sufficient for the development of dynamic vectorial organization of the cytoplasm oriented along the lines connecting the active edges with the central zones. Small cytoplasmic fragments, mechanically detached from the cell periphery, also develop a similar type of polarity (Albrecht-Buehler, 1980; McNiven *et al.* 1984; Gelfand *et al.* 1985; Euteneuer & Schliwa, 1986), and so do surface-spread anuclear platelets. Obviously, the cell nucleus is not necessary to this type of organization. We propose the term 'actinoplasts' for all types of motile, adherent and vectorized structures that contain an actin cortex, develop pseudopods at the periphery and exert tension towards their centre.

The whole cell, e.g. substratum-spread fibroblast or epitheliocyte, can be regarded as a single actinoplast. The fragment of cytoplasm cut from this cell is also an actinoplast with active edges and a new centre. On the other hand, several cells fused together form a single actinoplast, that is, they develop a united structure with a common centre and an active peripheral edge. Of course, these cells and fragments in most cases are not 'pure' actinoplasts. In contrast to colcemid-treated cells, they contain not only actin cortex but also functional microtubules and intermediate filaments. Often, e.g. in the epitheliocyte, the microtubular system is fully incorporated into the actinoplast. In other situations only a certain part of the cell may form a discrete actinoplast separated from the stable domains. These stable domains do not have lamellar areas and do not exhibit pseudopodial activity at the edge. Although these domains also contain actin cortex, they are particularly rich in microtubules and intermediate filaments. The growth cone at the end of the extending axon is an example of such a structure, that is, of a discrete actinoplast associated with stable domains (Fig. 1). Many types of morphogenesis include two types of process: (1) segregation of a cell into active and stable domains and (2) self-organization of active domains, actinoplasts. In this paper I will discuss some characteristics of both these types of process revealed in recent experiments by our group.

SEGREGATION OF ACTINOPLASTS AND STABLE DOMAINS

Effects of tumour promotor

New aspects of inter-relationships between active and stable cell parts were revealed by our recent experiments with the tumour promotor tetradecanoyl phorbol-acetate (TPA). These experiments show that TPA can induce fibroblasts to form long stable processes containing numerous microtubules and intermediate filaments. We have observed this previously unreported effect in the TPA-treated cultures of many fibroblastic lines, both transformed and non-transformed (Dugina *et al.* 1986). By screening we have found the line in which the effect of TPA was most pronounced and caused by the lowest concentrations of TPA (from 5 to 10 ng ml^{-1}). The following observations were made with this line. This line 152 consists of spontaneously transformed cloned mouse fibroblasts. The control cells had typical fibroblastic shape with one or several small active lamellae. At 20–30 min after the addition of TPA one could observe an extension of large fan-like lamellae from the cell edges; simultaneously the cell body contracted. Later (at 30–60 min) the newly formed lamellae contracted into narrow processes with occasional thicker areas ('bulbs'). Extension of new lamellae from other regions of the edge took place

Fig. 1. Separation of active (unstained) and stable (black) domains in various cells. From left to right: epitheliocyte; polarized fibroblast; TPA-treated fibroblast of the 152 cell line; neural cell with growing axon. Drawing by A. D. Bershadsky.

simultaneously with the retraction of the old ones. These extensions and retractions usually went on for many hours in the TPA-containing medium. Often they were accompanied by the translocation of the cell body. The body was displaced from time to time towards the newly extended lamella, while the tail part of the body contracted; these contractions led to elongation of the proximal parts of the narrow processes (Fig. 2A–C).

The effect of TPA was reversible; alterations of shape spontaneously disappeared after 24–36 h of incubation. Immunofluorescence microscopy and electron microscopy of the platinum replicas of cytoskeleton have shown that TPA-induced narrow processes are rich in microtubules and intermediate filaments but relatively poor in actin microfilaments; the lamellae and the cell body contained a dense network of microfilaments (Fig. 3). As actin-poor tail processes are formed by the retraction of actin-rich lamellae we have to conclude that, during this retraction, actin in some form moves along the microtubular framework. Experiments with inhibitors confirm that both microtubules and actin microfilaments are essential for the development of TPA-induced alterations in shape. Colcemid-induced depolymerization of microtubules led to rapid contraction and disappearance of TPA-induced processes; cytochalasin B prevented this contraction.

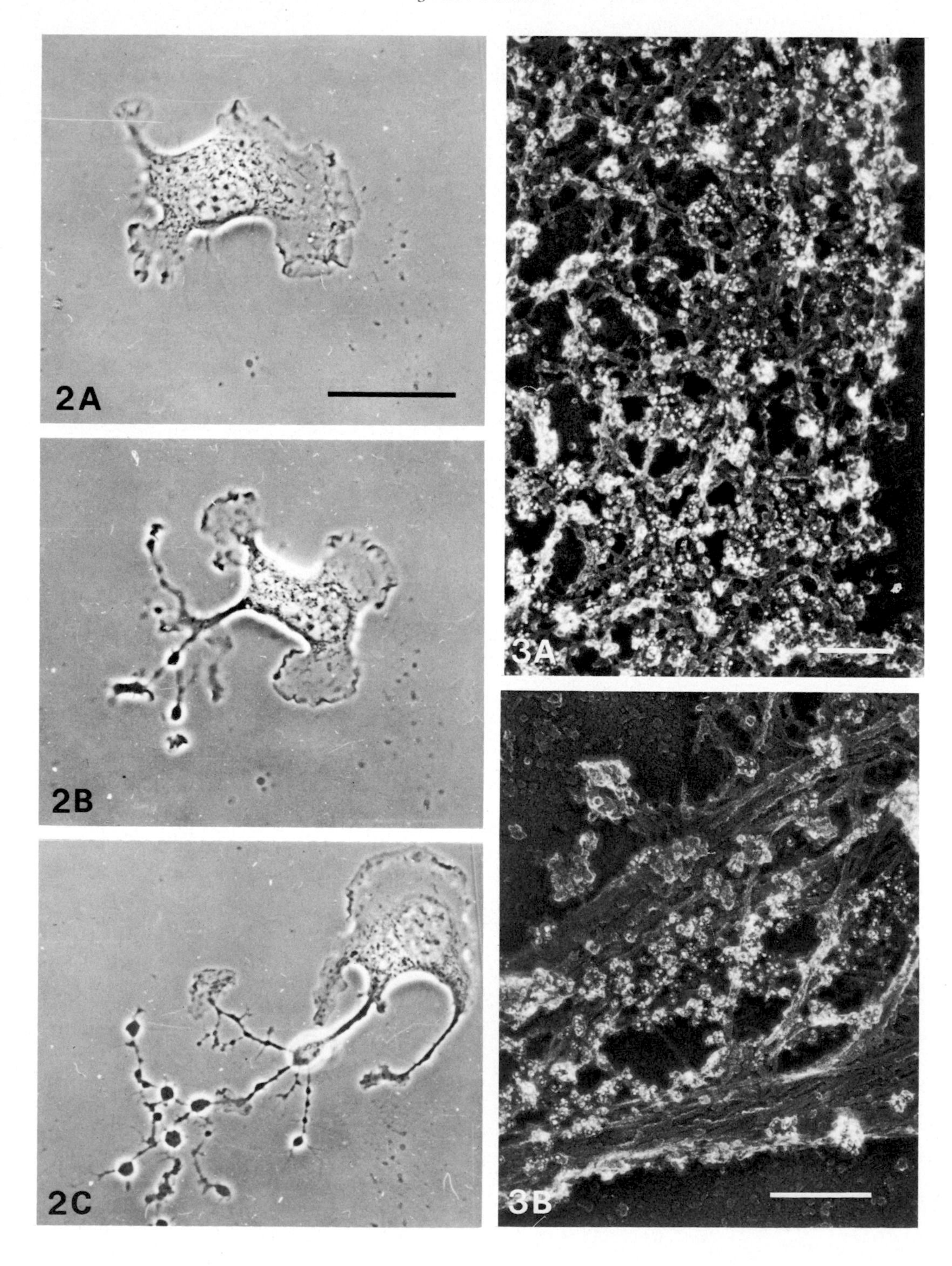
2A
2B
2C
3A
3B

Certain manifestations of the effects of TPA seen in these experiments, e.g. induction of ruffles and contraction of the cell body, are similar to those observed earlier in experiments with other cell types (Laszlo & Bissel, 1983; Schliwa *et al.* 1984). In our experiments these changes were associated with another effect; namely, with the reversible division of the cell into a motile body and long stable processes. As we have seen, there are reasons to suppose that, when the processes are formed, polymerized or depolymerized actin moves away from them along the microtubules. One may further suggest that these events are due to the modification of the normal extension–contraction cycle of the actin meshwork. It is well known that this meshwork is formed *de novo* in the extended pseudopods of various cells. The extended meshwork then contracts (review by Vasiliev, 1985; Newell, 1986; Fukui & Yumura, 1986). Microtubules and intermediate filaments linked to the meshwork of actin microfilaments may offer some resistance to its contraction. If the links between microfilaments and microtubules are firm, then a sufficient contractile force will overcome the resistance and the extended cell part will retract as a whole, carrying along other parts of the cytoskeleton. If, however, the main part of the extended actin cortex is not firmly linked to other cytoskeletal structures, it will retract, leaving microtubules and intermediate filaments behind. Stable processes are, possibly, formed in this way. Actin directionally transported from the old lamellae may form a microfilamentous network within the newly extended lamellae.

The exact mechanisms of the effects of TPA on the cytoskeleton remain obscure; TPA is a specific activator of protein kinase C. This enzyme normally participates in the transduction of membrane-generated signals. The long list of substrates of protein kinase C includes some cytoskeleton components, e.g. vinculin, vimentin, certain microtubule-associated proteins etc. Possibly, phosphorylation of one of these substrates by the enzyme modifies the interactions of the microtubules with the actin cortex. For instance, the enzyme may alter some proteins attaching the microtubules to the microfilaments. Alternatively, it may weaken the microfilamentous network (see Taylor & Fechheimer, 1982) in such a way that during contraction few microfilaments will remain attached to microtubules, while the main part of the meshwork will slide along them centripetally. The microtubular framework of the

Fig. 2. TPA-induced cell segregation into active and stable domains. The fibroblastic cell of the 152/15 line at various times after addition of TPA (5 ng ml^{-1}) to the medium: A, 10 min; B, 30 min; C, 90 min. The cell body, extending wide lamellae, gradually moves into the upper right corner of the photograph; a stable narrow branched tail process with bulbs is elongated during this movement. Phase-contrast. Bar, 20 μm. Photographs by V. Dugina.

Fig. 3. Electron microscopic platinum replicas of the cytoskeleton of 152/15 cells incubated with TPA (5 ng ml^{-1}) for 1 h. Cytoskeletons were stained for actin (A) or vimentin (B) using the indirect immunogold technique with 5 μm goat anti-rabbit colloidal gold particles (Janssen Pharmaceutica), rotary shadowed with platinum and carbon, and placed on electron microscope grids. Photographs are printed as negatives, so that gold particles appear as white dots. A. Network of labelled actin microfilaments at the leading edge of lamella. Labelling with anti-actin antibody. B. Tail process labelled with anti-vimentin antibody. The central part of the longitudinally split process contains numerous gold-labelled vimentin filaments; parallel actin microfilaments at the periphery remain unlabelled. Bar, 0·2 μm. Photographs by T. Svitkina.

stable processes is also, probably, changed in the course of their formation and elongation; these microtubules obviously grow, and their microtubule-organizing centre is likely to move forward, with the cell body.

Experiments with TPA suggest that the cell has a mechanism reversibly separating actin-rich motile domains, the actinoplasts, from the stable domains. This mechanism, possibly, acts not only in these very special conditions, that is, in the cells of certain lines treated with a special drug, TPA. Similar alterations may play important roles in normal morphogenesis of various cells. In the next paragraphs we will discuss possible reorganizations of this type in two groups of cells, fibroblasts and neurones.

Untreated fibroblasts

Normal fibroblasts moving in culture have a leading lamella with an active edge and a narrow tail. New actin-rich pseudopods are continuously formed at the active edge. As suggested by Dunn (1980), the material needed for the assembly of the actin meshwork in the pseudopods is, probably, transferred from the central parts of the cell towards the active edge; the assembled material may then move backward towards the centre. We do not yet know the exact way in which the pseudopodial material is transferred towards the edge.

As shown long ago, destruction of microtubules by colchicine and similar drugs disorganizes pseudopodial activity in such a way that all parts of the edge become active; stable lateral edges and the tail disappear. Possibly, the microtubular system is needed for the directional translocation of actin-rich pseudopodial material towards certain zones of the cell edge; in the absence of microtubules this transport is randomized. These movements require the presence not of isolated microtubules but of an integrated system of microtubules associated with an organizing centre. This conclusion is supported by experiments using taxol, which stabilizes the polymerized state of microtubules and transforms a united microtubular system into numerous groups of microtubules formed at many sites of cytoplasm and not connected with any centre. Taxol, like colchicine, inhibits cell elongation and the stabilization of the lateral cell edges (De Brabander *et al.* 1981; O. Ivanova & J. Vasiliev, unpublished results). Thus, two alternative processes, depolymerization of microtubules and their facilitated polymerization, paradoxically lead to the same morphological result, i.e. to the prevention of cell segregation into stable and active zones. Obviously, only a well-organized system of microtubules can direct the translocation of actin.

Thus, translocation of pseudopodial material from the tail to the leading lamella probably occurs in normal untreated fibroblasts. However, dissociation of active cell parts from the stable domains is much less pronounced in normal cells, than in the TPA-treated 152 cells described above. The tail of normal fibroblasts is elongated only to a certain degree; it remains contractile and is broken from time to time during movement. In other words, the TPA-induced separation of active and stable cell parts is, possibly, an exaggeration and modification of normal events that take place during the crawling movement of a fibroblast.

Neural cells

A growing neurone forms processes, which are divided into a stable microtubule-rich stem and a small terminal actinoplast, the growth cone. Pseudopods are extended and attached at the leading edge of the growth cone so that it gradually moves away from the cell body, while the rear edge of the growth cone retracts leaving behind the elongating stable part of the axon (see review by Bray, 1982). The similarity of these morphogenetic alterations to those characteristic of TPA-treated fibroblasts is obvious. In both cases the forward movement of the actinoplast is coupled with the elongation of a stable process connected with the rear edge of the actinoplast (Fig. 1). The main difference between these two systems is the nature and size of the actinoplast: small growth cone as against large lamella-forming cell body of the TPA-treated fibroblast.

Time-lapse cinematography of differentiating cells of mouse neuroblastoma 1300 in culture also revealed two other phenomena (O. Y. Ivanova, L. O. Domnina & J. M. Vasiliev, unpublished), which may be related to the translocation of the actin cortex along the microtubules. One of these phenomena is the formation of narrow cytoplasmic processes, neurites, by the contraction of active widely spread lamellae. As described many times before, the neuroblastoma cells have a non-differentiated morphology in the usual serum-containing medium: they have discoid shapes and large lamellae well-spread on the substratum (see review by Schubert *et al.* 1971). When these cultures are transferred into serum-free medium, most cells stop proliferating and undergo differentiation into neurone-like cells with long processes. At the early stage of differentiation one can often see the formation of holes in the lamellae and invaginations of the edges of these lamellae (Fig. 4). Widening of these holes and invaginations leads to the formation of curved narrow processes. This change is somewhat similar to the formation of narrow processes from the lamellae in TPA-treated cells.

Possibly, retraction of lamellae is one of the mechanisms of formation of processes at the early stages of differentiation of the neurone. Later, these processes grow by the usual growth cone mechanism.

Another very peculiar phenomenon, observed in neuroblastoma culture, is the movement of the nucleus-containing body of the neurone along the cytoplasmic process. The swollen part of the cell containing the nucleus and the main organelles started to move along the process; cytoplasm behind the moving body retracted forming the narrow tail. We have seen several cases of these translocations. They lasted for varying times and then stopped; the distances travelled by the body also varied. In one most spectacular case (Fig. 5) the body travelled all the way from one end to the other of a long process and then returned back along this process to the original position. The travel there and back lasted about 16 h.

Previous morphological investigations of sectioned material have led to the suggestion that certain neural cells in the course of normal development first extend their axons and then move the body along these axons; this was termed 'perikaryal translocation' (Domesik & Morest, 1977). Our observations show movement of a similar type in cultured cells. Possibly, this is another example of the movement of the actin-rich cell body along the microtubular framework. Unfortunately, these movements in culture remain unpredictable and we are still unable to induce them at

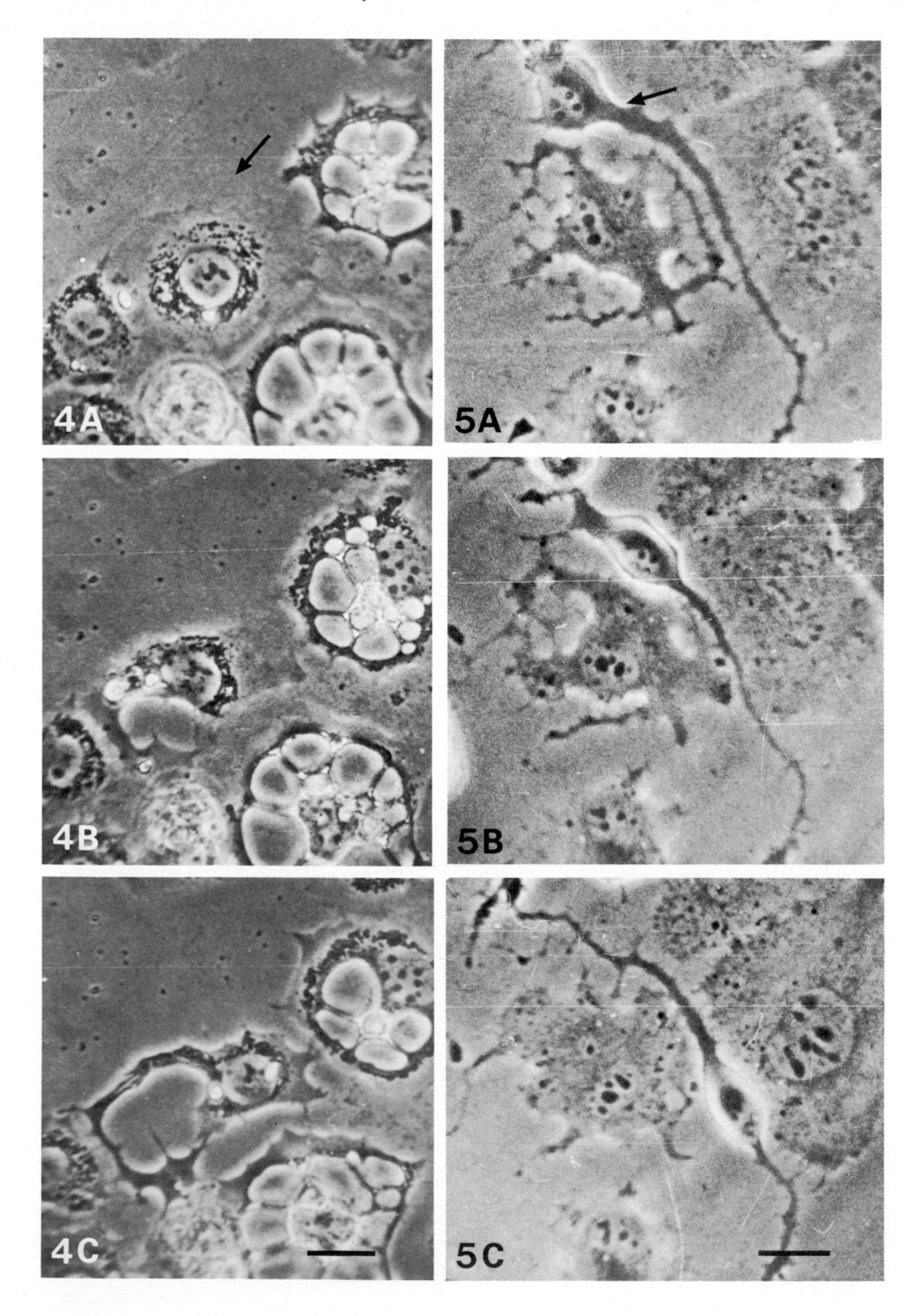

will and so study them in more detail. Thus, separation into active and stable domains, and further mutual translocations of these domains, seem to take place at various stages of the development of a neural cell: in the early stages of its differentiation from the well-spread precursor, during further growth of neurites, etc.

Possible mechanisms of segregation

We have discussed a number of rather diverse morphogenetic phenomena, which may be based on common types of mechanisms. These hypothetical mechanisms have the following main features: (1) material for the formation of a pseudopod is transferred towards the cell edge, is reorganized there into the actin network and contracts centripetally. (2) Both centrifugal and centripetal transport of pseudopodial material is directed and regulated by the microtubular system. (3) Contraction of the actin network can involve other parts of the cytoskeleton, that is, microtubules and intermediate filaments. Alternatively, the contracting network may become detached from the microtubules and intermediate filaments, which then form the core of the stable domains.

In certain cases actin movement may involve microtubule-organizing centres and various cellular organelles (see also next paragraph). Directions and degrees of centrifugal transport and retraction, as well as the degree of detachment of the actinoplasts from the stable zones, can vary in different systems and conditions, producing very diverse morphological results. As yet we know very little about the molecular basis of the various components of these mechanisms. Possibly, the mechanism of actin transport to the active edge is similar to that of slow axonal transport, which brings cytoskeletal components towards the tip of the axon. As suggested by Lasek (1986), this last type of transport is likely to be based on the sliding of cytoskeletal filaments along other filaments of the same or other types. As discussed above, microfilament–microfilament or microfilament–microtubule sliding may be involved in the detachment of actinoplasts from the stable domains. Translocation of actin and its segregation from microtubules are, probably, controlled by some membrane-generated signal. In fact, extension of pseudopods in many cell types can be induced by soluble or substrate-attached molecules acting on the corresponding membrane receptors (see review by Trinkaus, 1985; Vasiliev, 1985; Newell, 1986). The exact means of transduction of these signals to the cytoskeleton is unknown but, possibly, stimulation of protein kinase C is involved. As we have seen, the specific activator of this enzyme, TPA, can amplify and modify

Fig. 4. Collapse of wide lamella of undifferentiated mouse neuroblastoma cell (arrow) leads to formation of narrow axon-like process. A. 0 min; B, 200 min; C, 330 min. The culture was pre-incubated for 48 h in serum-free medium. Bar, 20 μm. Photographs by O. Ivanova and L. Domnina.

Fig. 5. Perikaryal translocation in differentiated cell (arrow) of mouse neuroblastoma. The culture was pre-incubated in serum-free medium for 48 h. A. 0 min; B, 200 min; C, 820 min. The nucleus-containing cell body gradually moves along the stable narrow process. Phase-contrast. Bar, 20 μm. Photographs by O. Ivanova and L. Domnina.

the extension and retraction of pseudopods in many cell types. In conclusion, I would like to stress once again that, the very existence of a common mechanism responsible for a number of the diverse morphogenetic phenomena described above is still only a working hypothesis.

SELF-ORGANIZATION OF ACTINOPLASTS

An actinoplast mechanically isolated or physiologically segregated from other cell parts is self-organized into a united structure that has its own centre. Possibly, the position of this centre is determined by the contractile tension of the cortex; when the stretched elastic film is cut into several fragments, each fragment contracts towards its own centre.

The actin cortex of each substratum-attached actinoplast may form several types of specialized substructures, e.g. networks, bundles of various types, microfilament sheaths etc. The pattern of these substructures seems to be determined by the extension–contraction cycles of the actin. The network of microfilaments is first formed in the newly extended pseudopods. A number of facts indicate that other substructures of the cortex are formed by the contracting pseudopodial network. For instance, as shown by Svitkina *et al.* (1986), treatment of mouse cells with an inhibitor of ATP formation, sodium azide, leads to almost complete destruction of all the actin structures, while other components of the cytoskeleton remain intact. When the inhibitor is washed off, restoration begins by the formation of ruffles at the edge and then the actin network is widened centripetally until the full cortex is formed. Centripetal formation of actin bundles was also observed in experiments where labelled actin was injected into cells (Wang, 1984). Thus, the pseudopodial network seems to be the formative part of the cortex, a kind of initial structure, from which other substructures develop. One particular aspect of the formative function of pseudopods is the development of the bundles of microfilaments and of associated focal contacts. These structures are highly dynamic and correlated with cell shape. For instance, the same cell, mouse fibroblast, in the course of its spreading on the flat substrate forms consecutively different patterns of bundles and contacts. We have studied these reorganizations using dynamic interference reflection microscopy as well as immunomorphological methods revealing focal contacts and various components of the actin cytoskeleton (I. S. Tint, A. D. Bershadsky & J. M. Vasiliev, unpublished). The spreading of fibroblasts has two main stages: first, spherical cells acquire a discoid shape (stage of radial spreading), later, they acquire an elongated shape (stage of polarization). It was found that during the first stage the cells form a ring of dot contacts at the ends of attached pseudopods (Fig. 6A,B). Later this ring of separate dots may be transformed into the continuous circular contact. At this stage the circular bundle is reorganized into a regular net of bundles connected by the star-like centres. This type of net was first described by Lazarides (1975). Simultaneously, the circular contact disappears and elongated contacts are formed at the advancing cell edges. Thus, at this stage there is no direct connection between each bundle and the contact. Rather, the whole system is attached to a few peripheral contacts by a few special 'suspenders', that is, with straight bundles radiating from the network (Fig. 6C,D).

Later, at 10–16 h, the circular pattern of the network is gradually lost and radial bundles become prominent (Fig. 6E,F). The system of interconnected straight bundles directly attached to focal contacts at their ends is formed; this pattern is characteristic of elongated cells.

Thus, three types of systems of bundles linked to the contacts, are formed consecutively in the course of spreading: a circular bundle, a network of bundles and a system of straight bundles (Fig. 7). It may be suggested that the bundles are developed from those parts of the pseudopodial network that became anchored to initial focal contacts formed at the periphery. As suggested previously (Wohlfarth-Bottermann & Isenberg, 1976), isometric contraction of these parts of the network may align microfilaments into parallel bundles. Alignment of microfilaments by externally applied tension was recently observed experimentally by Kolega (1986). The exact pattern of alignment may depend on the force of the tension and on the density of the contacts. At the first stage of spreading the tension towards the centre is low; at this stage the network between the nearby contacts contracts locally, so that the system of tangential bundles is formed. Later, the cell spreads further and, presumably, the centripetal tension in the cortex is increased. This tension stretches the circular bundle into a network with radial suspenders and then into a system of straight bundles. Dynamic observations of polarized cells during locomotion show that each alteration in the degree and in the orientation of tensions within the actin cortex causes realignment of the bundles and the focal contacts. For instance, when the cell begins to change the direction of its pseudopodial activity, the dot-like contacts located far away from the new leading edge are elongated in the direction of this edge. Moderate retraction of the cell caused by various factors, e.g. cooling or colchicine, induces simultaneous elongation of numerous dot-like contacts (O. Y. Ivanova, O. Y. Pletyuskins & J. M. Vasiliev, unpublished). It seems that we have here a novel and unusual type of structural reorganization, in which mechanically induced changes lead to chemical transformations. In particular, parallel alignment of microfilaments induced by isometric tension somehow leads to the regular distribution of myosin, α-actinin and other proteins characteristic of stress fibres. Alignment of microfilaments may also lead to some rearrangement of the membrane components involved in the elongation of contacts.

Colcemid-treated fibroblasts, that is, 'pure' actinoplasts, spread much less efficiently than control ones. Nevertheless, these cells acquire a flatened, discoid shape with an arc-like pattern of bundles and contacts (Lyass & Vasiliev, 1985). These patterns are much less regular than those of normal fibroblasts at the early stages of spreading. Obviously, individual actin bundles and contacts can be formed by 'pure' actinoplasts, but organization of highly regular patterns consisting of many bundles and contacts requires cooperation with microtubules.

Reciprocally, actin cortex can, probably, control the position of the microtubule-organizing centre (MTOC) and of the whole microtubular system. The MTOCs of translocating fibroblasts and epithelial cells usually move into the anterior part of the

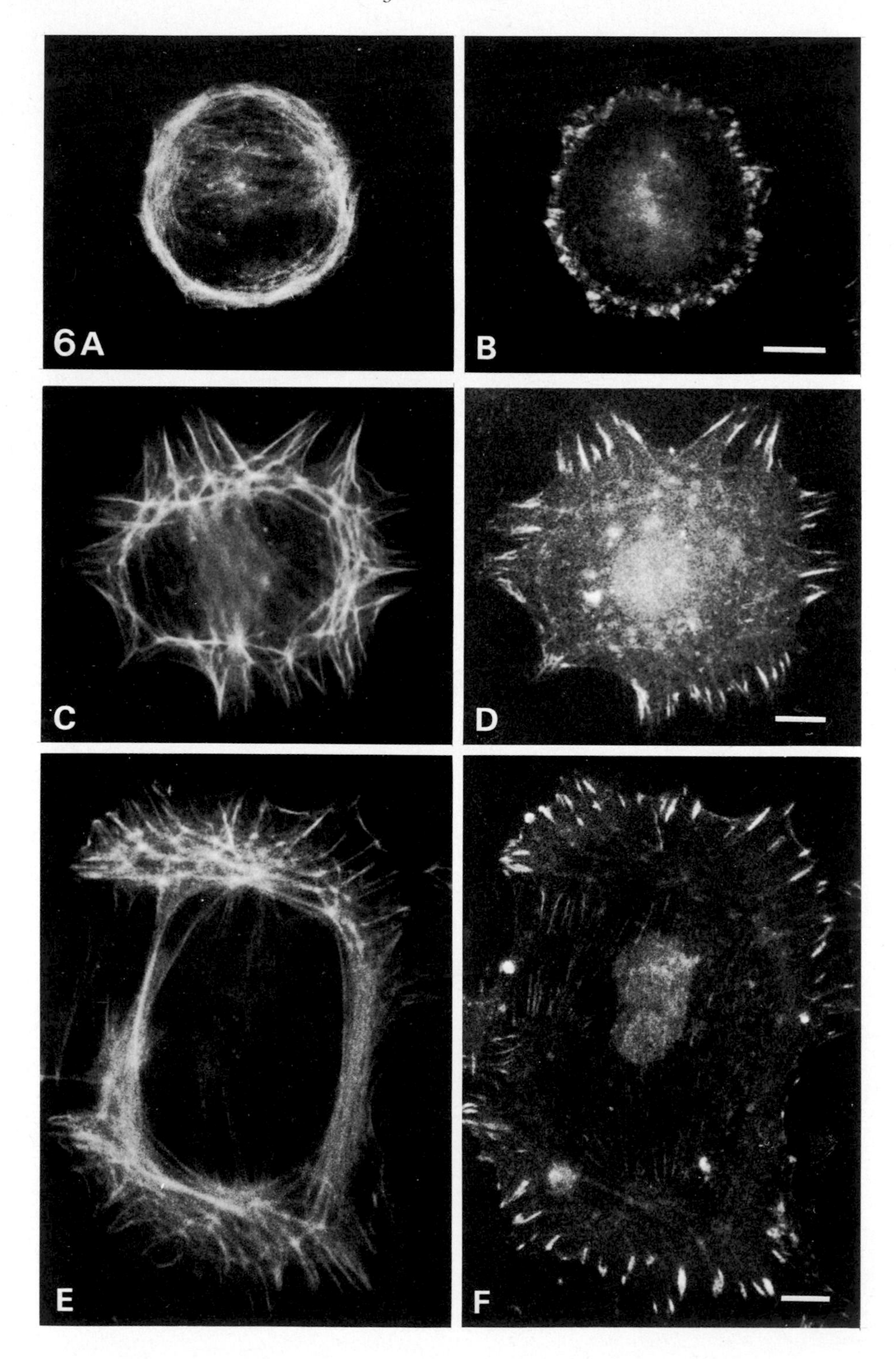
6A
B
C
D
E
F

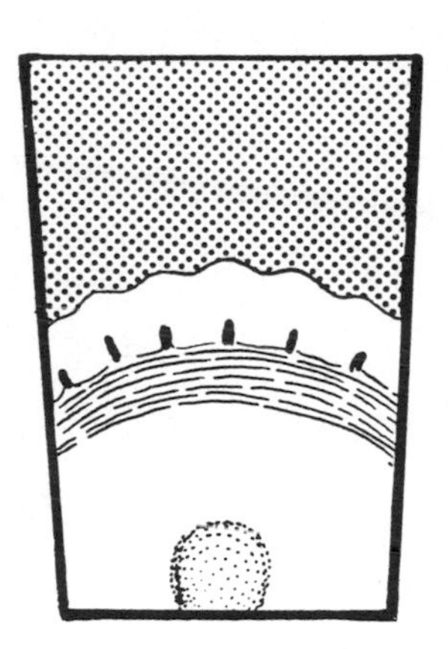

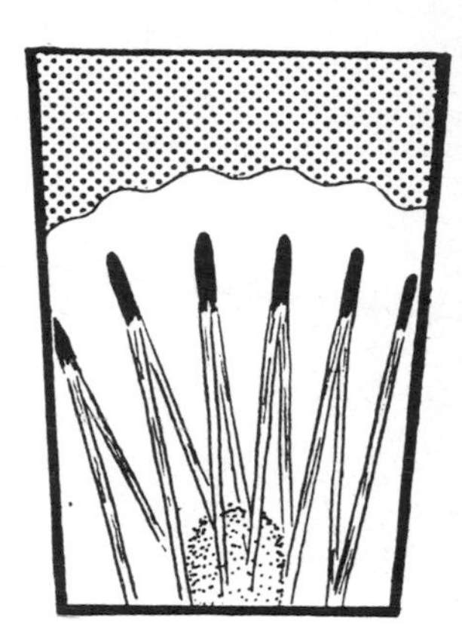

Fig. 7. Evolution of contact-bundle structures near active edges of spreading fibroblast. From left to right: pseudopodial network with dot-like contacts; circular bundle with peripheral circle of dot contacts; circular net of bundles with peripheral radial 'suspender' bundles attached to dash-like contacts; elongation of radial bundles and contacts during polarization. Drawing by A. D. Bershadsky.

cell, that is, into a position between the nucleus and the leading edge (Gotlieb *et al.* 1981; Kupfer *et al.* 1982). Polynorphonuclear leucocytes incubated with TPA increase considerably their spreading on the substratum; simultaneously their paired centrioles are separated and move away from one another; cytochalasin prevents this separation (Euteneuer & Schliwa, 1986). Probably, as suggested by Euteneuer & Schliwa, attached pseudopods exert tension on the microtubules and the associated MTOC. Owing to these interactions, the moving actin cortex in translocating cells may pull the more inert microtubular system. As discussed above, differences in the strength of these interactions may lead to various degrees of segregation of the advancing actinoplast from the rear microtubular system.

INACTIVATION OF THE EDGES OF ACTINOPLASTS BY CELL–CELL CONTACTS (CONTACT PARALYSIS)

The direction of translocation of actinoplasts on the substratum can be determined by the environmental factors controlling the extension and attachment of pseudopods, e.g. by gradients of concentrations of soluble molecules inducing pseudopod extension (chemotactic gradients), or by gradients of the substratum adhesiveness determining the probability of attachment and detachment of pseudopods (haptotactic gradient). Factors altering the attachments of pseudopods may also control their

Fig. 6. Evolution of contact-bundle structures during spreading of mouse embryo fibroblasts. Double staining with rhodamine–phalloidin to reveal actin (A,C,E), and with antibody against vinculin (B,D,F) to reveal focal contacts; anti-vinculin antibody distribution was visualized with second fluorescein-labelled antibody. A,B. 1 h; discoid cell with circular actin bundle and circle of dot-like contacts. C,D. 3 h; early stage of polarization. Circular net of bundles attached by radial 'suspenders' to focal contacts. E,F. 5 h; advanced stage of polarization. The net divided into two semi-circles connected by straight bundles. Fluorescence microscopy. Bar, 10 μm. Photographs by I. S. Tint.

further extension: previous attachments may act as signals inducing the new protrusions. The most mysterious factor affecting direction of movement is cell–cell contact. It is well known that cell contacts lead to local paralysis of pseudopodial activities (Abercrombie, 1970). Contact paralysis seems to be a general property of actinoplasts: it was observed not only in experiments with whole fibroblasts and epitheliocytes, but also in those using small cytoplasmic fragments prepared from these cells (Euteneuer & Schliwa, 1986) and with anuclear platelets spread on the substratum. I will briefly discuss here possible mechanisms for the alteration of pseudopodial activity by cell–cell contacts in epithelial sheets formed by various continuous cell lines. Electron-microscopic examination of these sheets (E. Fetisova, T. Svitkina & J. Vasiliev, unpublished) has revealed a considerable vertical asymmetry of contact paralysis. The upper surfaces of epithelial cells located above the rim of specialized cell–cell contacts had no significant pseudopodial extensions except for a few microvilli near this rim. In contrast, lateral surfaces under the rim of contacts formed lamellar protrusions; some of them were attached to the substratum. Often protrusions formed by a cell underlapped the lower surface of its neighbouring cell. This asymmetry was observed not only in isolated cultures but also in mixed cultures, at the boundaries between epithelial cells of different lines (Fig. 8). Heterologous cells, like homologous ones, formed specialized cell–cell contacts. The surface under the contacts have pseudopods, while that above the contacts is not active (Ivanova *et al.* 1981). Activity of the lower parts of the lateral surfaces of the contacting heterologous sheet was confirmed by the fact that the boundary between these sheets was not stationary but moved slowly in one direction, so that the cells of one line gradually pushed those of another line away from the substratum (Fig. 8). The pushed-out sheets often formed upward evaginations near the boundary with the pushing line. Electron microscopy has shown that lamellipodia of an advancing sheet often underlap the lower surface of a retreating sheet; the reverse type of underlapping was rare. These data show that the cells forming a united epithelial sheet may continue to compete with each other for the substratum, due to the pseudopodial activities of their lateral edges. The cell line, that more efficiently attaches its pseudopods to the substratum gradually dislodges the other line. Owing to the more efficient attachment of the pseudopods at the contact-free edges the cells can move directionally away from the contacting edge, that is, they can demonstrate contact inhibition of movement. Contact paralysis of the upper surface in our system is another phenomenon, which can be described not as the complete inhibition of the extension of pseudopods but as an inhibition of the upward movement of pseudopods from the lateral to the upper surface of contacting cells. At the contact-free edges, this movement leads to formation of ruffles; it is suppressed by the cell–cell contacts. The mechanism of this suppression remains to be studied. One possibility is that the upper parts of the actin cortexes of the contacting cells of the sheet are stretched by the tension parallel to the dorsal surface; the ruffles cannot move across this stretched cortex (see discussion, Vasiliev, 1982).

Thus, external signals control cell shape, orientation and position, mainly by regulation of pseudopodial reactions. These reactions continuously modify the cell

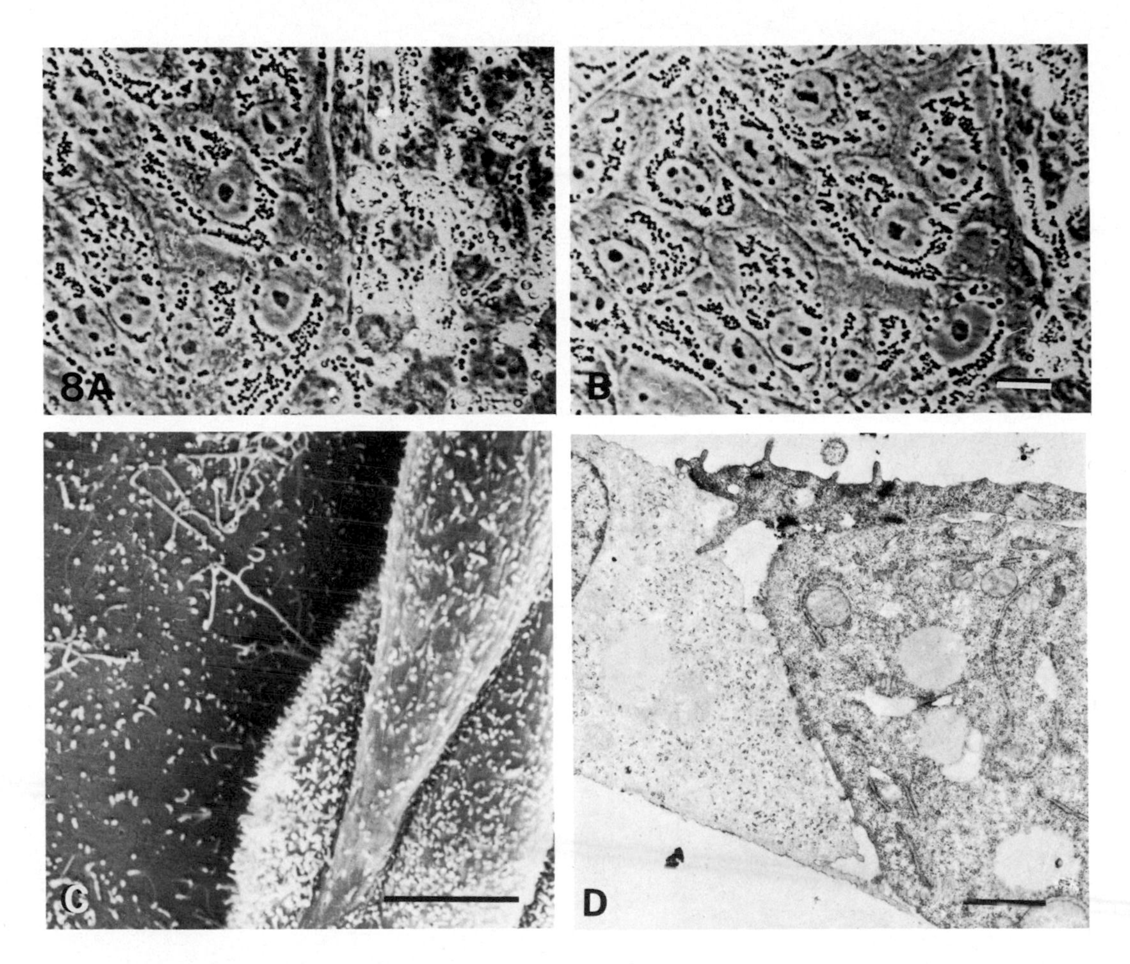

Fig. 8. Epithelial sheet of one mouse cell line (FBT) pushes away from the substrate the contacting sheet of another line (MPTR). A,B. Phase-contrast photographs of the contact zone between two cell lines taken with an interval of 1 h. The cells of the more spread FBT line (left) push the boundary with other line to the right. Bar, 20 μm. C. Scanning electron micrograph of the boundary zone. Crowding of MPTR cells underlapped by flat FBT cell (left). Bar, 20 μm. D. Transmission electron micrograph of the vertical section of the boundary between a FBT and a MPTR sheet. Lamellipod formed at the lower surface of less-dense FBT cell (left) underlaps the MPTR cell. Bar, 2 μm. Photographs by E. Fetisova and T. Svitkina.

cytoskeleton *via* the formation and contraction of actin networks. Alterations of the actin cortex may further lead to reorganization of the microtubular system stabilizing the direction of further pseudopodial activities. Another microtubule-independent way of stabilization is observed in the epithelial sheet. Owing to firm cell–cell contacts, moving marginal cells of the sheet carry their neighbours behind them. Although pseudopods continued to be formed, these neighbours decreased the efficiency of pseudopod attachment to the substratum at the posterior edges of the moving cells.

INTERMEDIATE FILAMENTS AND OTHER CYTOSKELETAL SYSTEMS

Thus far we have ignored the third main cytoskeletal component, intermediate filaments. The simple reason is that we know next to nothing about their role in cellular morphogenesis or their interactions with other cytoskeletal systems. The only well-established type of such an interaction is the determination of the distribution of vimentin-containing intermediate filaments by the microtubular system. Microtubules and intermediate filaments are exactly colocalized in the fully spread fibroblast. Depolymerization of microtubules by colchicine leads to retraction of intermediate filaments from the peripheral part of the cytoplasm and to their collapse in the perinuclear zone. In recent unpublished experiments (O. Pletyushkina & J. Vasiliev) fibroblasts were first incubated for several hours with colchicine, then cytochalasin D was added to the medium. This second drug partially unravelled the intermediate filaments that had been collapsed around the nucleus by the colchicine; some of these filaments left the perinuclear coil and penetrated into the peripheral parts of the cytoplasm.

These experiments suggest that some cytochalasin-sensitive (actin?) structures are involved in the maintenance of the collapsed state of intermediate filaments. The effect of these structures seems to be antagonistic to that of microtubules, which help to keep filaments in the extended state. Another fact that suggests that intermediate filaments can interact functionally with the actin cortex is the association of both these types of fibrils with focal contacts. Association of these contacts with actin microfilaments was, of course, established long ago (Heath & Dunn, 1978; Wehland *et al.* 1979). Recently, Bershadsky *et al.* (1987) using double immunofluorescence methods have shown that vinculin-containing adhesion plaques are associated with the ends of intermediate fibrils. Unfortunately, we have no data proving that selective alterations of intermediate filaments, e.g. injection of specific antibodies, alter the state of other cytoskeletal systems. The function of intermediate filaments remains a major unsolved problem in the study of cellular behaviour.

CONCLUSION

At the beginning of this paper I defined an actinoplast as a discrete adhesive and motile system organized by the actin cortex. A colcemid-treated fibroblast is a prototype of an actinoplast. By analogy, we can designate as 'tubuloplasts' cytoplasmic systems organized by microtubules. A cytochalasin-treated fibroblast is an actual cell that is sufficiently close to the theoretical prototype of a tubuloplast. This cell has drastically reduced actin cortex; it has no lamellae, but long narrow processes filled with microtubules and intermediate filaments. These processes can grow during spreading but otherwise remain stable (Bliokh *et al.* 1980). The normal cell can be regarded as a symbiosis of these two types of organization, of actinoplasts and of tubuloplasts. The two cytoskeletal systems, microtubules and actin cortex, compete and cooperate in the organization of the cytoplasm. In the course of morphogenesis the predominant type of organization can be altered. For instance, the undifferentiated neuroblastoma cell has the predominant 'actinoplast' organization, while the tubuloplastic organization becomes prominent during neural differentiation. Another important morphogenetic process discussed in some detail in this paper is the partial territorial segregation of actinoplasts and tubuloplasts in the same cell; actinoplasts can move with regard to one another and to tubuloplasts. The concept of two types of organization provides a convenient way of describing many morphogenetic processes based on the interactions of the actin cortex and the microtubular system. There is, however, still a very long way to go, before we will be able to describe these interactions in exact molecular terms.

REFERENCES

ABERCROMBIE, M. (1970). Contact inhibition in tissue culture. *In vitro* **6**, 128–142.

ABERCROMBIE, M. (1980). The crawling movement of metazoan cells. *Proc. R. Soc. Lond.* B **207**, 122–147.

ALBRECHT-BUEHLER, G. (1980). Autonomous movements of cytoplasmic fragments. *Proc. natn. Acad. Sci. U.S.A.* **77**, 6639–6644.

BERSHADSKY, A. D., TINT, I. S. & SVITKINA, T. M. (1987). Association of intermediate filaments with vinculin containing adhesion plaques of fibroblasts. *Cell Motil. Cytoskel.* (in press).

BLIOKH, Z. L., DOMNINA, L. V., IVANOVA, O. Y., PLETJUSHKINA, O. Y., SVITKINA, T. M., SMOLYANINOV, V. A., VASILIEV, J. M. & GELFAND, J. M. (1980). Spreading of fibroblasts in the medium containing cytochalasin B; formation of lamellar cytoplasm as a combination of several functionally different processes. *Proc. natn. Acad. Sci. U.S.A.* **77**, 5919–5922.

BRAY, D. (1982). Filopodial contraction and growth cone guidance. *Cell Behaviour. A Tribute to Michael Abercrombie* (ed. R. Bellairs, A. Curtis & G. Dunn), pp. 299–313. Cambridge University Press.

BRAY, D., HEATH, J. & MOSS, D. (1986). The membrane-associated 'cortex' of animal cell: its structure and mechanical properties. *J. Cell Sci. Suppl. 4*, 71–88.

DE BRABANDER, M., GEUENS, G., NUYDENS, R., WILLEBRORDS, R. & DE MEY, J. (1981). Taxol induces the assembly of free microtubules in living cells and blocks the organizing capacity of the centrosomes and kinetochores. *Proc. natn. Acad. Sci. U.S.A.* **78**, 5608–5612.

DOMESICK, V. B. & MOREST, D. K. (1977). Migration and differentiation of shepherd's crook cells in the optic tectum of the chick embryo. *Neuroscience* **2**, 477–491.

DUGINA, V. B., VASILIEV, J. M. & GELFAND, Y. M. (1986). Reversible reorganization of the cytoskeleton of cultured cells induced by 12-*O*-tetradecanoylphorbol-13-acetate. *Dokl. Acad. Nauk SSSR* **291**, 985–989 (in Russian).

DUNN, G. A. (1980). Mechanisms of fibroblast locomotion. In *Cell Adhesion and Motility* (ed. A. S. I. Curtis & J. D. Pitts), pp. 409–423. Cambridge University Press.

EUTENEUER, N. & SCHLIWA, M. (1986). The function of microtubules in directional cell movement. *Ann. N.Y. Acad. Sci.* **466**, 867–886.

FUKUI, Y. & YUMURA, S. (1986). Actomyosin dynamics in chemotactic amoeboid movement of *Dictyostelium*. *Cell Motil. Cytoskel.* **6**, 662–673.

GELFAND, V. I., GLUSHANKOVA, N. A., IVANOVA, O. Y., MITTELMAN, L. A., PLETYUSHKINA, O. Y., VASILIEV, J. M. & GELFAND, J. M. (1985). Polarization of cytoplasmic fragments microsurgically detached from mouse fibroblasts. *Int. Cell Biol. Rep.* **9**, 883–892.

GOTLIEB, A. I., MAY, L. M., SUBRAHMENYAN, L. & KALNINS, V. I. (1981). Distribution of microtubule organizing centers in migrating sheets of endothelial cell. *J. Cell Biol.* **91**, 589–594.

HEATH, J. P. & DUNN, G. A. (1978). Cell to substratum contacts of chick fibroblasts and their relation to the microfilament system. A correlated interference reflection and high-voltage electron microscopic study. *J. Cell Sci.* **29**, 197–200.

IVANOVA, O. Y., KOMM, S. G. & FETISOVA, E. K. (1981). Contact interactions of epithelial sheets. *Tsitologija* **23**, 1298–1303 (in Russian).

KOLEGA, J. (1986). Effects of mechanical tension on protrusive activity and microfilament and intermediate filament organization in an epidermal epithelium moving in culture. *J. Cell Biol.* **102**, 1400–1411.

Kupfer, A., Louvard, D. & Singer, S. I. (1982). The polarization of the Golgi apparatus and microtubule-organizing center in cultured fibroblasts at the edge of an experimental wound. *Proc. natn. Acad. Sci. U.S.A.* **79**, 2603–2607.

Lazarides, E. (1975). Immunofluorescence studies on the structure of actin filaments in tissue culture cells. *J. Histochem. Cytochem.* **23**, 507–528.

Lasek, R. J. (1986). Polymer sliding in axons. *J. Cell Sci. Suppl.* 5, 161–186.

Laszlo, A. & Bissel, M. J. (1983). TPA induces simultaneous alterations in the synthesis and organization of vimentin. *Expl Cell Res.* **148**, 221–234.

Lyass, L. A. & Vasiliev, J. M. (1985). Regulation of distribution of the microfilament bundles by the system of microtubules. *Ontogenes* **16**, 167–170 (in Russian).

McNiven, M. A., Wang, M. & Porter, K. R. (1984). Microtubule polarity and the direction of pigment transport reverse simultaneously in surgically severed melanophore arms. *Cell* **37**, 753–765.

Newell, P. C. (1986). The role of actin polymerization in amoebal chemotaxis. *BioEssays* **5**, 208–211.

Schliwa, M., Nakamura, T., Portex, K. R. & Enteneuer, U. (1984). A tumor promoter induces rapid and coordinated reorganization of actin and vinculin in cultured cells. *J. Cell Biol.* **89**, 1045–1059.

Schubert, D., Humphreys, S., Devitry, F. & Jacob, F. (1971). Induced differentiation of a neuroblastoma. *Devl Biol.* **25**, 514–546.

Svitkina, T. M., Neyfakh, A. A. & Bershadsky, A. D. (1986). Actin cytoskeleton of spread fibroblasts appears to assemble at the cell edges. *J. Cell Sci.* **82**, 235–248.

Taylor, D. L. & Fechheimer, M. (1982). Cytoplasmic structure and contractility: the solation-contraction coupling hypothesis. *Phil. Trans. R. Soc. Lond.* B **299**, 185–197.

Trinkaus, J. P. (1985). Protrusive activity of the cell surface and the initiation of cell movement during morphogenesis. *Expl Biol. Med.* **10**, 130–173.

Vasiliev, J. M. (1982). Spreading and locomotion of tissue cell; factors controlling the distribution of pseudopodia. *Phil. Trans. R. Soc. Lond.* B **299**, 159–167.

Vasiliev, J. M. (1985). Spreading of non-transformed and transformed cells. *Biochim. biophys. Acta* **780**, 21–65.

Vasiliev, J. M. & Gelfand, I. M. (1981). *Neoplastic and Normal Cells in Culture*. Cambridge University Press.

Wehland, J., Osborn, M. & Weber, K. (1979). Cell-to-substratum contacts in living cells: a direct correlation between interference-reflection and indirect immunofluorescence microscopy using antibodies against actin and α-actinin. *J. Cell Sci.* **37**, 257–273.

Wohlfarth-Bottermann, K. E. & Isenberg, G. (1976). Dynamics and molecular basis of the contractile system of *Physarum*. In *Contractile Systems in Non-muscle Tissues* (ed. S. V. Perry, A. Margreth & R. S. Adelstein), pp. 279–308. Amsterdam: Elsevier.

Wang, Y. L. (1984). Reorganization of actin filament bundles in living fibroblasts. *J. Cell Biol.* **99**, 1478–1485.

J. Cell Sci. Suppl. 8, 19–33 (1987)
Printed in Great Britain © *The Company of Biologists Limited 1987*

EFFECT OF PATTERNED SURFACES OF ADHESIVE ISLANDS ON THE SHAPE, CYTOSKELETON, ADHESION AND BEHAVIOUR OF SWISS MOUSE 3T3 FIBROBLASTS

G. W. IRELAND
Department of Human Anatomy, University of Oxford, S. Parks Rd, Oxford OX1 3QX, UK

P. DOPPING-HEPENSTAL*
NIMR, The Ridgeway, Mill Hill, London NW7 1AA, UK

P. JORDAN AND C. O'NEILL
ICRF, PO Box No. 123, Lincoln's Inn Fields, London WC2A 3PX, UK

SUMMARY

A pattern of circular islands of adhesive substratum can be used to control cell shape and behaviour. We have shown previously that the proportion of Swiss 3T3 cells that synthesize DNA varies with the area of the island to which they are attached, within the range 500–5000 μm^2. In this paper we investigate the cytoskeleton and adhesions of cells on islands using a variety of techniques including phalloidin staining and interference reflection microscopy. Islands of area 2000 μm^2 or less constrain cell shape, and cause focal contacts and actin microfilament bundles to accumulate in a circle at the margin. These changes are most obvious in islands of about 1000 μm^2, in which a complete ring of adhesion is sometimes formed in the periphery of the cell. This peripheral distribution is less common in cells on even smaller islands, and the focal contacts become smaller and less numerous. It is not yet clear whether any of these structural changes are associated directly with the proliferative stimulus due to contact with the substratum. However, we expect that the use of patterned substrata will contribute to the study of how cell shape and structure regulate many cell functions.

INTRODUCTION

Ordinary methods of tissue culture make use of plane surfaces, which have the important advantage over real tissues that all cells are available for examination or manipulation. In culture, the degree of cell spreading on the substratum and the particular shapes that cells adopt are often very variable. Cells move about over the substratum and make a variety of contacts with one another. Such interactions may be complicated further by multilayering, secretion of matrix or hormonal molecules and the appearance of differentiated subpopulations. We can simplify the study of cell behaviour by reducing the complexity of the contacts that the cell makes. This can be achieved to some extent by separating cells from each other or by devising techniques to study single cells. However, individual cell behaviour is very variable

* Present address: EM Unit, The Wellcome Research Laboratories, Langley Court, Beckenham, Kent BR3 3BS, UK

and therefore it is necessary to study populations of cells. These problems can be resolved by creating patterned substrata that control whole populations of cells. Such substrata can isolate cells, restrict their movement and control their shape.

TECHNIQUES FOR CONTROLLING CELL SHAPE

Folkman & Moscona (1978) introduced the use of the non-adhesive polymer poly-2-hydroxyethyl methacrylate (poly(HEMA)) to coat tissue culture dishes. They created substrata of different adhesivity by evaporation of ethanolic solutions containing different concentrations of the polymer. The average shape of the population of cells in the dish was related to the initial polymer concentration. At a low concentration, the cells were as well spread as on plastic, while higher concentrations were very effective in preventing cell attachment and spreading, and the cells remained rounded. It was originally thought that the adhesive properties of polymer coats produced in this way depend on the thickness of each coat. However, it has since been shown that thin films break down and reveal the underlying adhesive plastic surface; local variability in the integrity of the film is the reason for the existence of such a wide range of cell shapes at any particular poly(HEMA) concentration (Minett *et al.* 1984). There are also difficulties in obtaining reproducible coatings with this method, but the main problem is that there is a lack of accurate control over cell spreading. We have designed a method that uses patterned substrata, developed from earlier methods (Westermark, 1978; Ponten & Stolt, 1980), to limit spreading and control cell shape accurately.

The method makes use of the tendency of cells, when presented with two substrata differing widely in adhesiveness, to become confined to the more adhesive one (Carter, 1967; Harris, 1973). We used a completely non-adhesive coat of poly-(HEMA) on which small areas of palladium were deposited. First, coverslips were spun-coated with 1·5 % poly(HEMA) as described by Minett *et al.* (1984). Then palladium was evaporated onto this surface, under vacuum, through a copper mask fabricated by photolithographic techniques normally used in the production of integrated circuits (Fig. 1). By this method we could produce an array of palladium islands ranging in area from 400 to 5000 μm^2 (22·5–80 μm diameter) covering one coverslip or dish.

When freshly trypsinized cells were seeded onto a coverslip bearing islands, suspended cells in the medium immediately overlying the islands quickly became attached to them. After only 10 min, the distribution of attached cells was seen to be defined entirely by the pattern of evaporated palladium. Recruitment of cells to the islands continued until all had attached to an island (unless the unattached cells were removed by changing the medium). Even after many hours in culture, the spatial distribution of cells on the coverslip continued to be defined entirely by the pattern of evaporated palladium (Fig. 2).

Since cells only adhere to the palladium, the smaller islands prevented full cell spreading. Thus islands could force the cells to adopt circular outlines and lenticular shapes (Figs 3–7). On the smallest islands, cells could be seen to be almost

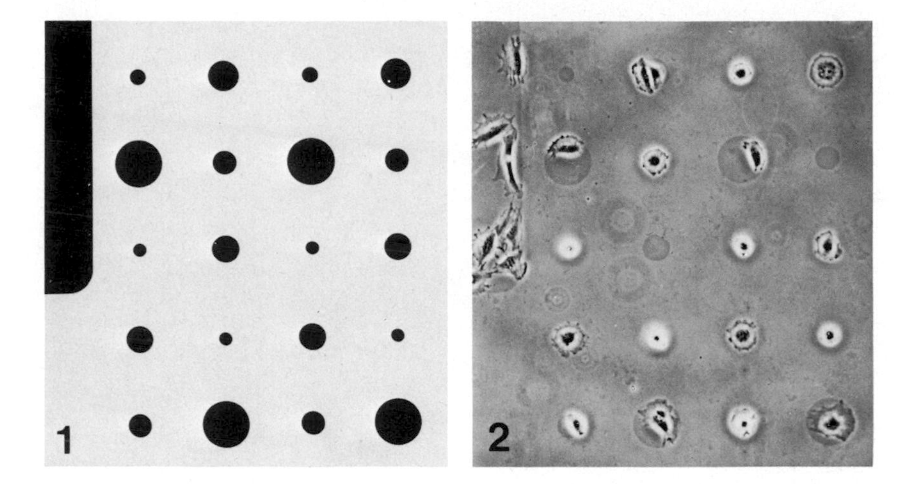

Fig. 1. This shows part of the master plate used for making the copper foil mask. It was made using the technique of photolithography by the Microelectronics Centre, Middlesex Polytechnic, London. Part of a large rectangle and part of the array of discs with centre-to-centre spacing of 150 μm are shown. The first row consists of alternate discs of area 930 and 3770 μm^2, the second row 5000 and 1230 μm^2, the third row 400 and 1625 μm^2, the fourth and fifth rows are the same as the third and second rows, respectively.

Fig. 2. This shows a phase-contrast micrograph of a patterned substrate, a similar area to that shown in Fig. 1, on which cells have been allowed to spread for 8 h. The substratum consists of a non-adhesive underlayer made by spin coating a coverslip with 1·5 % of poly(HEMA) (Hydron, Hydron Labs Inc, New Brunswick, New Jersey) using a photoresist spinner (Dynapert Precima Ltd, Colchester, Essex). The adhesive discs were made by evaporating palladium, under vacuum, through a copper foil mask (Alan Agar Ltd, Stanstead, Essex) made from the master plate shown in Fig. 1.

hemispherical in side-view microscopy (Fig. 3) (Boocock *et al.* 1985). On successively larger islands, the shapes adopted by cells were similar to successive stages of normal cell spreading on ordinary unconfined substrata. Cells on larger islands had smoother surfaces; cells on smaller islands had numerous filopodia and microvilli. Only cells on the largest islands were able to spread sufficiently to become elongated and polarized (Fig. 7), as they would appear on a uniformly adhesive substratum.

Time-lapse microscopy confirmed the resemblance of cells on different-sized islands to intermediate stages of normal spreading. Even after several days on the smaller islands, cells continued to protrude actively just as they would be expected to do during the first 20 min of normal spreading. Waves of protrusion were seen to circulate clockwise or anticlockwise around the margin of the cell. On islands of intermediate size, new lamellae often overlapped those already attached. They explored the surrounding poly(HEMA) substratum making temporary contacts, which were immediately followed by retraction.

CELL SHAPE AND PROLIFERATION

Normal cells require a substrate for proliferation: the loss of anchorage dependence is a familiar property of transformed and tumour cells (Stoker *et al.* 1968).

When deprived of anchorage, 3T3 cells rapidly become growth arrested in the G_1 phase of the cell cycle (Otsuka & Moskowitz, 1975). The full stimulus given by anchorage appears to be a consequence of shape changes rather than mere attachment. Maroudas (1973) showed that a full stimulus can be given to a single suspended cell by a tiny glass fibre. The stimulus depends critically on the length of the fibre, which needs to be sufficient to allow the cells to extend fully. Fibres shorter

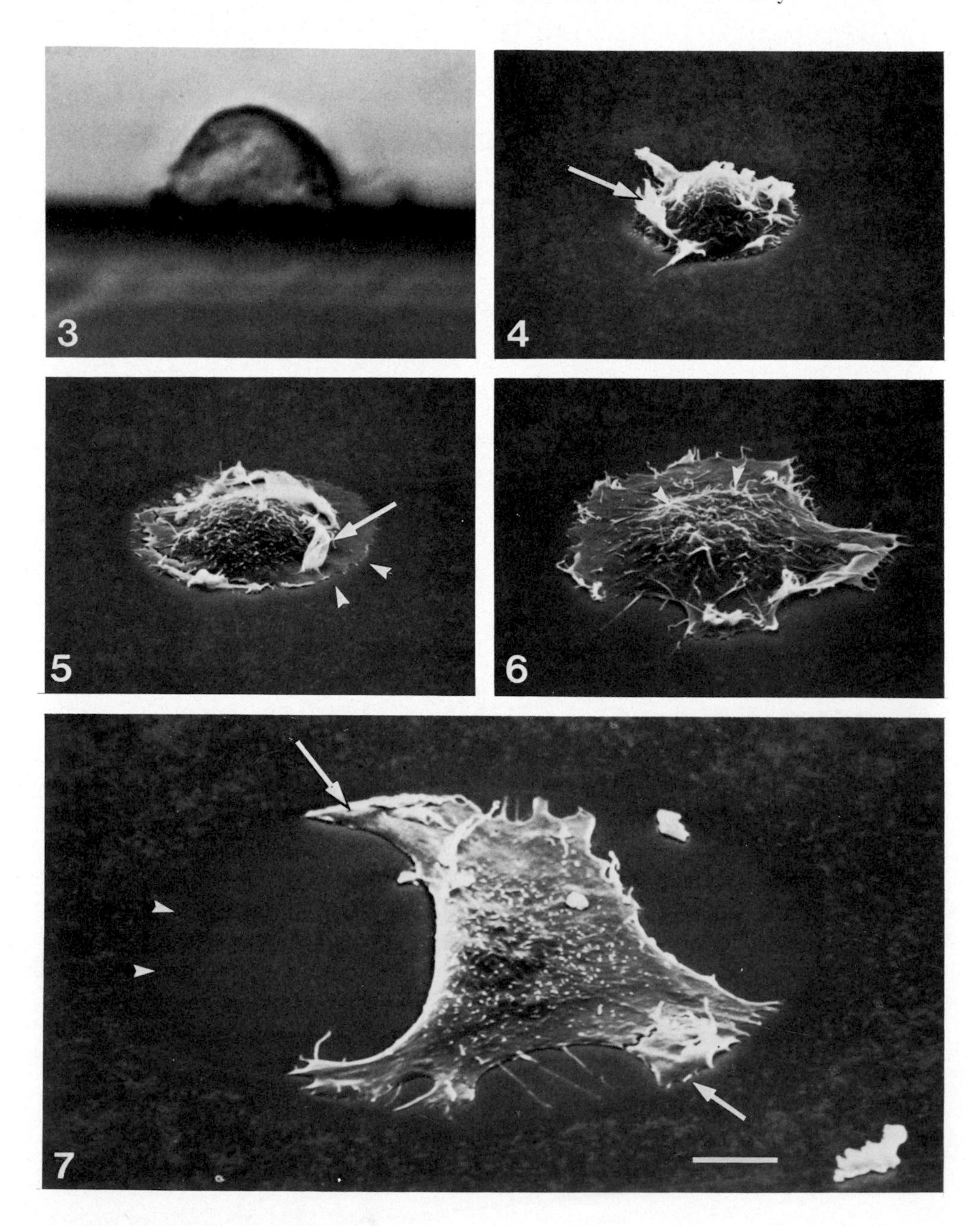

than 20 μm, although anchoring cells, did not stimulate proliferation; they were only fully effective when their length exceeded 200 μm. Folkman & Moscona (1978) showed that spreading in two dimensions has similar effects. Using poly(HEMA)-coated dishes, they showed that DNA synthesis varies with the mean height of the cell (a function of its spreading). Varying the overall adhesiveness of the substratum affects only the average extent of spreading in the population; it will vary widely between different cells and also between the same cell at different times. On the other hand, our circular islands will constrain cells to adopt circular outlines in which only the upper surface is not being determined.

We have shown that DNA synthesis depends on island size (O'Neill *et al.* 1986). Similar data are shown in Fig. 8. The [^{3}H]thymidine labelling index of simian virus 40 (SV40)-transformed 3T3 cells is unaffected by island size, while the labelling index of normal 3T3 cells is dependent on the area of the islands on which they spread (provided that it is less than 5000 μm^2). This means that neither movement on the substratum nor contact between the cells is necessary for stimulation of DNA synthesis; contact with the substratum is sufficient. It is possible that, in principle, cell–substratum contact has this effect partly because it causes an increase in surface to volume ratio, since it is known that diffusion can be limiting to growth (Stoker, 1973; Dunn & Ireland, 1984). However, it is quite clear that this aspect cannot account for all the stimulation seen in 3T3 cells, since we have estimated (O'Neill *et al.* 1986) that the surface to volume ratio becomes constant when the islands are 650 μm^2, yet the labelling index is sixfold higher on islands of about this area than it is in suspended cells. This stimulus must be derived more directly from interaction with the substratum and its matrix of adsorbed proteins and seems likely to be mediated by changes in cell structure.

CELL–SUBSTRATUM ADHESION AND ITS RELATION TO THE CYTOSKELETON

Attachment and spreading on plane substrata involves the dynamic reorganization of three filamentous structures: microtubules, microfilaments and intermediate

---

Fig. 3. Cell on 530 μm^2 island photographed in side-view using a standard microscope and the technique described by Boocock *et al.* (1985).

Figs 4–7. Scanning electron micrographs of Swiss 3T3 cells on islands. Cells on island patterned coverslips were fixed in 2·5 % glutaraldehyde in 0·1 M-cacodylate buffer at 37 °C for 30 min. Pieces of coverslip were dehydrated in ethanol and acetone and critical point dried (Polaron E3000). They were then given a 15 nm coating of gold in a sputter-coater (Baltzers Union) and photographed in a scanning electron microscope (Jeol JSM-T20). Bar, 10 μm.

Fig. 4. Cell on island of area 530 μm^2. Note the extensive ruffling (arrow).

Fig. 5. Cell on island of area 930 μm^2. The cell is able to spread more fully but still has its outline constrained by the edge of the adhesive island. Extensive ruffling is seen (arrow) behind the attached margin (arrowheads).

Fig. 6. Cell on island of area 2165 μm^2. The cell no longer fills the island but is still unable to become polarized. The dorsal surface has many filopodial projections (arrowheads).

Fig. 7. Cell on island of area 5000 μm^2. The cell is now able to become polarized and only a few parts of the margin are curved (arrows) as indicated by the edge of the island (arrowheads). Fewer microprojections are seen on the dorsal surface.

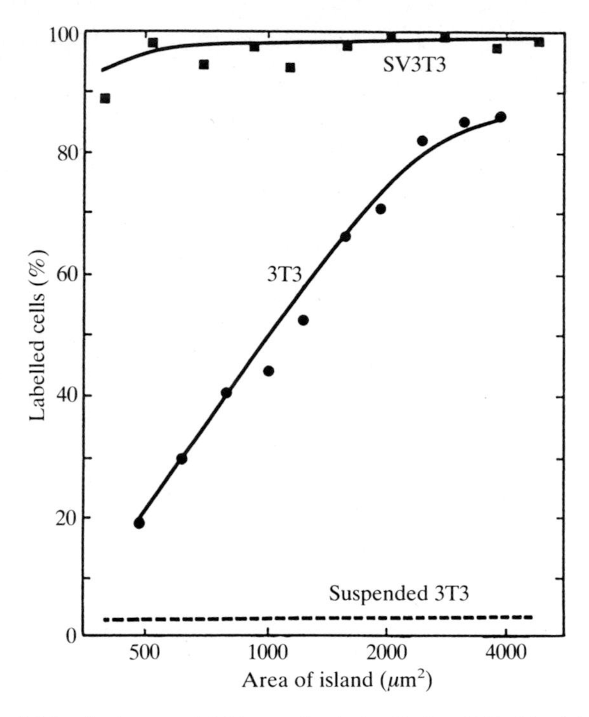

Fig. 8. Effect of island size on DNA synthesis in Swiss 3T3 fibroblasts. Cells were labelled with [^{3}H]thymidine while growing for 24 h in normal medium containing 10 % serum. Autoradiography was performed and the graph shows the percentage of cells with labelled nuclei on islands of different size. Normal Swiss 3T3 cells (●——●) and SV40-virus transformed 3T3 cells (■——■) are shown. The lower line (----) shows the proportion of normal Swiss 3T3 cells undergoing DNA synthesis when kept in suspension in agar in the same dish (98 % of SV3T3 cells in suspension were labelled).

filaments. Of particular interest is the relationship of actin to cell–substratum adhesions. Several different types of cell–substratum adhesion have been described, in a variety of cell types, using the technique of interference reflection microscopy (IRM), including *close contacts* and *focal contacts* (Abercrombie & Dunn, 1975; Izzard & Lochner, 1976; Ireland & Stern, 1982). Each focal contact is the ventral membrane terminus of an actin microfilament bundle (Heath & Dunn, 1978; Rees *et al.* 1978; Wehland *et al.* 1979). Both vinculin and talin are also associated with the cytoplasmic face of the focal contact (Geiger, 1979; Connell & Burridge, 1982).

We have found that IRM can be used to detect adhesions between live cells and the adhesive islands, provided that the thickness of both the palladium and poly(HEMA) coats are carefully controlled. The palladium islands can be seen as grey discs, slightly darker than the background (see Fig. 15). During the initial attachment of cells to an island of any size the first contacts to appear were uniformly grey and of the close-contact type. Later, spread cells appeared mostly white or grey but also had dark streaks, the latter representing specialized cell–substratum adhesions or focal contacts (see Fig. 15). Focal contacts were found to be distributed widely over the under-surface of the cell (Fig. 15). Bundles of actin microfilaments, which could be visualized using rhodamine-conjugated phalloidin (Fig. 9), were often orientated with the long axis of the cell. Some passed close to the ventral membrane and inserted into the focal contacts. Another set of microfilament bundles was found closer to the dorsal cell membrane. These were not always orientated in parallel arrays, but often several bundles converged to form intersections or foci (Lazarides, 1976; Ireland & Voon, 1981). At the cell margin, lamellipodia often overlapped the poly(HEMA) and were frequently found to be lifted away from the substratum as ruffles (Fig. 9). They contained a dense weave of microfilaments, most of which were orientated radially. Thus the type, size and distribution of cell–substratum contacts seen on these larger islands were very similar to those seen on plain glass. However, focal contacts were seen only in the parts of the cell over the palladium and never in regions overlapping the poly(HEMA) (Fig. 15).

CELLS ON SMALL ISLANDS SHOW DIFFERENT PATTERNS OF ADHESIONS AND ARRANGEMENTS OF THEIR ACTIN CYTOSKELETON

If cells are examined on successively smaller islands (Figs 9–19) three general changes are observed. First, the size of the focal contacts decreases. Second, their arrangement changes so that, instead of being widely distributed, they become arranged around the periphery of the island, a tendency that reaches its peak on islands of about 1000 μm^2. Third, the orientation of microfilament bundles changes; instead of spanning the island, they become arranged just inside and following the curved margin of the island.

Islands of areas 1500–2500 μm^2, which begin to constrain cell shape, also alter the distribution of adhesions. They are no longer found in the central region of the island, but instead become confined to within a few micrometres of the periphery. Microfilament bundles were found that traversed from a set of adhesions at one side of the island to a set on the other side (Fig. 10). They also often followed the concave margin of the cell between adjacent groups of focal contacts forming catenary curves (Fig. 10). The peripheral arrangement of focal contacts was most obvious on islands of about 1000 μm^2, when they were found to be distributed evenly in a ring at the margin of the island (Fig. 17). In the extreme case, the contacts appeared to form virtually a complete ring of adhesion (Fig. 19). Microfilament bundles now followed an arc just inside the edge of the island (Figs 11, 12) and they could also be seen in thin glancing sections parallel to the substratum (Fig. 21). In transverse sections, large plaque-like structures were observed on the cytoplasmic face of the ventral membrane close to the edge of the island (Fig. 20).

Cells on islands of area less than 1000 μm^2 still had curved microfilament bundles inside the island margin, but some small microfilament bundles were found close to the ventral membrane and were often arranged in a fan shape (Fig. 13). However, the arrangement of adhesions became less ordered, with small focal contacts being found further towards the centre of the island (Fig. 18), although many cells lacked visible focal contacts. Microfilament bundles were seen in lamellipodial protrusions

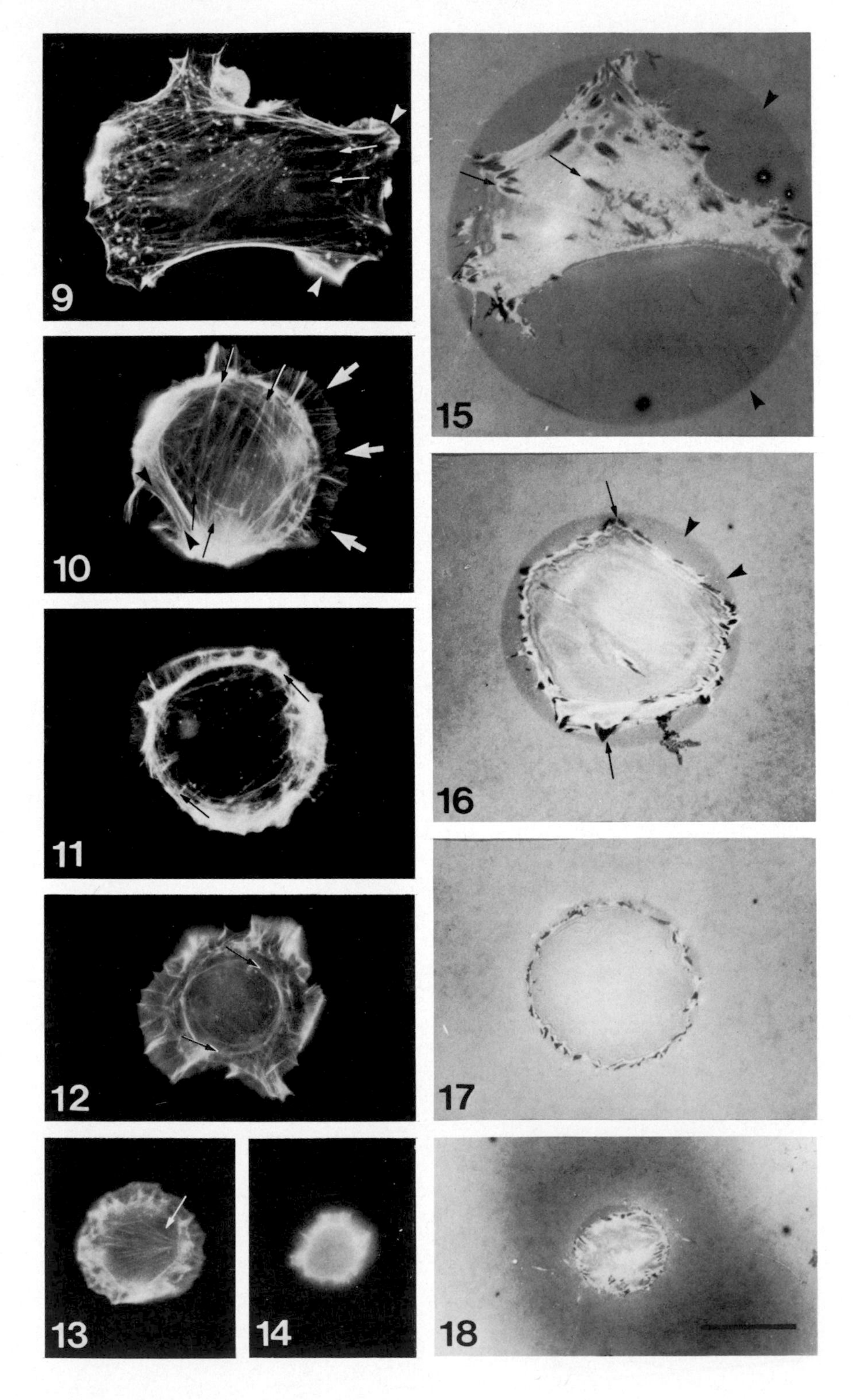
9
10
11
12
13
14
15
16
17
18

projecting from the dorsal cell surface of cells on small islands but no clear bundles were seen in cells not attached to islands (Fig. 14).

It is perhaps interesting that some of the features we observed in cells on islands resemble those seen at particular stages of normal cell spreading.

COMPARISON OF NORMAL CELL SPREADING WITH CELLS ON ISLANDS

Spreading of a fibroblast cell is usually initiated by the formation of a uniformly grey close contact, although formation of focal contacts within a few minutes has

Figs 9–14. Filamentous actin distribution in Swiss 3T3 cells on islands. For rhodamine–phalloidin staining, cells were grown on island patterned coverslips for 5 h. They were then fixed in 0·25 % glutaraldehyde in phosphate buffer for 5 min, permeabilized in 0·1 % Triton X-100 for 15 min, and then fixed again in 0·25 % glutaraldehyde for a further 5 min. The preparation was quenched in 2 mg ml^{-1} borohydride on ice, blocked with 1 % BSA and stained with rhodamine-conjugated phalloidin (kindly provided by Professor T. Wieland). The coverslips were mounted in buffer and observed using Zeiss epi-fluorescence optics.

Fig. 9. Cell on island of area 3770 μm^2. At the margin of the cell small protrusions (or ruffles) can be seen (arrowheads). Large microfilament bundles (arrows) can be seen in the rest of the cell, orientated similarly to the long axis of the cell.

Fig. 10. Cell on island of area 1625 μm^2. Many microfilament bundles still traverse the cell from one side of the island to the other (arrows). On one side a broad lamellipodium (broad arrow) protrudes beyond the edge of the island. It can be seen to contain short radial microfilament bundles. A microfilament bundle forming a short catenary curve is shown (arrowheads).

Fig. 11. Cell on island of area 1230 μm^2. A dense circular band of microfilament bundles (arrows) can be seen just inside the margin of the cell. A few thin microfilament bundles still traverse the cell.

Fig. 12. Cell on island of area 930 μm^2. The cell has produced a lamellipodium around most of its margin. Microfilament bundles arranged in arcs (arrows) are seen just inside the edge of the island.

Fig. 13. Cell on island of area 530 μm^2. Microfilament bundles are more difficult to visualize on these more-rounded cells. A few thin microfilament bundles are arranged in a fan shape close to the substrate.

Fig. 14. Cell not on island. Brightly staining protrusions are seen but no clear microfilament bundles.

Figs 15–19. IRM of Swiss 3T3 cells on islands. Cells were seeded onto island patterned coverslips mounted on Cooper dishes (Falcon) modified by drilling a hole in the lid. The bottom of the dish was also modified by replacing the plastic with a coverslip mounted with silicon grease; the whole assembly could be gassed with 15 % CO_2. A Zeiss microscope (Universal) equipped with epifluorescence optics, a HPL-POL reflector, narrow band pass filter (46-78-07), polarizer and analyser was used for IRM. All IRM was performed on live cells observed with a 63× Antiflex objective.

Fig. 15. Cell on island of area 5000 μm^2. The palladium island is seen as a disc (arrowheads) slightly darker than the background. The focal contacts (two shown with arrows) are seen distributed amongst the white and grey parts of the cell undersurface further away from the substratum.

Fig. 16. Cell on island of area 2165 μm^2. The cell almost fills the island (arrowheads) and its focal contacts are mostly arranged in its periphery near the edge of the island (arrows). Arrow-shaped contacts are seen.

Fig. 17. Cell on island of area 1230 μm^2. The cell fills the island and small focal contacts are found only at the margin, distributed in a ring.

Fig. 18. Cell on island of area 400 μm^2. A few very small contacts can be seen but are not strictly confined to the margin of the island. Bar, 20 μm.

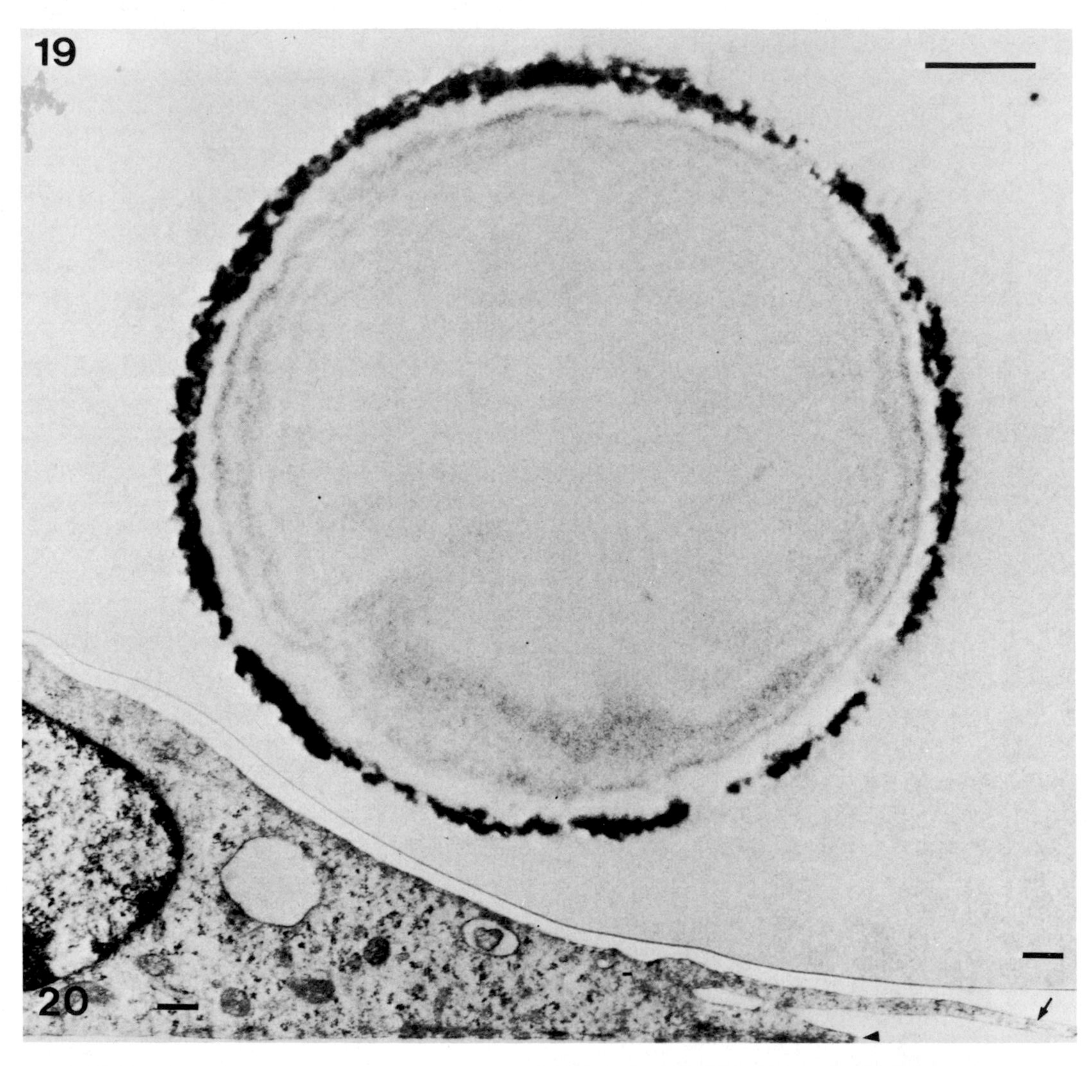
19
20

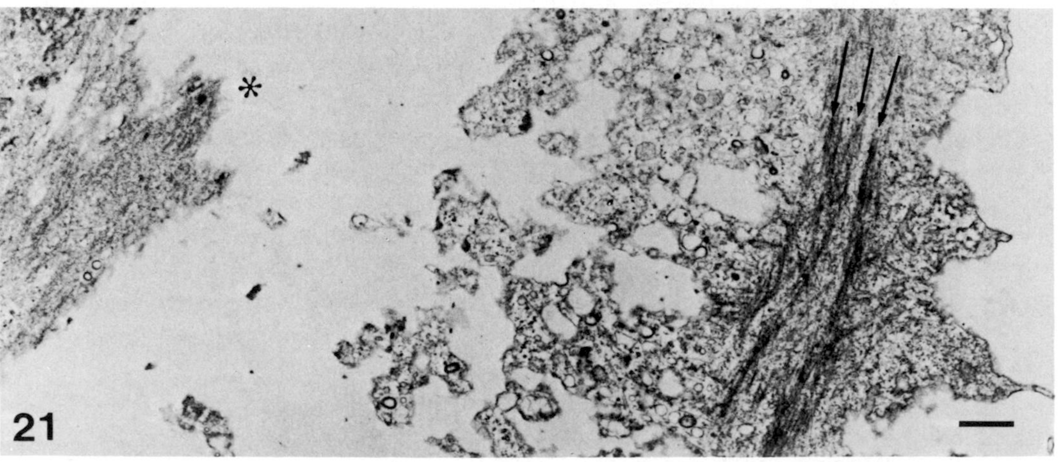
*
21

been observed in some cells (Heaysman *et al.* 1982). At the discoid stage of cell spreading, a circumferential ring of microfilaments is seen in the lamella margin (Vasiliev, 1982). This feature is also characteristic of epithelial cells even when they are fully spread. Further flattening and spreading of the cell is accompanied by the formation of radially orientated microfilament bundles (Soranno & Bell, 1982). The circular outline is lost as discrete lamellipodia develop and the cell assumes a stellar shape. Finally, parts of the margin become stabilized and protrusion of lamellipodia is confined to a particular region, resulting in a polarized shape (Vasiliev, 1982).

A major difference between spreading cells and those on islands is that in the first case any particular shape is only experienced transiently, while in the second it is held for several days. Comparisons between cells on islands and cells spreading on continuous palladium surfaces revealed at least two differences. First, focal contacts were present on many relatively unspread cells, such as those on islands 400 and 530 μm^2 in area, whereas in unconfined cells focal contacts were not seen until cells were spread to a much greater extent. Second, when cells were filmed by time-lapse video microscopy it was found that the turnover of adhesions was different on islands of different size. On large islands, which permit some locomotion (since spread cells do not cover the entire surface of the island), focal contacts were formed and disappeared in a way similar to that occurring during normal locomotion. On islands of intermediate size (700–1500 μm^2) the focal contacts were stable and their number often increased. However, on islands smaller than 700 μm^2 in area, the small focal contacts that were found were apparently more labile and appeared and disappeared readily. Thus, the stability of focal contacts seems to be associated with their arrangement in a ring at the margin of the cell.

When a complete ring of adhesion is formed around the periphery of the cell, the space between the ventral cell membrane and the substratum may become a separate compartment from the bulk of the culture medium. By IRM and electron microscopy (EM), the ventral membrane appeared to be lifted away from the substratum. In time-lapse IRM video films the reflection pattern changed during observation; the changes were interpreted as slow movement of the cell membrane

---

Fig. 19. Cell on island of area 930 μm^2. Single focal contacts are not observed; instead, there is a complete ring of adhesion around the margin of the island. Bar, 5 μm.

Figs 20, 21. TEM of Swiss 3T3 cells on islands. Cells were grown on island patterned coverslips and then fixed by replacing the medium with 2·5 % glutaraldehyde in cacodylate buffer for 30 min. The cells were rinsed and postfixed in 1 % osmium tetroxide. Dehydration was carried out through a graded ethanol series and the specimens embedded in the water-soluble resin Quetol 651 (Polaron). Selected areas were sawn from the block and the coverslip removed by repeated cooling in liquid nitrogen. Sections were cut and stained with uranyl acetate and lead citrate.

Fig. 20. Cell on island of area 1230 μm^2. This section is normal to the substratum and shows the plaque structure on the cytoplasmic face of the ventral cell membrane. A lamellipodium (arrow) appears to have protruded over the attached cell margin (arrowhead) onto the poly(HEMA). Bar, 0·5 μm.

Fig. 21. Similar cell to Fig. 20 but sectioned parallel and very close to the plane of the substratum. The circumferential band of microfilaments is seen just inside the cell margin (arrows). Further towards the centre of the island (*) little structure is seen, because the ventral membrane was lifted away from the island. Bar, 1 μm.

away from the substratum, followed by rapid movement towards it. Epithelial sheets are known to pump intracellular sodium across their basal membrane and water follows passively, resulting in the formation of the characteristic 'domes' seen in tissue culture (Leighton *et al.* 1969). This is thought to be due to the concentration of sodium pumps in the basal membrane. It seems possible that limiting substrata, by determining the arrangement of the cytoskeleton, could alter the pattern of ion and fluid transport of a fibroblastic cell to make it resemble the pattern characteristic of epithelial cells. Clearly, this may be just another example of how the cytoskeleton might act to alter the position and activity of membrane proteins. The best example is found during capping in lymphocytes and fibroblasts (Flanaghan & Koch, 1978; Heath, 1983). If the cytoskeleton influences the number and activity of receptors for growth factors, either directly or indirectly, this might have important consequences for the control of proliferation.

STRUCTURAL CORRELATES OF PROLIFERATIVE CONTROL

The relationship between entry into *S* phase and structural parameters is unclear. Primary explants of chick heart fibroblasts develop large stable focal contacts, often called 'focal adhesions' during their proliferative phase (Couchman & Rees, 1979). However, in most cell lines these stable adhesions are more characteristic of cells made quiescent by serum starvation. Such cells undergo dramatic changes in their actin cytoskeleton following stimulation with platelet-derived growth factor (Mellstrom *et al.* 1983; Heath & Ireland, 1985) and there is evidence that drugs that disrupt actin structure inhibit the ability of serum growth factors to stimulate DNA synthesis (Maness & Walsh, 1982). Treatment of cells with platelet-derived growth factor can cause the dissociation of vinculin from focal contacts (Herman & Pledger, 1985). Focal contacts have also been implicated in changes that occur following transformation. Certain oncogene products, known to be tyrosine-specific protein kinases, have been localized in focal contacts (Rohrschneider, 1980) and vinculin has been shown to contain elevated levels of phosphotyrosine following transformation (Sefton *et al.* 1981).

We sought to examine whether there is any direct relationship between the pattern of adhesion and commitment to *S* phase. In this experiment we scored 3T3 cells for the presence or absence of focal contacts and the same cells for labelling with [^{3}H]thymidine (Table 1). On the smallest islands (400 μm^2), about one third of the cells were labelled and many of them had no visible focal contacts during the time they would be committed to the G_1–S transition. Although cells with focal contacts were more likely to become labelled there was no significant predictive value of the adhesion pattern for entry into *S* phase.

CONCLUSIONS AND FUTURE PROSPECTS

These findings demonstrate that 'contact stimulation' can be given by small substrata on which cells are still quite rounded in shape. Focal contacts can form,

Table 1. *Focal contacts and commitment to S phase*

	Focal contacts	Few or no focal contacts
Labelled nuclei	16	5
Not labelled	32	19

Quiescent 3T3 cells were seeded on island patterned coverslips. After 5 h, cells on 400 μm^2 islands were scored for the presence or absence of focal contacts using IRM. All the cells were exposed to [^{3}H]thymidine for 18 h and then prepared for autoradiography. The same cells in which adhesions had been recorded earlier were then scored for labelled nuclei.

even on these small substrata, but it is not clear how closely these, and the concomitant changes in the actin cytoskeleton, are involved in the changes in cell activity that follow contact. They do not seem to be involved directly since their presence or absence cannot be used to predict entry into *S* phase. This is perhaps not surprising since much previous work has suggested the stochastic nature of the G_1–S transition (Smith & Martin, 1973). Other studies have shown that the speed of locomotion of cells cannot predict eventual age at mitosis, even though the mean speed of the population can be closely correlated with mean age at mitosis (O'Neill *et al.* 1985). It seems that both the structural changes we have described here and locomotion are only manifestations of some unknown regulatory activity.

The findings reported here support the suggestion that the cytoskeleton could act as a modulator between the cell surface and the nucleus. Evidence is emerging that gene expression of cytoskeletal proteins can be influenced both by their polymerization state and by cell shape. This appears to occur at both the transcriptional and translational levels (Cleveland *et al.* 1981; Farmer *et al.* 1983; Ungar *et al.* 1986). There is also evidence that cell shape can affect the post-translational processing of proteins leading to secretion when the cells are able to spread, or their retention in the membrane when cells are kept rounded (Kabat *et al.* 1985). It is interesting to compare the focal contacts we see here with the patches that accompany the stimulation of lymphocytes to proliferate. Both involve the anchoring of ligand–receptor complexes to cytoskeletal elements and it is possible that patches and focal contacts convey similar signals to the cell interior (Vasiliev & Gelfand, 1982).

Patterned substrata allow us to control cell structure, without recourse to drugs, while many other variables are kept constant. Using homogeneous island sizes, which force all the cells in a dish to adopt similar shapes, we will be able to study the proliferative stimulus using biochemical techniques. Thus patterned substrata open the door to the study of the relationship between cell structure and the regulation of cellular metabolism.

Part of this work was done at the MRC Cell Biophysics Unit, London, while G.W.I. and P.D.-H. were funded by NIMR, Mill Hill, London. G.W.I. was also in receipt of grants from the Nuffield Foundation and the Cancer Research Campaign. We would like to thank Dr D. A. Rees for encouragement and support, Dr C. Stern for commenting on the manuscript and Professor T. Wieland for his gift of rhodamine phalloidin.

REFERENCES

Abercrombie, M. & Dunn, G. A. (1975). Adhesions of fibroblasts to substratum during contact inhibition observed by interference reflection microscopy. *Expl Cell Res.* **92**, 57–62.

Boocock, C. A., Brown, A. F. & Dunn, G. A. (1985). A simple chamber for observing microscopic specimens in both top and side views. *J. Microsc.* **137**, 29–34.

Carter, S. B. (1967). Haptotaxis and the mechanism of cell motility. *Nature, Lond.* **213**, 256–260.

Cleveland, D. W., Lopata, M. A., Sherline, P. & Kirschner, M. W. (1981). Unpolymerised tubulin modulates the level of tubulin mRNAs. *Cell* **25**, 537–546.

Connell, L. & Burridge, K. (1982). A new protein of the adhesion plaque. *J. Cell Biol.* **95**, 299a.

Couchman, J. R. & Rees, D. A. (1979). The behaviour of fibroblasts migrating from chick heart explants: changes in adhesion, locomotion and growth, and in the distribution of actomyosin and fibronectin. *J. Cell Sci.* **39**, 149–165.

Dunn, G. A. & Ireland, G. W. (1984). New evidence that growth in 3T3 cell cultures is a diffusion-limited process. *Nature, Lond.* **312**, 63–65.

Farmer, S. R., Wan, K. M., Ben-Ze'ev, A. & Penman, S. (1983). Regulation of actin mRNA levels and translation responds to changes in cell configuration. *Molec. cell. Biol.* **3**, 182–189.

Flanaghan, J. & Koch, G. L. E. (1978). Cross-linked Ig attaches to actin. *Nature, Lond.* **273**, 278–281.

Folkman, J. & Moscona, A. (1978). Role of cell shape in growth control. *Nature, Lond.* **273**, 345–349.

Geiger, B. (1979). A 130K protein from chicken gizzard; its localisation at the termini of microfilament bundles in cultured chicken cells. *Cell* **18**, 193–205.

Harris, A. K. (1973). Behaviour of cultured cells on substrata of variable adhesiveness. *Expl Cell Res.* **77**, 285–297.

Heath, J. P. (1983). Direct evidence for microfilament-mediated capping of surface receptors on crawling fibroblasts. *Nature, Lond.* **302**, 532–534.

Heath, J. P. & Dunn, G. A. (1978). Cell to substratum contacts of chick fibroblasts and their relation to the microfilament system. A correlated interference reflection and high voltage electron microscope study. *J. Cell Sci.* **29**, 197–212.

Heath, J. P. & Ireland, G. W. (1985). Morphology and behaviour of fibroblasts after stimulation by growth factors. *Eur. J. Cell Biol* **36**, Suppl. 8, 15.

Heaysman, J. E. M., Pegrum, S. M. & Preston, T. M. (1982). Spreading chick fibroblasts. A correlated study using phase contrast microscopy, RIM, TEM, and SEM. *Expl Cell Res.* **140**, 85–93.

Herman, B. & Pledger, W. J. (1985). Platelet-derived growth factor-induced alterations in vinculin and actin distribution in BALB/c–3T3 cells. *J. Cell Biol.* **100**, 1031–1040.

Ireland, G. W. & Stern, C. D. (1982). Cell–substrate contacts in cultured chick embryonic cells: an interference reflection study. *J. Cell Sci.* **58**, 165–183.

Ireland, G. W. & Voon, F. C. T. (1981). Polygonal networks in living chick embryo cells. *J. Cell Sci.* **52**, 55–69.

Izzard, C. S. & Lochner, L. R. (1976). Cell-to-substrate contacts in living fibroblasts: an interference reflection study with an evaluation of the technique. *J. Cell Sci.* **21**, 129–159.

Kabat, D., Gliniak, B., Rohrschneider, L. & Polonoff, E. (1985). Cell anchorage determines whether mammary tumour virus glycoproteins are processed for plasma membranes or secretion. *J. Cell Biol.* **101**, 2274–2283.

Lazarides, E. (1976). Actin, α-actinin and tropomyosin interaction in the structural organisation of actin filaments in non-muscle cells. *J. Cell Biol.* **68**, 202–219.

Leighton, J., Brada, F., Estes, L. W. & Justh, G. (1969). Secretory activity and oncogenicity of a cell line (MDCK) derived from canine kidney. *Science* **163**, 472–473.

Maness, P. F. & Walsh, R. C. (1982). Dihydrocytochalasin B disorganises actin architecture and inhibits initiation of DNA synthesis in 3T3 cells. *Cell* **30**, 253–262.

Maroudas, N. G. (1973). Growth of fibroblasts on linear and planar anchorages of limiting dimensions. *Expl Cell Res.* **81**, 104–110.

Mellstrom, K., Hoglund, A.-S., Nister, M., Heldin, C.-H., Westermark, B. & Lindberg, U. (1983). The effect of platelet-derived growth factor on morphology and motility of human glial cells. *J. Muscle Res. Cell Motil.* **4**, 589–609.

MINETT, T. W., TIGHE, B. J., LYDON, M. J. & REES, D. A. (1984). Requirements for cell spreading on polyhema coated culture substrates. *Cell Biol. Int. Rep.* **8**, 151–159.

O'NEILL, C. H., JORDAN, P. & IRELAND, G. W. (1986). Evidence for two distinct mechanisms of anchorage stimulation in freshly-explanted and 3T3 Swiss mouse fibroblasts. *Cell* **44**, 489–496.

O'NEILL, C. H., RIDDLE, P. N. & ROZENGURT, E. (1985). Stimulating the proliferation of 3T3 fibroblasts by peptide growth factors or by agents which elevate cellular cyclic AMP levels has opposite effects on motility. *Expl Cell Res.* **156**, 65–78.

OTSUKA, H. & MOSKOWITZ, M. (1975). Arrest of 3T3 cells in G1 phase in suspension culture. *J. cell. Physiol.* **87**, 213–220.

PONTEN, J. & STOLT, L. (1980). Proliferation control in cloned normal and malignant human cells. *Expl Cell Res.* **129**, 367–375.

REES, D. A., BADLEY, R. A., LLOYD, C. W., THOM, D. & SMITH, C. G. (1978). Glycoproteins in the recognition of substratum by cultured fibroblasts. In *Cell–Cell Recognition, SEB Symp. XXXII*, pp. 241–260. Cambridge University Press.

ROHRSCHNEIDER, L. R. (1980). Adhesion plaques of Rous sarcoma virus-transformed cells contain the *src* gene product. *Proc. natn. Acad. Sci. U.S.A.* **77**, 3514–3518.

SEFTON, B. M., HUNTER, T., BALL, E. H. & SINGER, S. J. (1981). Vinculin: a cytoskeletal target of the transforming protein of Rous sarcoma virus. *Cell* **24**, 165–174.

SMITH, J. A. & MARTIN, L. (1973). Do cells cycle? *Proc. natn. Acad. Sci. U.S.A.* **70**, 1263–1267.

SORANNO, T. & BELL, E. (1982). Cytostructural dynamics of spreading and translocating cells. *J. Cell Biol.* **95**, 127–136.

STOKER, M. G. P. (1973). Role of diffusion boundary layer in contact inhibition of growth. *Nature, Lond.* **246**, 200–203.

STOKER, M., O'NEILL, C., BERRYMAN, S. & WAXMAN, V. (1968). Anchorage and growth regulation in normal and virus-transformed cells. *Int. J. Cancer* **3**, 683–693.

UNGAR, F., GEIGER, B. & BEN-ZE'EV, A. (1986). Cell contact- and shape-dependent regulation of vinculin synthesis in cultured fibroblasts. *Nature, Lond.* **319**, 787–791.

VASILIEV, J. M. (1982). Spreading and locomotion of tissue cells: factors controlling the distribution of pseudopodia. *Phil. Trans. R. Soc. Lond.* B **299**, 159–167.

VASILIEV, J. M. & GELFAND, I. M. (1982). Possible common mechanism of morphological and growth-related alterations accompanying neoplastic transformation. *Proc. natn. Acad. Sci. U.S.A.* **79**, 2594–2597.

WEHLAND, J., OSBORN, M. & WEBER, K. (1979). Cell to substratum contacts in living cells: a direct correlation between interference reflection and indirect-immunofluorescence microscopy using antibodies against actin and α-actinin. *J. Cell Sci.* **37**, 257–273.

WESTERMARK, B. (1978). Growth control in miniclones of human glial cells. *Expl Cell Res.* **111**, 295–299.

J. Cell Sci. Suppl. 8, 35–54 (1987)
Printed in Great Britain © *The Company of Biologists Limited 1987*

THE PHYSICS OF CELL MOTILITY

GEORGE F. OSTER

Departments of Biophysics, Entomology & Zoology, University of California, Berkeley, CA 94720, USA

AND ALAN S. PERELSON

Theoretical Division, Los Alamos National Laboratory, Los Alamos, NM 87545, USA

SUMMARY

Cell locomotion begins with a protrusion from the leading periphery of the cell. What drives this extension? Here we present a model for the extension of cell protuberances that unifies certain aspects of this phenomenon, and is based on the hypothesis that osmotic pressure drives cell extensions. This pressure arises from membrane-associated reactions, which liberate osmotically active particles, and from the swelling of the actin network that underlies the membrane.

INTRODUCTION: WHAT ARE THE FORCES DRIVING CELL MOTILITY?

Cells possess several mechanisms for exerting forces on their surroundings. In particular, a number of mechanochemical enzymes have been identified, including myosin, dynein and kinesin; other molecules will probably be identified in the future. All of these molecules share a common characteristic: they enable the cell to exert only contractile forces. This is a puzzling situation, since in order to move about cells must also be capable of generating protrusive forces. Placing cells in hypertonic media seems to suppress all protrusive activity, suggesting that protrusive force generation may be produced by simple osmotic pressure (Harris, 1973; Trinkaus, 1984, 1985). But osmotic pressure is an isotropic force: it acts equally in all directions. Therefore, in order to use pressure for protrusion, the cell must devise means to focus the force in particular directions. In the next section we propose a mechanism by which osmotic forces drive cell protrusion, and which is coordinated with the polymerization of the actin network that fills such protrusions. This model is an extension of two previous models we have proposed for lamellipod and acrosomal extension.

MODELS FOR CELL PROTRUSION

Cells move by extending their periphery in a number of motile appendages. These protrusions are usually classified according to their appearance: lamellae, filopods, microspikes, pseudopods or blebs (Trinkaus, 1984). The chemical steps involved in creating these appendages are turning out to be extraordinarily complex, and it is easy to lose sight of a simple fact of physics: in order to extend its periphery the cell must generate a protrusive force. Since actin polymerization is generally associated with protrusive activity, there seems to be a general feeling that this polymerization can 'push' the cell periphery outwards. Upon closer examination, however, this idea seems untenable, for there is no evidence that the event of actin polymerization is associated with any conformational change that could produce a mechanical force, such as that produced by myosin head movements. But if the chemical process of polymerization cannot itself generate a protrusive force, how can one explain the intimate association of actin polymerization with protrusive activity? We propose here a physicochemical mechanism for resolving this apparent paradox. Our model is built on the notion that the processes involving actin polymerization upset the local osmotic pressure equilibrium, and it is this unbalanced osmotic force that drives protrusion. However, there are several ways in which a cell can generate and control an osmotic pressure differential. We begin with a particularly simple system: the acrosomal process in the sea cucumber, *Thyone*.

Elongation of the acrosomal process in Thyone

One of the most dramatic examples of cell protrusive activity is the elongation of the acrosomal process in the sperm of echinoderms. In the sea cucumber, *Thyone*, the acrosome can extend 90 μm in less than 10 s. The acrosomal process is filled with actin fibres; Tilney & Kallenbach (1979), on the basis of evidence cited below, concluded that actin polymerization must drive the elongation process. As we will show, however, it turns out that actin polymerization is too slow to account for the dramatically rapid growth of the *Thyone* acrosomal process, and so we present an alternative explanation (Oster *et al.* 1982): that osmotically generated hydrostatic forces drive the extension and that actin polymerization acts to form and stabilize the tube-like shape of the growing structure. That is, actin ultimately forms a rigid supporting structure that allows the acrosome to keep its shape once equilibrium is reached, but actin polymerization does not push the acrosome outwards.

Does actin polymerization drive acrosomal extension? Fig. 1 is a schematic illustration of the acrosomal reaction in *Thyone*. When the sperm comes in contact with the jelly coat of an egg the acrosomal reaction is initiated. The acrosomal vacuole fuses with the plasma membrane, and actin monomers stored in the periacrosomal cup begin polymerizing from the actomere, a nucleation site on the cell nucleus (Tilney *et al.* 1983). Once nucleated, filaments grow outward from the actomere. Labelling with myosin subfragment 1 indicates that the growing fibres are unidirectionally polarized with their barbed end oriented toward the plasma membrane (Tilney & Kallenbach, 1979). The actin within the periacrosomal cup is not free, but is complexed with profilin and two other actin binding proteins to prevent spontaneous nucleation within the periacrosomal cup (Tilney *et al.* 1983).

Experiments by Tilney & Inoué (1982, 1985) show that, as the acrosome grows, its length increases in proportion to the square root of time, a dependence that is generally characteristic of diffusion processes. If monomer has to diffuse from the periacrosomal cup to the growing tip of a fibre before it can polymerize, one might expect the rate of fibre growth to be limited by the rate of monomer diffusion, and hence the length of the fibres would increase as the square root of time. If this is the

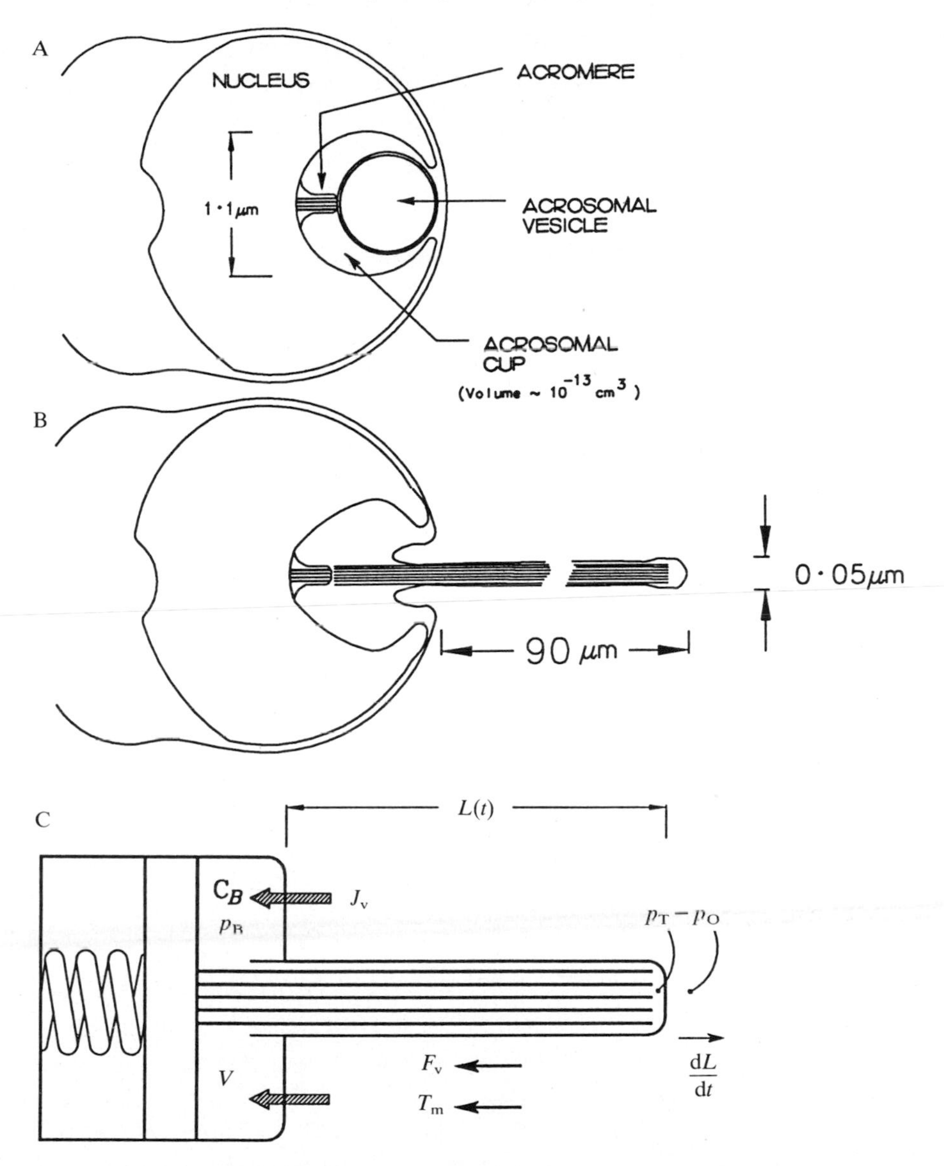

Fig. 1. A. A schematic diagram of the acrosomal process in *Thyone*. The acrosomal process grows from the acromere, a nucleating structure at the base of the acrosomal cup, which contains concentrated actin–profilin complexes. B. Upon activation, the membrane of the acrosomal vesicle fuses with the plasma membrane and there ensues a rapid influx of water into the acrosomal cup, doubling its volume in some 70 ms. The acrosomal cup is filled with profilin–actin complexes, which diffuse to the growing tip, dissociate, and the G-actin polymerizes onto the ends of the actin fibres. The acrosomal process extends some 90 μm in less than 10 s (see Tilney *et al.* 1978; Tilney & Inoué, 1982, 1985; Oster *et al.* 1982). Note the bulbous tip region, which may indicate osmotic swelling in this region. C. A schematic diagram of the model acrosome. After inflation by osmotic influx of water, J_v, the acrosomal cup has a volume $V \approx 10^{-13}\,\text{cm}^3$. Because of the elasticity of the cup, there is a hydrostatic pressure, p_B. The tip extends at velocity dL/dt, where $L(t)$ is the length of the acrosome at time t. The driving force for extension is the pressure drop at the tip: $p_T - p_0$, where p_0 is the external pressure. The only forces opposing the extension are frictional drag, F_v, and membrane tension T_m.

case, then would this not prove that the extension of the acrosome is driven by the actin polymerization reaction? The answer appears to be no. We show in Appendix 1 that diffusion of monomer and actin polymerization at the growing tip does lead to a fibre growth rate that is proportional to $t^{\frac{1}{2}}$. However, unlike estimates made by Tilney & Kallenbach (1979), we find that the growth rate of the acrosomal process, when limited by monomer diffusion, is approximately an order of magnitude smaller than that observed.

Hydrostatic pressure could drive the elongation of the acrosome. The periacrosomal cup contains a very high concentration of protein. Tilney & Inoué (1982) estimated the concentration of actin, profilin and other actin binding proteins to be 370 mg ml^{-1}. The protein would occupy a substantial fraction of the volume of the periacrosomal cup and, because of excluded volume effects, would generate a considerable osmotic pressure (cf. Minton, 1983). The molecular weights of actin and haemoglobin are similar. Using the data in fig. 3 of Minton (1983) for haemoglobin we conclude that at a concentration of 370 mg ml^{-1} profilactin would generate an osmotic pressure of approximately 400 torr (T).

Experiments by Dan *et al.* (1964, 1967) on the early events in the acrosomal reaction demonstrated that in the sea-urchin sperm there is roughly a threefold volume increase in the region occupied by actin, and an even larger increase in volume in starfish sperm. Inoué & Tilney (1982) found that within 50–70 ms after induction, the volume of the acrosomal region nearly doubles and there is a precipitous drop in the refractive index of the periacrosomal region. Taken together, these data indicate that there is a considerable influx of water into the periacrosomal region of the sperm (see also Green, 1978). We believe that such a rapid water influx could create a temporary hydrostatic pressure increase, which could extend the acrosomal process. The rapid water influx could be considered analogous to taking a deep breath when about to blow up a balloon, and then exhaling, which relieves the increase in pressure and inflates the balloon, analogous to the extending acrosomal process.

Oster *et al.* (1982) constructed a detailed mechanical model for such a mechanism. This model for acrosomal elongation assumes that a pressure differential drives the elongation. Interestingly, the model also predicted that the length of the acrosome should grow in proportion to the square root of time. Further they were able *quantitatively* to fit the data of Tilney & Inoué (1982) for the rate of acrosomal extension with their data. Because the mechanical properties of the acrosomal membrane have not been measured, there is still some uncertainty as to whether the parameter values Oster *et al.* chose to fit the data are realistic. However, this modelling exercise does show that hydrostatic pressure can drive acrosomal elongation at realistic rates. In order to test these predictions, Tilney & Inoué (1985) varied the tonicity of the medium outside the sperm. As predicted by the model, increasing the osmolarity of the medium, which would reduce the osmotic driving force for water inflow and hence the subsequent hydrostatic pressure increase, decreased the rate of acrosomal elongation and the final length the process obtained. At a tonicity of 1·5 times that of normal sea water acrosomal process formation is

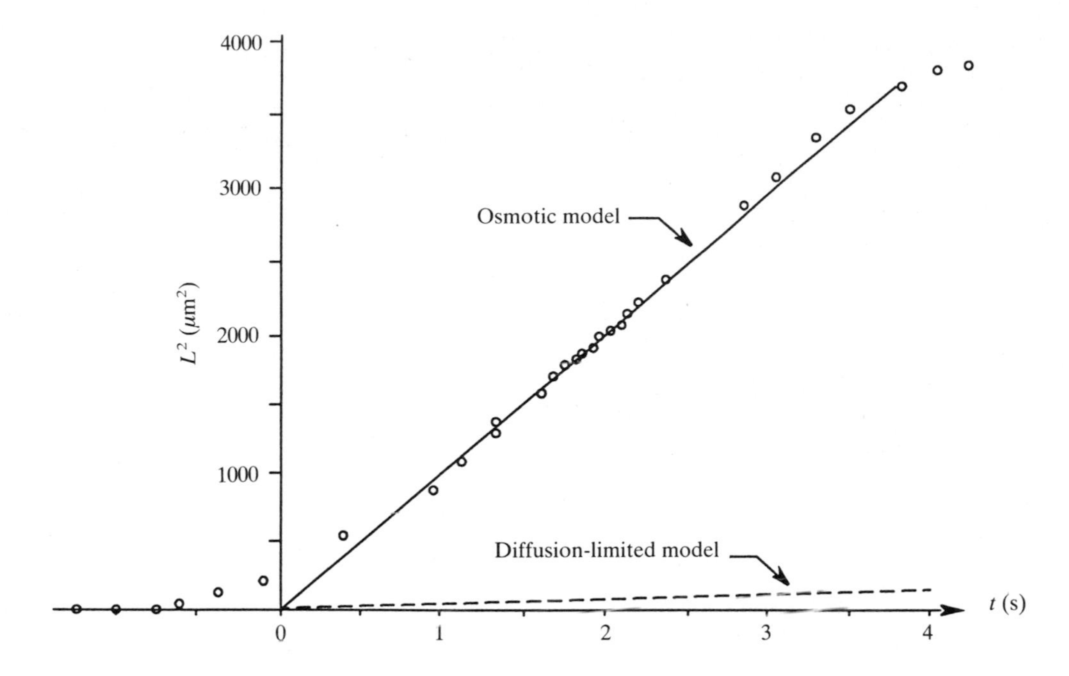

Fig. 2. A plot of the square of the acrosome length, L^2, as a function of time, t. The data points are from the experiments of Tilney & Inoué (1982, 1985); the continuous line is computed from the osmotic model (see Oster *et al.* 1982, for the exact parameter values employed in the simulation). The broken line is computed from the diffusion-limited polymerization model (Perelson & Coutsias, 1986). Even assuming polymerization is instantaneous, the slope of the diffusion model is less than 35 $\mu m^2 s^{-1}$, compared with 960 $\mu m^2 s^{-1}$ for the experimental points. Therefore diffusion-limited polymerization of actin at the tip of the acrosome cannot drive the extension process fast enough.

completely inhibited. Conversely, decreasing the tonicity of the suspending medium (which should increase the osmotic driving force) led to an increased rate of acrosomal elongation and increased the final length of the process.

Water inflow into the acrosome is a transient process. Thus it can create the force necessary to extend the acrosome, but it cannot maintain that force. The pressure will eventually equalize throughout the system, and unless a cytoskeletal rearrangement occurs, the acrosomal process cannot remain extended. However, during its transient existence the hydrostatic pressure imbalance can do more than simply extend the membrane of the acrosome: it can also drive flows of cytoplasm up the acrosome and hence transport profilactin at a rate that is greater than that attainable by pure diffusion. At this increased rate of transport actin polymerization could keep up with the growth of the acrosomal process, so that the acrosome always appeared to be filled with actin filaments.

Simulation of the model acrosome. The model acrosome is shown schematically in Fig. 1B; the equations are given in Appendix 2. Fig. 2 shows a plot of the square of the acrosome length as a function of time. The osmotic pressure model can fit the data quite well, for the frictional drag forces on the acrosomal cylinder conspire to produce a linear L^2 *versus* t plot just as a pure diffusion process would (cf. Appendix 1).

Data from Tilney & Inoué (1985) show that varying the osmotic environment of the sperm changes both the extension rate and the maximum length of the acrosomal process. The osmotic model is capable of simulating the extension rate quite well (Perelson & Oster, unpublished data); however, this should not be taken as *proof* that the acrosome is driven by osmotic pressure from the acrosomal cup. We can only make two claims. First, simple diffusion of actin is not fast enough to account for the extension rate. Second, the osmotic model can account for the linear relation between the square of the length and time as well as the dependence of the slope on external osmolarity. At the very least, the success of the model in fitting the data should call attention to controlled osmotic forces as a general mechanism for cell protrusion. With this encouragement, we shall outline below a model for other kinds of extension processes in motile cells. First, however, we shall investigate a modification of the above model that incorporates some additional considerations, which may explain the bulbous tip of the acrosomal process (see Fig. 1B).

Osmotically coupled polymerization. In the above model the driving force for elongation was generated in the acrosomal cup by its large concentration of profilactin. This may not be the complete story, however. In order to form actin filaments, actin–profilin complexes diffuse to the tip of the acrosome where they dissociate into actin and profilin, the actin adding to existing filaments and extending them (Tilney *et al.* 1983). Why does the actin–profilin complex dissociate only at the acrosome tip? One possibility is that there are cleaving enzymes associated with the tip structure. In this connection, Lassing & Lindberg (1985) showed that the inositol lipid, phosphatidylinositol 4,5-bisphosphate (PIP_2) can mediate the cleavage of profilactin into actin monomer and profilin. This cleavage increases the particle number at the membrane and, coupled with consequent counterion changes, may drive an osmotic influx of water at the growing tip of the acrosome. One might expect the tip to take on a slightly bulbous shape due to this water influx, and indeed this is observed (Tilney & Inoué, 1982, 1985).

In order to quantify possible osmotic effects associated with dissociation of profilactin, we have developed a model for acrosomal extension that couples osmotic drive due to profilactin dissociation and actin polymerization. We call this process *osmotically coupled polymerization* (Fig. 3). We assume that profilactin stored in the base of the acrosome diffuses to the tip of the growing acrosome. At the tip it is cleaved (e.g. by PIP_2) into actin and profilin. The free actin diffuses within the acrosome and adds to filament free ends *via* a reversible reaction. The free profilin also diffuses within the acrosome away from its source of generation, the acrosomal tip. The tip of the acrosome is assumed to move outwards due to the generation of an osmotically driven inflow. We impose volume conservation so that each μm^3 of water that enters increases the volume of the acrosome by the same amount. As space is created and actin monomers released, actin filaments are able to elongate until they reach the membrane. The equations describing the model are given in Appendix 3 (full details of the model will be published elsewhere).

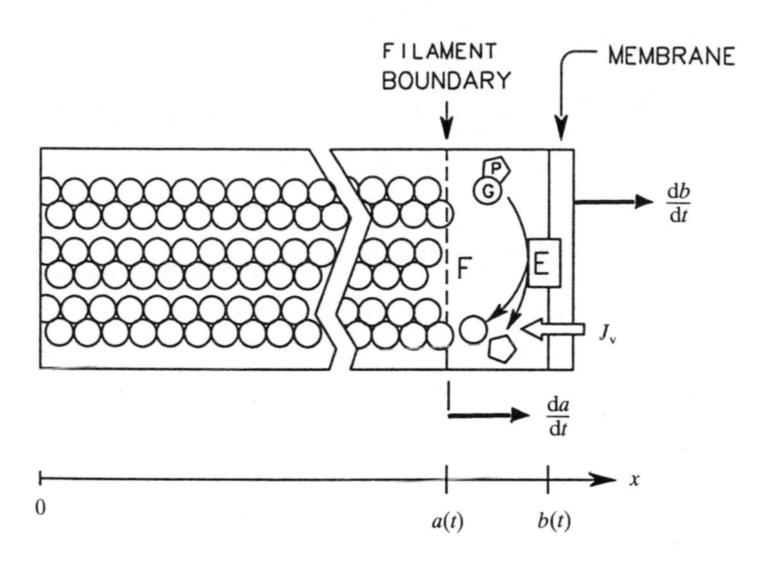

Fig. 3. The osmotically coupled polymerization model. Actin–profilin complexes diffuse to the plasma membrane where they are cleaved by the enzyme, E, to G-actin and profilin. The particle gain creates an osmotic influx, J_v, which drives the boundary, $b(t)$ to the right at velocity db/dt. The G-actin polymerizes onto the fibres, F, which grow at a rate da/dt.

Preliminary simulations of this model indicate that, as a model for acrosomal elongation, it suffers from the same diffusional limitations as does the pure polymerization model of Appendix 1. That is, the rate of diffusion of profilactin from the periacrosomal cup to the membrane limits the rate of elongation of the acrosomal process below that observed by Tilney & Inoué. If enough osmotically active particles are created at the tip per profilactin cleaved, then the acrosome will be able to elongate at speeds consistent with observation. However, under such circumstances the actin fibres will not be able to keep up with the elongating membrane and a gap will form between the two. A combined model, which takes into consideration convective transport of prolifactin to the tip, due to osmotic water inflows at the base, along with osmotic extension of the tip due to reactions associated with the cleavage of profilactin, may well be able to account for all of the experimental observations. We shall report on this model elsewhere. Indeed, it is likely that the acrosome extension is driven by a two-step process, the initial extension being driven by the hydrostatic pressure generated at the base, and the final stages by the osmotic influx at the tip.

While our analysis of the acrosomal process demonstrates that osmotic forces are physically capable of driving the acrosomal extension, it does not prove that acrosomal elongation actually works this way; this issue can only be settled experimentally. For protuberances, such as microspikes and lamellipodia, which grow much more slowly than the acrosome, the speed of diffusional transport of profilactin to the growing membrane would not be limiting, and the osmotically coupled polymerization model may be appropriate. In any event, such a model is useful for it provides a unified view of how force generation and actin polymerization are coordinated during cell locomotion.

Protrusion of the cell periphery: microspikes and lamellipodia

Two common locomotory appendages are lamellipodia and microspikes. Lamellipodia are broad, flat cytoplasmic sheets, filled with an actin network, and largely devoid of other organelles. Microspikes are slender protuberances that resemble the acrosomal process, except that the actin fibres do not terminate in an electron-dense cap, as in the acrosome, but flare into a meshwork gel, i.e. they often appear to terminate in tiny lamellipodia. Typically, microspikes and lamellipodia are extended and retracted during motile activity; when they adhere to the substratum, the retractive forces pull the cell forward. Frequently, a neural growth cone will advance by 'filling in' a lamellipod web between two microspikes. Here we shall present a model for the protrusion of these organelles, but we shall not address the problem of attachment or of subsequent retraction.

In a previous model for lamellipodia we suggested that the swelling of the actin gel could drive protrusion (Oster, 1984; Oster & Perelson, 1985). Since then, however, the role of inositol lipids regulating protrusive activity has received much attention. In the light of these recent findings we propose an elaboration of our earlier model*.

Cortical events accompanying protrusion. When a chemoattractant binds to cell surface receptors it triggers a complex sequence of events that culminates in extension of the cell surface in the neighbourhood of those receptors. The chemical reactions that cascade from the ligand–receptor interaction are quite complex, and have yet to be completely elucidated (Omann *et al.* 1987). Even were they known, it would be idle to attempt a model that incorporates all of these reactions. However, by focusing only on the mechanical consequences of the biochemistry, one can make some progress in understanding the physics underlying cell protrusion. Fig. 7B summarizes some of the cortical events that may be involved.

1. *Inositol lipid metabolism.* Binding of a ligand to a chemoattractant receptor initiates a sequence of reactions in the cell cortex. The ligand binding event is first translated into an intracellular signal through the agent of a G-protein, which, by binding GTP, activates a phosphodiesterase on the cytoplasmic face of the plasma membrane (Berridge, 1986; and Fig. 4). This lipase cleaves the inositol lipid, phosphatidylinositol 4,5-bisphosphate (PIP_2), into diacylglycerol (DAG) and inositol triphosphate (IP_3). Each of these substances participates in subsequent reactions, which have the following mechanical effects on the cell cortex. (1) *Membrane bending moments.* The cleavage of PIP_2 into DAG can produce a mechanical effect since the shape of the lipid changes from cylindrical to conical (Cullis & Hope, 1985; Chernomordik *et al.* 1985). Thus the DAG that remains in the

*Most of the ideas for this proposal grew from conversations with T. Stossell, K. Zaner, P. Janmey, J. Hartwig & H. Yin, of the Hematology & Oncology Unit of the Massachusetts General Hospital.

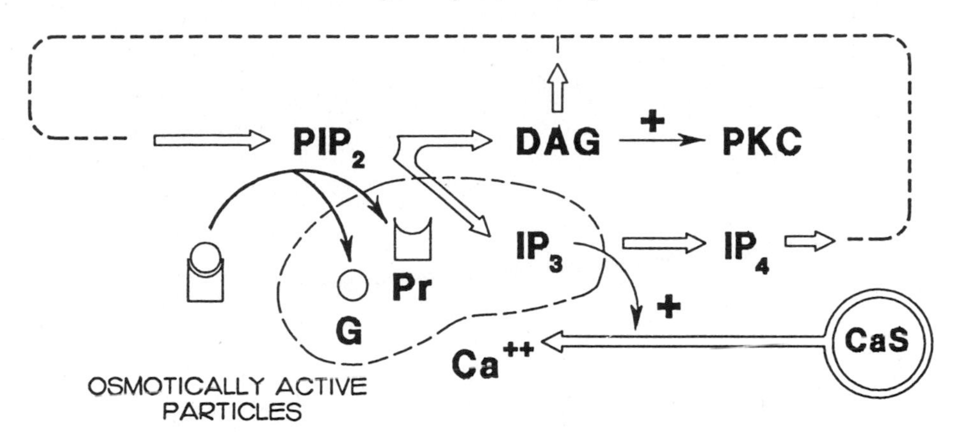

Fig. 4. Part of the inositol lipid pathway that affects cell protrusion. PIP_2, phosphatidylinositol 4,5-bisphosphate; IP_3, inositol triphosphate; DAG, diacylglycerol; PKC, protein kinase C; G, G-actin; Pr, profilin; CaS, calcium sequestered in the endoplasmic reticulum. PIP_2 cleaves profilactin into G + Pr, and is itself cleaved into DAG and IP_3. IP_3 is released into the cytoplasm where it joins G and Pr as osmotically active particles. The broken line indicates the resynthesis pathway for PIP_2.

membrane generates a bending moment that can be several orders of magnitude above kT. This bending moment can buckle the membrane outwards if the local concentration of DAG is sufficiently high. While we do not believe this effect is very important in cell protrusion, we do not have enough information to discount its importance. (2) *Interfacial osmotic effects.* The receptor–ligand signal initiates several reactions that result in the release of osmotically active particles at the cytoplasmic face of the plasma membrane. These arise from the following sources: (a) PIP_2 can cleave profilactin into actin and profilin, resulting in a net doubling of the particle count (Lassing & Lindberg, 1985). We note in passing that, since G-actin is negatively charged and profilin positively charged, there can be a counterion osmotic effect; its magnitude will depend on the titration properties of the macromolecules. Unfortunately, there seems to be little titration data on cortical proteins. (b) Cleavage of PIP_2 releases IP_3 into the cytoplasm. This hydrolysis may also expose charge, which will induce counterions that are osmotically active.

2. *Calcium release and remodelling of the cortical actin gel.* IP_3 releases sequestered calcium from the endoplasmic reticulum (Berridge, 1986). Ip_3 (i.e. Ins(1,4,5)P3) is thence phosphorylated to IP_4 (i.e. Ins(1,3,4,5)P4). This appears to open Ca^{2+} channels in the plasma membrane, which may serve to replenish the release of internally sequestered Ca^{2+} (Houslay, 1987). While this rise in cytosolic Ca^{2+} also produces an osmotic effect, it is likely to be negligible compared to the osmolarity of the cortical cytoplasm. The rise in cytosolic Ca^{2+} produces a number of important mechanical effects on the actin network adjacent to the plasma membrane (cf. Fig. 5). (1) *The elastic modulus* of the cortical cytogel is regulated by solation and gelation proteins. An important class of cortical proteins regulates the degree of gelation of the cortical actin. For example, gelsolin binds two Ca ions, which appear to activate it to bind one or two actin monomers. With one bound actin, the

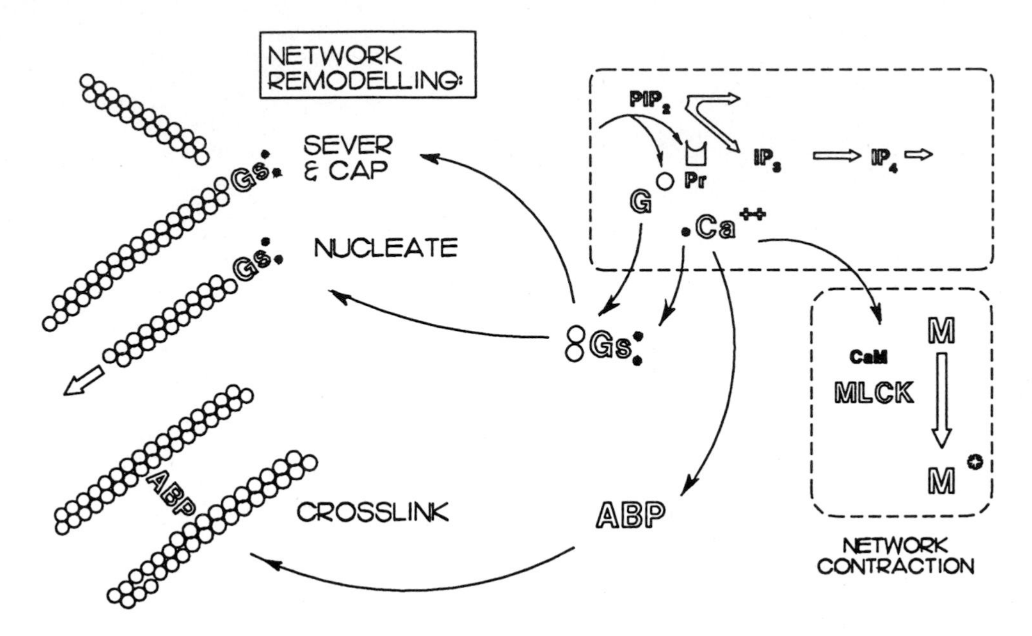

Fig. 5. Remodelling of the actin network during extension. Gelsolin (Gs) binds two calciums and either one or two G-actins. With one bound actin it can solate the actin gel by severing F-actin fibres, and cap the barbed end. With two bound actins it can nucleate the growth of new fibres. Crosslinking proteins, some of which may be calcium activated, promote gelation. Calcium also stimulates the slower process of contraction *via* calmodulin (CaM) and myosin light chain kinase (MLCK), which phosphorylates myosin: $M \rightarrow M^*$ (cf. Oster, 1984).

actin–gelsolin complex (AGs) can sever actin filaments and cap the (barbed) ends, thus preventing further elongation from the barbed ends. However, monomers can still add to the free (pointed) ends, since the concentration is probably above the critical concentration for elongation. Moreover, with two bound actins the complex (A_2Gs) can nucleate the growth of new filaments. The net effect is an increase in F-actin. Because of excluded volume effects, this probably causes a rise in osmotic pressure (K. Zaner, personal communication; Minton, 1983). More importantly, severing of the network weakens its elastic modulus, which enables it to expand under its gel osmotic pressure (Oster, 1984; Oster & Perelson, 1985). There are a number of other actin solation and gelation factors. However, for the purpose of modelling the cortical cytogel we can lump them all into a surrogate substance that can modulate the gelation state, and thus the elastic modulus, of the cytogel.

It is worth emphasizing that the osmotic pressure of a gel is different from the interfacial osmotic pressure generated by the collisions of solute particles with a membrane interface. Solute osmotic pressure induces water influx through the plasma membrane, and the resulting hydrostatic pressure is distributed uniformly over the cell. Gel swelling, however, is localized to the vicinity of the network disruption (Oster, 1984). (2) *Network reannealing.* While the calcium-activated gelsolin severs network strands and nucleates new strands, actin binding proteins

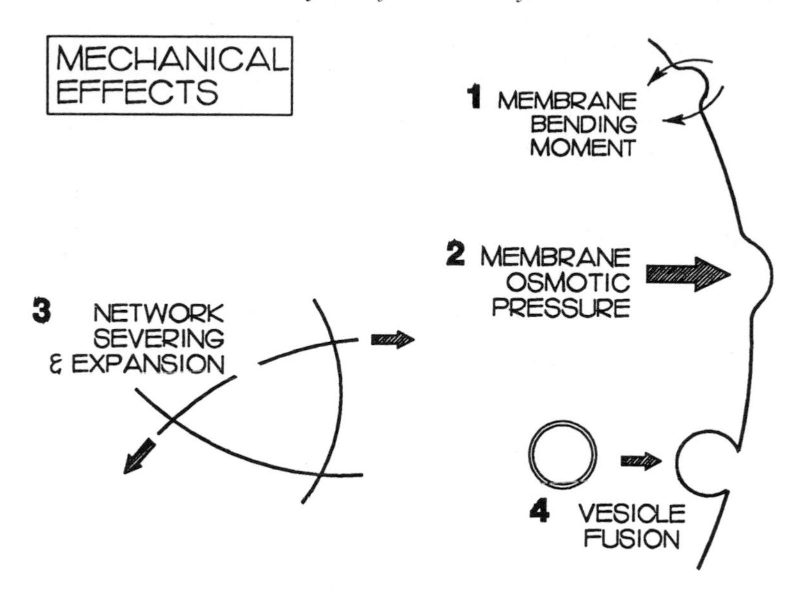

Fig. 6. Summary of the mechanical effects accompanying protrusion of the cell surface. 1. Cleavage of PIP_2 into DAG creates a membrane bending moment. 2. Profilin, G-actin and IP_3 (and perhaps counterions) create a membrane osmotic pressure. 3. Severing of F-actin by solating factors allows the network to expand under its gel swelling pressure. 4. Calcium stimulates fusion of vesicles with the plasma membrane, to supply the extra membrane for protrusion.

(ABP) are crosslinking the strands and reannealing the gel (ABPs are generally calcium-independent). Thus, the shift in gel–sol equilibrium results in remodelling of the network: first, it swells under its internal osmotic pressure as the fibres are severed, then it resolidifies as the new and remodelled fibres are crosslinked. (3) *Other calcium-stimulated events.* In addition to the foregoing events, the rise in cytosolic calcium also initiates many other reactions. Two that are relevant to protrusion are: (a) *Contraction of the gel.* Calcium release initiates phosphorylation of myosin light chain kinase, which leads to contraction of the gel. This is a slower process than protrusion; however, we shall not deal with this phase of the motility cycle here (Oster, 1984). (b) *Exocytosis of vesicles.* In many systems calcium stimulates exocytosis of membrane vesicles (Moore *et al.* 1987). Since protrusion necessitates an increase in the membrane area of the leading periphery, new membrane must either be inserted at the protuberance, or there must be surface flow of lipid into the region (Bretscher, 1984). Indeed, solation of the cortical cytoskeleton may facilitate the insertion of vesicles into the plasma membrane (Perrin *et al.* 1987).

The mechanochemical events listed above are summarized in Fig. 6 and Table 1. The theory cannot predict what fraction of the protrusive force arises from each of these processes: this will have to be settled by experiments.

A dynamical model for cortical protrusion. The cortical chemistry that accompanies protrusion is quite complex, and the description we outlined above will certainly have to be extended as more details become known. However, since our focus is on the physics of protrusion rather than the chemistry, we can give the

Table 1. *Some cortical reactants and their mechanical effects*

Component	Biochemical effect	Physical effect
PIP_2	Cleaves profilactin	
DAG	Activates PKC	Creates membrane bending moment
IP_3	Releases intracellular calcium	Osmotic solute
Profilin	Binds G-actin, prevents polymerization	Osmotic solute
Gelsolin	Binds calcium, severs F-actin, caps barbed end, nucleates fibres	Solation: reduces elastic modulus Gelation: increases elastic modulus
Calcium	Regulation of gelation and solation factors, activation of PKC	Negligible osmotic effect; possible counterion effect

PIP_2, phosphatidylinositol 4,5-bisphosphate; IP_3, inositol triphosphate; DAG, diacylglycerol; PKC, protein kinase C.

following scenario for extension of the cell periphery (cf. Fig. 7A). A complete mathematical treatment and numerical study of the model will be presented elsewhere; however, the equations of motion are very similar to that described in Appendix 3 for the acrosome model, with an additional contribution from swelling of the solated actin gel, a contribution probably not present in the acrosome.

Profilactin is free to diffuse in the cytoplasm. We regard the cytoplasmic face of the plasma membrane as a catalytic surface, where actin–profilin complexes are split (e.g. by PIP_2). There is a net particle gain at the cytoplasmic interface due to this cleavage and through the release of other osmotically active particles (e.g. IP_3). The effect of this release is to draw water in through the leading edge. (In writing the model equations, the net particle gain, including the counterion contributions, is incorporated into the osmotic coefficients of the actin and profilin.) Meanwhile, the actin network is being solated by the calcium-activated solation factors (e.g. gelsolin). This leads to an osmotic expansion of the network as its elastic modulus is weakened (Oster, 1984). The combined effects of the two osmotic forces push the leading edge outwards. In the model calculations we have not explicitly included membrane insertion coupled to the calcium release, nor have we modelled the growth and reannealing of the network due to nucleation and crosslinking. The effects of these processes are sufficiently complex to require separate treatment.

DISCUSSION

The physical chemistry underlying cell protrusion is quite complex, with reactions involving not only cytoskeletal components, but membrane-associated reactants as well. We have attempted to cut through this complexity by focusing on the mechanical forces that drive cortical extensions. We propose that osmotic forces of two sorts power these motions. First, interfacial osmotic pressure is generated on the cytoplasmic face of the plasma membrane by the release of osmotically active particles into the cytoplasm. Some of these reactions probably involve the inositol lipids, since PIP_2 is known to cleave profilactin into profilin and G-actin, and is itself

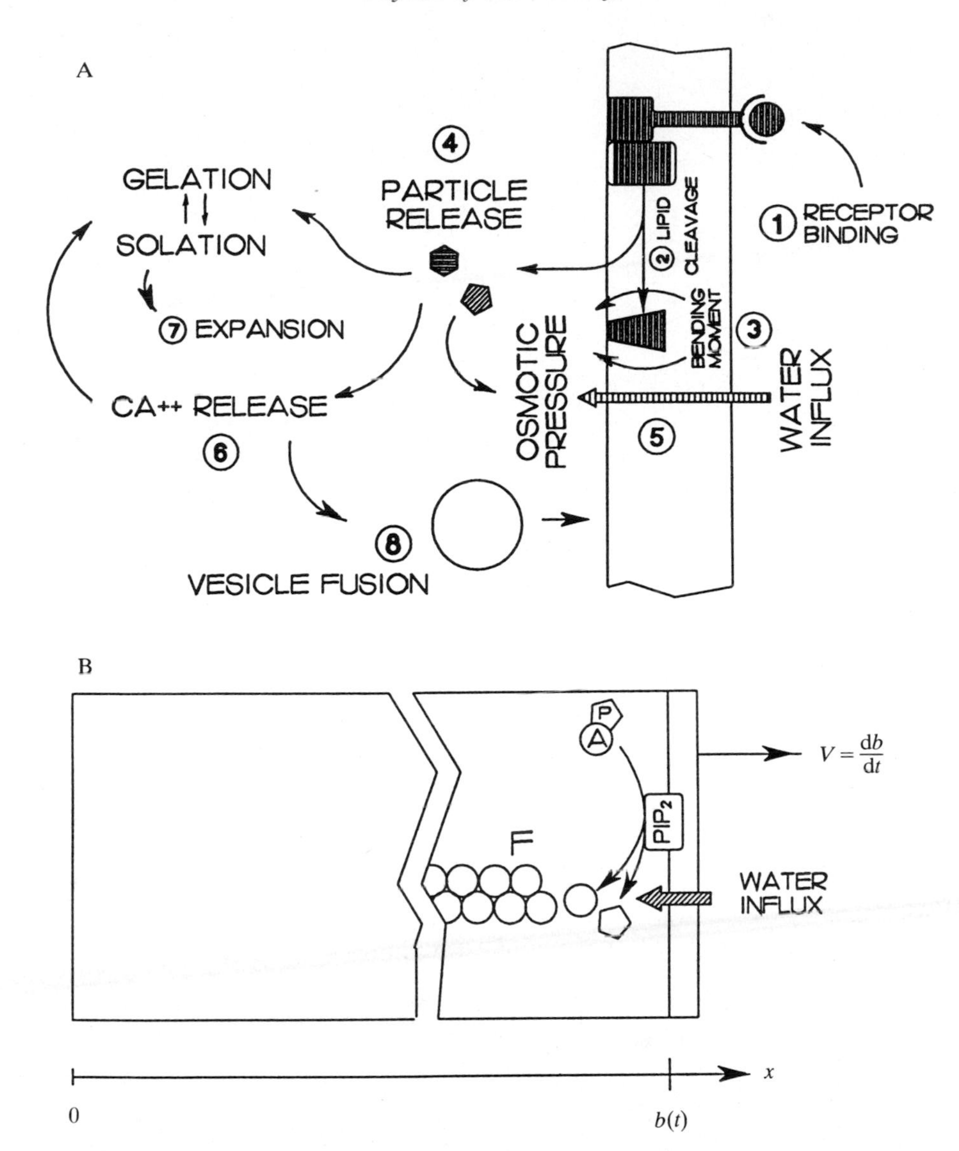

Fig. 7. A. The sequence of events accompanying cell protrusion. Receptors bind a chemoattractant (1), which, *via* a G-protein, stimulates lipid cleavage (2), which creates a bending moment (3). Osmotic particles are released (4) creating a membrane osmotic pressure, which drives a water influx (5). Calcium release (6) stimulates solation of the actin network allowing it to expand (7), and triggers vesicle fusion to supply membrane to the protrusion site (8). B. Schematic drawing of the model for microspike extension (from Perelson, Glasser & Oster, unpublished). Actin–profilin complexes are split, the free actin polymerizing onto the fibres (F). The osmotically driven water influx resulting from the particle gain and from the gel expansion pushes the boundary ($b(t)$) to the left at velocity $V = \mathrm{d}b/\mathrm{d}t$.

cleaved to DAG and IP_3, with the latter being released into the cytoplasm. Second, IP_3 triggers the release of intracellular calcium. Calcium, in turn, activates solating factors such as gelsolin, which sever actin strands, thus reducing its elastic modulus and enabling it to expand due to its gel osmotic swelling pressure. In addition to solating the gel, solating factors create free growing ends and new nucleating sites for the growth of actin fibres. Therefore, the expanded network can be quickly reannealed into a stable dilated configuration by crosslinking proteins such as ABP. Indeed, without reannealing the protrusion formed by the osmotic forces would collapse, as happens during the formation of blebs.

In order to investigate this scenario, we have modelled a simple protrusive system: the acrosome of *Thyone*. We find that osmotic forces can reproduce the experimental observations. The model is entirely consistent with the observation that increasing external osmolarity slows the extension process. Moreover, we can show that a process that involves only actin polymerization at the growing tip, with actin monomers supplied by diffusion, cannot match the speed of extension.

Finally, our analysis suggests that, using the inositol lipid pathway, cells can control local osmotic conditions so as to achieve directed locomotion in response to external stimuli. If this view has merit, it may suggest some new experimental interventions, and help explain the ubiquitous inhibition hyperosmotic conditions impose on cell protrusive activity.

APPENDIX 1

Diffusion is not fast enough to drive the acrosomal process

Perelson & Coutsias (1986) provided a detailed mathematical analysis of diffusion-limited actin filament growth. They analysed two models, one first presented by Tilney & Kallenbach (1979) and based on work of Hermans (1947), and a more realistic model that includes the reversibility of the polymerization reaction and the required movement of cytoplasm into the acrosome as it grows. Both models lead to roughly the same conclusion; here we present only the simpler analysis.

Assume the periacrosomal cup contains monomer at concentration c_0. For simplicity we shall assume c_0 remains constant throughout the growth process. This will overestimate the rate of acrosomal elongation, since depletion of monomer would slow down the growth process. Further, we assume that a set of fibres are nucleated and begin growing in one dimension from $x=0$ to a position $x=L(t)$ at time t. Monomer must diffuse from the reservoir at $x=0$ to the fibre tip at $x=L(t)$, where they can add to the end of the fibre and extend it. To calculate the maximal possible rate of growth we shall assume that the polymerization reaction is irreversible and that monomer addition occurs infinitely fast; that is, as soon as a monomer gets to $x=L(t)$ it instantaneously adds to the end of the fibre. This implies that c, the concentration of free monomer at $x=L(t)$ is zero, i.e. $c(L,t)=0$. Between $x=0$ and $x=L(t)$ monomer simply diffuses and hence must obey the diffusion equation:

$$\frac{\partial c}{\partial t}=D\frac{\partial^2 c}{\partial x^2}, \tag{1}$$

where D is the diffusion coefficient. The motion of the fibre tip at $x=L(t)$ is determined by mass conservation. The number of molecules reaching a unit area of the tip per unit time is the diffusional flux at $x = L(t)$. Assume that at the tip there are f fibres per unit area. Each time a monomer adds a fibre grows by a length λ. If there were 50 fibres per unit area and 100 molecules arrived per second then fibres would elongate at a rate of 2λ. Thus, f/λ is the concentration of free ends at the tip, where the following relation must hold:

$$\frac{dL}{dt} = \lambda \left[\frac{-D\frac{\partial c}{\partial x}\big|_{x=L}}{f} \right]. \tag{2}$$

Perelson & Coutsias (1986), following Hermans (1947), show that the solution to the diffusion equation (1) with the boundary moving as in equation (2) is:

$$c(x,t) = c_0\left[1 - \left(\frac{erf(x/\sqrt{4Dt})}{erf(L/\sqrt{4Dt})} \right) \right], \tag{3}$$

where $erf(x)$ is the error function (Abramowitz & Stegun, 1964), and the motion of the fibre tip at $x = L(t)$ is the solution of the equation:

$$ze^{z^2}erf(z) = \text{constant} = \frac{1}{\sqrt{\pi}}\frac{c_0\lambda}{f}, \tag{4}$$

where $z^2 = L^2/4Dt$.

Once we solve equation (4) for z we can determine the speed at which polymerization can drive acrosomal elongation*. Tilney & Kallenbach (1979) estimate that the diffusion coefficient for actin (or profilactin) is approximately $5\times10^{-7}\,\text{cm}^2\,\text{s}^{-1}$. More recent experimental measurements confirm that this is probably the fastest that actin diffuses within a cell. Each actin filament contains 370 monomers per μm and hence $\lambda = 2{\cdot}7\times10^{-3}\,\mu$m. Electron microscopic pictures of the acrosomal process show that on average it contains 60 filaments (Tilney & Inoué, 1982). Correcting for possible sample shrinkage in EM pictures, Tilney estimates that the diameter of the acrosomal process is approximately $0{\cdot}05\,\mu$m. Thus $f = 3\times10^4\,\mu\text{m}^{-2}$. The last parameter required is c_0, the actin monomer concentration in the periacrosomal cup. Tilney & Inoué (1982) estimated that the fully developed acrosomal process contains $1{\cdot}1\times10^6$ actin monomers. If we assume that the periacrosomal cup, whose volume is approximately $0{\cdot}5\,\mu\text{m}^3$ (Tilney & Inoué, 1982), contains twice this number of monomers (a clear overestimate) then $c_0 = 4{\cdot}4\times10^6\,\mu\text{m}^{-3}$. Using these values, the right-hand side of equation (4) $= 0{\cdot}226$. Solving for z and using the value of D given above we find $L^2/t = 35\,\mu\text{m}^2\,\text{s}^{-1}$. Hence in 10 s, with no depletion of monomer from the periacrosomal cup, the acrosome would only grow $18{\cdot}7\,\mu$m. The more refined model of Perelson & Coutsias (1986) predicts that the acrosome would only extend $10\,\mu$m in 10 s. Both of these estimates are considerably smaller than the experimental value of $90\,\mu$m.

To summarize our mathematical analysis we find that growth limited by diffusion of monomer to the growing tip would lead to a rate of growth in which L^2 increased

* Tilney & Inoué incorrectly use the actin concentration at the tip, C_T, rather than the concentration of free ends, f/λ. This yields a constant on the right-hand side of four orders of magnitude too large.

linearly with t as was found in the experiments of Tilney & Inoué (1982, 1985). However, if actin polymerization from the barbed end of the actin filaments were the sole driving force responsible for the extension of the acrosome, the acrosome would grow considerably slower than observed.

APPENDIX 2

The osmotic model for acrosomal protrusion

Oster *et al.* (1982) provided a detailed model for the growth of the acrosome driven by osmotic forces. Here we summarize the highlights of that model.

The model is derived by taking into account three dynamic processes: (1) the mechanical motion of the acrosomal process through the fluid medium; (2) an osmotically driven influx of water, which increases the volume of the periacrosomal region of the acrosome; and (3) the transport of profilactin to the growing tip of the acrosome. For each process we can write a kinetic equation.

The mechanical equation of motion is derived from a balance of forces. If there is a hydrostatic pressure difference, $p_T - p_0$, between the tip of the growing process and the external medium, it will drive the elongation of the process. This driving force will be counter-balanced by the drag forces and any membrane tension. Thus,

$$(p_T - p_0)A_T = F_D + T_m , \tag{5}$$

where A_T is the area of the growing tip across which the force is acting, F_D are the drag forces caused by the movement of the acrosomal membrane through the external medium and the cell's cytoplasm, and T_m is the membrane tension. The drag forces will be proportional to the velocity at which the acrosome moves, dL/dt, and to the surface area of the acrosome, which in turn is proportional to its length L. During the acrosomal reaction new plasma membrane appears to be inserted at the base of the acrosome (Sardet & Tilney, 1977; Tilney & Inoué, 1982) and thus T_m is probably negligible. If excess membrane becomes depleted, then T_m could become appreciable and cause a cessation of growth. Note that if the pressure difference remains approximately constant during some period of acrosomal growth, then equation (5) predicts that $L\,dL/dt$ is constant or that L^2 grows linearly with t.

The osmotically induced water influx leads to an increase in the volume of the periacrosomal region and the growing acrosomal process. For water transport driven by osmotic and hydrostatic pressure differences we have:

$$-L_p A_B [(p_B - p_0) - \Delta\pi] = \frac{dV_B}{dt} + A_x \frac{dL}{dt} , \tag{6}$$

where L_p is the hydraulic permeability coefficient and A_B the area of the membrane through which water is flowing. For convenience we refer to this region as the 'base of the acrosome' and hence the subscript B. The hydrostatic pressure difference between the base and the medium is $p_B - p_0$, while the osmotic pressure difference is $\Delta\pi$. Here $\Delta\pi$ refers to the total effective osmotic pressure difference caused by both ions and macromolecules. If the membrane is not ideally semipermeable, then a reflection coefficient would be included in $\Delta\pi$, which would decrease its magnitude. The base increases in volume at rate dV_B/dt, whereas the growing tube with cross-sectional area A_x increases in volume at the rate $A_x dL/dt$.

To complete the model we need to relate the hydrostatic pressure in the tip, p_T, to the hydrostatic pressure in the base, p_B, and relate the pressure in the base to its volume. To a good approximation one can show that:

$$p_T = p_B - \text{constant } L\frac{dL}{dt}. \qquad (7)$$

Central to this model is the assumption that as the volume of the periacrosomal region increases pressure is built up. We thus treat this region as an elastic vessel, i.e. we assume:

$$p_B - p_0 = K(V_B - V_0), \qquad (8)$$

where K is the elastic modulus of the vessel and V_0 is its original unstressed volume. Because we assume that there is excess membrane, the elasticity comes not from the membrane, but rather from the cytoplasmic material in this region.

Combining equations (7), (8) and (5) we find that:

$$\frac{dL^2}{dt} = c_1(V_B - V_0) - c_2 T_m, \qquad (9)$$

where c_1 and c_2 are constants. As shown by Oster *et al.* (1982) the rate of change of V_B can be determined from equation (6). However, since in *Thyone* the base doubles in volume in 50–70 ms, we can simply assume that V_B is initially twice V_0 and then study the development of the acrosomal process on a time-scale of seconds. Since the total volume of the extended acrosomal process is only a small fraction of $2V_0$, the enlarged volume of the base (≈18 % if we assume the process to be a 90 μm long cylinder with a 0·05 μm diameter), we can assume V_B remains approximately constant during acrosomal elongation. (Oster *et al.* did not make this approximation, but rather considered in detail the osmotic flows, the dilution of the material in the base due to water inflow and the transport of profilactin to the growing tip. From our analysis we conclude that V_B is approximately constant.) Thus as long as T_m remains negligible one should observe growth in which L^2 increases linearly with time. However, once excess membrane runs out T_m will become appreciable and the elongation process will slow down and eventually stop.

APPENDIX 3

Osmotically coupled polymerization

In this Appendix we summarize the osmotically coupled polymerization model. We assume that substantial variations in the chemical concentrations of actin, profilin, etc. only occur in one dimension (see Fig. 3, main text). Along this axis, which we call the x-axis, the tip of the acrosome is located at $x = b(t)$. The left boundary at $b(t)$ is free to move. The boundary of the actin filaments is assumed to lie at $x = a(t)$; this boundary will move to right as the filaments elongate. Our goal is to determine the motion of the boundaries $a(t)$ and $b(t)$.

The model is built around the following assumptions:

(1) G-actin (A) is combined with profilin (P) to form profilactin, an actin–profilin complex (PA).

(2) PIP_2 cleaves the complex (PA) into profilin (P) and actin. The reaction is localized at the membrane, $x = b(t)$, and its rate is given by Michaelis–Menten kinetics:

$$\mathcal{J}_r = \frac{v_{max}[PA]}{K_m + [PA]} \, . \tag{10}$$

(3) The freed monomeric actin diffuses away from the membrane to the actin filament boundary at ($x = a(t)$) and polymerizes onto an F-actin fibre according to the overall reaction:

$$F + A \rightleftharpoons F, \tag{11}$$

where F is the F-actin filament tip concentration.

If f is the number of actin fibre tips per unit cross-sectional area, and λ is the length a filament extends when an actin monomer adds to the end, then at $x = a(t)$ actin disappears at a rate (Perelson & Coutsias, 1986):

$$-\frac{dA}{dt} = \frac{f}{\lambda}(k_1 A(x = a) - k_2), \tag{12}$$

and the actin boundary located at $a(t)$ moves to the right with a velocity given by:

$$\frac{da}{dt} = \lambda[k_1 A - k_2], \tag{13}$$

where k_1 and k_2 are the forward and reverse rate constants at the barbed end.

(4) The net particle gain in the reaction at the membrane and boundary interface generates an osmotic pressure, which drives a water influx:

$$\mathcal{J}_v = L_p \Pi = L_p RT([PA + A + P]_{x=b} - C_0) \, , \tag{14}$$

where C_0 is the concentration of osmotically active material in the solution surrounding the cell and L_p is the hydraulic permeability of the acrosomal tip membrane. Note that we can incorporate the contributions of other osmotically active solutes by adjusting the osmotic coefficients of A, P and PA.

(5) The membrane is driven to the right by the water influx at a rate proportional to $\mathcal{J}_v$, i.e.:

$$\frac{db}{dt} = k_3(PA + A + P - C_0) \, . \tag{15}$$

(6) Each of the component particles diffuses according to Fick's law, and reacts

only at the membrane or the actin–filament interface. Denote by y_1, y_2 and y_3 the concentrations of actin, profilin and actin–profilin complex, respectively. Then:

$$\frac{\partial y_1}{\partial t} = D_1 \frac{\partial^2 y_1}{\partial x^2} - \frac{f}{\lambda}(k_1 y_1(a) - k_2 \delta(x-a) \quad (16)$$

$$\frac{\partial y_2}{\partial t} = D_2 \frac{\partial^2 y_2}{\partial x^2} \quad (17)$$

$$\frac{\partial y_3}{\partial t} = D_3 \frac{\partial^2 y_3}{\partial x^2}, \quad (18)$$

where $\delta(x-a)$ is the Dirac delta function.

(7) As initial conditions, we assume that at $t=0$ profilactin is present throughout the domain, but that free actin and free profilin have not yet been generated. Thus:

$$y_1(0,x) = 0, \quad y_2(0,x) = 0 \quad \text{and} \quad y_3(0,x) = y_{30}. \quad (19)$$

(8) As boundary conditions, we assume that at $x = 0$ conditions are as in the interior of the cell (periacrosomal cup). Thus:

$$y_i = c_i, \quad i = 1,2,3, \quad (20)$$

$$\text{Actin:} \quad -D_1 \frac{\partial y_1}{\partial x} = y_1 \frac{db}{dt} - \frac{v_{max}[PA]}{K_m + [PA]}. \quad (21)$$

$$\text{Profilin:} \quad -D_2 \frac{\partial y_1}{\partial x} = y_2 \frac{db}{dt} - \frac{v_{max}[PA]}{K_m + [PA]}. \quad (22)$$

$$\text{Actin–profilin:} \quad -D_3 \frac{\partial y_1}{\partial x} = y_3 \frac{db}{dt} + \frac{v_{max}[PA]}{K_m + [PA]}. \quad (23)$$

Thus the problem reduces to a set of linear diffusion-reaction equations with the two moving boundaries, $a(t)$ and $b(t)$. These equations were solved numerically by means of a moving finite-element algorithm (Perelson *et al.* unpublished).

We thank Lew Tilney for supplying us with his data, and for many stimulating conversations. J. P. Trinkaus made valuable comments on the manuscript. G.F.O. was supported by NSF grant MCS-8110557. A.S.P. was supported by the Department of Energy.

REFERENCES

ABRAMOWITZ, M. & STEGUN, I. A. (1964). *Handbook of Mathematical Functions*. Washington, DC: National Bureau of Standards.

BERRIDGE, M. J. (1986). Cell signalling through phospholipid metabolism. *J. Cell Sci. Suppl. 4*, 137–153.

BRETSCHER, M. (1984). Endocytosis: relation to capping and cell locomotion. *Science* **224**, 681–686.

CHERNOMORDIK, L., KOZLOV, M., MELIKYAN, G., ABIDOR, I., MARKIN, V. & CHIZMADZHEV, YU. (1985). The shape of lipid molecules and monolayer membrane fusion. *Biochim. biophys. Acta* **812**, 643–655.

CULLIS, P. & HOPE, M. (1985). Physical properties and functional roles of lipids in membranes. In *Biochemistry of Lipids and Membranes* (ed. D. Vance & J. Vance). Menlo Park: Benjamin/Cummings.

DAN, J. C. & HAGIWARA, Y. (1967). Studies on the acrosome. IX. Course of acrosome reaction in the starfish. *J. Ultrastruct. Res.* **18**, 562–579.
DAN, J. C., OHORI, Y. & KUSHIDA, H. (1964). Studies on the acrosome. VII. Formation of the acrosomal process in sea urchin spermatozoa. *J. Ultrastruct. Res.* **11**, 508–524.
GREEN, D. (1978). The osmotic properties of the acrosome of guinea-pig sperm. *J. Cell Sci.* **32**, 165–176.
HARRIS, A. (1973). Cell surface movements related to cell locomotion. In *Locomotion of Tissue Cells. Ciba Fdn Symp.* 14 (new series), pp. 3–26. Amsterdam: North Holland.
HERMANS, J. J. (1947). Diffusion with discontinuous boundary. *J. Coll. Sci.* **2**, 387–398.
HOUSLAY, M. (1987). Egg activation unscrambles a potential role for IP4. *Trends Biochem. Sci.* **12**(1), 1–2.
INOUÉ, S. & TILNEY, L. G. (1982). The acrosomal reaction of *Thyone* sperm. I. Changes in the sperm head visualized by high resolution video microscopy. *J. Cell Biol.* **93**, 812–820.
LASSING, I. & LINDBERG, U. (1985). Specific interaction between phosphatidylinositol 4,5-biphosphate and profilactin. *Nature, Lond.* **314**, 472–474.
MINTON, A. P. (1983). The effect of volume occupancy upon the thermodynamic activity of proteins: some biochemical consequences. *Molec. cell. Biochem.* **55**, 119–140.
MOORE, H.-P. H., ORCI, L. & OSTER, G. (1987). Biogenesis of secretory granules. In *Protein Transfer and Organelle Biogenesis* (ed. R. C. Das & P. W. Robbins). New York: Academic Press (in press).
OMANN, G., ALLEN, R., BOKOCH, G., PAINTER, R., TRAYNOR, A. & SKLAR, L. (1987). Signal transduction and cytoskeletal activation in the neutrophil. *Physiol. Rev.* **67**, 285.
OSTER, G. F. (1984). On the crawling of cells. *J. Embryol. exp. Morph.* **83** (Suppl), 329–364.
OSTER, G. F. & PERELSON, A. S. (1985). Cell spreading and motility: a model lamellipod. *J. math. Biol.* **21**, 383–388.
OSTER, G. F., PERELSON, A. S. & TILNEY, L. G. (1982). A mechanical model for elongation of the acrosomal process in *Thyone* sperm. *J. math. Biol.* **15**, 259–265.
PERELSON, A. S. & COUTSIAS, E. A. (1986). A moving boundary model of acrosomal elongation. *J. math. Biol.* **23**, 361–379.
PERRIN, D., LANGLEY, O. K. & AUNIS, D. (1987). Anti-α-fodrin inhibits secretion from permeabilized chromaffin cells. *Nature, Lond.* **326**, 498–501.
SARDET, C. & TILNEY, L. G. (1977). Origin of the membrane for the acrosomal process: Is actin complexed with membrane precursors? *Cell Biol. Int. Rep.* **1**, 193–200.
TILNEY, L. G., BONDER, E. M., COLUCCIO, L. M. & MOOSAKER, M. S. (1983). Actin from *Thyone* sperm assembles on only one end of an actin filament: a behavior regulated by profilin. *J. Cell Biol.* **97**, 112–124.
TILNEY, L. G. & INOUÉ, S. (1982). The acrosomal reaction of *Thyone* sperm. II. The kinetics and possible mechanism of acrosomal process elongation. *J. Cell Biol.* **93**, 820–827.
TILNEY, L. G. & INOUÉ, S. (1985). Acrosomal reaction of the *Thyone* sperm. III. The relationship between actin assembly and water influx during the extension of the acrosomal process. *J. Cell Biol.* **100**, 1273–1283.
TILNEY, L. G. & KALLENBACH, N. (1979). Polymerization of actin. VI. The polarity of the actin filaments in the acrosomal process and how it might be determined. *J. Cell Biol.* **81**, 608–623.
TILNEY, L., KICHART, D., SARDET, C. & TILNEY, M. (1978). Polymerization of actin. IV. Role of Ca^{++} and H^{+} in the assembly of actin and in membrane fusion in the acrosomal reaction of echinoderm sperm. *J. Cell Biol.* **77**, 536–550.
TRINKAUS, J. P. (1984). *Cells into Organs. The Forces that Shape the Embryo*, 2nd edn. Englewood Cliffs, NJ: Prentice-Hall.
TRINKAUS, J. P. (1985). Protrusive activity of the cell surface and the initiation of cell movement during morphogenesis. *Expl Biol. Med.* **10**, 130–173.

J. Cell Sci. Suppl. 8, 55–79 (1987)
Printed in Great Britain

NOVEL METHODS FOR THE GUIDANCE AND MONITORING OF SINGLE CELLS AND SIMPLE NETWORKS IN CULTURE

J. A. T. DOW[1], P. CLARK[1], P. CONNOLLY[2], A. S. G. CURTIS[1] AND C. D. W. WILKINSON[2]

[1]*Departments of Cell Biology and* [2]*Electronic and Electrical Engineering, University of Glasgow, Glasgow G12 8QQ, Scotland*

SUMMARY

The effects of the topography, adhesiveness and chemistry of surfaces in modulating the behaviour of cells *in vivo* and *in vitro* have been extensively researched. However, few natural systems are simple enough to allow straightforward conclusions to be drawn, as many different cues are likely to be present at one time. Microelectronic fabrication, normally employed in making integrated circuits, can produce substrates patterned on scales highly relevant to studies of cell behaviour.

In this paper, we describe progress in fabricating simple artificial substrata both at the micrometre and sub-micrometre scales. The former can be considered as models for contact guidance along other cells or axonal processes: the latter, models for guidance along aligned collagen matrices. We have systematically studied the reactions of different cell types to simple cues (steps and grooves). Additionally, it may be possible to produce fine-resolution patterns with differential adhesiveness, or with other cell-specific surface-chemical properties, such as the differential deposition of proteins, e.g. cell adhesion molecules. We also describe early results in using topographic and other cues to guide cells onto patterned metal electrodes, forming simple electrically active networks of controlled design, from which long-term recordings can conveniently be made.

INTRODUCTION

Our group is adopting a multidisciplinary approach to certain problems in cell biology, particularly in neurobiology. In this article, current models for cell guidance during development, in particular contact guidance, are reviewed. The techniques of electronic microfabrication are discussed from a biological standpoint, and their application to the formation of specific topographies is outlined. The use of computers in the analysis of cell behaviour is outlined, and prospects for the formation of simple neuronal/electronic hybrid networks discussed. The possibilities opened by such experiments could be exciting, from both the standpoint of pure science and that of medical therapeutics.

CUES FOR CELL GUIDANCE

In the developing embryo, cells display an ability to navigate rather precisely over considerable distances in order to form the functional tissues of the adult. The study of this problem, and the elucidation of the cues involved, is one of the most important areas of cell biology. In particular, the specificity of formation of neuronal connections has attracted considerable interest, and there is evidence to support several hypotheses of cell guidance (Dunn, 1982). Sperry's (1963) theory of chemoaffinity is generally favoured (with some modification); and many contemporary workers believe that specific cell-surface markers hold the key to neuronal specificity (Goodman & Bate, 1981; Goodman & Bastiani, 1984; Zipser & McKay, 1981; Bonhoefer & Huf, 1980). There is now some evidence to support the plausible hypothesis that positional information can be gained from morphogenetic fields of diffusible morphogens (Wolpert, 1978; Tickle *et al.* 1982), and that some growth factors (Gundersen & Barrett, 1980; Lumsden & Davies, 1986) or even neurotransmitters (Hume *et al.* 1983; Young & Poo, 1983; Patel *et al.* 1985) may affect the terminal guidance of neurones. Experiments showing that the morphology of developing neurones *in vivo* and *in vitro* is similar (Banker & Cowan, 1979; Role & Fischbach, 1987) suggest that certain components of neuronal shape are intrinsically determined. Galvanotaxis of cells and galvanotropism of neuronal growth cones have been demonstrated *in vitro* (Hinkle *et al.* 1981; McCaig, 1986; Nuccitelli & Erickson, 1983; Cooper & Schliwa, 1985), and these effects are believed to occur at physiological electric field strengths (Barker *et al.* 1982; Patel *et al.* 1985). Haptotaxis on patterns of differential adhesivity (Hammarback *et al.* 1985; Mason, 1985; Hammarback & Letourneau, 1986) has been demonstrated; and the results explained as reflecting the differential grip obtained by filopodia on opposite sides of a cell or growth cone, within a haptotactic gradient, for successful traction (Bray, 1982).

A frequent explanation for cell guidance during morphogenesis is that of contact guidance (Dunn, 1982); in its narrow interpretation, cells are thought to be sensitive to the topographical features in their environment. As a multiplicity of cues is present, contact guidance is very difficult to demonstrate unambiguously *in vivo*, although there is some evidence from studies of retinotectal projection (Scholes, 1979; Horder & Martin, 1979), and in the developing fish fin (Wood & Thorogood, 1984). As with other morphogenetic cues, most of the evidence for the contact guidance hypothesis has been amassed *in vitro*. There are several explanations that have been proffered to explain contact guidance: Dunn (1982) suggested that cytoskeletal inflexibility limits the ability of cells to form successful (i.e. load-bearing) focal adhesions over topographic discontinuities, such as shallow prisms (Dunn & Heath, 1976); O'Hara & Buck (1979) suggested that, on finely grooved substrata, the orientation of the focal adhesions themselves is constrained, and that this restricts the ability of the cytoskeleton to exert traction in directions other than the orientation of the substratum; Lackie (1986) suggested that topographic cues might affect the *probability* of forming a successful protrusion. These models may not be incompatible, and merit further study.

Over the years, cell reactions to a wide range of substrata, such as spiders' webs, gramophone records, diffraction gratings, tubes and fibres, have been studied. Recently, studies of contact guidance have been made easier by the advent of microfabrication techniques, normally employed in the manufacture of integrated circuits. It is now possible to produce arbitrary topographies, of controlled surface chemistry, in a wide range of substrata, and with great precision. Furthermore, the two disciplines can be integrated to the extent of producing electrode arrays for the extracellular monitoring of electrical activity in neuronal networks (Pickard, 1979; Kruger, 1983; Eichenbaum & Kuperstein, 1986).

MICROFABRICATION TECHNIQUES

Microfabrication techniques, as applied to biology, have been usefully reviewed elsewhere (White *et al.* 1983; Eichenbaum & Kuperstein, 1986); photolithography is basically a contact-printing process, capable of producing either positive or negative relief images. Substrata of most materials (silicon, silicon dioxide, silicon nitride, glass, sapphire, titanium, perspex) can be patterned either by etching away of bulk material, or by deposition of further material. Selectivity is obtained by using a mask of an inert material, which protects part of the substratum from the processes of etching or deposition.

Masks are generally made by spin-coating a photosensitive resist onto the substratum, to produce a thin, continuous layer of perhaps a micrometre in depth. The resist is then either cross-linked or depolymerized by the action of light (generally contact-printed through a metal mask), and the less-polymerized material dissolved away by a developer, leaving a relief image of the mask in photoresist. In practice, the resolution achievable by such photolithographic techniques is around 1–2 μm, and the maximum area that can be patterned up to about 25 cm^2. This makes photolithography highly suitable for the production of patterns on the biological scale; spread cells 'might' be around 20–50 μm in diameter appear strongly oriented by features of 1–10 μm in period.

The limitation on resolution in conventional photolithography is the contact-printing process: small particles of dust between mask and photoresist cause blurring of the image. Even smaller patterns are produced by the technique of electron-beam lithography. In this maskless technique, the resist is exposed directly by a scanning electron microscope beam. The resolution attainable by this technique is limited only by the spot size of the scanning beam; details as fine as 3 nm are feasible. Although ideal for research and prototyping, this technique is much too slow for direct commercial wafer production; it can be used instead to produce masks, which are then used for conventional photolithography.

Extracellular electrodes, for stimulating or recording, are produced by coating a metal (usually gold or platinum) onto the substratum, bonding wires to the contact pads, spin-coating an insulating layer of resist onto the electrodes, then exposing windows of resist above the electrode terminals. The impedance of such electrodes rises sharply with decreasing diameter (Prohaska *et al.* 1986); in practice, window diameters of about 25 μm^2 provide the best signal-to-noise ratio (Edell, 1986).

The biocompatibility of these materials must be considered, both for cultured cells, and for the surrounding tissue in the case of prosthetic implants. In this case, most structures can be functionally separated into three layers: substratum, electrodes and insulator. Popular substrata include sapphire, glass and silicon.

Electrodes have been made of nickel/iron, silver/silver chloride, gold, platinum, titanium and indium/tin oxide. The electrode material of choice is usually gold, although the resistance of these electrodes can be reduced tenfold by platinization. Insulation is generally provided by polyimide (Kapton), or a photoresist: most photoresists are toxic, but some have proved biocompatible over extended periods. The resulting structures have been used successfully *in vitro* for several months (Droge *et al.* 1986), in rabbit peripheral nerve implants for a year (Edell, 1986), and in the case of human cochlear implants for several years *in vivo*, without ill effects (Hochmair-Desoyer *et al.* 1983).

TOPOGRAPHY: BEHAVIOUR OF CELLS ON ARTIFICAL SURFACES

Steps

The most common type of artificial surface used in work on cell alignment is an array of parallel ridges or grooves (Weiss, 1945; Curtis & Varde, 1964; Brunette *et al.* 1983; Brunette, 1986; Dunn & Brown, 1986). However, there are several variables to consider in such analyses, namely ridge width, groove width, groove depth, groove profile, choice of substratum and uniformity of substratum. The simplest possible aligning cue would be a single intersection between two planes; this was studied by Dunn & Heath (1976), who found that single cells could not move over the top of a shallow prism if the angle of pitch exceeded 16°. We decided to look at the next simplest structure possible, a single step, or discontinuity in a flat plane. The pattern thus exposed the cell to two right angles, one external and one internal. This pattern could in turn be viewed as 'half' of a groove (Fig. 1).

Steps of varying depth were cut into perspex using conventional photolithographic techniques (Curtis *et al.* 1985; Clark *et al.* 1987), and the reactions of various cells studied. The standard experimental subject for these studies was the baby hamster kidney (BHK) cell (Fig. 1A). Cells were tracked by video microscopy, and the interactions of cells encountering a step analysed. A distinction was made between *crossing*, where the whole body of the cell moved from one side of the step to the other, and *alignment*, where the long axis of the cell was adjudged to be within about 10° of the axis of the step. Alternative outcomes, such as reflection or refraction, were rare under these conditions; effectively all encounters resulted either in crossing or alignment. The results obtained for various step heights are shown in Fig. 2. As can be seen, crossings declined monotonically with increasing step height, so that at a step height of 18 μm, only 10 % of cells crossed the step in either direction (Fig. 2A) (and that, conversely, 90 % of cells aligned: Fig. 2B). Interestingly, there was no systematic difference between cells encountering the step from the upper or the lower side, implying that the order in which the external and internal angles were encountered did not significantly affect the outcome.

The pattern established for BHK cells was also seen for a variety of cell types (Fig. 3). On encountering a step of 5 μm (which approximately 30 % of BHK cells crossed), a similar fraction of primary chick heart fibroblasts crossed. Growth cones were not filmed directly, but crossing was scored under phase-contrast microscopy;

Fig. 1. Scanning electron micrographs (SEM) of cultured cells encountering a step in a perspex substrate. A. BHK cell aligning along the top of a 10 μm step. Bar, 20 μm. Note the roughening of the etched (lower) surface. B. Embryonic chick hemisphere neurite aligning along a 4 μm step in poly-L-lysine-coated perspex. Bar, 10 μm. (Reproduced from Clark *et al.* (1987), with permission.)

again, around a quarter of the neurites crossed a 5 μm step in either direction. The exception was afforded by neutrophil leucocytes, which were not seriously impeded from crossing. This difference may reflect the relative lability of neutrophil cytoskeletal organization (Clark *et al.* 1987); the models of both Dunn & Heath (1976) and O'Hara & Buck (1979) for contact guidance lay stress on cytoskeletal organization.

Grooves

We have begun to work on grooved surfaces, both at light and electron microscopic resolution. Conventional photolithography permits the easy production of sheer-walled grooves of any mark/space ratio and aspect ratio (groove depth: width) up to around unity, with a minimum period (groove + ridge repeat distance) or around 1 μm; while interferometric techniques allow us to produce smoothly undulating

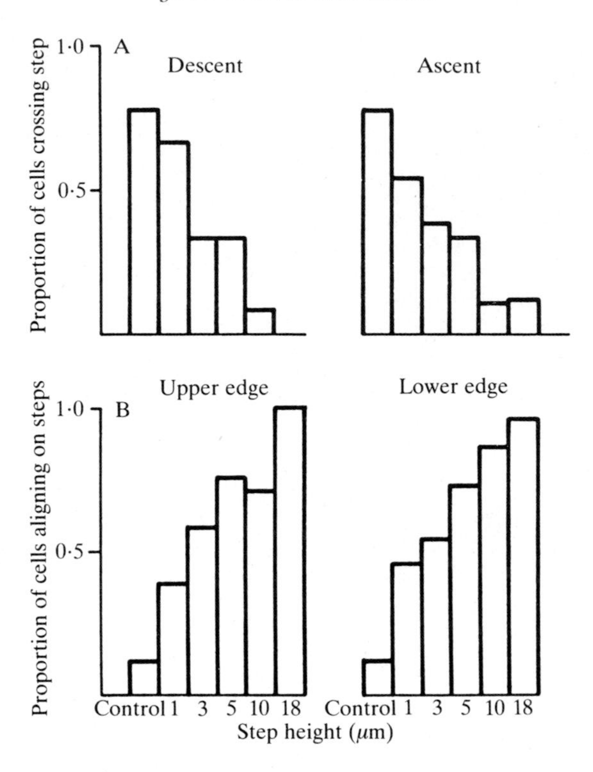

Fig. 2. Crossing (A) and alignment (B) of BHK cells at steps of increasing height, as related to their direction of approach. (Reproduced from Clark *et al.* (1987), with permission.)

gratings with very much shorter periods (as low as 300 nm), of the same order of size as collagen fibrils.

Our preliminary findings are that, together with period, depth is a significant influence on alignment for gratings with a period in the 4–24 μm range. (Above this range, of course, the pattern encountered by any cell begins to resemble a single step, as this is all that one cell could bridge.) Gratings with a period of 6 μm, and a depth of only 2 μm, can align BHK cells very strongly (Fig. 4). In fact, depths of 0·7 μm are quite capable of producing alignment (Dunn & Brown, 1986).

It seems that the degree of alignment relates to the number of grooves that a cell could bridge, were it not aligned. It should be noticed (Fig. 4) that, even on fine grooves, most cells align along a single ridge, even though they become greatly elongated. It would be tempting to speculate on the cytoskeletal constraints imposed on cells by such structures. Dunn & Brown (1986) showed that the elongation observed in aligned cells can be described as a simple mathematical transformation of normal (unaligned) cell morphology.

Spirals

On the basis of the previous set of experiments, one might expect that a cell lying on a narrow ridge with curved boundaries would spread to a greater extent on regions

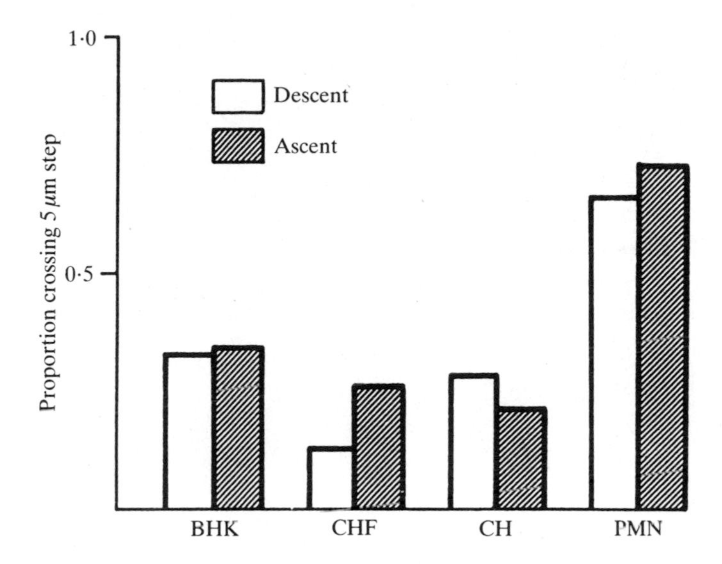

Fig. 3. The crossing reactions of different cell types to a step of 4 μm, related to their direction of approach. BHK, baby hamster kidney cell line C13; CHF, primary culture of embryonic chick heart fibroblasts; CH, primary culture of embryonic chick hemisphere neurones; PMN, rabbit neutrophils, prepared by peritoneal lavage (Vicker *et al.* 1986). (Reproduced from Clark *et al.* (1987), with permission.)

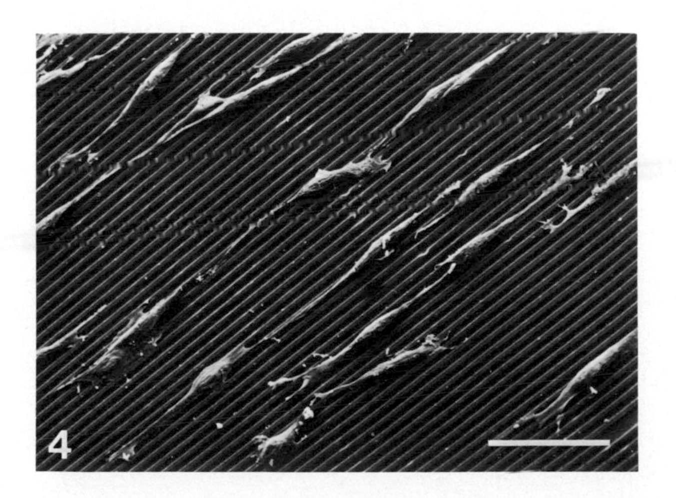

Fig. 4. SEM of BHK cells aligned on repeated grooves, of period 6 μm and depth 2 μm, etched into perspex. Bar, 50 μm.

of lower curvature. This problem is also related to the studies of cell spreading inside and outside glass cylinders of varying radius (Abercrombie, 1980; Dunn & Heath, 1976). An experimental pattern that simultaneously provides a continuously graded set of curvatures in two dimensions is afforded by an eteched spiral, as shown in Fig. 5. Cells near the centre of the spiral are unable to spread completely, and thus to

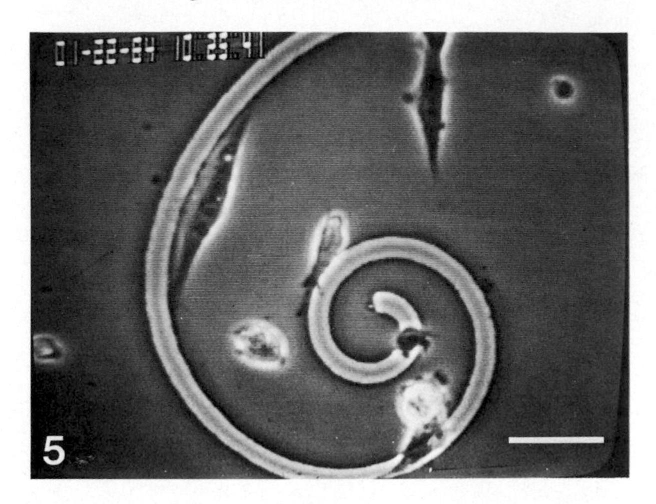

Fig. 5. Light micrograph of BHK cells aligned by a spiral of width 10 μm and depth 3 μm, etched into quartz. Phase-contrast; bar, 50 μm.

move; this resembles the fate of cells adhering to spheres of radius too low to permit efficient spreading (Dunn, 1982). Further out, cells spread progressively more completely, and tend to move into regions of lower curvature (i.e. away from the centre); one could speculate that, near the centre, the degree of permitted spreading could vary noticeably from one side of a cell to the other; a more-spread cytoskeleton on one side could suffice to produce the outward movement described. This pattern is of interest in that not just an alignment, but also a polarized movement, of cells is produced.

Hillocks and dolines

Another way of systematically constraining the cytoskeleton is to punctuate a planar substrate with a regular array of hillocks or dimples ('dolines'). These resemble the surface of an epithelial sheet of cells in curvature and scale. Such structures are powerfully aligning for cells (Fig. 6). Cells align so as to minimize the changes in substrate height that they must accommodate; in this case, there are only two perfectly flat domains, and these are narrow, and orthogonal. Indeed, this structure could be seen as a pair of orthogonally intersecting groove patterns.

HOW DOES TOPOGRAPHY AFFECT CELL ORIENTATION?

There is a theme underlying the results described above; it is that cells seem to align so as to minimize distortions in their cytoskeleton. In the nearly two-dimensional systems described here, this implies that cells tend to find the flattest or least curved area of substratum available, even if this involves elongation far beyond that normally occurring on planar substrata. This accords with Dunn & Brown's (1986) amalgamation of earlier (Dunn & Heath, 1976; O'Hara & Buck, 1979) theories of contact guidance. Additionally, there seems to be an arithmetic rule for

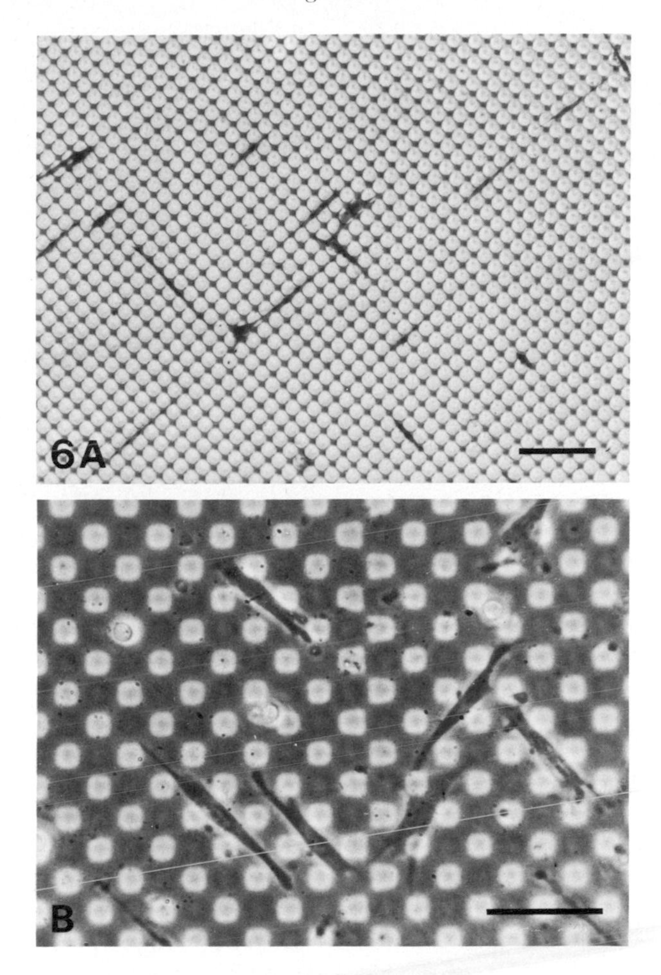

Fig. 6. Light micrograph of BHK cells aligned by a landscape of hillocks of height 3 μm, etched into glass in an orthogonal array of repeat interval 20 μm. Hillocks were made by patterning photoresist onto glass, and baking at a high enough temperature to produce some flow, before etching with HF. Such landscapes strongly oriented cells along the diagonals. Phase-contrast. Bars: 100 μm (A), 50 μm (B).

alignment at repeated features; cells are aligned very highly by repeated grooves or features at a depth far less than that required to produce alignment at a single step.

While the results argue strongly for a dominant role of the cytoskeleton in contact guidance, it is not clear whether they allow us to distinguish between the models of Dunn & Heath (1976) and O'Hara & Buck (1979) for contact guidance. It is hard to reconcile the ability of cells to cross fairly high steps with their failure to cross a much more modest feature, a prism of 16° angle. Unless a cell is able to bridge a step completely with a protrusion, detecting the planar surface beyond the step, one would expect a large degree of cytoskeletal deformability to be required to obtain crossing; and that the cytoskeletal constraints imposed by crossings in opposite directions would be very different. However, our results suggest that there is not a large difference between upward and downward crossings; Clark *et al.* (1987) argued that this is because in terms of cytoskeletal deformation the upper (convex) edge of a step presents a far more serious obstacle to cells than the lower (concave) edge. Thus, although the three elements of the step topography (top edge, step height and bottom edge) can be encountered in different orders, the cells' reactions are mainly affected by a single element, the top edge.

It remains to be seen whether contact guidance will suffice to produce ordered arrays of cells. Certainly, spirals seem to act as a trap for cells, and it should be possible to construct grooves or ridges deep enough so that crossing is almost totally inhibited. It is thus quite likely that 'confrontation culture' experiments of a type already producing interesting results in developmental biology (Bonhoeffer & Huf, 1985) could easily be performed using photolithographic landscapes. However, whether topographic cues alone will suffice to produce specific neuronal structures remains to be investigated.

CELL TRACKING

Two types of measurement are central to many studies of cell behaviour. These are the *static* measures of cell spread area, orientation and elongation; and the *dynamic* measures of speed and position of moving cells. The manual execution of either technique is painstaking: in the case of static measures, the cells must be photographed, their outlines cut out of the print, and the areas measured by weighing. Orientations and elongations, though requiring the use of only ruler and protractor, require the subjective assessment of the 'long axis' of the cell, a notoriously inaccurate procedure. Dynamic measures require the post-analysis of video tape or ciné film, and the manual plotting of loci of the experimenter's subjective assessment of the centres of the cells in successive frames.

It is not surprising, therefore, that both of these measurements have been automated, usually on minicomputers (Noble & Levine, 1986; Huijsmans *et al.* 1986; Donovan *et al.* 1986; Dunn & Brown, 1986). In our Department, driven by necessity, these automated measures have been implemented on standard laboratory microcomputers (Dow *et al.* 1986, 1987).

In our configuration, cells are viewed through a conventional microscope, fitted with a TV camera and phase-contrast optics. The video signal is viewed on a monitor, and sent to a framegrabber, which is connected to a BBC microcomputer. Digitized images are stored in screen memory to a resolution of 256×640 points at two intensity levels, and then processed by a short program written in BASIC and machine code. With appropriate care in controlling illumination, satisfactory images of living cells can be obtained (see Fig. 10, below). The software calculates the visual centroid of all non-background pixels in a square search area; this is called a 'box search' (Dow *et al.* 1987). This simple approach is capable of error, but only in predictable circumstances, which can be precluded by experimental design (Dow *et al.* 1987).

This system has proved highly successful in tracking neutrophil leucocytes, which are ideal subjects for such systems because of their clear phase image and relatively high speed. They have thus been studied extensively by other authors (Noble & Levine, 1986). Our tracking system can routinely follow (in real time) an arbitrary number (e.g. 50) of cells, sampling every 20 s for an arbitrary period (e.g. 30 min). The cell densities used are comparable with those previously employed in manual tracking studies, so no special experimental changes were dictated by switching to a computer-centred system; the resulting tracks are broadly similar to those obtained previously (Fig. 7), although the far higher yield of tracked cells per experiment (50 compared with 20 previously) allows more extensive statistical analysis.

A model proposed by Dunn (1983) suggests that neutrophil locomotion can be characterized by just two parameters, speed and persistence. The model likens neutrophil locomotion to a random-walk with persistence of direction, made up of a series of linear movements of constant speed, punctuated by changes of direction. Thus speed, in terms of the model, is simply total displacement divided by total time while persistence is a measure of the mean time between direction changes, and thus has units of time. This model has the advantage of parsimony in that only two

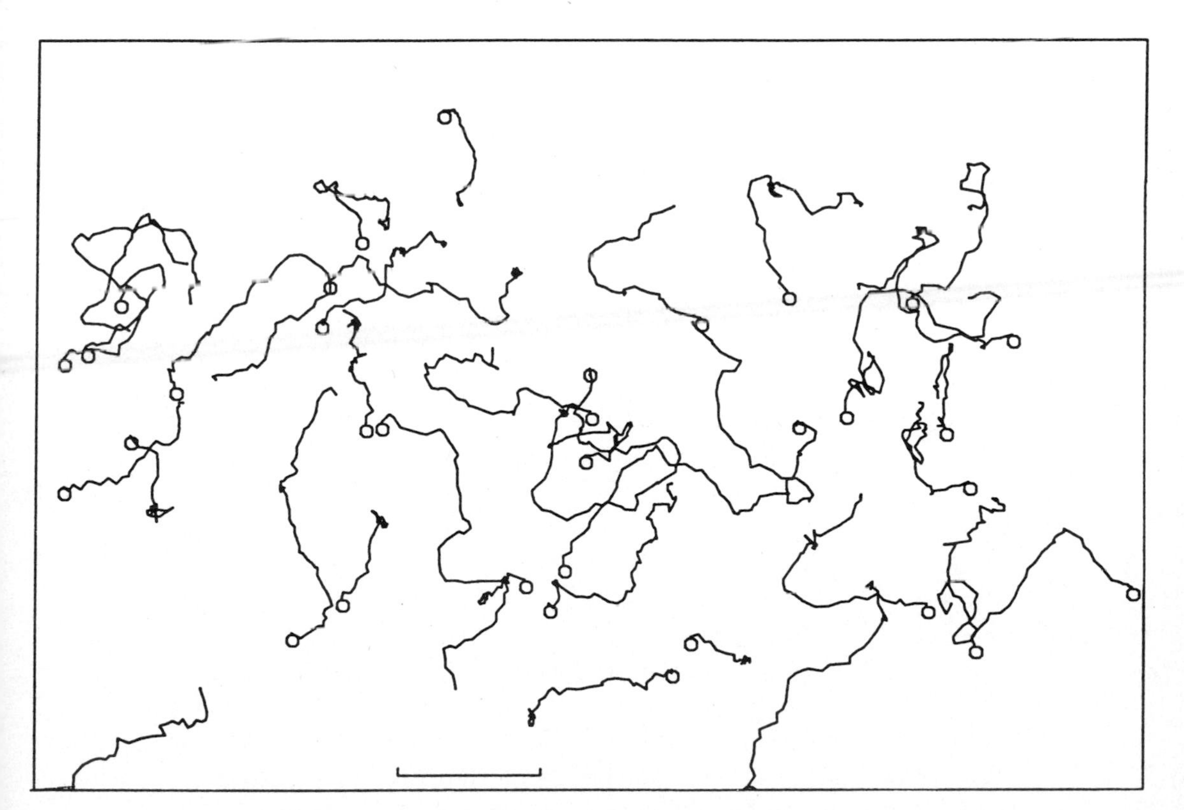

Fig. 7. Computer plot of rabbit neutrophils tracked in real time during a typical experiment: 45 cells were selected by the computer at the beginning of the experiment: 35 produced the satisfactory tracks shown here. The experiment lasted 30 min; samples were taken every 30 s. Bar, 100 μm. (Courtesy Mr K. V. Crocket.)

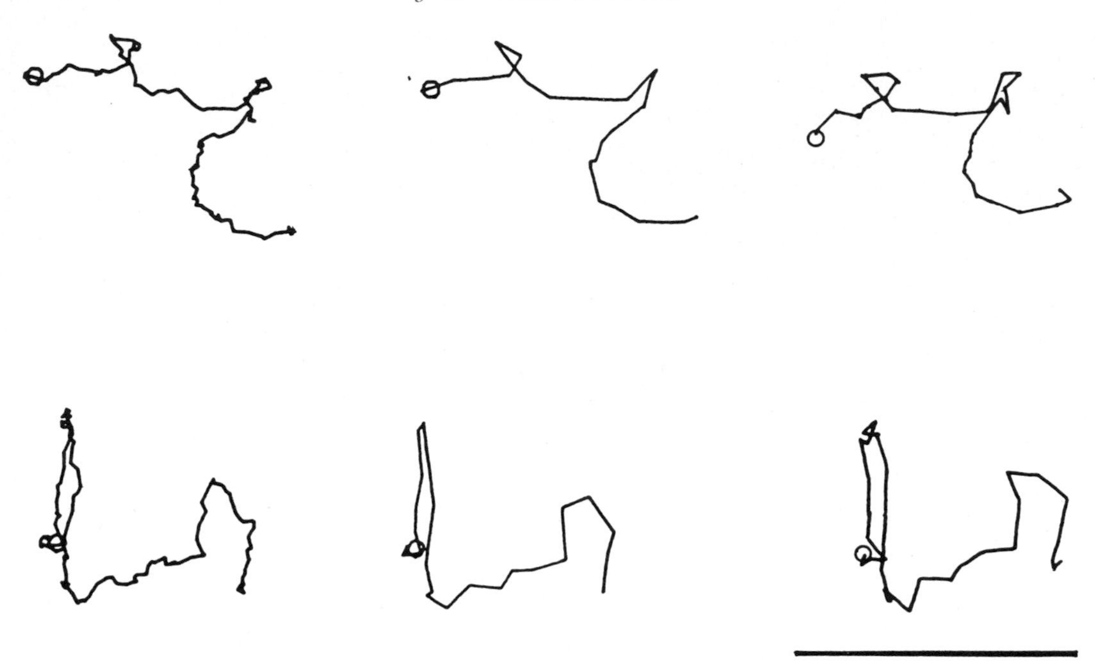

Fig. 8. The smoothing effect of manual tracing can be mimicked by computer. Two cells (top and bottom rows) were recorded on film and the sequence analysed both manually and by computer. Left column: cells tracked by computer, sampling every 12 s. Centre column: cells tracked by computer, sampling every 60 s. Right column: cells tracked by hand, sampling every 60 s. Bar, 100 μm. (Reproduced from Dow *et al.* (1987), with permission.)

parameters are needed to describe the population movement fully, and the nature of the parameters accords with our knowledge of locomotion. For example, bacterial locomotion is made up of a series of linear 'runs', interspersed with random 'tumbles' (Berg, 1975; Lackie, 1986). The greater volume of data available with computer tracking systems have enabled this model to be subjected to detailed scrutiny.

Interestingly, there are some systematic differences between computer and manual tracking. Our experiments have shown that manually produced cell tracks are noticeably smoother than those produced by a computer (Dow *et al.* 1987), and only partly due to the increased sampling interval (60 s *versus* 20 s) in manual tracking experiments (Fig. 8). Computer tracks are noticeably more angular than those produced manually, resulting in higher speeds and lower persistences, although these effects are minimal at sampling intervals as great as those used manually. However, computer analysis allows us to vary the sampling interval systematically. When this is done, it becomes clear that speed, and particularly persistence, are sensitive to sampling interval (Fig. 9). To some extent, these findings can be explained in terms of noise in the measurement of individual position. For a constant error in position measurement, the error in calculated speed is inversely proportional to the sampling interval. This is not, of course, a problem peculiar to computer

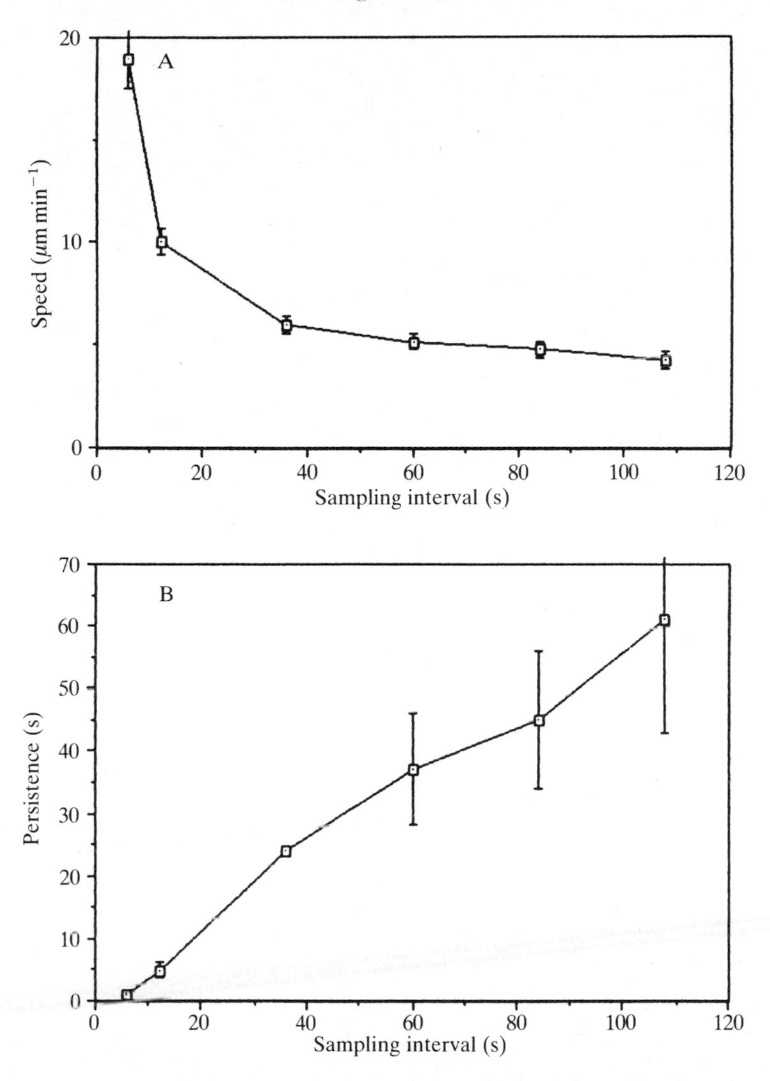

Fig. 9. Apparent speed (A) and persistence (B) of rabbit neutrophils as a function of sampling interval. A ciné film of rabbit neutrophils was analysed by computer, at various sampling intervals. Data are plotted as population means ± S.D. for four independent computer analyses of the same sequence.

systems; manual errors in the subjective estimate of cell centroids are at least as large, but very few workers have endured the tedium necessary to analyse films manually at such a fine time resolution.

There are, however, other possibilities for anomalous speeds at short sampling intervals: cells may make rapid shape changes, on much shorter time-scales than gross translocation. This is a perfectly valid parameter to measure, and is in principle separable from computer noise by imaging the cells at higher magnification: cell movements would remain absolute in magnitude, whereas computer errors are proportional to the number of micrometres spanned by each pixel.

However, while it is clear from Fig. 9 that speeds of cells are consistent above a certain threshold sample interval (in the case of a 10× lens, 20 s), the same cannot be said for persistence. This shows a direct proportionality with sample interval, calling into question its suitability as an independent variable in the analysis of neutrophil locomotion. This may not undermine its value as a descriptive measure: for a constant sampling interval, apparent persistences vary systematically with the application of agents known to affect neutrophil activation. In the light of the improved ability of the computer tracking system to follow large numbers of cells, the question of modelling neutrophil locomotion will be studied further.

These experiments draw our attention to the possibility that we may be able to characterize cell locomotion at several different levels; at the gross scale, there are population displacements on the scale of millimetres and periods of hours; and on a fine scale, there may be rapid fluctuations on a scale of micrometres and a period of seconds. The same mathematical models are unlikely to apply at both ends of the scale; nor is it surprising that path-length is apparently a fractal measure (Mandelbrot, 1977). Computer-based data acquisition, rather than clouding the issue, can perform the routine calculations rapidly and objectively, enabling the experimenters to concentrate on the question of what should be measured.

The limitations of our method for computer tracking should be acknowledged. In spread cells, an optical centroid may not be an appropriate measure of cell position, and may be unduly sensitive to non-locomotory changes in cell shape. This may be overcome by tracking one of the nucleoli at higher magnification, provided that these are prominent (Dunn & Brown, 1986). In our hands, satisfactory images of spread cells, and of individual neuronal growth cones, can be obtained (Fig. 10), suggesting that the tracking system might be suitable for use on a wide range of cultured cells.

Framegrabber hardware does not provide for the automatic subtraction of background from the image. This can be a serious problem as image intensity is rarely constant across a field. Both the illumination intensity of the microscope and the sensitivity of the camera tube may vary markedly. This 'shading' artefact may result in systematic errors in cell areas across the screen, or even in the disappearance of cells in some regions of the screen (Ramm & Kulick, 1985). In our experience, shading was not a serious problem when tracking neutrophils, but necessitated extreme care when following other cell types.

ELECTRICAL RECORDING

There are several popular approaches in attempting to understand neuronal function. At one extreme are the behaviourists and psychologists, who believe that inner workings can be inferred from the actions of the subject; while at the other extreme lie the *in vitro* neurophysiologists, who believe that an understanding of the excitatory process in individual cells and across single synapses is crucial. In between lies the middle ground of classical neurobiology, which seeks to study the firing patterns and interactions of ever more tightly defined classes of neurones in the intact organism.

In classical neurobiology, rapid progress has been made with simpler model systems. Vertebrate neurophysiologists have made major advances, for example in the understanding of visual processing (Masland, 1986); but they can work only with defined *classes* of neurone, such as spinal motorneurones or retinal ganglion cells. However, invertebrate biologists are able to work with identified *single* neurones, with predictable positions, morphology, interconnections and behaviour. In this way, the neural circuitry underlying several simple types of behaviour, such as locomotion, ventilation and feeding, have been thoroughly studied. For example, simple systems have contributed greatly to our understanding of memory; in *Aplysia*, a simple model for memory in avoidance reflexes (Kandel, 1979; Kandel & Schwartz, 1982) has implicated serotonin modulation of cyclic AMP levels; the same second messenger is implicated by memory-deficient mutants of *Drosophila* (Dudai, 1985), and so the study of such systems can lead to a more general understanding of these functions in vertebrates.

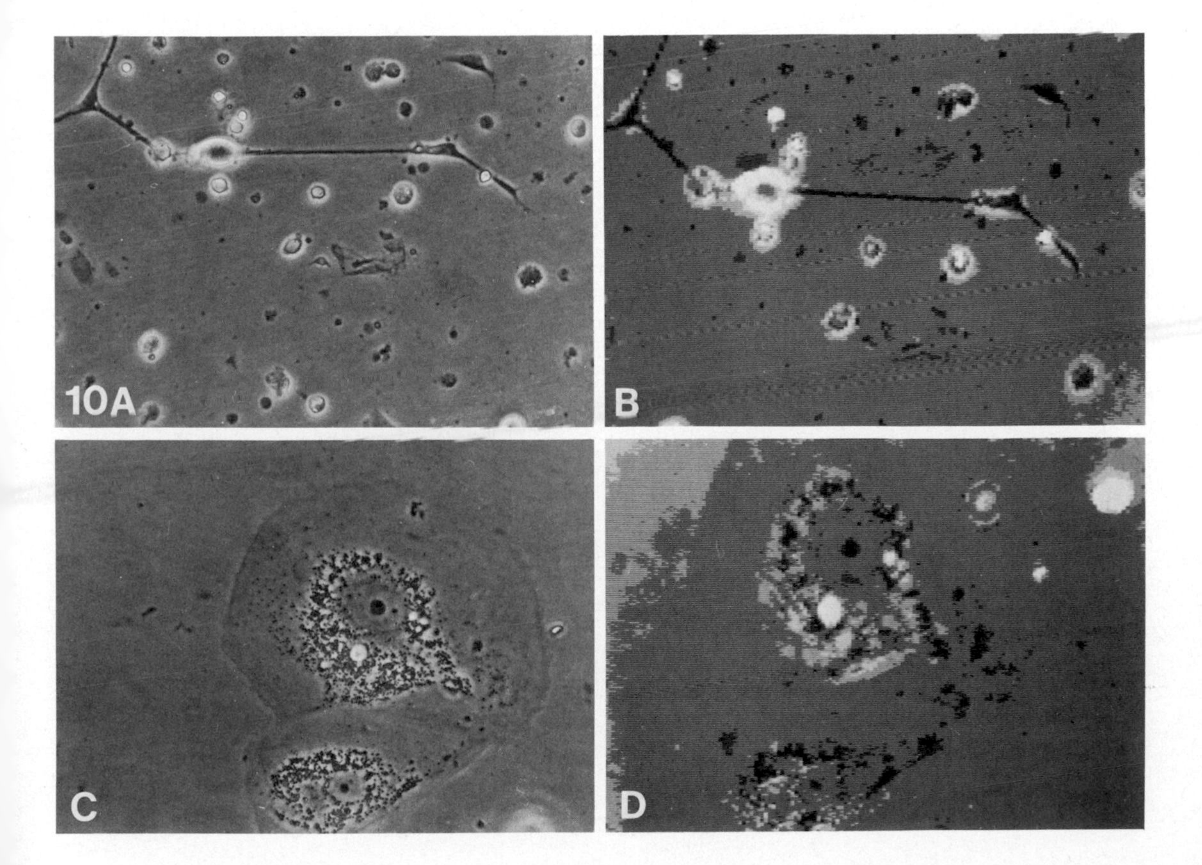

Fig. 10. Phase-contrast micrographs and computer images, digitized to a resolution of 256×160 pixels, with 8 grey levels. Embryonic chick dorsal root ganglion cell with neurite and growth cone; phase-contrast (A), digitized (B). MDCK cells; phase-contrast (C), digitized (D).

However, even in invertebrate systems, the behavioural pathways that are susceptible to the classical approach tend to be rather simple and stereotyped, involving only a handful of neurones. More complex behaviour produces intractable problems in wiring; even a simple animal may have many thousands of neurones, and each neurone may make many synaptic contacts. Our group has as its goal the controlled and repeatable formation of simple neural networks of between two and a few dozen neurones, allowing us to study neuronal function in a series of hypothetical simple animals that do not exist in the real world. While the first to admit that this approach has its pitfalls, we would argue that there are clear benefits to be obtained.

ARE CULTURED NERVE CELLS VALID MODELS OF THE INTACT NERVOUS SYSTEM?

It is important to establish that cultured nerve cells resemble *in situ* neurones in their morphology and function, before they can be considered as adequate model systems. Cultured nerve cells do not necessarily display all of the properties associated with electrical activity; they do not always express a full range of voltage-gated channels, and they may not make functional synapses. However, provided that these limitations are borne in mind, cultured cells have proved to be most useful model systems for a variety of studies (Nelson, 1975; Nelson & Lieberman, 1981). In developmental biology, the rate of outgrowth of identified *Helisoma* neurones, and the morphology and pharmacological sensitivities of their growth cones, have been found to mirror those observed in the embryo (Haydon *et al.* 1985). Similarly, the morphology of the neuronal outgrowth of hippocampal neurones *in vitro* matches that observed in the embryo (Banker & Cowan, 1979). Ciliary ganglion neurones in culture show a shift from multipolar to unipolar organization (Role & Fischbach, 1987), and a rise in choline acetyl transferase (Nishi & Berg, 1987), which mimic those found in the developing embryo. So it seems that certain determinants of neuronal morphology and biochemical maturation are intrinsic in nature, and little affected by the transition to cell culture.

Electrophysiologists have used cultured cells for years; the absence of interfering glial cells and connective tissue has made cell culture a common experimental manipulation for patch clamp studies (Sakmann & Neher, 1983). It seems that when an ion channel is found in cultured cells, it displays the normal (i.e. physiological) properties. Electrical excitability and spontaneous activity are also seen *in vitro*. Mouse and chick cells from a variety of sources, spinal cord (Fischbach & Dichter, 1974; Ransom *et al.* 1977*b*); sympathetic ganglia (Walicke *et al.* 1977; Patterson *et al.* 1978) and dorsal root ganglion (Fischbach, 1972; MacDonald *et al.* 1983) show normal action potentials *in vitro*. Most of these tissues develop electrical activity only after some time in culture, typically 1 month; however, embryonic chick ciliary ganglion cells are electrically active immediately after isolation (Role & Fischbach, 1987). In general, invertebrate neurones are much larger and hardier: they can display normal electrical activity much earlier after isolation (Lees *et al.* 1985; Fuchs *et al.* 1981; Goodman & Spitzer, 1981; Schacher & Proshansky, 1983; Dagan &

Levitan, 1981); the drawback is that invertebrate cell culture techniques are not as far advanced as those for vertebrate cells.

Another property that some cultured neuronal cells share with intact cells is synaptic activity. Normally, sympathetic neurones grown in culture contain adrenaline, and may even make (electrically silent) 'autapses' on themselves: however, on coculture with myoblasts, functional cholinergic and dual-transmitter synapses result (Walicke *et al.* 1977; Patterson *et al.* 1978). In cocultures between dorsal root ganglia (DRG) and spinal cord neurones (SC). DRG to SC and SC to SC synapses are observed, both in chick (Fischbach & Dichter, 1974) and in mouse (Ransom *et al.* 1977*a*; MacDonald *et al.* 1983). *Aplysia* neurones reliably form synapses *in vitro* (Camardo *et al.* 1983; Schacher & Proshansky, 1983; Bodmer *et al.* 1984; Schacher *et al.* 1985), which match the specificity observed *in vivo* (Kandel, 1979). Certain identified neurones from the leech segmental ganglion have been thoroughly characterized *in vivo* (Nicholls & Baylor, 1968), and have been successfully cultured *in vitro*. When placed close together, Retzius cells (responsible for mucous secretion) and P cells (which normally respond to cutaneous pressure) form interdigitating processes, and functional chemical synapses of the Retzius cell onto the P cell frequently result in 3–4 days (Fuchs *et al.* 1981, 1982; Henderson *et al.* 1983; Arechiga *et al.* 1986).

Although there would seem to be great benefit to be derived from investigating neuronal cell lines, in which each cell is uniform and capable of replication, there seem to be severe drawbacks. Neuronal cells do not normally divide and, in cell lines, it seems that the dividing cell population is not excitable; neuronal properties, such as excitability, neurotransmitter production and neurite production, occur only when the cells differentiate under conditions of low serum, or under the influence of certain growth factors (Prasad, 1975). For example, the phaeochromocytoma line PC12 differentiates under the influence of low serum, pH, nerve growth factor or cyclic AMP to form neurone-like cells, with vigorous process growth (Connolly *et al.* 1985; O'Lague & Huttner, 1980), continued accumulation and release of catecholamines (the diagnostic property of the *in vivo* tumour), and the development of a Ca^{2+}/K^{+}-based action potential (Dichter *et al.* 1977), as found in other developing neurones (Grinvald & Farber, 1981). In the longest differentiated cultures, a sodium current also develops (Dichter *et al.* 1977). However, these properties do not result in an action potential *per se*; it is only unmasked under certain experimental conditions (O'Lague *et al.* 1985). NG108 cells, produced by fusing a neuroblastoma and a glioma, show some excitability, and also the accumulation of acetylcholine vesicles at synapse-like regions. Both NG108-15 and adrenergic mouse neuroblastome line N1E-115 demonstrate Na^{+}/K^{+} action potentials; additionally, several slow Ca^{2+} currents are revealed under Na^{+}-free, TEA perfusion conditions (Moolenar & Spector, 1978; Fishman & Spector, 1981). Acetylcholine-induced hyperpolarization of N1E-115 cells is potentiated by cyclic AMP (Tsunoo & Narahashi, 1984). So, although not possessing fully neuronal properties, cell lines are valuable model systems for the study both of individual ion channels, and of the regulation of neuronal gene expression.

ELECTRICAL RECORDING

In our studies, we have used chick cardiac myocytes because the cells have been well studied, because the electric fields generated by these cells are rhythmic and large, and because visual confirmation of the occurrence of each action potential is possible, as excitation is accompanied by contraction. Thus microelectrodes need not be used routinely to correlate electrical activity of the cells with the recordings

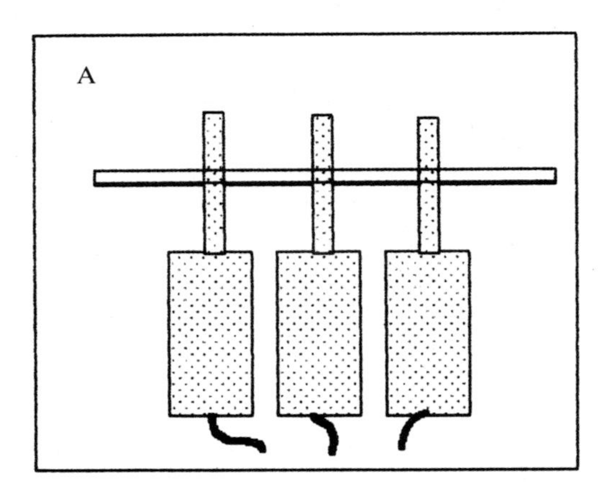

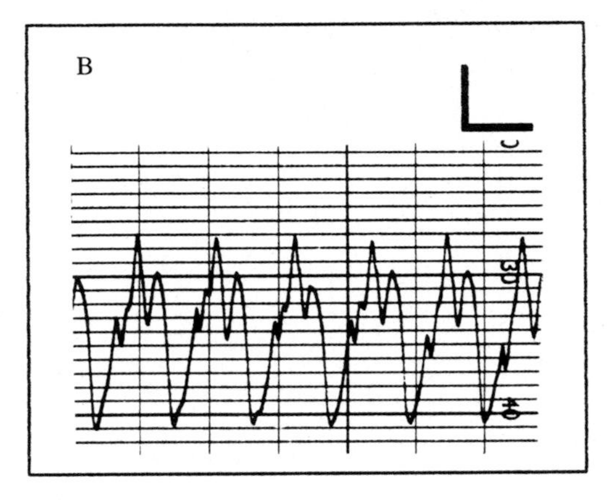

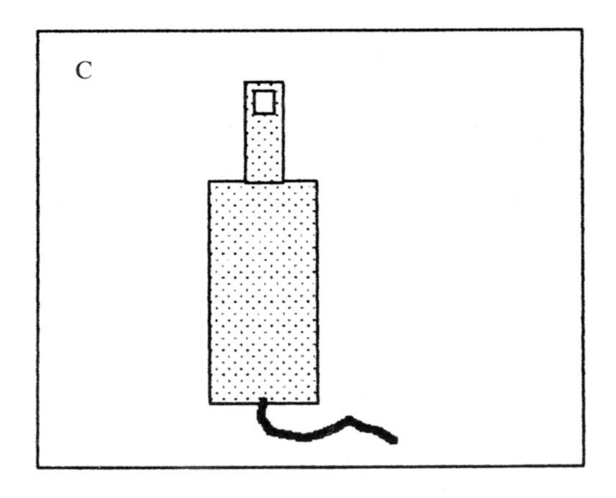

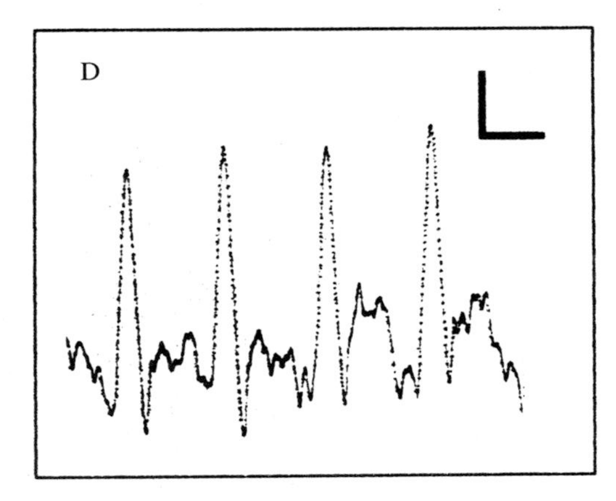

Fig. 11. Extracellular recordings of embryonic chick heart muscle explants from patterned electrodes. A. Diagram of grooved electrode; a channel 20 μm wide was cut through the overlying insulator, exposing the 100 μm-wide gold electrode beneath. B. Results with grooved electrode. C. Diagram of window electrode; electron-beam lithography was used to expose a 6 μm $\times$ 8 μm window in a 1 μm thick polymethylmethacrylate insulating layer above a gold electrode; the window was subsequently developed away. D. Results from window electrode. Bars: B,D, 1 s (ordinate), 20 μV (abscissa).

Fig. 12. Extracellular recordings from isolated leech segmented ganglion from 6 μm $\times$ 8 μm window electrode, as described in legend to Fig. 11. A. Background recording, with ganglion distant from electrode; B, extracellular recording, with ganglion overlying electrode; C, as for B, but with expanded time-scale. Bars: 20 μV (abscissa); 100 ms (ordinate) (A,B) or 10 ms (C).

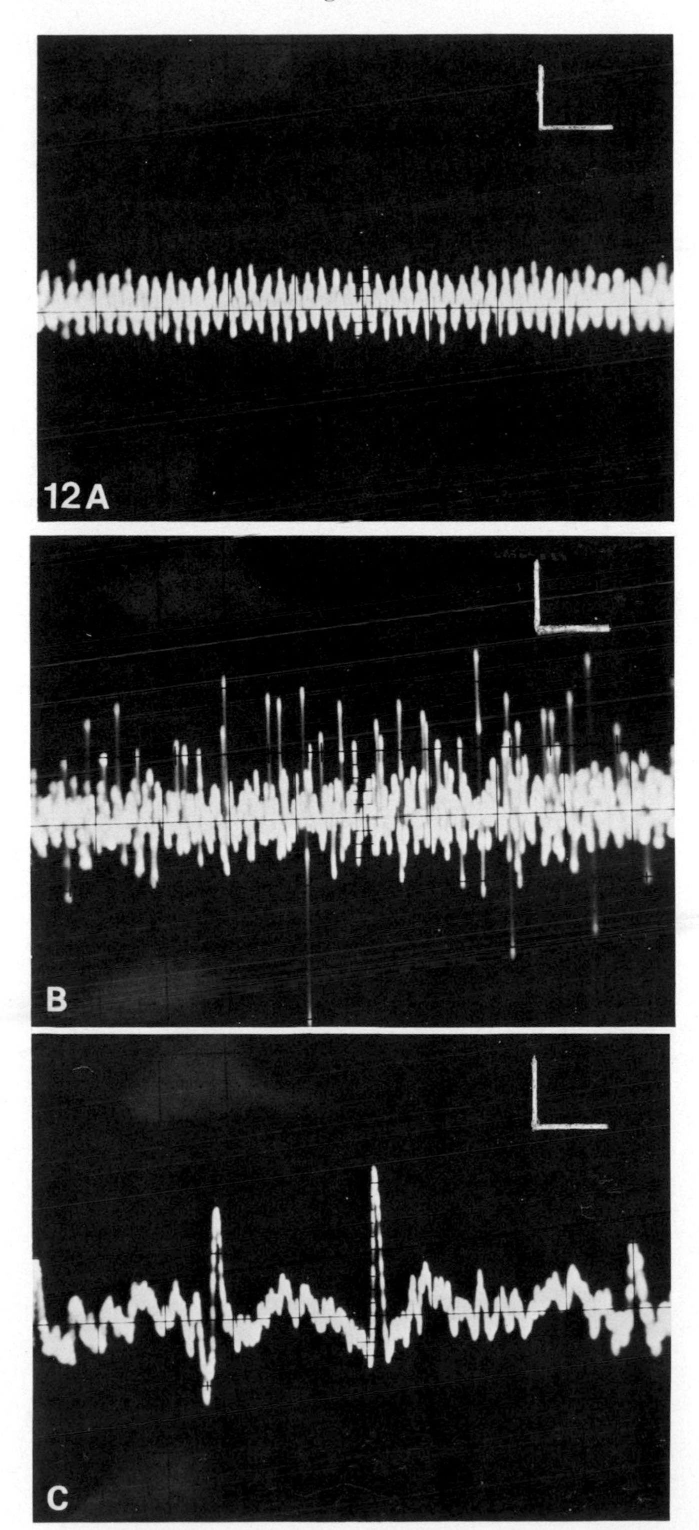
12 A
B
C

obtained by the solid-state electrodes. The chick heart muscle culture system has been used by other workers for similar reasons (Thomas *et al.* 1972; Israel *et al.* 1984). The electrodes we have used have been of two main designs; a small-area electrode, based on a groove cut in an insulating layer, cut at right angles to a series of thin, underlying gold electrodes (Fig. 11A); and a simple rectangular window of arbitrary size, cut through an insulating layer, and exposing a small area of a metal film electrode below (Fig. 11C). Both of these systems have proved suitable for recording muscle action potentials (Fig. 11). Interestingly, the voltage detected by each of the electrode designs ($30\,\mu V$) is similar; it is the signal-to-noise ratio that distinguishes them. A degradation in signal-to-noise ratio for small-area metal electrodes is well known (Edell, 1986). We are currently evaluating these electrode systems for use with neurones. Preliminary results with electron-beam lithographic window electrodes have been encouraging, and extracellular recordings have been obtained from leech segmental ganglia (Fig. 12), as a preliminary to recording from identified leech neurones in culture.

Electrode arrays offer certain advantages over conventional glass or metal microelectrodes when used *in vivo* (Kruger, 1983); they enable many recordings to be made at predictable relative geometries; they increase the chances that a viable extracellular recording will be made from at least one of the electrodes; and they enable systematic differences in neuronal activity to be mapped over a small geographical region of the brain, such as the visual cortex. Such arrays are now in widespread use in vertebrate (Kruger, 1983; Eichenbaum & Kuperstein, 1986) and invertebrate (Pickard & Wellberry, 1976; Pickard *et al.* 1978; Pickard, 1979; Novak & Wheeler, 1986) systems, where their performance is fully comparable with conventional extracellular electrodes. When used on cultured cells *in vitro*, such arrays permit stable electrical monitoring of cells for periods far longer than would be possible with conventional electrodes, with no damage inherent in cell penetration, and without risking the sterility of the culture. However, nerve cells in culture form a thin network in loose contact with the substratum, and surrounded by relatively low-resistivity medium. Such circumstances make electrical extracellular recording technically far harder than it is in intact brain tissue; however, satisfactory results have so far been obtained by several workers (Gross *et al.* 1985; Droge *et al.* 1986).

Metal microelectrodes can also be used in a simpler fashion, to detect the presence of adherent cells (Giaever & Keese, 1984, 1986). In this case, a small-amplitude a.c. field is applied between the microelectrode and the indifferent electrode in the medium, and the presence of cells on the electrode inferred from fluctuations in impedance. In this way, Giaever & Keese suggest that not just the cell's presence can be detected, but that high-frequency fluctuations, on a time-scale and size consistent with lamellipodial extensions, can be resolved. However, the large area of their electrode ($200\,\mu m \times 100\,\mu m$) relative to the area of a typical spread cell might make this appear optimistic. Additionally, experiments in our laboratory have suggested that impedance changes brought about by temperature changes and cell conditioning of the medium might be larger than those brought about by cell locomotion, under similar experimental conditions (P. Connolly *et al.* unpublished).

PROSPECTS

The use of topographical cell contact guidance in the construction of simple neuronal networks could be termed 'bioengineering' in its most literal sense. Quite apart from the benefits to our basic understanding of cell behaviour, there may be certain applied benefits. In medicine, it is now conceivable that spinal prosthetic implants may be able to monitor neuronal activity in severed nerves, and to activate directly the relevant muscles. A suitable recording device has been tested in rabbit (Edell, 1986). Active electrode arrays, which incorporate their own amplifiers, have already been built and tested (Jobling *et al.* 1981). In audiology, such prostheses are even nearer to reality; human patients with multi-electrode implants in the cochlea or adjacent to the moliolar nerve show satisfactory discrimination between spoken monosyllabic words (Hochmair-Desoyer *et al.* 1983). Such implants are biocompatible over a period of years, and electrical stimulation does not cause nerves to die back from the implant (Brummer & Robblee, 1983). Work with *Aplysia* neurones inspired the building of a new class of parallel processor that can solve the 'travelling salesman' problem, one of the most complex in computing science (Anon, 1986). Similarly, the study of artificial intelligence is intertwined with studies of human neuronal circuitry (Ullman, 1986). It seems likely that this will be an expanding area of cell biology in the future.

The authors gratefully thank John Lackie and Ken Crocket for their help with neutrophils; Susannah Blackshaw and Douglas Neil, for their help with neurophysiology; and Lois Hobbs, Bill Monaghan, Mike McGrath and Susan Kitson for their assistance. This work was funded by the BP Venture Research Group, and by the General Fund of the University of Glasgow.

REFERENCES

ABERCROMBIE, M. (1980). The crawling movement of metazoan cells. *Proc. R. Soc. Lond.* B, **207**, 129–147.

ANON. (1986). "Neuron" chips emulate brain cells, hold promise of much faster processors. *Byte* **November**, 9.

ARECHIGA, H., CHIQUET, M., KUFFLER, D. P. & NICHOLLS, J. G. (1986). Formation of specific connections in culture by identified leech neurones containing serotonin, acetylcholine and peptide transmitters. *J. exp. Biol.* **126**, 15–31.

BANKER, G. A. & COWAN, W. M. (1979). Further observations on hippocampal neurons in dispersed cell culture. *J. comp. Neurol.* **187**, 469–494.

BARKER, A. T., JAFFE, L. F. & VANABLE, J. W. (1982). The glabrous epithelium of cavies contains a powerful battery. *Am. J. Physiol.* **242**, R358–366.

BERG, H. C. (1975). Bacterial behaviour. *Nature, Lond.* **254**, 389–392.

BODMER, R., DAGAN, D. & LEVITAN, I. B. (1984). Chemical and electrotonic connections between *Aplysia* neurons in primary culture. *J. Neurosci.* **4**, 228–233.

BONHOEFFER, F. & HUF, J. (1980). Recognition of cell types by axonal growth cones *in vitro*. *Nature, Lond.* **288**, 162–164.

BONHOEFFER, F. & HUF, J. (1985). Position-dependent properties of retinal axons and their growth cones. *Nature, Lond.* **315**, 409–410.

BRAY, D. (1982). Filopodial contraction and growth cone guidance. In *Cell Behaviour* (ed. R. Bellairs, A. S. G. Curtis & G. A. Dunn), pp. 299–317. Cambridge University Press.

BRUMMER, S. B., ROBBLEE, L. S. & HAMBRECHT, F. T. (1983). Criteria for selecting electrodes for electrical stimulation: theoretical and practical considerations. *Ann. N.Y. Acad. Sci.* **405**, 159–171.

BRUNETTE, D. M. (1986). Fibroblasts on micromachined substrata orient heirarchically to grooves of different dimensions. *Expl Cell Res.* **164**, 11–26.

BRUNETTE, D. M., KENNER, G. S. & GOULD, T. R. L. (1983). Grooved titanium surfaces orient growth and migration of cells from human gingivial explants. *J. dent. Res.* **62**, 1045–1048.

CAMARDO, J., PROSHANSKY, E. & SCHACHER, S. (1983). Identified *Aplysia* neurons form specific chemical synapses in culture. *J. Neurosci.* **3**, 2614–2620.

CLARK, P., CONNOLLY, P., CURTIS, A. S. G., DOW, J. A. T. & WILKINSON, C. D. W. (1987). Topographical control of cell behaviour. I. Simple step cues. *Development* **99**, 439–448.

CONNOLLY, J. L., SEELEY, P. J. & GREEN, L. A. (1985). Regulation of growth cone morphology by nerve growth factor: a comparative study by scanning electron microscopy. *J. Neurosci. Res.* **13**, 183–198.

COOPER, M. S. & SCHLIWA, M. (1985). Electrical and ionic controls of tissue cell locomotion in DC electric fields. *J. Neurosci. Res.* **13**, 223–244.

CURTIS, A. S. G., CLARK, P., CONNOLLY, P., DOW, J. A. T. & WILKINSON, C. D. W. (1985). The control of neurite extension by surface topography. *J. Cell Biol.* **101**, 128a.

CURTIS, A. S. G. & VARDE, M. (1964). Control of cell behaviour: topological factors. *J. natn. Cancer Inst.* **33**, 15–26.

DAGAN, D. & LEVITAN, I. B. (1981). Isolated identified *Aplysia* neurons in cell culture. *J. Neurosci.* **1**, 736–740.

DICHTER, M. A., GREENE, L. A. & TISCHLER, A. S. (1977). Nerve growth factor induced increase in electrical excitability and acetylcholine sensitivity of a rat phaeochromocytoma cell line. *Nature, Lond.* **268**, 501–504.

DONOVAN, R. M., GOLDSTEIN, E., KIM, Y., LIPPERT, W., CHEUNG, A. T. W. & MILLER, M. E. (1986). A quantitative method for the analysis of cell shape and locomotion. *Histochemistry* **84**, 525–529.

DOW, J. A. T., LACKIE, J. M. & CROCKET, K. V. (1986). Moving neutrophils can be tracked with a low-cost video/microcomputer system. *Proc. R. microsc. Soc.* **21**, S82.

DOW, J. A. T., LACKIE, J. M. & CROCKET, K. V. (1987). A simple microcomputer-based system for real-time analysis of cell behaviour. *J. Cell Sci.* **87**, 171–182.

DROGE, M. H., GROSS, G. W., HIGHTOWER, M. H. & CZISNY, L. E. (1986). Multielectrode analysis of coordinated, multisite, rhythmic bursting in cultured CNS monolayer networks. *J. Neurosci.* **6**, 1583–1592.

DUDAI, Y. (1985). Genes, enzymes and learning in *Drosophila*. *Trends Neurosci.* **8**, 18–20.

DUNN, G. A. (1982). Contact guidance of cultured tissue cells: a survey of potentially relevant properties of the substratum. In *Cell Behaviour* (ed. R. Bellairs, A. S. G. Curtis & G. A. Dunn). Cambridge University Press.

DUNN, G. A. (1983). Characterising a kinesis response: time averaged measures of cell speed and directional persistence. *Agents Actions Suppl.* **12**, 14–33.

DUNN, G. A. & BROWN, A. F. (1986). Alignment of fibroblasts on grooved surfaces described by a simple geometric transformation. *J. Cell Sci.* **83**, 313–340.

DUNN, G. A. & HEATH, J. P. (1976). A new hypothesis of contact guidance of tissue cells. *Expl Cell Res.* **101**, 1–14.

EDELL, D. J. (1986). A peripheral nerve information transducer for amputees: long-term multichannel recordings from rabbit peripheral nerves. *IEEE Trans. Biomed. Eng.* **33**, 203–214.

EICHENBAUM, H. & KUPERSTEIN, M. (1986). Extracellular neural recording with multichannel microelectrodes. *J. Electrophysiol. Tech.* **13**, 189–209.

FISCHBACH, G. D. (1972). Synapse formation between dissociated nerve and muscle cells in low density cell cultures. *Devl Biol.* **28**, 407–429.

FISCHBACH, G. D. & DICHTER, M. A. (1974). Electrophysiologic and morphologic properties of neurons in dissociated chick spinal cord cell culture. *Devl Biol.* **37**, 100–116.

FISHMAN, M. C. & SPECTOR, I. (1981). Potassium current suppression by quinidine reveals additional calcium currents in neuroblastoma cells. *Proc. natn. Acad. Sci. U.S.A.* **78**, 5245–5249.

FUCHS, P. A., HENDERSON, L. P. & NICHOLLS, J. G. (1982). Chemical transmission between individual Retzius and sensory neurones of the leech in culture. *J. Physiol.* **323**, 195–210.

FUCHS, P. A., NICHOLLS, J. G. & READY, D. F. (1981). Membrane properties and selective connexions of identified leech neurons in culture. *J. Physiol.* **316**, 203–223.

GIAEVER, I. & KEESE, C. R. (1984). Monitoring fibroblast behaviour in tissue culture with an applied electric field. *Proc. natn. Acad. Sci. U.S.A.* **81**, 3761–3764.

GIAEVER, I. & KEESE, C. R. (1986). Use of electrical fields to monitor the dynamical aspect of cell behaviour in tissue culture. *IEEE Trans. Biomed. Eng.* **33**, 242–255.

GOODMAN, C. S. & BASTIANI, M. J. (1984). How embryonic nerve cells recognise one another. *Sci. Am.* **251**(6), 50–58.

GOODMAN, C. S. & BATE, M. (1981). Neuronal development in the grasshopper. *Trends Neurosci.* **4**, 163–169.

GOODMAN, C. S. & SPITZER, N. C. (1981). The development of electrical properties of identified neurons in grasshopper embryos. *J. Physiol.* **313**, 385–403.

GRINVALD, A. & FARBER, I. C. (1981). Optical recording of calcium action potentials from growth cones of cultured neurons with a laser microbeam. *Science* **212**, 1164–1167.

GROSS, G. W., WEN, W. Y. & LIN, J. W. (1985). Transparent indium–tin oxide electrode patterns for extracellular, multisite recording in neuronal cultures. *J. neurosci. Meth.* **15**, 243–252.

GUNDERSEN, R. W. & BARRETT, J. N. (1980). Characterization of the turning response of dorsal root neurites toward nerve growth factor. *J. Cell Biol.* **80**, 546–554.

HAMMARBACK, J. A. & LETOURNEAU, P. C. (1986). Neurite extension across regions of low cell–substratum adhesivity: implications for the guidepost hypothesis of axonal pathfinding. *Devl Biol.* **117**, 655–662.

HAMMARBACK, J. A., PALM, S. L., FURCHT, L. T. & LETOURNEAU, P. C. (1985) Guidance of neurite outgrowth by pathways of substratum-absorbed laminin. *J. Neurosci. Res.* **13**, 213–220.

HAYDON, P. G., COHAN, C. S., MCCOBB, D. P., MILLER, H. R. & KATER, S. B. (1985). Neuron-specific growth cone properties as seen in identified neurons of *Helisoma*. *J. Neurosci. Res.* **13**, 135–147.

HENDERSON, L. P., KUFFLER, D. P., NICHOLLS, J. & ZHANG, R.-J. (1983). Structural and functional analysis of synaptic transmission between identified leech neurons in culture. *J. Physiol.* **340**, 347–358.

HINKLE, L., MCCAIG, C. D. & ROBINSON, K. R. (1981). The direction of growth of differentiating neurones and myoblasts from frog embryos in an applied electric field. *J. Physiol.* **314**, 121–135.

HOCHMAIR-DESOYER, I. J., HOCHMAIR, E. S. & BURIAN, K. (1983). Design and fabrication of multiwire scala tympani electrodes. *Ann. N.Y. Acad. Sci.* **405**, 173–182.

HORDER, T. J. & MARTIN, K. A. C. (1979). Morphogenetics as an alternative to chemospecificity in the formation of nerve connections. *Symp. Soc. exp. Biol.* **32**, 275–359.

HUIJSMANS, D. P., LAMERS, W. H., LOS, J. A. & STRACKEE, J. (1986). Towards computerized morphometric facilities: a review of 58 software packages for computer-aided three dimensional reconstruction, quantification and picture generation from parallel serial sections. *Anat. Rec.* **216**, 449–470.

HUME, R. L., ROLE, L. & FISCHBACH, G. D. (1983). Acetylcholine release from growth cone detected by patches of acetylcholine receptor-rich membrane. *Nature, Lond.* **305**, 632–634.

ISRAEL, D. A., BARRY, W. H., EDELL, D. J. & MARK, R. G. (1984). An array of microelectrodes to stimulate and record from cardiac cells in culture. *Am. J. Physiol.* **247**, H669–H674.

JOBLING, D. T., SMITH, J. G. & WHEAL, H. V. (1981). Active microelectrode array to record from the mammalian central nervous system *in vitro*. *Med. biol. eng. Comput.* **19**, 553–560.

KANDEL, E. R. (1979). Small systems of neurons. *Sci. Am.* **241**, 60–70.

KANDEL, E. R. & SCHWARTZ, J. H. (1982). Molecular biology of learning: modulation of transmitter release. *Science* **218**, 433–443.

KRUGER, J. (1983). Simultaneous individual recordings from many cerebral neurons: techniques and results. *Rev. physiol. biochem. Pharmacol.* **98**, 177–233.

LACKIE, J. M. (1986). *Cell Movement and Cell Behaviour*. London: Allen & Unwin.

LEES, G., BEADLE, D. J., BOTHAM, R. P. & KELLY, J. S. (1985). Excitable properties of insect neurons in culture. A developmental study. *J. Insect Physiol.* **31**, 135–144.

LUMSDEN, A. G. & DAVIES, A. M. (1986). Chemotropic effect of specific target epithelium in the developing mammalian nervous system. *Nature, Lond.* **323**, 538–539.

MACDONALD, R. L., PUN, R. Y. K., NEALE, E. A. & NELSON, P. G. (1983). Synaptic interactions between mammalian central neurons in cell culture. I. Reversal potential for excitatory postsynaptic potentials. *J. Neurophysiol.* **49**, 1428–1441.

MANDELBROT, B. B. (1977). *Fractals, Form, Chance and Dimension.* San Francisco: W. H. Freeman.
MASLAND, R. H. (1986). The functional architecture of the retina. *Sci. Am.* **255** (6), 90–99.
MASON, C. (1985). How do growth cones grow? *Trends Neurosci.* **July**, 304–306.
MCCAIG, C. D. (1986). Dynamic aspects of amphibian neurite growth and the effects of an applied electric field. *J. Physiol.* **375**, 55–69.
MOOLENAR, W. H. & SPECTOR, I. (1978). Ionic currents in cultured mouse neuroblastoma cells under voltage clamp conditions. *J. Physiol.* **278**, 265–286.
NELSON, P. G. (1975)., Nerve and muscle cells in culture. *Physiol. Rev.* **55**, 1–61.
NELSON, P. G. & LIEBERMAN, M. eds (1981). *Excitable Cells in Tissue Culture.* NY: Plenum.
NICHOLLS, J. G. & BAYLOR, D. A. (1968). Specific modalities and receptive fields of sensory neurons in CNS of the leech. *J. Neurophysiol.* **31**, 740.
NISHI, R. & BERG, D. K. (1977). Dissociated ciliary ganglion neurons *in vitro:* survival and synapse formation. *Proc. natn. Acad. Sci. U.S.A.* **74**, 5171–5175.
NOBLE, P. B. & LEVINE, M. D. (1986). *Computer-assisted Analyses of Cell Locomotion and Chemotaxis.* Baton Rouge, Florida: CRC Press.
NOVAK, J. L. & WHEELER, B. C. (1986). Recording from the *Aplysia* abdominal ganglion with a planar microelectrode array. *IEEE Trans. Biomed. Eng.* **33**, 196–202.
NUCCITELLI, R. & ERICKSON, C. A. (1983). Embryonic cell motility can be guided by physiological electric fields. *Cell Motil.* **2**, 243–255.
O'HARA, P. T. & BUCK, R. C. (1979). Contact guidance *in vitro.* A light, transmission and scanning electron microscopic study. *Expl. Cell Res.* **121**, 235–249.
O'LAGUE, P. H. & HUTTNER, S. L. (1980). Physiological and morphological studies of rat phaeochromocytoma cells (PC-12) chemically fused and grown in culture. *Proc. natn. Acad. Sci. U.S.A.* **77**, 1701–1705.
O'LAGUE, P. H., HUTTNER, S. L., VANDENBERG, C. A., MORRISON-GRAHAM, K. & HORN, R. (1985). Morphological properties and membrane channels of the growth cones induced in PC12 cells by nerve growth factor. *J. Neurosci. Res.* **13**, 301–321.
PATEL, N. B., XIE, Z.-P., YOUNG, S. H. & POO. M.-M. (1985). Response of nerve growth cone to focal electric currents. *J. Neurosci. Res.* **13**, 245–256.
PATTERSON, P. H., POTTER, D. D. & FURSHPAN, E. J. (1978). The chemical differentiation of nerve cells. *Sci. Am.* **239**, 38–47.
PICKARD, R. S. (1979). Printed circuit microelectrodes. *Trends Neurosci.* **2**, 259–261.
PICKARD, R. S., COLLINS, A. J., JOSEPH, P. L. & HICKS, R. C. J. (1978). Flexible printed-circuit probe for electrophysiology. *Med. biol. eng. Comput.* **17**, 261–267.
PICKAR, R. S. & WELBERRY, T. R. (1976). Printed circuit microelectrodes and their application to the honeybee brain. *J. exp. Biol.* **64**, 39–44.
PRASAD, K. N. (1975). Differentiation of neuroblastoma cells in culture. *Biol. Rev.* **50**, 129–265.
PROHASKA, O. J., OLCAAYTUG, F., PFUNDNER, P. & DRAUGAUN, H. (1986). Thin-film multiple electrode probes: possibilities and limitations. *IEEE Trans. Biomed. Eng.* **33**, 223–229.
RAMM, P. & KULICK, J. H. (1985). Principles of computer-assisted imaging in autoradiographic densitometry. In *The Microcomputer in Cell and Neurobiology Research* (ed. R. R. Mize), pp. 311–334. New York: Elsevier.
RANSOM, B. R., CHRISTIAN, C. N., BULLOCK, P. N., NELSON, P. G. (1977*a*). Mouse spinal cord in cell culture. II. Synaptic activity and circuit behaviour. *J. Neurophysiol.* **40**, 1151–1162.
RANSOM, B. R., NEALE, E., HENKART, M., BULLOCK, P. N. & NELSON, P. G. (1977*b*). Mouse spinal cord in cell culture. I. Morphology and intrinsic neuronal electrophysiologic properties. *J. Neurophysiol.* **40**, 1132–1150.
ROLE, L. W. & FISCHBACH, G. D. (1987). Changes in the numbr of ciliary ganglion neuron processes with time. *J. Cell Biol.* **104**, 363–370.
SAKMANN, B. & NEHER, E., eds (1983). *Single Channel Recording.* New York: Plenum.
SCHACHER, S. & PROSHANSKY, E. (1983). Neurite regeneration by *Aplysia* neurons in cell culture. *J. Neurosci.* **3**, 2403–2413.
SCHACHER, S., RAYPORT, S. G. & AMBRON, R. T. (1985). Giant *Aplysia* neuron R2 reliably forms strong chemical connections *in vitro*. *J. Neurosci.* **5**, 2851–2856.
SCHOLES, J. H. (1979). Nerve fibre topography in the retinal projection to the tectum. *Nature, Lond.* **278**, 620–624.

SPERRY, R. W. (1963). Chemoaffinity in the orderly growth of nerve fibre patterns and connections. *Proc. natn. Acad. Sci. U.S.A.* **50**, 703–710.

THOMAS, C. A., SPRINGER, P. A., LOEB, G. E., BERWALD-NETTER, Y. & OKUN, L. M. (1972). A miniature microelectrode array to monitor the bioelectric activity of cultured cells. *Expl Cell Res.* **74**, 61–66.

TICKLE, C., ALBERTS, B., WOLPERT, L. & LEE, J. (1982). Local application of retinoic acid to the limb mimics the action of the polarising region. *Nature, Lond.* **296**, 564–566.

TSUNOO, A. & NARAHASHI, T. (1984). Cyclic AMP-mediated potentiation of muscarinic hyperpolarisation in neuroblastoma cells. *Brain Res.* **294**, 123–126.

ULLMAN, S. (1986). Artificial intelligence and the brain: computational studies of the visual system. *A. Rev. Neurosci.* **9**, 1–26.

VICKER, M. G., LACKIE, J. M. & SCHILL, W. (1986). Neutrophil leucocyte chemotaxis is not induced by a spatial gradient of chemoattractant. *J. Cell Sci.* **84**, 263–286.

WALICKE, P. A., CAMPENOT, R. B. & PATTERSON, P. H. (1977). Determination of transmitter function by neuronal activity. *Proc. natn. Acad. Sci. U.S.A.* **74**, 5767–5771.

WEISS, P. (1945). Experiments on cell and axon orientation *in vitro*: the role of colloidal exudates in tissue organization. *J. exp. Zool.* **100**, 353–386.

WHITE, R. L., ROBERTS, L. A., COTTER, N. F. & KWON, O.-H. (1983). Thin-film electrode fabrication techniques. *Ann. N.Y. Acad. Sci.* **405**, 183–190.

WOLPERT, L. (1978). Pattern formation in biological development. *Sci. Am.* **239**, 154–164.

WOOD, A. & THOROGOOD, P. (1984). An analysis of *in vivo* cell migration during teleost fin morphogenesis. *J. Cell Sci.* **66**, 205–222.

YOUNG, S. H. & POO, M.-M. (1983). Spontaneous release of transmitter from growth cone of embryonic neurone. *Nature, Lond.* **305**, 634–637.

ZIPSER, B. & MCKAY, R. (1981). Monoclonal antibodies distinguish identifiable neurones in the leech. *Nature, Lond.* **289**, 549–554.

J. Cell Sci. Suppl. 8, 81–102 (1987)

A UNIFIED APPROACH TO ANALYSING CELL MOTILITY

G. A. DUNN AND A. F. BROWN
MRC Cell Biophysics Unit, 26–29 Drury Lane, London WC2B 5RL, UK

SUMMARY

The quantitative analysis of cell motility in culture has several important functions. First, it gives a concise and accurate description of the motile process and can detect subtle differences in motility due to different genetic makeup or experimental conditions. Second, its objectivity means that results can be communicated precisely and used unambiguously to test hypotheses about motility. Third, it may be used to derive a mathematical model with the same statistical properties as the motile process and thus elucidate the mechanism of motility.

In this paper, we introduce a general procedure for analysing cell motility in a wide variety of circumstances. We describe a pilot project for the analysis of simple geometrical data obtained from randomly moving fibroblasts. Finally, as an example, we show how an analysis of the translocation of the fibroblasts can lead to insights into the mechanism of motility that are arguably not obtainable by any other approach.

WHY ANALYSE CELL MOTILITY?

An outstanding problem in the study of cell motility is how the locomotory machinery is controlled and coordinated. What are the overall dynamics of it? The analysis of the molecular components of the locomotory machinery, and their interactions, has made great progress over the last 15 years or so, particularly in those interactions where there is a clear homology with muscle. The dynamics of assembly and disassembly of these components are now also beginning to emerge and we are perhaps not far from understanding many of the basic molecular interactions of cell motility. How are we going to relate these properties at the molecular level to the behavioural properties of the whole cell?

At the level of cell behaviour, it is often convenient to discuss the mechanism of cellular retraction, traction, protrusion or persistence in direction as if they were isolated processes and it is tempting to associate each with a separate molecular mechanism. For example, the first might involve actin–myosin interactions, and the second might require an additional transmembrane molecular linkage system; the third might require actin assembly and the fourth tubulin assembly and interactions with other proteins. However, most investigators agree that these processes have a degree of interdependence, even if only that they utilize common molecular pools and are jointly affected by such global factors as changes in ion concentrations. Nevertheless, there is still a danger in treating the motile system as if it were a collection of relatively independent subsystems susceptible to individual analysis. The possibility exists, for example, that the processes are interdependent at a deeper level. Traction, retraction, protrusion and persistence in direction may be merely superficial properties of a single fundamental process. The understanding of these processes at the molecular level will eventually require hard information on the structure of their mutual interdependence.

Although, in principle, a thorough knowledge of the molecular interactions should be sufficient to predict all the properties of a biological system such as the motile machinery of a cell, there is now a growing realization that this sort of information, on its own, may not help very much. A classic analogy is the Belousov–Zhabotinsky reaction in which fairly simple autocatalytic reactions combine to produce lifelike changing patterns of unexpected complexity (Fig. 1). Manipulation of the experimental parameters reveals new aspects of the patterns that are unpredictable in practice from a knowledge of the underlying molecular interactions (Agladze & Krinsky, 1982). Interestingly, the experimenters use methods for studying the reaction, such as prodding with a needle, that would be familiar to a cell biologist. It is not an inadequate knowledge of the chemistry of the underlying reactions that is hampering progress in understanding this phenomenon but an inadequate knowledge of the dynamics of the patterns and of the theory of the dynamics of autocatalytic systems. These new properties of bulk systems that arise, often unexpectedly, from the underlying properties at a lower level of organization have been called 'emergent properties' (Cottrell, 1977).

The emergent properties of many living processes are now thought by Prigogine and colleagues to be the result of 'far from equilibrium' thermodynamics similar to the Belousov–Zhabotinsky reaction (Prigogine & Stengers, 1984). For example, there is a close parallel between this reaction and the aggregation of slime moulds. Fig. 2 shows two pictures of a spreading fibroblast from Heath (1983) and, comparing them with Fig. 1, there is even an intriguing suggestion that actin-based motility in fibroblasts has some similarities with the dynamics of the Belousov–Zhabotinsky reaction. If we take Prigogine's point of view, then our eventual understanding of the control of the motile process will depend on a knowledge of the stability properties of the system as a whole, and the pattern of intercommunication

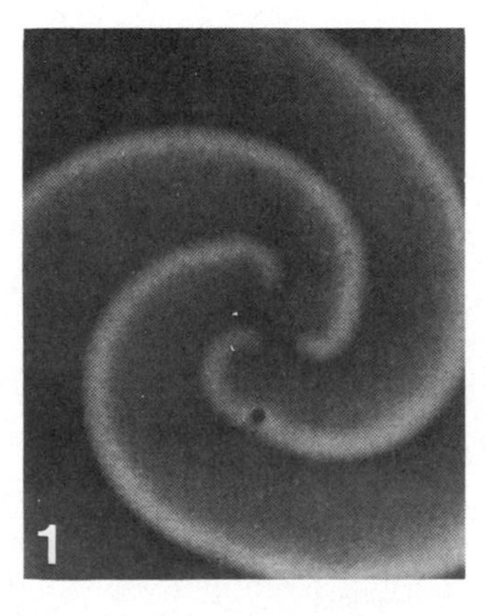

Fig. 1. A rotating three-armed vortex produced by manipulating the Belousov–Zhabotinsky reaction (reproduced from Agladze & Krinsky, 1982).

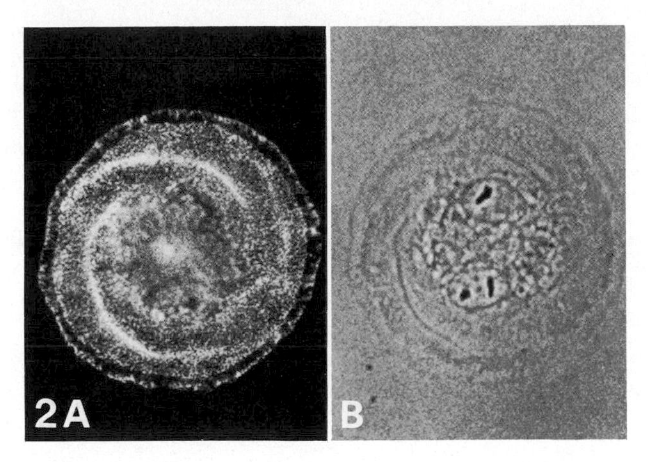

Fig. 2. A three-armed spiral of anti-CSN receptors on the surface of a spreading fibroblast (A) and a corresponding spiral in the underlying cortical microfilaments (B) (reproduced from Heath, 1983).

between its parts, rather than on a detailed knowledge of the individual molecular interactions. If we could know eventually where all the molecules in a moving cell are, and how they are all moving, we might still find ourselves in the position where, in Cottrell's words, 'we would then know everything about the piece of matter in question but understood nothing about it'.

There is, however, one approach to understanding how the dynamic properties might arise from the underlying interactions. This is to model the molecular interactions using a computer and to observe the bulk properties that emerge in the model. We can see from the previous presentation (see Oster, this volume) that this approach has considerable potential for studying cell motility. If the appropriate properties do not emerge then the model is obviously inadequate; the power of this sort of modelling is its usefulness for rejecting hypotheses about the molecular interactions. Unfortunately, if the appropriate properties do emerge it does not prove that the model is correct nor does it necessarily mean that we will be able to understand how the properties emerge in the model. Even so, this approach is probably one of the most promising for relating properties at the two levels since it bypasses the need to understand how the properties emerge. It is important to realize that the performance of any such model can only be judged by how well it matches the dynamics at both levels.

Whether to test the validity of a model, or to examine the effects on motility of an experimental or genetic change, or simply to study the emergent properties in their own right, a detailed knowledge of the dynamics of motility at the level of the whole cell will eventually be required. There has already been a great deal of experimentation on the emergent properties of cell motility but few attempts to describe these properties quantitatively. It may seem obvious, but it needs emphasizing, that any explanation of a process can only go as far as the characterization of the process. The process of motility in tissue cells appears to be a probabilistic or stochastic process and its quantitative description will therefore consist of the joint statistical properties of a collection of variables that each describe some aspect of the process. The aim of analysing cell motility is to discover the interdependence between these different aspects of the motile process.

Apart from being an accurate, objective description of motility, a quantitative analysis can lead to important insights into mechanism. Its limitations are that it says nothing about the molecular mechanism of motility, unless some of the variables are contrived to represent molecular events, and it is notoriously hard to interpret statistical dependence as cause/effect relationships. Given these limitations, the method presents a short-cut to answering such questions as 'is the mechanism of changing speed of a cell independent of its mechanism of changing direction?' and 'what are the time constants in the interdependence of protrusion and retraction?' If Prigogine is right, then attacking these problems directly, at the level of the emergent properties, and then seeking a molecular explanation is likely to be more efficient than trying to predict the emergent properties from a study of the molecular interactions.

A UNIFIED APPROACH

It may seem a hopeless task to specify a general approach to the analysis of cell behaviour, in view of the many different types of variable whose interrelationships we want to examine, but such an approach is widely employed in the fields of meteorology, economics, sociology and industrial process control. One powerful and very general statistical approach is known as the analysis of time series and the requirements of analysis in the field of cell behaviour coincide so well with the requirements in these other fields that it is surprising that the methods of time-series analysis have been largely ignored by cell behaviourists.

The aim is usually to determine the statistical dependence between successive observations in a sequence of data in the hope of predicting the future development of the sequence or of visualizing the underlying process. The method is to express this dependence structure initially by estimating, for each variable, a large matrix of correlations from the data. Autocorrelations express how the value of the variable at any one time depends on its previous values and cross-correlations express how it depends on present and previous values of other variables of the system. This description usually requires simplification before it can be interpreted and the next step is to express the salient features of the correlation matrix as a model, often a stochastic difference equation, that has the same statistical properties as the original observations. Finally, the model that fits the discrete observations might be refined to produce a model based on differential equations that represents the underlying continuous process. Ideally, we end up with a model that has the same statistical properties as the underlying process regardless of how frequently or even of how erroneously we have observed the process.

Several schemes have now been published whereby the procedure for arriving at this final model is almost automatic (Box & Jenkins, 1970; Chatfield, 1975; Pandit & Wu, 1983). Computer routines for implementing these schemes are readily available and we mainly use the time-series analysis section (G13) of the NAg FORTRAN Library (Numerical Algorithms Group Ltd).

CHOOSING THE VARIABLES

There are no hard-and-fast rules to guide the choice of variables. The conventional microscope image of a moving fibroblast in culture presents literally an infinity of potentially measurable variables. Each variable represents a continuous process and can take as many values as we like within a given time interval. Yet other potential variables may be introduced by special techniques for imaging the living cell and its motile apparatus or by experimental procedures.

There are, however, some rough guidelines. The process of motility should be sampled at uniform time increments, with no missing values for the variables, if the majority of available methods of analysis are to be useful. The sampling interval should be short enough to detect a dependence between successive values of a given variable. Another guideline is that it may be uninformative to look at the relationship between variables that are known *a priori* to be carrying similar information. For example, it tells us little about cell motility that the length of a nucleus is strongly related to its area. Finally, a desirable though not essential property is that each process represented by a variable should be stationary. This means that, although each variable obviously varies with time, its statistical properties should not vary with time. For example, the displacement of a cell from a given starting point is not a stationary process because we expect that its value will tend to increase with time. But we might expect that the cell displacement over successive short time increments, say 1-min intervals, will not show a general tendency to increase or decrease with time provided that the experimental conditions remain constant. The first is a measure of the total motility from the start of the experiment whereas the second is a measure of the level of motility.

A PILOT PROJECT

For a pilot project, we have chosen a simple form of cell motility: the so-called 'random' motility or free wandering of isolated fibroblasts cultured on a planar two-dimensional substratum. We use primary chick heart fibroblasts and these are cultured under agar so that cell protrusions tend to be confined to the image plane of the microscope. The fibroblasts are filmed in phase contrast using time lapse at 1-min intervals. Data from these films are put into a computer by projecting each image onto a digitizing tablet and tracing with the cursor around the margin of each cell and then around the margin of its nucleus. For a typical fibroblast filmed over 5 h, the raw data in the computer consist of representations of the positions of 300 irregular polygons, each with about 120 vertices, and 300 more with about 40 vertices. These represent the relative positions and orientations of the cell and nuclear outlines at

1-min intervals. Fig. 3 shows the sequence of cell outlines obtained from one fibroblast.

The variables chosen fall into four categories depending on whether they carry vector or scalar information and whether they are calculated directly from an outline or from the differences between successive outlines. Vectors in two dimensions require two numbers for their specification whereas scalars require only one. Dealing with vector variables presents some difficulties since the available software for time series analysis generally accepts only scalar variables. Splitting a vector variable into a magnitude variable and a direction variable is unsatisfactory for examining correlations since there is always a discontinuity in the use of angles to describe directions (e.g. 0° is equivalent to 360°). However, many programmes will accept a correlation matrix instead of raw data as input and so for these it is only necessary to define correlation for vectors. Instead of accumulating sums of products as in an ordinary correlation, we do this by accumulating sums of scalar (dot) products of the vectors (Tchen, 1952) as shown below. Note that all the vectors we use are assumed to be distributed isotropically in large samples of cells and we therefore assume a population mean magnitude of zero instead of taking deviations from sample means. Entering the programme with a correlation matrix also permits the data from several cells to be pooled whereas programmes that accept raw data will generally deal with only one time series for each variable.

Fig. 3. A total of 300 cell outlines taken at successive 1-min intervals from a chick heart fibroblast cultured under agar. Bar, 100 μm.

The sample autocovariance function, c_k, for a series of displacement vectors $\mathbf{d}_i$ $(i = 1, 2, \ldots, n)$ is:

$$c_k = \frac{1}{n-k} \sum_{i=1}^{n-k} (\mathbf{d}_i \cdot \mathbf{d}_{i+k}) \qquad (k = 0, 1, \ldots)$$

and the sample autocorrelation function, r_k, is:

$$r_k = c_k / c_0 \qquad (k = 1, 2, \ldots).$$

Pooled estimates of c_k, and hence of r_k, may be obtained from N cells by summing the dot products over all N series and dividing by $(n_1 + n_2 + \ldots + n_N - Nk)$, were each n is the length of the series from each cell.

Cell displacement over fixed short time increments is an example of a vector variable calculated from the first differences of successive position vectors. The position of a cell can be defined in many ways but the two obvious ways of calculating it from our data are to use the geometrical centroids of the cell and nuclear outlines. We use both of these with the aim of finding which gives the simpler description of cell motility. These variables are representations of the changing velocity of the cell (actually average velocity over short time increments) and, even on their own, they contain a great deal of information about the nature of cell motility. Since the variables take vector values, they contain information about variation in direction as well as variation in speed. We will describe a preliminary analysis of them in the next section.

Protrusion and retraction are examples of scalar variables calculated from differences between successive outlines. Protrusion is all the area of substratum covered by an outline but not covered by the previous outline and retraction is all the area not covered by an outline but covered by the previous outline as shown in Fig. 4. The magnitudes and dispositions of protrusion and retraction together fully determine the displacement and so we would expect some strong relationships between their magnitudes and the magnitude of displacement. But the relationship between protrusion and retraction is probably much more informative since it represents a basic level of control of the motile system: it will give the parameters of the feedback loop that stabilizes the spread area of the moving cell. Such a feedback mechanism must exist otherwise the whole process of motility would show a runaway instability. Fig. 5 is taken from a series of experiments performed by Dunn & Heath, which show that, if the tail of a moving fibroblast is artificially detached from the substratum, it rapidly retracts and there follows, after a short delay, a wave of increased protrusion at the leading margin of the cell (Dunn, 1980; Chen, 1981). Examining the time-lagged correlations between these two variables in a freely moving fibroblast will give information about the symmetry of the control loop: whether it is retraction that generally drives protrusion or *vice versa* or whether their roles are symmetrical.

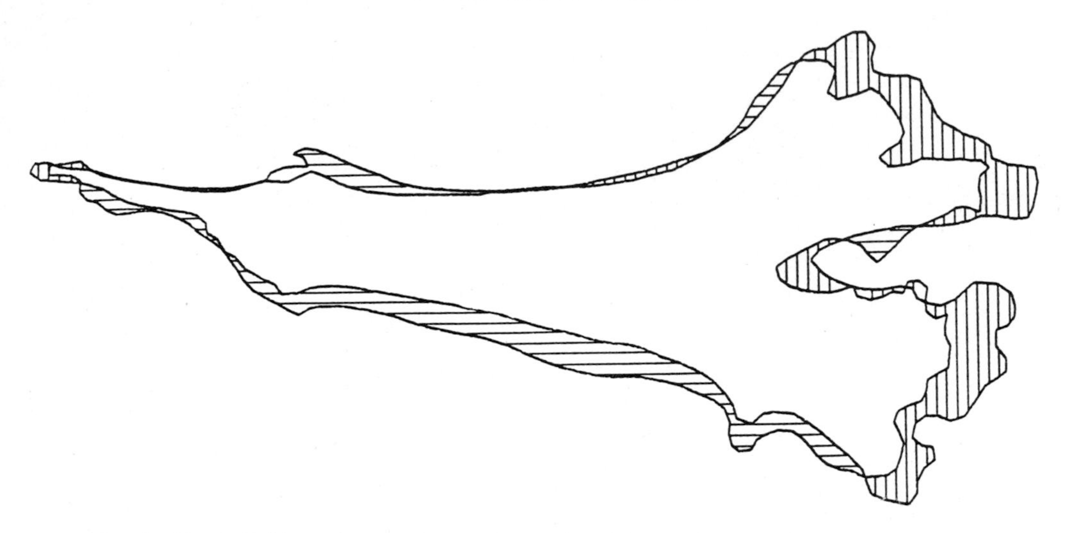

Fig. 4. The definition of protrusion and retraction. The total area with vertical shading is a measure of protrusion and the total area with horizontal shading is a measure of retraction.

Another reason why these dynamics are of interest is the possibility that these processes represent separate but interactive molecular events. Chen (1981) has shown that tail retraction is, at least partly, probably an active contraction of the actin–myosin meshwork and Dunn (1980) has suggested that during locomotion this meshwork in contracting continuously and a steady state is maintained by parallel continuous processes of disassembly, transport, and reassembly of the meshwork at the active margin of the cell. The time lag between retraction and protrusion would then indicate the time delay required for the intervening processes of disassembly and transport. To examine both time lags in freely moving cells will probably require a better time resolution than the 1-min intervals that we are using in the pilot project and we will reserve this analysis for a later paper.

The spread area of a moving cell is an example of the simplest type of scalar variable that can be calculated from a single outline. By an extension of the mathematical theory that underlies the calculation of the area and centroid of an outline, we can derive an automatic method for describing the position, size, shape and orientation of a single outline to any degree of accuracy that we please. This description is known as the series of moments (m) and for a two-dimensional image they are defined as follows (Hall, 1979):

$$m_{pq} = \int_{-\infty}^{\infty} \int_{-\infty}^{\infty} x^p \, y^q \, f(x,y) \, dx \, dy \, .$$

For describing outlines, function $f(x,y)$ takes the value 1 if the point (x,y) lies within the polygon defining the outline and 0 otherwise. p and q can each take any integer value greater than or equal to zero. Moments where $p + q = n$ are known as moments of the nth order.

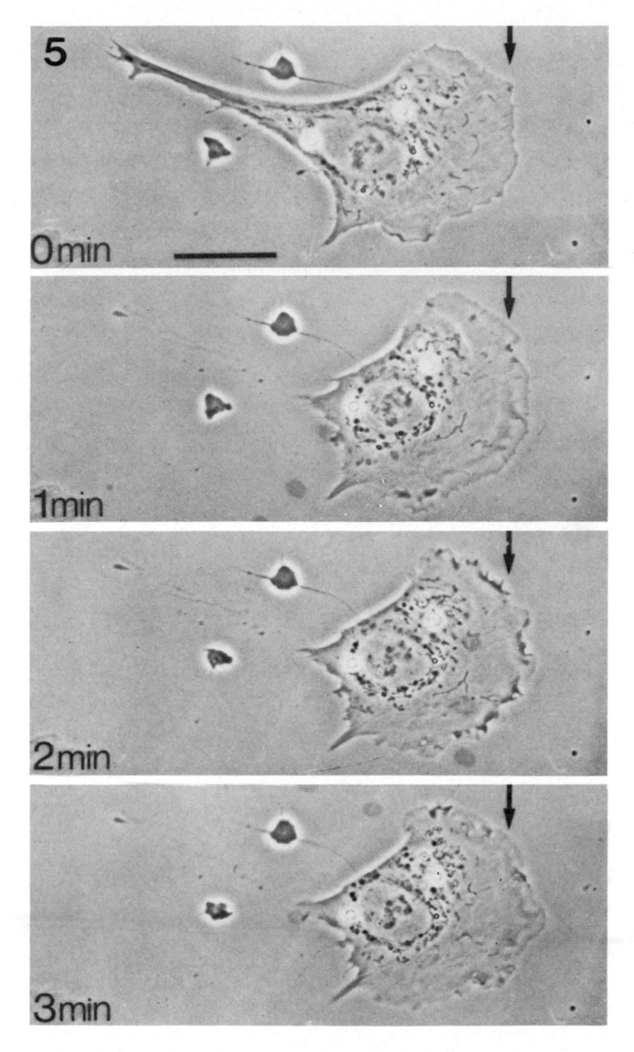

Fig. 5. Retraction and protrusion after detaching the tail of a chick heart fibroblast using micromanipulation. Most of the tail retraction is completed within the first minute and the lag of about 20 s before the increased protrusion starts is not resolved at 1-min intervals. Bar, 20 μm.

For each cell outline and each nucleus outline, we routinely calculate all 10 moments up to and including the third order. We have previously described how moments are calculated from the pixels of a digitized image of cells (Dunn & Brown, 1986) but a more sophisticated algorithm is required to calculate them from polygonal outlines and we will shortly be describing this in another publication. The moment m_{00} simply represents the area of the outline and the moments m_{10} and m_{01} are required together with this moment for calculating the position of the cell centroid. Exactly how to derive sensible measures of shape and orientation from the higher-order moments ceases to be an entirely automatic procedure, but the idea is generally to segregate the information on size, position, shape and orientation into separate variables. Hu (1962) described how to obtain a series of seven rotationally invariant measures of shape from moments up to the third order. We described measures of shape and orientation, calculated from moments up to the second order, that are easier to interpret as measures of compactness and elongation etc. of the cell (Dunn & Brown, 1986*). Three vector variables can be calculated from the third-order moments; each can be interpreted as the magnitude and direction of a local maximum in asymmetry of the cell shape. Some fibroblast outlines together with representations of some of these variables are shown in Fig. 6 and it can be seen that the largest asymmetry vector points in the direction opposite to the obvious direction of motion of the two polarized cells.

It is clear from the foregoing that a thorough analysis of even the data available from outlines could develop into a major project, especially since there are at least two more radically different ways of quantitatively describing cell shape (using

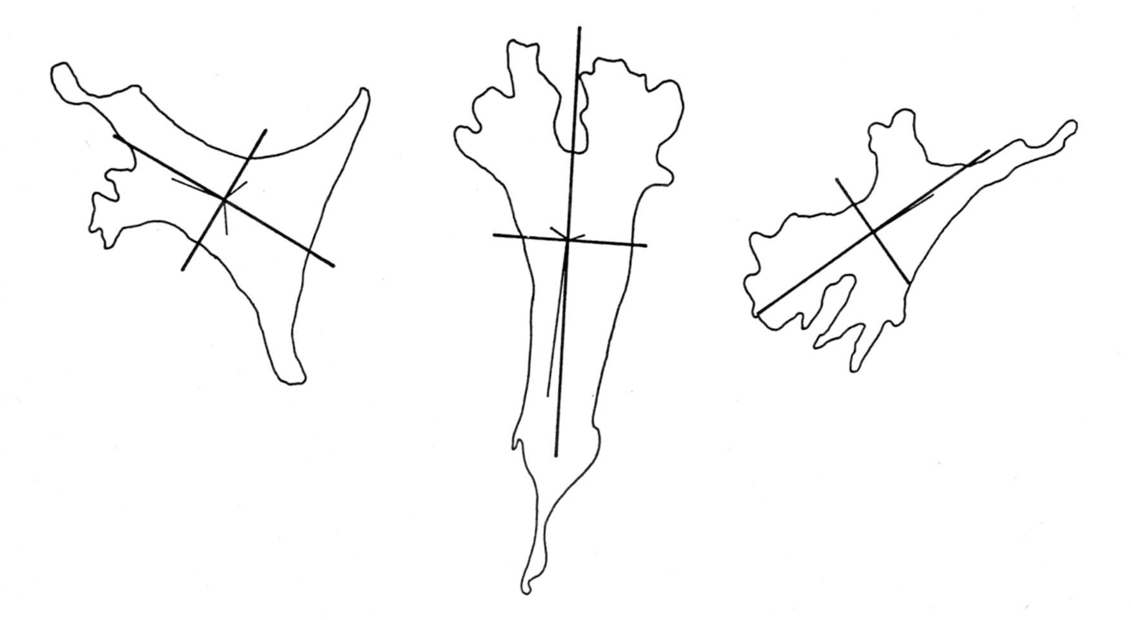

Fig. 6. Some outlines of chick heart fibroblasts together with graphical representations of some measures of shape and orientation. The bold cross represents the two principal axes of the momental ellipse defined by second-order moments (see Dunn & Brown, 1986). The three fine lines are the principal directions and magnitudes of the third-order moments.

* In this paper we gave the theoretical values of dispersion for a triangle and a parallelogram for use as a check on results. Unfortunately, these were calculated using natural logarithms instead of $\log_2$ as in the rest of the paper and the correct values should be 0·2741 and 0·0665, respectively.

Fourier transforms and median axis transforms) that may lead to simpler descriptions of cell motility. A series of multivariate time-series analyses using each of the behavioural variables (e.g. 1 min velocity, 1 min protrusion etc.) as output series and one or several of the shape and orientation descriptions as input series will give information on how shape, orientation of elongation, orientation of asymmetry etc. are related to protrusion, retraction and the speed and direction of travel. More importantly, for gaining an insight into the mechanism of motility, they will also give information on the time precedence of the relationships. For example, is a particular change in behaviour characteristically preceded by a change in shape, orientation or symmetry or do these changes follow the change in behaviour? We hope that the following preliminary analysis of a subset of the data will illustrate some of the potential of the approach.

A PRELIMINARY ANALYSIS OF DISPLACEMENTS

Fig. 7 is a histogram of the autocorrelations at time lags of 1–100 min for 1-min displacements of the centroid of the cell outlines from a single fibroblast filmed over approximately 5 h. This correlogram is a picture of the migration ability of the cell because the area under the autocorrelation curve, together with the variance of displacement, determine the total square displacement D^2 of the cell after n 1-min steps:

$$D^2 = c_0 \left(n + 2 \sum_{k=1}^{n-1} (n-k)\, r_k \right).$$

The expected values of c_0 and r_k in the theoretical population of all similar cells are designated γ_0 and ρ_k. These are better estimated using the pooled values of c_0 and r_k from a sample of similar cells and a correlogram pooled from three fibroblasts is shown in Fig. 8. The expected total square displacement, $E[D^2]$, for any new cell drawn from a population of similar cells, is given by:

$$E[D^2] = \gamma_0 \left(n + 2 \sum_{k=1}^{n-1} (n-k)\, \rho_k \right).$$

Another way of looking at the correlogram is that it is a fingerprint of the pattern of persistence in motion of the cells. If there are no significant correlations, then there is no detectable persistence and the cells do not get very far because they are pure random walkers. Incidentally, although a cell might appear to be a pure random walker, if observed very infrequently, it is physically impossible for any real moving body to be a pure random walker in continuous time. If a cell appears to move with no persistence we can only conclude that the sampling interval is too long to detect the persistence.

The largest lag in the correlogram associated with a significant autocorrelation shows the extent of the cells' persistence in motion. In Fig. 8 this largest lag indicates

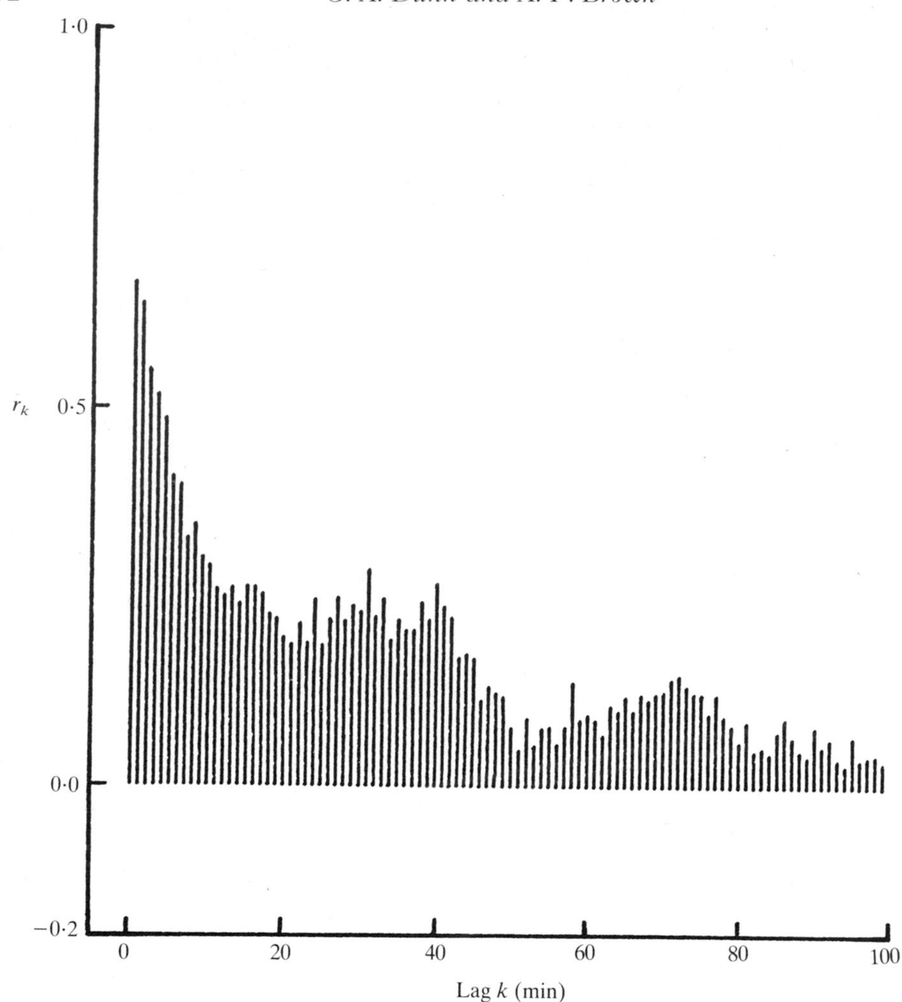

Fig. 7. Correlogram of 1-min displacements for a single fibroblast.

that the velocities of the cells are significantly related to their velocities of approximately 1 h earlier. This retention span of 1 h does not mean, however, that the cells have any sort of separate memory other than that retained in the motility itself. A very simple form of autocorrelated process, known as a first-order autoregressive or Markov process, also has this property. It is as if a traveller in a desert is trying to walk in a straight line by making each step line up accurately with the direction of the previous step. No memory is required for this apart from remembering the previous step, but the direction of travel at any instant is related to that of many steps ago.

A way of revealing if the fibroblasts have a more sophisticated memory of their previous motility is the partial correlogram. In this, each correlation is corrected for the effect of correlations at smaller lags. The second partial autocorrelation, for example, measures the similarity between all pairs of displacements that are separated by an intervening displacement after allowing for the fact that adjacent

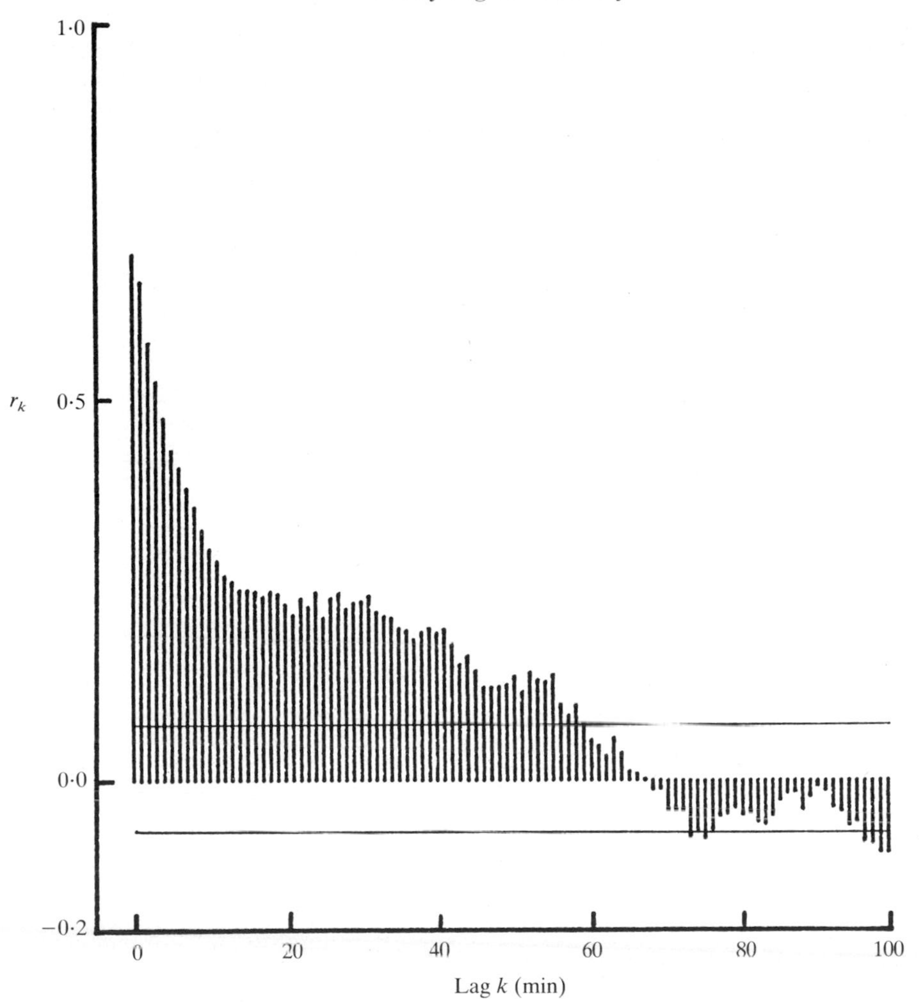

Fig. 8. Pooled correlogram of 1-min displacements for three fibroblasts. The horizontal lines are 95 % confidence limits.

displacements are similar. The pooled partial correlogram of Fig. 9 is calculated from the pooled autocorrelations using NAg routine G13ACF. It appears from this partial correlogram that the first two or three partial autocorrelations might be significantly positive. For a discrete Markov process such as the desert traveller's walk, there ought to be only one non-zero partial autocorrelation. This suggests that the fibroblasts are able to maintain their speed and direction of motility more accurately than can be explained by the similarity between each displacement and the immediately previous one. It suggests the presence of a separate memory or piloting system that brings the fibroblasts' travel back on course after small deviations lasting for 2 or 3 min.

Although 2 or 3 min is not a very long time considering that it takes a fibroblast about an hour to cover its own length, it is important for understanding the

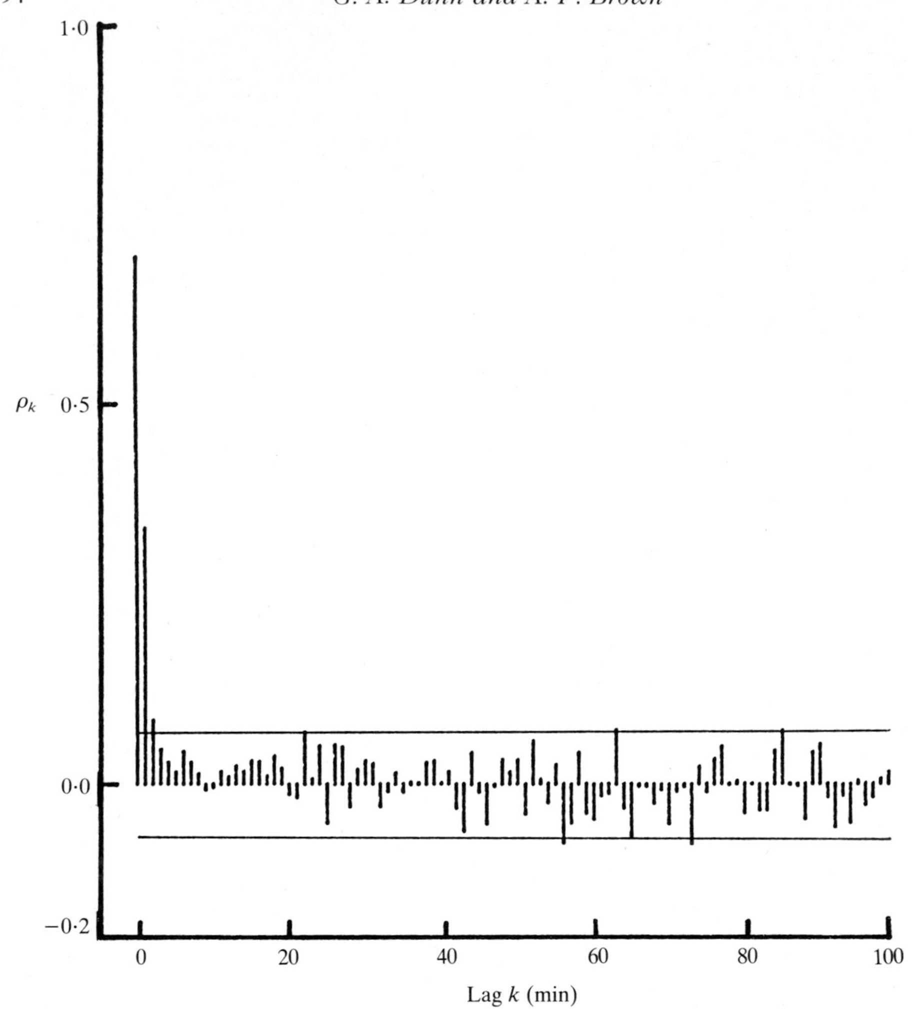

Fig. 9. Pooled partial correlogram for the three fibroblasts. The horizontal lines are 95 % confidence limits.

mechanism of motility to discover whether this apparent evidence for a short-lived memory is misleading. There are two effects inherent in the observation of cell motility that can combine to produce spurious partial autocorrelations. The first is that the observed process consists of samples at discrete intervals whereas the underlying process of motility is continuous. The second is that some error is inevitable in estimating the positions; the apparent small deviations of the fibroblasts from their route might well be due to such errors. In order to explain how these partial autocorrelations might arise, we must introduce some theory of continuous stochastic processes and observational errors.

The simplest type of continuous, autocorrelated, random motion is known as the Ornstein–Uhlenbeck (O.U.) process (Uhlenbeck & Ornstein, 1930). In this process, the projections of motion on to orthogonal axes gives one-dimensional motions that are statistically similar but independent. The velocity process on each axis $\{v(t)\}$ satisfies the Langevin equation:

$$\frac{dv(t)}{dt} = -\beta v(t) + n(t).$$

This differential equation simply states that the change in motion at any instant can be resolved into two components: a deterministic component $-\beta v(t)$ that tends to oppose the motion and a purely random 'white noise' component $n(t)$ that has a mean of zero. Once the process has settled down (i.e. become stationary) then its statistical properties are entirely determined by the constant β and a constant α, which can be thought of as the variance of $n(t)$ (variance is undefined for continuous white noise and so α is more properly called the variance parameter or spectrum of the white noise).

To move from the continuous O.U. process to the discrete process of displacements observed over uniform time increments, Doob (1942) gave a general formula for the correlations between displacements in the O.U. process that can be simplified to deal specifically with uniform time increments. The resulting theoretical autocorrelation structure of the sampled process depends only on the Langevin parameter β and on the duration τ of the uniform sampling interval. Surprisingly, although the O.U. process is a continuous Markov process, the sampled process turns out to be slightly more complicated than a discrete Markov process. In the language of time-series theory, it is recognizable as belonging to a class of mixed autoregressive, moving-average processes known as ARMA(1,1) processes (Chatfield, 1975). In such a process, the projection of each displacement $\mathbf{d}_i$ onto a single axis is related to the projection of the previous displacement by the stochastic equation:

$$\mathbf{d}_i = \phi \mathbf{d}_{i-1} + \mathbf{z}_i + \theta \mathbf{z}_{i-1} \, ,$$

where the process (z_i) is discrete random noise, normally distributed with a mean of zero. A discrete Markov process, or AR(1) process, would not require the last term in the equation.

An ARMA(1,1) process that is derived by sampling a continuous O.U. process in this way can be recognized by the fact that θ depends on ϕ, since both depend on the underlying parameter β. The details of this relation are quite complicated and we may publish them later in a more theoretical paper. It must suffice here to say that, if the sampling interval is fairly short, so that the value of ϕ is well above 0·5, then θ should have a value close to $2-\sqrt{3}$ or approximately 0·268. It does not matter that we have derived this result from consideration of a one-dimensional process; it is easy to show that the dot autocorrelations we have defined above have the same expectations as the conventional autocorrelations of the motion projected onto any axis. The sample dot autocorrelations merely provide twice as much information about the motion and therefore permit better estimates of the population values.

It can be further shown that the effect of random errors in cell position is to produce an even more complicated stochastic process known as an ARMA(1,2)

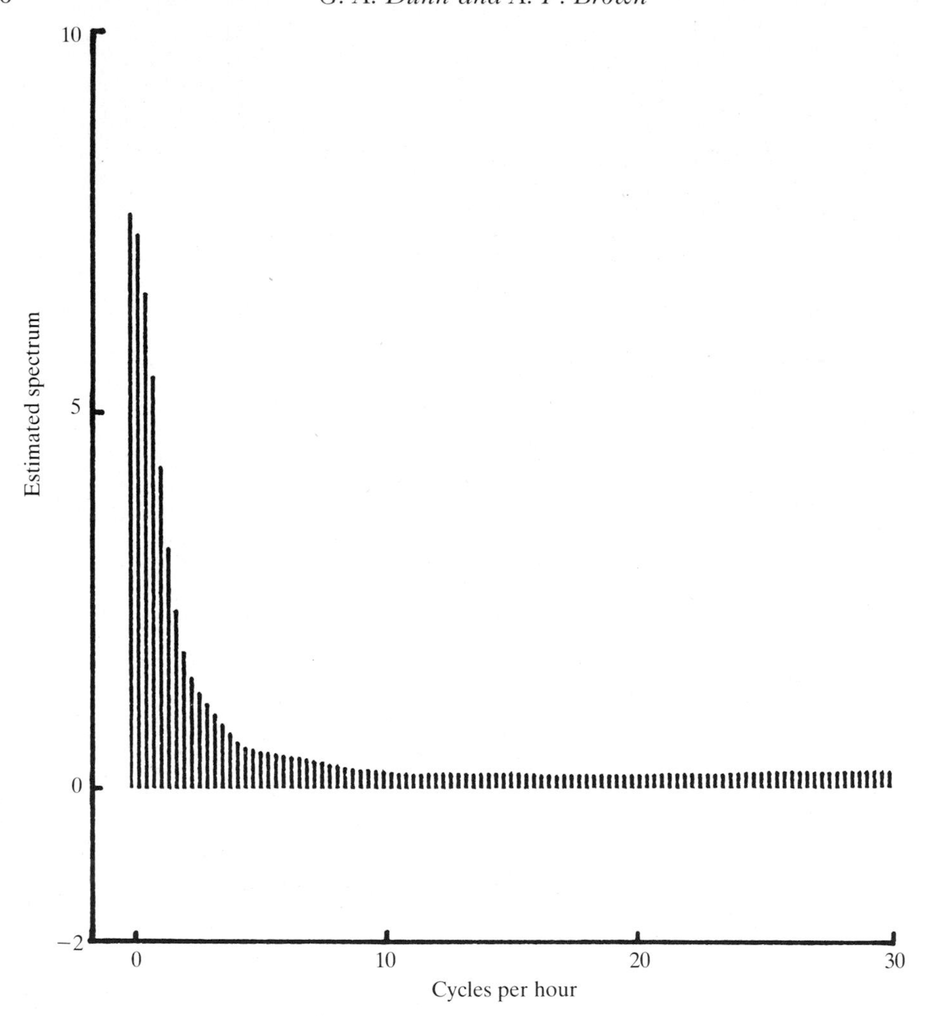

Fig. 10. Pooled power spectrum for the three fibroblasts (using Tukey smoothing window, bandwidth 0·279).

model. This complication can be avoided by compensating the autocovariances for the effects of observational errors before fitting an ARMA model to the cell translocation data. c_0 should be reduced by twice the variance of the errors and c_1 should be increased by the variance of the errors. However, this requires knowing the variance of the errors beforehand and an alternative approach is to find out if the observed fibroblast motility looks like an O.U. process with positional errors introduced during sampling.

Fig. 10 is the power spectrum of the pooled fibroblast 1-min displacements obtained from the autocorrelation function using NAg routine, G13CAF. This shows how the variations in speed and direction of the cells are distributed at different frequencies. Theoretically, the spectrum of a sampled O.U. process should fall off exponentially as the frequency increases and the effect of random positional error is to add another spectrum that increases sigmoidally from zero to a plateau at $2/\pi$ times the variance of the errors at the high frequency end. This is exactly what the spectrum in Fig. 10 looks like. The slowly changing speed and direction of the moving cells result in a large concentration at the low frequency end of the spectrum, whereas the rapid random wiggles introduced into the cell tracks by observational errors are represented by a noise level that gradually increases towards the high-frequency end. The error variance estimated from the level of the high-frequency plateau is $0{\cdot}314\,\mu m^2$. When the autocorrelations are compensated for this estimated error and an ARMA(1,1) process is fitted, the estimated value of θ is 0·245, which is very close to the expected value 0·268. The spectrum obtained from the compensated autocorrelations is shown in Fig. 11. Therefore, after compensating for observational errors of only $0{\cdot}560\,\mu m$ standard deviation, the autocorrelation structure is almost exactly what would be expected from a sampled O.U. process.

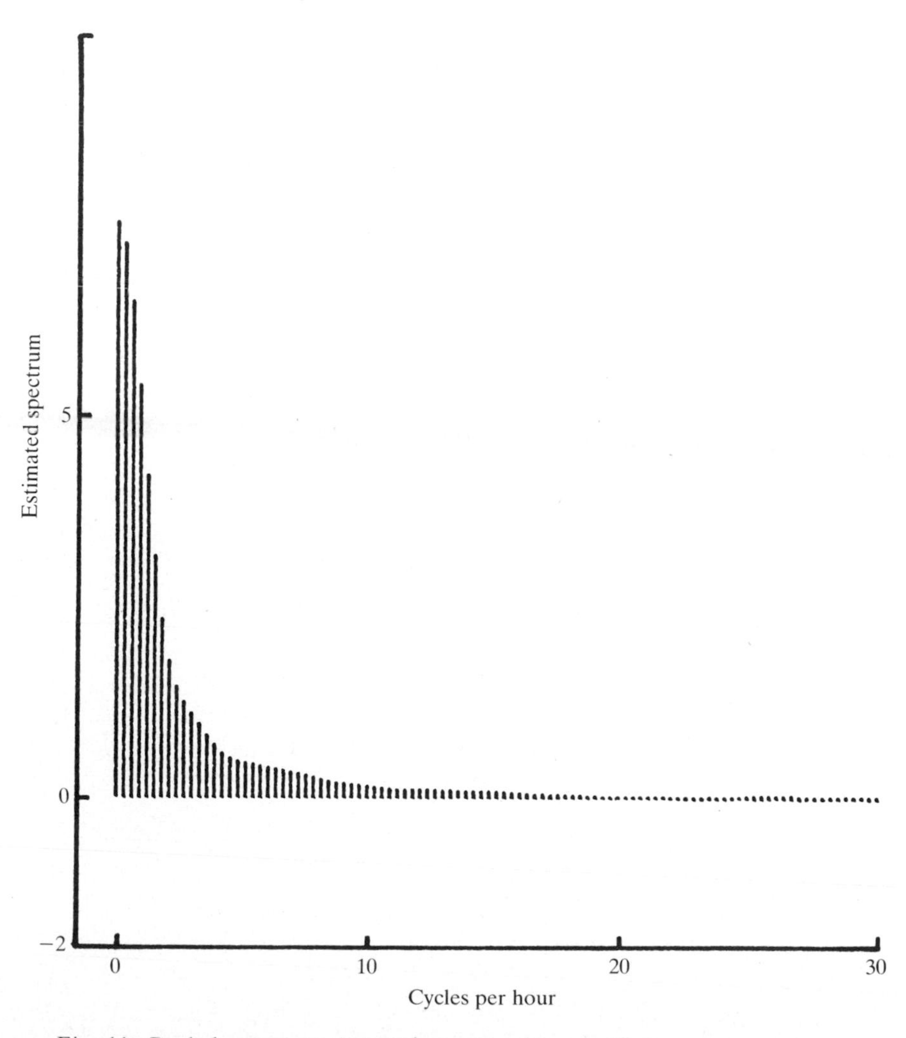

Fig. 11. Pooled power spectrum after error compensation.

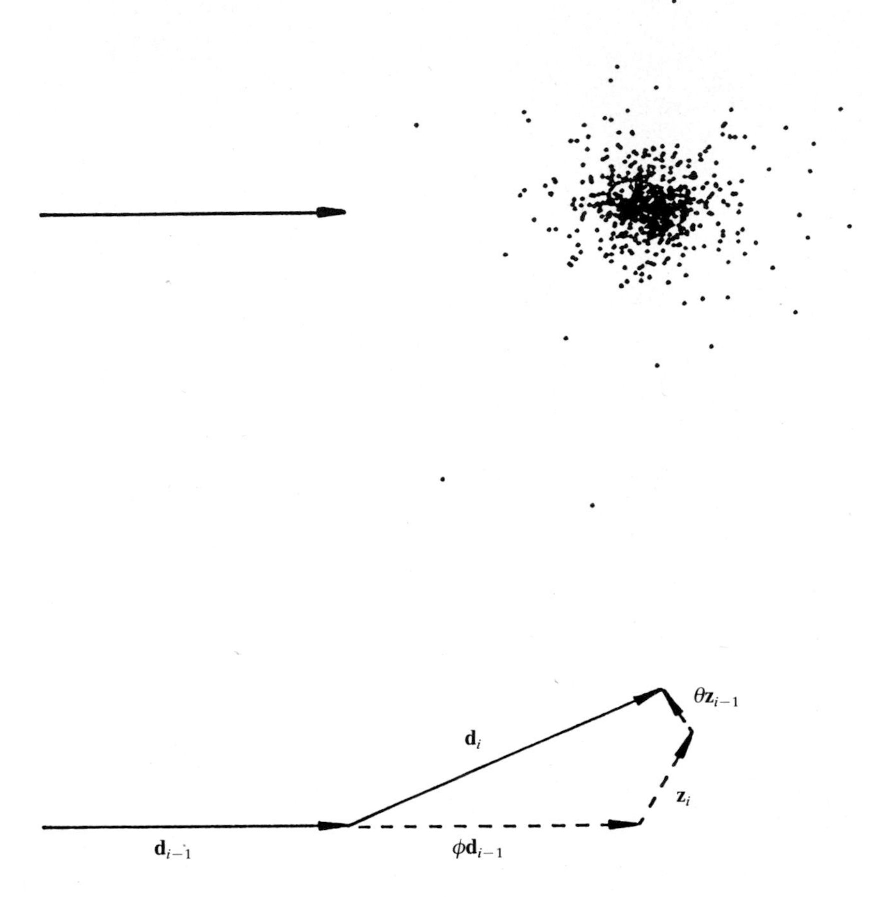

Fig. 12. Each 10-min displacement $\mathbf{d}_i$ of the pooled fibroblast data is shown relative to the previous displacement $\mathbf{d}_{i-1}$ by applying the same transformation to $\mathbf{d}_i$ that is required to give $\mathbf{d}_{i-1}$ a length of 1 and a direction horizontally to the right in the figure. The common $\mathbf{d}_{i-1}$ is shown as a prominent arrow. Each $\mathbf{d}_i$ starts at the arrowhead and the position where it ends up is marked by a dot. The lower diagram represents the theoretical equation relating $\mathbf{d}_i$ and $\mathbf{d}_{i-1}$ (see the text).

So far, we have considered only the one-dimensional aspects of the O.U. process but a further property is that the projection of the two-dimensional motion onto two orthogonal axes should give two independent processes. This can be represented by writing the ARMA(1,1) model in two dimensions:

$$\mathbf{d}_i = \phi \mathbf{d}_{i-1} + \mathbf{z}_i + \theta \mathbf{z}_{i-1} ,$$

where $\mathbf{d}_i$ and $\mathbf{z}_i$ are now two-dimensional vectors and $\mathbf{z}_i$ has an isotropic variance. On the other hand, if the fibroblast has separate mechanisms for varying speed and direction, the $\mathbf{z}_i$ is likely to have a different variance along the axis of travel than it does along the perpendicular axis. Unless there is a pure coincidence, we would expect the random kicks that change the speed of the cell to be different in strength from the random kicks that change the direction of cell travel. Fig. 12 is a graphical representation of the displacements of the fibroblasts compared with a graphical representation of the above stochastic equation; 10-min instead of 1-min intervals have been used in order to reduce the effect of observational errors. If $\mathbf{z}_i$ has an isotropic variance then the scatter in the horizontal axis should be very similar to the scatter in the vertical axis (the horizontal scatter should be slightly larger because of a correlation between $\mathbf{d}_{i-1}$ and $\mathbf{z}_{i-1}$). In fact, the ratios of horizontal to vertical standard deviations (after transforming to make the distributions normal) for the three fibroblasts are 1·15, 1·03 and 1·29. This suggests that the random fluctuations in motility are a single isotropic process as they are expected to be in a sampled O.U. process.

IMPLICATIONS OF THE DISPLACEMENT ANALYSIS

In summary, we have found no evidence that fibroblast translocation is other than the simplest form of continuous stochastic process in two dimensions: the O.U. process. The data set is as yet quite small, with a total of 1378 outlines, and small but significant deviations from the O.U. process might emerge as more data are collected. In particular, the finding that the random kicks to motility have the same strength along the axis of travel as they do across this axis might turn out to be a mere coincidence as different fibroblasts are examined in different circumstances. It is clear, however, that the 1-min sampling frequency approaches the practical limits of time resolution for the analysis of fibroblast displacement. Although the estimated errors in determining the cell centroid have a standard deviation of only 0·560 μm, the standard deviation of observed displacements for the pooled fibroblasts over 1-min intervals is only 1·97 μm. Interestingly, the estimated errors using the centroids of nuclear outlines instead of cell outlines are larger with a standard deviation of 0·831 μm. This could mean that the observational errors are larger with nuclei, since their outlines are often not so well defined as the cell outlines, or it could be that the nuclear centroid is a less fundamental marker of the motile process.

The O.U. process is a continuous Markov process, which means that the future progress of the process depends only on its present state. The implication for fibroblasts is that they do not have a detectable memory of their earlier motility. It might be thought, for example, that the cytoplasmic microtubule system could constitute a relatively stable piloting system that brings the direction of locomotion back on course after small deviations. Or it could be that the whole locomotory machinery oscillates in a deterministic manner like the locomotion of most multicellular organisms. Neither of these possibilities is supported by the analysis. Nor does it appear that the changes in direction are controlled by a separate steering mechanism, which might again have been the microtubule system, since the changes in speed appear to be caused by the same random kicks as the changes in direction.

An implication from the practical point of view is that the persistence in motion of fibroblasts can be described using a single number instead of giving the full autocorrelation structure. It has been known for some years that the random motion of a variety of cell types can be adequately characterized using only two numbers, provided that the level of motility is fairly constant or, more formally, provided that the velocity process is stationary (Gail & Boone, 1970; Wilkinson & Allen, 1978; Dunn, 1983). This is done by fitting a function in two parameters to data obtained from the displacements of cells over a range of time intervals. Dunn suggested using root-mean-square speed and persistence in direction as the parameters. We can now see that an alternative is to use the two parameters, α and β, of the Langevin equation. In fact, these two approaches are mathematically identical. Doob (1942) gives the expected square speed $E[s^2]$ and the expected square displacement $E[D^2]$ during time t for a one-dimensional O.U. process as:

$$E[s^2] = \frac{\alpha}{2\beta} \qquad E[D^2] = \frac{\alpha}{\beta^3}(\beta t - 1 + e^{-\beta t}).$$

Since, by Pythagoras's theorem, the expected square speed and square displacement for the two-dimensional process are simply twice those of the one-dimensional process, the function for expected displacement squared described by Dunn is easily derived from the above equations. The persistence parameter is simply the reciprocal of the parameter β of the Langevin equation and this should be called persistence in velocity or simply persistence in motion since it is a combination of persistence in direction and persistence in speed.

At a deeper level there is the implication that the Langevin equation might in some sense represent the physical mechanism of cell motility. This would suggest that certain experimental treatments might be able to affect the parameters α and β independently of each other. Any effect on α would alter the speed but the persistence should only be affected transiently whereas an effect on β would alter both speed and persistence. It is interesting in this respect that Wilkinson *et al.* (1984) discovered an experimental treatment that affects the speed of neutrophil motility but not the persistence. A prediction from this is that a treatment might be found that affects the persistence in the same ratio as the mean-square speed, but that it is unlikely that a treatment will affect the persistence alone.

Of course, it is too early to speculate on the molecular processes represented by α and β, but it is clear what sort of processes they might represent. The small and rapidly changing fluctuations or random kicks represented by $n(t)$ in the Langevin equation accumulate to determine the current motile state, or speed and direction, of the O.U. process. The parameter α measures the strength of these fluctuations and the parameter β measures how quickly their effect on the motility fades away. If we consider that the current motile state of the cell is determined by the current state of asymmetry in its locomotory machinery, then an obvious explanation of the accumulation of the random fluctuations is that they are fluctuations in the assembly of some component(s) of the locomotory machinery. The parameter α would then represent the strength of fluctuation and β might represent the rate of turnover of the assembled structures. β would thus determine how rapidly the asymmetry drifts in magnitude and direction with time or, in other words, it would determine the lack of persistence in motility.

The fact that fibroblast translocation appears to be a very simple stochastic or non-deterministic process argues in favour of self-organization of the locomotory machinery by a process akin to Prigogine's formation of far-from-equilibrium or dissipative structures. In the words of Ji (1985) "the equilibrium structures of the cell may impart machine-like, deterministic properties, whereas the dissipative structures may be responsible for non-machine like, non-deterministic and unpredictable, life-like behaviors of the living cell. The machine-like properties of the cell result from the tendency of all molecules to search for their minimum free-energy states which are determined by the structural complementarity of interacting molecules. The non-machine-like properties reflect the ability of far-from-equilibrium systems to evolve into new steady states beyond a critical threshold, and these new states are unpredictable because they are influenced by thermal fluctuations and microenvironmental factors".

Whether or not the ideas of Prigogine and Ji are applicable to the process of cell motility, it is clear that the basic mechanism that we have to explain is how asymmetry develops from the perfectly symmetrical circular state of a newly spread fibroblast; the fibroblast can only translocate after it has developed this asymmetry. It seems from our analysis that the asymmetry is due to an accumulation of rapid fluctuations that are random in direction as well as in strength. The asymmetry does not seem to be built in from the start as it might be if it were determined, for example, by the position of the centrosome in relation to the nucleus. It will be interesting in this respect to see if the time course of the start of locomotion in a freshly plated fibroblast matches that of starting the O.U. process with a velocity of zero. Prigogine's ideas give us a hypothetical mechanism for the development of this asymmetry: the origin of the fluctuations may be an amplification of thermal motion and other microenvironmental factors, which is thought to be a common mechanism for breaking symmetry in chaotic systems. If this view is correct then the apparent directional organization of the fibroblast might be as much a result of directed translocation as a cause of it. These issues can only be resolved by a much more detailed examination of the overall dynamics of cell motility.

We are grateful to Miss A. K. Kernaghan for her excellent technical assistance. This work was supported by the Medical Research Council.

REFERENCES

AGLADZE, K. I. & KRINSKY, V. I. (1982). Multi-armed vortices in an active chemical medium. *Nature, Lond.* **296**, 424–426.

BOX, G. E. P. & JENKINS, G. M. (1970). *Time-series Analysis, Forecasting and Control*. San Francisco: Holden-Day.

CHATFIELD, C. (1975). *The Analysis of Time Series: Theory and Practice*. London: Chapman and Hall.

CHEN, W.-T. (1981). Mechanism of retraction of the trailing edge during fibroblast movement. *J. Cell Biol.* **90**, 187–200.

COTTRELL, A. (1977). Emergent properties of complex systems. In *The Encyclopaedia of Ignorance* (ed. R. Duncan & M. Weston-Smith), pp. 129–135. Oxford: Pergamon.

DOOB, J. L. (1942). The Brownian movement and stochastic equations. *Ann. Math.* **43**, 351–369.

DUNN, G. A. (1980). Mechanisms of fibroblast locomotion. In *Cell Adhesion and Motility* (ed. A. S. G. Curtis & J. D. Pitts), pp. 409–423. Cambridge University Press.

DUNN, G. A. (1983). Characterising a kinesis response: time averaged measures of cell speed and directional persistence. In *Leukocyte Locomotion and Chemotaxis* (ed. H. Keller & G. O. Till), pp. 14–33. Basel: Birkhauser Verlag.

DUNN, G. A. & BROWN, A. F. (1986). Alignment of fibroblasts on grooved surfaces described by a simple geometric transformation. *J. Cell Sci.* **83**, 313–340.

GAIL, M. H. & BOONE, C. W. (1970). The locomotion of mouse fibroblasts in tissue culture. *Biophys. J.* **10**, 980–993.

HALL, E. L. (1979). *Computer Image Processing and Recognition*. New York: Academic Press.

HEATH, J. P. (1983). Direct evidence for microfilament-mediated capping of surface receptors on crawling fibroblasts. *Nature, Lond.* **302**, 532–534.

HU, M. K. (1962). Visual pattern recognition by moment invariants. *I. R. E. Trans. Information Theory* IT-8, pp. 179–187.

JI, S. (1985). The Bhopalator: a molecular model of the living cell based on the concepts of conformons and dissipative structure. *J. theor. Biol.* **116**, 399–426.

PANDIT, S. M. & WU, S.-M. (1983). *Time Series and System Analysis with Applications*. New York: Wiley.

PRIGOGINE, I. & STENGERS, I. (1984). *Order out of Chaos. Man's New Dialogue with Nature*. London: Fontana.

TCHEN, C. M. (1952). Random flight with multiple partial correlations. *J. chem. Phys.* **20**, 214–217.

UHLENBECK, G. E. & ORNSTEIN, L. S. (1930). On the theory of Brownian motion. *Phys. Rev.* **36**, 823–841.

WILKINSON, P. C. & ALLEN, R. B. (1978). Assay systems for measuring leucocyte locomotion: an overview. In *Leucocyte Chemotaxis* (ed. J. I. Gallin & P. G. Quie), pp. 1–24. New York: Raven Press.

WILKINSON, P. C., LACKIE, J. M., FORRESTER, J. V. & DUNN, G. A. (1984). Chemokinetic accumulation of human neutrophils on immune-complex-coated substrata: analysis at a boundary. *J. Cell Biol.* **99**, 1761–1768.

J. Cell Sci. Suppl. 8, 103–119 (1987)
Printed in Great Britain

LEUCOCYTE LOCOMOTION: BEHAVIOURAL MECHANISMS FOR ACCUMULATION

P. C. WILKINSON

Bacteriology and Immunology Department, University of Glasgow, Western Infirmary, Glasgow G11 6NT, UK

SUMMARY

The behavioural mechanisms that may contribute to the accumulation of leucocytes (e.g. in inflammatory sites) are reviewed. Almost all of the neutrophils and monocytes of blood are motile and capable of migrating into tissues, but many blood lymphocytes are non-motile. They can however be induced to acquire locomotor capacity by culture with growth activators such as anti-CD3 antibodies. Resting lymphocytes become motile after entering the G_1 phase of the cell cycle. Chemotaxis is well-studied in neutrophil leucocytes and is an efficient mechanism for cell accumulation. Possible mechanisms by which leucocytes respond to attractant gradients are discussed. Non-chemotactic mechanisms may also lead to cell accumulation, and evidence is reviewed that shows that an adhesive trapping mechanism causes leucocytes that cross an adhesion boundary to accumulate in the absence of a chemotactic gradient. Leucocytes migrating through aligned connective tissue show contact guidance in the axis of alignment of the tissue. Contact guidance can reinforce or hinder the response of neutrophils to chemotactic gradients.

INTRODUCTION

Leucocytes have much to offer to the student of cell locomotion. Neutrophil leucocytes are easily available in high purity and good yield as suspensions of single cells. They move rapidly and show good chemotactic responses, the study of which has been stimulated greatly by the identification of the synthetic, chemotactic formyl peptides (Schiffmann *et al.* 1975; Showell *et al.* 1976) and of their associated receptors (Williams *et al.* 1977; Aswanikumar *et al.* 1977). Much is now known about the biochemistry of these receptors and their associated signal transduction apparatus (Snyderman, 1984). Behavioural studies have also made progress, albeit more slowly, and in this review I shall discuss some recent findings on behavioural responses of leucocytes to environmental stimuli and their implications for the accumulation of these cells at inflammatory foci. Though chemotaxis is probably the most important determinant of this accumulation, the role of other responses such as chemokinesis, contact guidance, etc. is not negligible and needs to be discussed.

The major classes of leucocyte are the neutrophil (or polymorphonuclear) leucocyte, the mononuclear phagocyte (monocytes and macrophages) and the lymphocyte. Locomotion and chemotaxis have been best studied in neutrophils, but we also know something of locomotor behaviour in the other classes. Locomotion of leucocytes *in vivo* is chiefly thought of in the context of inflammation, immunity and defence against infectious disease. The cells accumulate at the site of tissue injury by leaving the bloodstream and migrating through the intervening tissues. In different types of inflammatory disease characteristic accumulations are seen, predominantly of neutrophils in acute bacterial diseases, and of macrophages and lymphocytes in chronic inflammatory disease associated with specific immune reactions (e.g. delayed-type hypersensitivity). Neutrophil locomotion *in vivo* allows rapid recruitment of cells to sites of tissue injury. Mononuclear phagocytes and lymphocytes also migrate into these sites, in which they accumulate more slowly than neutrophils, but they show additional, ill-understood patterns of migration. For example, blood monocytes move into normal uninjured tissues, e.g. lymphoid tissues, the liver and spleen, serous cavities, the pulmonary alveoli, the skin, bone (osteoclasts), etc., where they differentiate into macrophages whose function within each tissue is specialized. Lymphocytes recirculate between blood and lymph, a unique migratory pathway that requires them to traverse the specialized high endothelial venules (HEV) of lymphoid tissue (Ford *et al.* 1978; Parrott & Wilkinson, 1981; Jalkanen *et al.* 1986). This migration may involve separate signals and possibly different cells, from migration across non-specialized endothelia into inflammatory tissues.

The following categories of leucocyte behaviour, some of which were defined by Keller *et al.* (1977) will be discussed: (1) the intrinsic locomotor capacity of the cells; (2) chemokinesis; (3) chemotaxis; (4) contact guidance and other forms of contact behaviour. These terms will be used in the sense defined by Keller *et al.* (1977).

INTRINSIC LOCOMOTOR CAPACITY: CELL MATURATION AND LOCOMOTION

It is obvious that the cells that leave the blood and accumulate in inflammatory foci must have locomotor capacity. Leucocyte precursors may lack this capacity and acquire it during maturation.

Neutrophils

In vitro over 95% of blood neutrophils become polarized and move within a few minutes of challenge with an optimal concentration of chemotactic factors such as formylMet-Leu-Phe (FMLP) or C5a (Shields & Haston, 1985). This locomotor capacity is acquired during maturation in the bone marrow and before neutrophils leave it for the bloodstream. The promyelocyte line HL-60 is non-motile. Agents such as dimethylformamide or dimethylsulphoxide induce maturation of HL-60 cells to mature neutrophil forms. They acquire increased numbers of chemotactic factor receptors as they mature and concomitantly acquire locomotor capacity (Niedel *et al.* 1980; Fontana *et al.* 1980). Similar findings have been reported with developing myeloid cells from normal bone marrow (Giordano *et al.* 1973; Rabinovitch & de Stefano, 1978). Locomotor capacity is absent in myeloblasts but is acquired during the myelocyte and metamyelocyte stages of development.

Monocytes and macrophages

Several reports indicate that a subpopulation of about 60% of blood monocytes carries receptors for FMLP, C5a and other chemoattractants (Falk & Leonard, 1980; Cianciolo & Snyderman, 1981) and that the remaining 40% lack these receptors and therefore presumably constitute a non-motile population. Results from our laboratory (Islam, 1987), however, suggest that over 85 % of blood monocytes can be induced to move by mixtures containing one or more of the above defined attractants together with unidentified factors found in activated serum. We therefore think that most blood monocytes are motile, but that a minority of them respond only to undefined factors.

Tissue macrophages also are heterogeneous in respect to locomotor capacity. The 'resident' population of mouse peritoneal macrophages is poorly motile. Less than 20 % of these cells respond to chemotactic gradients from *Candida albicans* spores, whereas, after intraperitoneal injection of an inflammatory stimulus (thioglycollate) over 70 % of the macrophages taken 4 days later are motile in the same assay (Wilkinson, 1982*a*). These inflammatory macrophages are newly recruited from the blood monocyte population. Macrophages in many tissues are described as sessile and have formed firm attachments with nearby cells. Cells such as Kupffer cells, which line the hepatic sinusoids and pick up particles from the blood flowing past, perform this function without any requirement to translocate.

Lymphocytes: locomotor capacity and activation of growth

Many observations both *in vivo* and *in vitro* suggest that unactivated small lymphocytes from the lymphoid tissues of unprimed animals or from normal blood are mostly non-motile *in vitro*, either because they lack locomotor capacity or because specialized stimuli, such as those that cause them to cross HEV *in vivo*, are needed to activate locomotion. In recent studies (Wilkinson, 1986; Wilkinson & Higgins, 1987*a*), we were unable to induce polarization or locomotion into collagen gels of more than 40 % of human lymphocytes freshly separated from blood. However, following antigenic or mitogenic challenge, the growing lymphocytes, e.g. cells from mouse lymph nodes draining the challenge site, showed high motility, (Wilkinson *et al.* 1977; Shields *et al.* 1984). When human blood lymphocytes were cultured in the presence of mitogens (PHA, anti-T3, etc.) or antigen (PPD), up to 80 % of the cells acquired locomotor capacity during the next 48 h. This acquisition of locomotor capacity was inhibited by inhibiting protein synthesis (cycloheximide) but unaffected by inhibiting DNA synthesis (mitomycin). Two subpopulations of cells were observed. One remained small and non-motile and showed little synthesis of RNA or protein. These cells presumably lacked the capacity to respond to the activator under study. The other consisted of growing cells synthesizing RNA and protein (Fig. 1). The latter cells showed polarized morphologies and were able to invade collagen gels. These results suggest that activators that cause lymphocytes to enter the cell cycle also activate locomotor capacity. This activation is evident during the first 24 h of growth, while the cells are in G_1 (Fig. 2). Cyclosporin A, a drug that inhibits expression of mRNA for certain lymphokines during G_1, also inhibits mitogen-induced locomotor activation (Wilkinson & Higgins, 1987*b*).

Among the most interesting activators of lymphocyte locomotion are monoclonal antibodies (OKT3) against the cell-membrane CD3 (T3) protein (Wilkinson & Higgins, 1987*a*). This protein is non-covalently bound to the T-cell antigen receptor,

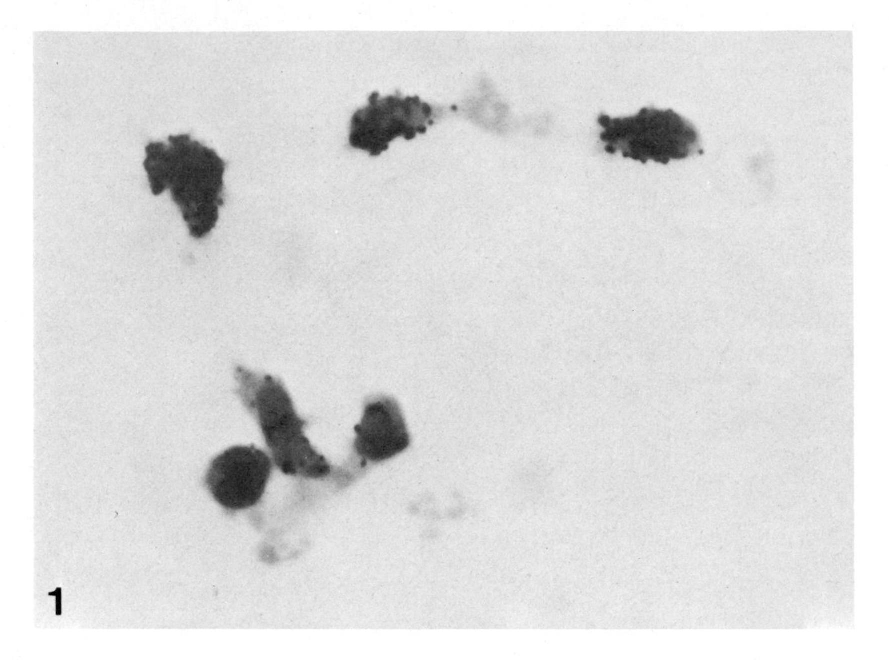

Fig. 1. Autoradiograph of human blood lymphocytes, pulsed with [^{3}H]uridine after 24 h culture in PHA (1 μg ml^{-1}). Most of the cells are in polarized morphology and have taken up uridine. A single round cell in this field has few grains.

and activation through CD3 may be a good model for antigen-stimulated lymphocyte activation. CD3 is believed to transduce activation signals delivered when antigen binds to its T-cell receptor. It is phosphorylated on stimulation of the cells, both with phorbol esters that stimulate protein kinase C, and with antigen (Cantrell *et al.* 1987). Within 24 h of stimulation with anti-CD3, most of the T cells of human blood have increased in size, become polarized and motile (Fig. 2). Anti-CD3 antibody (OKT3) activates locomotor capacity in T cells only in the presence of Fc-receptor-positive cells (FcR^+), to which the Fc portion of the antibody binds, thus cross-linking the T cells to the FcR^+ cells (Wilkinson & Higgins, 1987*a*). Cell–cell contact is required for the activation of locomotor capacity. By the same token, it is likely that antigen-activated locomotion requires binding of the T-cell antigen receptor to a cell-surface bearing self-MHC + antigen, as is the case for other antigen-driven forms of lymphocyte activation.

Many reports suggest that the lymphocytes that enter inflammatory sites *in vivo* are mainly activated cells and the findings outlined above are consistent with this. Stimulation with mitogen *in vitro*, and by implication with antigen *in vivo*, yields a population of motile lymphocytes with high locomotor capacity, which are available for recruitment into immune lesions. Note that specific mitogens recruit only the populations they activate, e.g. anti-CD3 recruits T cells, whereas B-cell-specific mitogens such as the Cowan *Staphylococcus* activate locomotion in a predominantly B-cell population (Wilkinson & Higgins, 1987*b*).

While the *in vitro* findings reported above may be pertinent to the migration of lymphocytes into inflammatory foci *in vivo*, they may bear no relation to the migration of recirculating cells across HEV. The recirculating pool consists chiefly of small, non-activated cells. It is believed that specialized surface molecules on the lymphocytes, e.g. MEL-14 in the mouse, are required for attachment to HEV (Jalkanen *et al.* 1986), though it is not known what role active locomotion plays in migration across HEV. HEV-attachment molecules such as MEL-14 (Dailey *et al.* 1983) may be lost from the lymphocyte surface when the cells are activated with mitogens.

CHEMOKINESIS

Leucocyte attractants are not only chemotactic factors but also stimulate locomotion when present at uniform concentration. Under these conditions the leucocytes show a 'persistent random walk' (Allan & Wilkinson, 1978), which is probably typical of all tissue cells (Gail & Boone, 1970). The speed of locomotion is concentration-dependent, thus the locomotor reaction to the stimulus can be classified as *orthokinesis*. The turning frequency of leucocytes (klinokinesis) may also be modified by attractants (Keller *et al.* 1984*a*) and at high concentrations of formyl

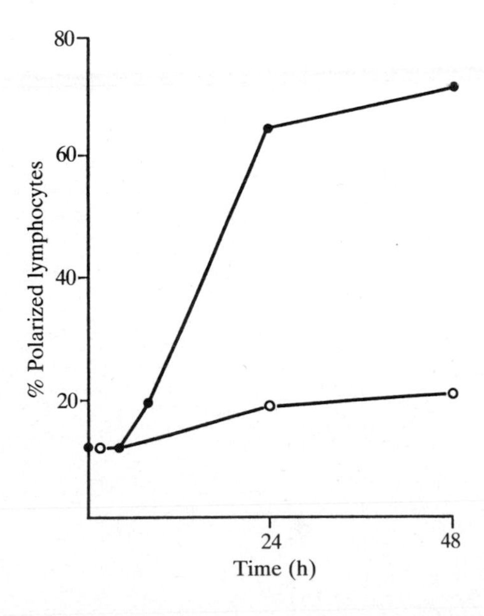

Fig. 2. Time-course showing polarization of human blood lymphocytes during culture with an anti-CD3 antibody (OKT3, 2·5 ng ml^{-1}, ●——●) and in the absence of the antibody (○——○). The cells were cultured in RPMI+2% foetal calf serum.

peptide neutrophils show exaggerated turning behaviour (Shields & Haston, 1985), but this may reflect the inability of the cells to distinguish between different signals at these high concentrations rather than an intrinsic property possessed by cells moving under ideal conditions.

While the generalization that all chemotactic factors are also orthokinetic factors may hold (I should be surprised if there were exceptions to it), the reverse is not the case. Agents may affect cell speed without being chemotactic factors. Obviously many physical factors such as the adhesiveness of substrata, temperature, etc. affect the speed of cell movement without influencing its direction. Other agents alter cell speed by biochemical mechanisms that by-pass cell surface receptors. For example, colchicine causes polarization of a high proportion of leucocytes, and these cells become motile and will invade three-dimensional collagen gels. However, colchicine does not cause leucocytes to orientate if presented in a gradient. Polarization induced by colchicine and other microtubule-depolymerizing agents (including chilling) develops slowly in both neutrophils (Keller *et al.* 1984*b*) and lymphocytes (Wilkinson, 1986), suggesting an intracellular action, presumably on microtubules. It is not at all clear why preventing microtubule polymerization should, in the absence of any other stimulus, cause leucocytes to change from a spherical to a polarized shape and to move. This seems to mimic the activity of chemotactic factors, but from an intracellular signal, so that the cell gains no directional information.

As long as the concentration of a chemokinetic agent remains uniform, no accumulation of the cell population will ensue. The average displacement of the cells of the population will be greater or smaller as the absolute concentration of the attractant is changed, but since the direction of the cells is random, there will be no net displacement of the population from its source other than that due to statistical fluctuation. However, where the concentration of a chemokinetic agent is anisotropic, cell accumulation can result even in the absence of chemotactic cues. This is illustrated by experiments in which the behaviour of neutrophils was studied at a boundary between two fields differing in chemokinetic properties (Wilkinson *et al.* 1984). Coverslips were coated with bovine serum albumin (BSA) providing a surface that is favourable for cell locomotion. Then across the midline of each coverslip was streaked a strip of IgG–anti-BSA to form a sharp linear boundary between BSA-coated glass and BSA–anti-BSA immune complex-coated glass. Neutrophils were seeded onto the surface and their behaviour was studied by filming fields crossed by the boundary. Locomotion was analysed by tracking, and a computer program was used to calculate the true speed (S) of the cells and their persistence index (P) as measures of orthokinesis and klinokinesis, respectively. The displacement (R) can be calculated directly from P and S: $2S^2P = R$. The justification for this was presented by Dunn (1983) and the procedures were described by Wilkinson *et al.* (1984). These experiments showed that S was higher on BSA than on the immune complexes, but there was no difference in P on the two sides of the boundary. Because cells crossing from the BSA to the immune complexes slowed down, their likelihood of crossing back was reduced and gradual accumulation of cells on the immune complexes was observed. The mechanism was increased adhesiveness on the immune complexes.

Neutrophils bear Fc receptors capable of binding to the substratum-bound IgG and, on immune-complex-coated surfaces, these receptors become redistributed to the under surface of the cell (Michl *et al.* 1979). This can be tested by an Fc-rosetting assay. The neutrophils on the BSA coat formed rosettes with IgG-antibody-coated sheep red cells, but the neutrophils on the immune complexes, which no longer had available Fc receptors on their dorsal surfaces, failed to form rosettes (Fig. 3).

In this example, cells accumulated where they were moving most *slowly*, due to a difference in the adhesive properties of the substratum on the two sides of the boundary. This is probably relevant to situations that occur *in vivo*, since neutrophils are known to accumulate at sites of immune complex deposition, for example in the joints in rheumatoid arthritis or on the glomerular capillary basement membrane in glomerulonephritis. In the latter situation, cells flowing in the blood are likely to attach, and we showed similar attachment of neutrophils flowing at a regulated rate across an immune-complex-coated surface in a chamber *in vitro* (Wilkinson *et al.* 1984). This 'adhesive trap' mechanism for cell accumulation would be enhanced if serum were added to the system, since immune complexes activate complement and a chemotactic gradient across the boundary would be generated. In

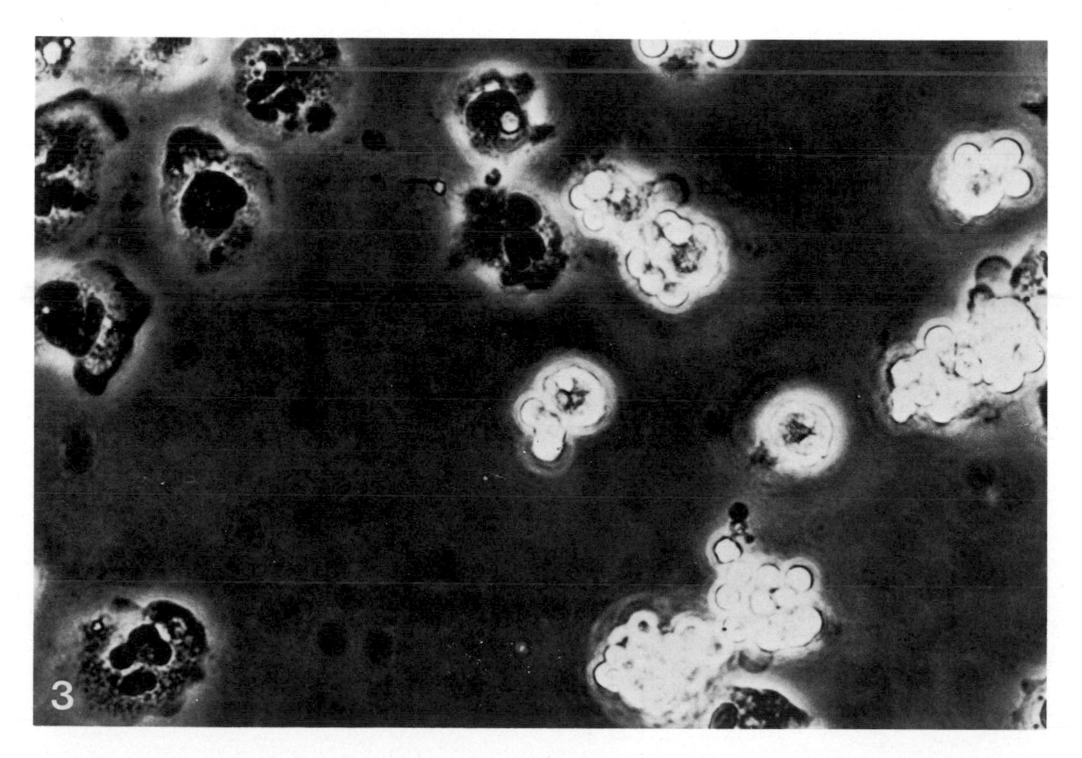

Fig. 3. Fc-rosetting of human blood neutrophils at a boundary between surfaces with BSA alone (right) and BSA–anti-BSA immune complexes (left). The boundary runs vertically down the middle of the picture. The cells on BSA show Fc rosettes, but those on immune complexes do not. The latter cells have redistributed their Fc receptors to the under surface (bound to IgG) and are not able to bind IgG-coated sheep red cells. (From Wilkinson *et al.* (1984).)

our serum-free system, no chemotaxis was present and cell accumulation could be ascribed purely to differences in cell speed on either side of the boundary.

CHEMOTAXIS

Chemotaxis is a special form of locomotor response to chemical signals in which the responding cell becomes oriented in, and moves up, a concentration gradient of an attractant. The same attractant present in isotropic concentration activates locomotion through the same biochemical pathways, but without providing an external bias, so that in this case locomotion is random in direction. Thus attractants are not only chemotactic factors but also chemokinetic factors, and in addition activate a wide range of cell functions unrelated to locomotion (Wilkinson, 1982*b*). Study of attractant-induced locomotion in neutrophils and monocytes is greatly facilitated by the availability of several well-defined attractants such as the formyl peptides, leukotriene B_4 and C5a. These factors do not stimulate locomotion in lymphocytes, attractants for lymphocytes are not well-defined nor is lymphocyte chemotaxis well understood. The ensuing discussion is concerned exclusively with neutrophils.

Leucocytes probably do not move unless stimulated to do so by an external signal. When purified carefully, blood neutrophils remain spherical (Shields & Haston, 1985; Haslett *et al.* 1985). If a chemotactic factor is added at optimal concentration (e.g. 10^{-8} M-FMLP), >95% of these neutrophils take up a typical, polarized locomotor morphology within the next few minutes (Zigmond *et al.* 1981; Smith *et al.* 1979; Shields & Haston, 1985). On an appropriate surface, the cells then move in a direction determined by this anteroposterior polarity. Morphological polarization is accompanied by forward redistribution of cell-surface receptors, both those specific for the activating chemotactic ligand (Sullivan *et al.* 1984) and other receptors such as Fc and C3b receptors (Fig. 4), and, in lymphocytes, Thy-1 (Walter

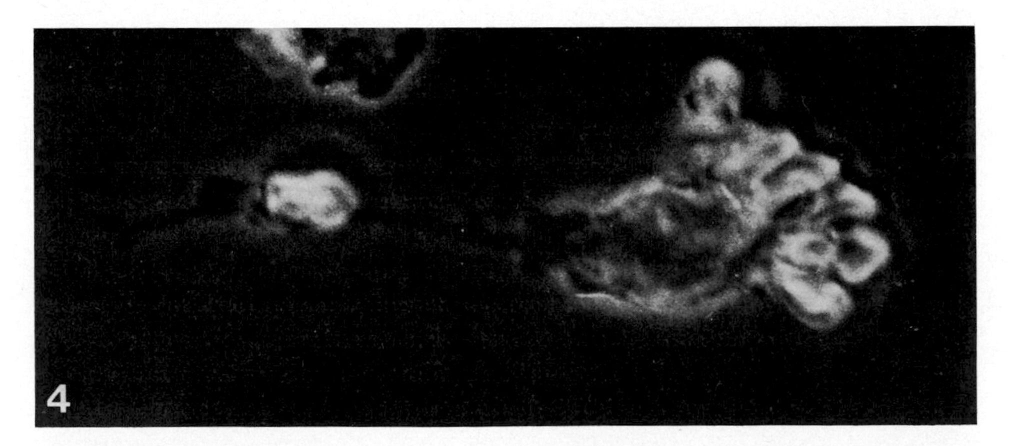

Fig. 4. Redistribution of Fc receptors to the leading edge of a polarized human blood neutrophil. Cells were allowed to polarize for 30 min in 10^{-8} M-FMLP at 37 °C, then rosetting with IgG-antibody-coated sheep cells was carried out at 0 °C for 60 min. (From Wilkinson *et al.* (1980).)

et al. 1980; Wilkinson *et al.* 1980; Shields & Haston, 1985). All of these events take place, not only in gradients, but also in isotropic concentrations of ligand. Therefore, cell polarization and subsequent locomotion cannot be responses to a gradient *per se*. The most likely explanation of this is that the cell responds by polarizing in the direction of the first hit by the ligand, provided the ligand concentration is low enough for the cell to distinguish between a first and subsequent hits. If the ligand concentration is isotropic, the first hit by ligand on the different cells in a population will be random in direction, and the polarization of the different cells in response to that ligand will also be random in direction. Thus the polarization response is stochastically determined. This being so, it follows that cells orient and move up chemotactic concentration gradients, because the first contact with ligand is statistically most likely to be on the up-gradient side of most cells of the population, where the concentration is highest, so that most cells become polarized in that direction. The idea has been discussed more fully elsewhere that chemotaxis is more likely to be a stochastic process than to result from either a spatial or a temporal 'reading' of concentration differences by the cell (Shields & Haston, 1985; Wilkinson & Haston, 1988; Haston & Wilkinson, 1987). This idea has the virtue of simplicity, since it requires of the cell neither spatial computations nor a memory. Adaptation would be required to prevent cells from responding to hits after the first hit. Once adaptation was lost, the forward receptor distribution would presumably increase the likelihood of further stimulation at the anterior pole. Bacteria adapt to chemotactic gradients, i.e. for a time after stimulation they are refractory to further signals but eventually recover responsiveness. It has been suggested that neutrophils also show adaptation (Zigmond & Sullivan, 1979); at high and uniform concentrations of ligand (e.g. 10^{-6} M-FMLP: well above the K_d) neutrophils seem unable to adapt, but put out several pseudopods at different points (Shields & Haston, 1985). Presumably, at these concentrations many ligand molecules bind simultaneously at different point on the cell surface so that the cell is unable to distinguish a first hit. Even after prolonged exposure to attractants at these concentrations, the cells never establish a well-defined anteroposterior polarity.

Neutrophils migrate up chemotactic gradients in straight paths with few and narrow turns (Zigmond, 1974; Allan & Wilkinson, 1978). This is an excellent mechanism for tracking microorganisms and for accumulation at sites of injury. The asymmetric distribution of receptors to the forward part of the cell will strengthen the chances of the cell continuing to respond to signals from the direction of the gradient source, and thus assist it to migrate up-gradient, but cells also need to respond to new gradients from new sources. Studies of neutrophils exposed to new gradients at the rear of the cell show that they frequently make U-turns, as would be expected of a cell whose receptors were concentrated at the front (Keller & Bessis, 1975; Zigmond *et al.* 1981; Gerisch & Keller, 1981). However, if the new gradient from the rear is very intense, as was the case in some of the experiments of Gerisch & Keller (1981) with local gradients from formyl-peptide-filled micropipettes, the cell may protrude a new pseudopod at its rear end. Clearly some receptors must remain at the tail for this to happen (Sullivan *et al.* 1984). Possibly, in polarized cells, the receptors are still able to diffuse, but some unknown mechanism favours concentration of receptors in a forward position.

CONTACT GUIDANCE

Mechanisms

Contact guidance is usually understood to mean the locomotor response of cells to the curvature of the surfaces that they contact as they move, using the word curvature in a broad sense to imply all deviations from the planar (Lackie, 1986). The mechanisms are not clearly understood. Weiss (1934) originally suggested that cells moving along aligned protein fibres were responding to the molecular configuration of polymerized protein arrays, nevertheless most cell biologists nowadays consider contact guidance to be a response to physical, rather than chemical, properties of surfaces. Dunn (1982) has reviewed postulated mechanisms, mostly based on work with strongly adhesive cells such as fibroblasts. On rigid surfaces, there are constraints on the deformability of adherent cells imposed by the curvature of the surface. On elastic substrata, such as connective tissue matrices, an adherent cell pulling at an angle on elastic fibres (e.g. those lateral to it) might distort these fibres more than fibres that it pulled in the axis of alignment of the fibre. In the latter case, since the fibre did not distort, traction by the cell would be more efficient and the cell would displace more efficiently (Dunn, 1981). This could provide an explanation for the preferential locomotion of cells in the axis of fibre alignment, and has been termed 'anisotropic elasticity'.

It is perhaps not surprising that leucocytes show guidance, since many cell types show similar responses to axial anisotropy of the surfaces on which they move. The fact that leucocytes do show guidance may have some relevance to the mechanisms, mostly based on adherence, that have been suggested for guidance, since neutrophils form much weaker adhesions to substrata than fibroblasts do; and lymphocyte adherence is weaker still. We observed contact guidance of leucocytes moving through aligned gels of collagen or fibrin (Wilkinson *et al.* 1982). Neutrophils showed a clear preference for locomotion in the axis of alignment of three-dimensional (3-D) gels. They showed no guidance on dried-down aligned two-dimensional (2-D) collagen surfaces, suggesting that the cells were not simply responding by preferential adhesion along the line of the oriented fibrous polymer. Moreover lymphocytes completely failed to adhere to, and did not move on, 2-D aligned polymers, whereas they showed excellent contact guidance in 3-D gels. This suggested that an adhesive mechanism for guidance of leucocytes was rather unlikely, since the locomotion of lymphocytes in gels (Haston *et al.* 1982) is probably independent of adhesion, and the cells put out blebs into gaps in the gel, which they perhaps use as fixed traction points for movement. Neutrophils in gels probably use similar mechanisms (Brown, 1982).

The reaction of leucocytes to elastic substrata was studied on elastic collagen films prepared by drying collagen gels and then aligning them by tension (Haston *et al.* 1983). Fibroblasts became oriented along the axis of stretch of these films, but did so poorly if the films were attached to glass slides and chemically fixed to reduce their elastic properties. Neutrophils failed to orient on aligned elastic collagen films, but did so within aligned 3-D gels. These findings suggest that fibroblasts, but not neutrophils, are responsive to the elastic properties of the substratum. The difference between the two cell types seems likely to be related to differences in the strength or duration of their adhesion to the substrata studied.

Contact guidance and chemotaxis

Contact guidance has obvious implications for accumulation of cells in inflammatory lesions. The tissues that these cells must traverse are patterned. Connective tissue in the body is normally under tension and therefore aligned. Other tissues have much more complex geometry. An obvious question to ask is what effect guidance in aligned tissues has on the ability of leucocytes to respond to chemotactic gradients. We tackled this by setting up gradients of FMLP in aligned fibrin gels using the assay shown in Fig. 5 and studied the behaviour of neutrophil leucocytes: (1) moving up a gradient parallel to the guidance field, and (2) moving up a gradient at right angles to the guidance field (Wilkinson & Lackie, 1983). The result of an experiment of this sort is shown in Fig. 6. Clearly, migration towards the FMLP source is much more efficient in the axis of gel alignment than across it. Perhaps some of the observed differences in predisposition to infection in different tissues may result from differences in ease of recruitment of leucocytes, which have to traverse those tissues to reach the infection site.

The possibility that contact guidance of leucocytes is itself some specialized form of chemotaxis needs to be excluded, since leucocytes can release enzymes such as

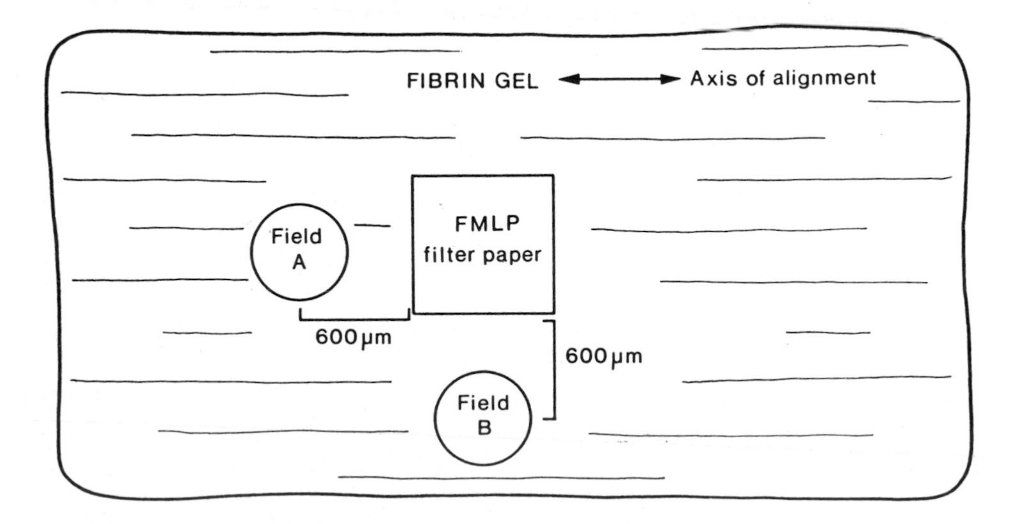

Fig. 5. Schematic drawing to show how locomotion of neutrophils through aligned gels towards FMLP gradients was assayed. In field A, the gradient is parallel to the axis of gel alignment; in field B, it is perpendicular to it. Cells were filmed and their tracks analysed in both fields. (From Wilkinson & Lackie (1983).)

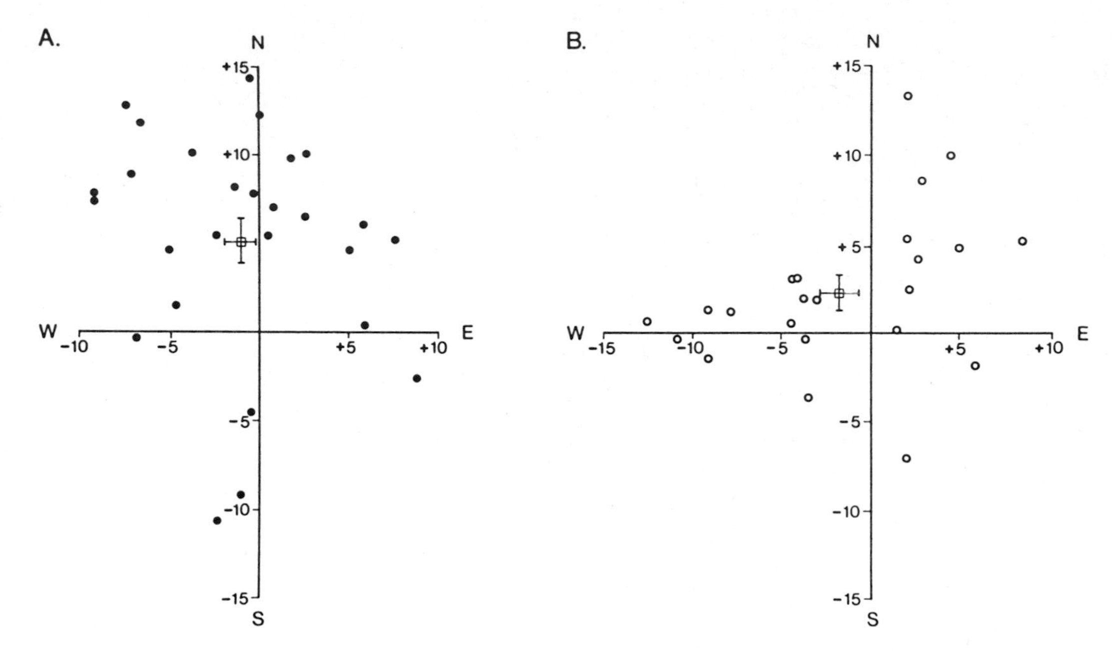

Fig. 6. Vector scatter diagrams showing neutrophil displacement (μm min^{-1}) in field A (left) and field B (right) from Fig. 5. In A, the guidance axis is N–S and the gradient source is at N. In B, the guidance axis is E–W and the gradient source is at N. The dots are displacements of individual cells. Mean displacement ± S.E.M. in *x* and *y* axes is indicated by the crosses. (From Wilkinson & Lackie (1983).)

collagenase or plasminogen activator, which can degrade fibrous proteins, thus forming local gradients of breakdown products. There is indirect evidence that this is not so: in a sensitive assay, [^{3}H]collagen peptide cleavage by collagenases released by neutrophils migrating in gels was undetectably low (Crocket & Lackie, personal communication), and the presence of protease inhibitors such as α_2M had no effect on neutrophil migration in gels (Forrester *et al.* 1983). If chemotaxis were involved, then, since chemotaxis is characterized by polarization towards the gradient source, it should be found that lamellipodia are protruded more frequently in the axis of alignment of the gel than perpendicular to it. In fact, lamellipodium formation in an aligned gel was random in direction (Table 1), which is not consistent with a chemotactic response. Lamellipodia advanced in the axis of alignment tended to persist, but when they were formed at right-angles to it their formation was often not followed by cell displacement in that direction. Though this might be explained on the 'anisotropic elasticity' hypothesis, we failed to show a response to elastic substrata in leucocytes. It is also possible that forward movement in the direction of a lamellipodium that has met a barrier is less likely than when there is no hindrance to forward flow. Contact guidance of leucocytes in aligned gels may result from nothing more than the fact that the sum of forces impeding movement perpendicular to the axis of gel alignment is greater than the sum of forces impeding movement parallel to that axis.

OTHER CONTACT BEHAVIOUR

Among other factors that are likely to contribute to leucocyte accumulation are contact interactions with other cells. These are essentially adhesive interactions perhaps more appropriately discussed in a symposium on cell adhesion than on locomotion. This is a large and complicated subject. Nevertheless, since these interactions are undoubtedly important for leucocyte locomotion in inflammation, I shall simply list them here with reference to appropriate reviews.

(1) *Leucocyte interactions with endothelium.* This is the initial event in inflammation and of obvious importance. Changes in the neutrophil and the endothelial cell may both take place in vessels in inflamed sites. Lackie & Smith (1980) reviewed much of the work up to a few years ago, which suggested that changes in the properties of blood neutrophils may determine their capacity to bind to and to traverse endothelium. Since then a related family of leucocyte surface molecules has been shown to play a role in many adhesive interactions of leucocytes, e.g. with endothelium, in phagocytosis, in T-cell cytotoxicity and in other functions. These include LFA-1, the C3bi receptor (CR3) of neutrophils and macrophages, and gp150,95, a neutrophil surface glycoprotein (Gallin, 1985). Adhesive function is abrogated both by monoclonal antibodies to these molecules (Anderson *et al.* 1986) and, more importantly, in patients who lack them and who suffer from severe, recurrent infections (Anderson *et al.* 1985). The specialized molecules that may be involved in lymphocyte adhesion to HEV have already been mentioned. There is also recent evidence that endothelial cells are rendered more adhesive for leucocytes by treatment, e.g. with LPS or interleukin-1 (Bevilacqua *et al.* 1985; Schleimer & Rutledge, 1986; Pohlman *et al.* 1986; Cavender *et al.* 1986). This is a burgeoning field in which rapid progress should be expected.

(2) *Homotypic cell contacts.* Addition of chemotactic factors to neutrophils causes reversible aggregation not only *in vitro* but also *in vivo*, for example, if C5a is generated within the circulation (e.g. in patients on haemodialysis) (Craddock *et al.* 1979).

(3) *Contact inhibition.* Leucocytes are invasive cells that might be expected not to show heterotypic contact inhibition type I, and there is experimental evidence to

Table 1. *Effect of fibre alignment on direction of lamellipodium formation by human neutrophils in collagen gels*

Direction	No. of lamellipodia formed in each direction was		% Cells in which lamellipodium formation succeeded by locomotion in the same direction		
N	49	*P* NS	76	*P* 0·001	Higher than expected
S	39	*P* NS	77	*P* 0·002	Higher than expected
E	52	*P* NS	21	$P<0·001$	Lower than expected
W	50	*P* NS	42	*P* NS	

Axis of fibre alignment: N–S.
P values derived by Chi-squared test. NS, not significant.
In a control experiment in a non-aligned gel, 76% of all lamellipodia were formed in the direction of an FMLP gradient, of which 86% were followed by locomotion in that direction.

show that they do not do so (Armstrong & Lackie, 1975; Lackie & de Bono, 1977; Lackie *et al.* 1985). However, it is possible that contact between two moving cells (homotypic or heterotypic) may modify their locomotory behaviour in subtle ways. This has not been properly measured, partly because methods for doing so have only recently been described (Paddock & Dunn, 1986).

(4) *Clustering of immune cells.* Induction of T-dependent immune responses requires contact of T helper cells with accessory cells that present antigen in association with syngeneic MHC. Obviously, for this to happen the relevant cells must find each other, though we do not know how this is done. The morphological concomitant of immune induction is clustering of lymphocytes around macrophages, which has been studied by a number of groups (McFarland *et al.* 1966; Lipsky & Rosenthal, 1975). There is no information to suggest how this clustering takes place. Are chemotactic signals involved? In unpublished time-lapse filming studies of such cells responding to antigen or to mitogens, we did not demonstrate chemotaxis, but rather, clusters appeared to form between cells that met by random contact. This is a field in which some basic cell behaviour studies are needed to complement the molecular knowledge already available.

The author's work was supported by the MRC. I thank Dr John Lackie for helpful suggestions about this manuscript.

REFERENCES

ALLAN, R. B. & WILKINSON, P. C. (1978). A visual analysis of chemotactic and chemokinetic locomotion of human neutrophil leucocytes. *Expl Cell Res.* **111**, 191–203.

ANDERSON, D. C., MILLER, L. J., SCHMALSTIEG, F. C., ROTHLEIN, R. & SPRINGER, T. A. (1986). Contributions of the Mac-1 glycoprotein family to adherence-dependent granulocyte functions: structure–function assessments employing subunit-specific monoclonal antibodies. *J. Immun.* **137**, 15–27.

ANDERSON, D. C., SCHMALSTIEG, F. C., FINEGOLD, M. J., HUGHES, B. J., ROTHLEIN, R., MILLER, L. J., KOHL, S., TOSI, M. F., JACOBS, R. L., WALDROP, T. C., GOLDMAN, A. S., SHEARER, W. T. & SPRINGER, T. A. (1985). The severe and moderate phenotypes of heritable Mac-1 LFA-1 deficiency. *J. infect. Dis.* **152**, 668–689.

ARMSTRONG, P. B. & LACKIE, J. M.(1975). Studies on intracellular invasion *in vitro* using rabbit peritoneal neutrophil granulocytes (PMNs). I. Role of contact inhibition in locomotion. *J. Cell Biol.* **65**, 439–462.

ASWANIKUMAR, S., CORCORAN, B., SCHIFFMANN, E., DAY, A. R., FREER, R. J., SHOWELL, H. J., BECKER, E. L. & PERT, C. B. (1977). Demonstration of a receptor on rabbit neutrophils for chemotactic peptides. *Biochem. biophys. Res. Commun.* **74**, 810–817.

BEVILACQUA, M. P., POBER, J. S., WHEELER, M. E., COTRAN, R. S. & GIMBRONE, M. A. (1985). Interleukin-1 acts on cultured human vascular endothelium to increase the adhesion of polymorphonuclear leukocytes, monocytes and related leukocyte cell lines. *J. clin. Invest.* **76**, 2003–2011.

BROWN, A. F. (1982). Neutrophil granulocytes: adhesion and locomotion on collagen substrata and in collagen matrices. *J. Cell Sci.* **58**, 455–467.

CANTRELL, D., DAVIES, A. A., LONDEI, M., FELDMAN, M. & CRUMPTON, M. J. (1987). Association of phosphorylation of the T3 antigen with immune activation of T lymphocytes. *Nature, Lond.* **325**, 540–542.

CAVENDER, D. E., HASKARD, D. O., JOSEPH, B. & ZIFF, M. (1986). Interleukin-1 increases the binding of human B and T lymphocytes to endothelial cell monolayers. *J. Immun.* **136**, 203–207.

CIANCIOLO, G. J. & SNYDERMAN, R. (1981). Monocyte responsiveness to chemotactic stimuli is a property of a subpopulation of cells that can respond to multiple attractants. *J. clin. Invest.* **67**, 60–68.

CRADDOCK, P. R., HAMMERSCHMIDT, D. E., MOLDOW, C. F., YAMADA, O. & JACOB, H. S. (1979). Granulocyte aggregation as a manifestation of membrane interactions with complement: possible role in leukocyte margination microvascular occlusion and endothelial damage. *Semin. Hemat.* **16**, 140–147.

DAILEY, M. O., GALLITIN, W. M., WEISSMAN, I. L. & BUTCHER, E. C. (1983). Surface phenotype and migration properties of activated T cells and T cell clones. In *Intercellular Communication in Leucocyte Function* (ed. J. W. Parker & R. L. O'Brien), pp. 645–648. New York: Wiley.

DUNN, G. A. (1981). Chemotaxis as a form of directed cell behaviour: some theoretical considerations. In *Biology of the Chemotactic Response* (ed. J. M. Lackie & P. C. Wilkinson), pp. 1–26. Cambridge University Press.

DUNN, G. A. (1982). Contact guidance of cultured tissue cells: a survey of potentially relevant properties of the substratum. In *Cell Behaviour* (ed. R. Bellairs, A. S. G. Curtis & G. A. Dunn), pp. 247–280. Cambridge University Press.

DUNN, G. A. (1983). Characterising a kinesis response. *Agents Actions, Suppl.* **12**, 14–33.

FALK, W. & LEONARD, E. J. (1980). Human monocyte chemotaxis: migrating cells are a subpopulation with multiple chemotaxis specificities on each cell. *Infect. Immun.* **29**, 953–959.

FONTANA, J. A., WRIGHT, D. G., SCHIFFMANN, E., CORCORAN, B. A. & DIESSROTH, A. B. (1980). Development of chemotactic responsiveness in myeloid precursor cells: studies with a human leukemia cell line. *Proc. natn. Acad. Sci. U.S.A.* **77**, 3664–3668.

FORD, W. L., SMITH, M. E. & ANDREWS, P. (1978). Possible clues to the mechanism underlying the selective migration of lymphocytes from the blood. *SEB Symp.* **32**, 359–392.

FORRESTER, J. V., LACKIE, J. M. & BROWN, A. F. (1983). Neutrophil behaviour in the presence of protease inhibitors. *J. Cell Sci.* **59**, 213–230.

GAIL, M. H. & BOONE, C. W. (1970). The locomotion of mouse fibroblasts in tissue culture. *Biophys. J.* **10**, 980–993.

GALLIN, J. I. (1985). Leukocyte adherence-related glycoproteins LFA-1, Mo1 and p150, 95: A new group of monoclonal antibodies, a new disease, and a possible opportunity to understand the molecular basis of leukocyte adherence. *J. infect. Dis.* **152**, 661–664.

GERISCH, G. & KELLER, H. U. (1981). Chemotactic reorientation of granulocytes stimulated with fMet-Leu-Phe. *J. Cell Sci.* **52**, 1–10.

GIORDANO, G. F., LICHTMAN, M. A. & NAYLE, E. (1973). Marrow cell egress: The central interaction of barrier pore size and cell maturation. *J. clin. Invest.* **52**, 1154–1164.

HASLETT, C., GUTHRIE, L. A., KOPANIAK, M. M., JOHNSTON, R. B. & HENSON, P. M. (1985). Modulation of multiple neutrophil functions by preparative methods or trace concentrations of bacterial lipopolysaccharide. *Am. J. Path.* **119**, 101–110.

HASTON, W. S., SHIELDS, J. M. & WILKINSON, P. C. (1982). Lymphocyte locomotion and attachment on 2-dimensional surfaces and in 3-dimensional matrices. *J. Cell Biol.* **92**, 747–752.

HASTON, W. S., SHIELDS, J. M. & WILKINSON, P. C. (1983). The orientation of fibroblasts and neutrophils on elastic substrata. *Expl Cell Res.* **146**, 117–126.

HASTON, W. S. & WILKINSON, P. C. (1987). Gradient perception by neutrophil leucocytes. *J. Cell Sci.* **87**, 373–374.

ISLAM, L. N. (1987). Studies on chemoattractant-induced polarisation and locomotion of human blood leucocytes. Ph.D. thesis, University of Glasgow.

JALKANEN, S., REICHERT, R. A., GALLATIN, W. M., BARGATZE, R. F., WEISSMAN, I. L. & BUTCHER, E. C. (1986). Homing receptors and the control of lymphocyte migration. *Immun. Rev.* **91**, 39–60.

KELLER, H. U. & BESSIS, M. (1975). Migration and chemotaxis of anucleate cytoplasmic leucocyte fragments. *Nature, Lond.* **258**, 723–724.

KELLER, H. U., MEIER, G. & ZIMMERMANN, A. (1984*a*). Klinokinesis in polymorphonuclear leucocytes. *Blood Cells* **10**, 505–509.

KELLER, H. U., NAEF, A. & ZIMMERMANN, A. (1984*b*). Effects of colchicine, vinblastine and nocodazole on polarity, motility, chemotaxis and cAMP levels of human polymorphonuclear leukocytes. *Expl Cell Res.* **153**, 173–185.

KELLER, H. U., WILKINSON, P. C., ABERCROMBIE, M., BECKER, E. L., HIRSCH, J. G., MILLER, M. E., RAMSEY, W. S. & ZIGMOND, S. H. (1977). A proposal for the definition of terms related to locomotion of leucocytes and other cells. *Clin. exp. Immun.* **27**, 377–380.

LACKIE, J. M. (1986). *Cell Movement and Cell Behaviour*, p. 207. London: Allen & Unwin.

LACKIE, J. M. & DE BONO, D. (1977). The aggregation of rabbit polymorphonuclear leucocytes (PMNs). Effects of agents which affect the acute inflammatory response and correlation with secretory activity. *Inflammation* **2**, 1–15.

LACKIE, J. M. & SMITH, R. P. C. (1980). Interactions of leucocytes and endothelium. *Cell Adhesion and Motility* (ed. A. S. G. Curtis & J. D. Pitts), pp. 235–272. Cambridge University Press.

LACKIE, J. M., URQUHART, C. M., BROWN, A. F. & FORRESTER, J. V. (1985). Studies on the locomotory behaviour and adhesive properties of mononuclear phagocytes from blood. *Br. J. Haemat.* **60**, 567–581.

LIPSKY, P. E. & ROSENTHAL, A. S. (1975). Macrophage–lymphocyte interaction. II. Antigen-mediated physical interactions between immune guinea pig lymph node lymphocytes and syngeneic macrophages. *J. exp. Med.* **141**, 138–154.

MCFARLAND, W., HEILMAN, D. H. & MOORHEAD, J. F. (1966). Functional anatomy of the lymphocyte in immunological reactions *in vitro*. *J. exp. Med.* **124**, 851–858.

MICHL, J., PIECZONSKA, M. M., UNKELESS, J. C. & SILVERSTEIN, S. (1979). Effects of immobilized immune complexes on Fc- and complement-receptor function in resident and thioglycollate-elicited mouse peritoneal macrophages. *J. exp. Med.* **150**, 607–621.

NIEDEL, J., KAHANE, I., LACHMAN, L. & CUATRECASAS, P. (1980). A subpopulation of cultured human promyelocytic leukaemia cells (HL-60) displays the formyl peptide chemotactic receptor. *Proc. natn. Acad. Sci. U.S.A.* **77**, 1000–1004.

PADDOCK, S. W. & DUNN, G. A. (1986). Analysing collisions between fibroblasts and fibrosarcoma cells: fibrosarcoma cells show an active invasionary response. *J. Cell Sci.* **81**, 163–187.

PARROTT, D. M. V. & WILKINSON, P. C. (1981). Lymphocyte locomotion and migration. *Prog. Allergy* **28**, 193–284.

POHLMAN, T. H., STANNESS, K. A., BEATTY, P. G., OCHS, H. D. & HARLAN, J. M. (1986). An endothelial cell surface factor(s) induced *in vitro* by lipopolysaccharide, interleukin 1 and tumor necrosis factor-α increases neutrophil adherence by a CDw-18-dependent mechanism. *J. Immun.* **136**, 4548–4553.

RABINOVITCH, M. & DE STEFANO, M. J. (1978). *In vitro* chemotaxis of mouse bone marrow neutrophils. *Proc. Soc. exp. Biol. Med.* **158**, 170–173.

SCHIFFMANN, E., CORCORAN, B. A. & WAHL, S. A. (1975). *N*-formylmethionyl peptides as chemoattractants for leukocytes. *Proc. natn. Acad. Sci. U.S.A.* **72**, 1059–1062.

SCHLEIMER, R. P. & RUTLEDGE, B. K. (1986). Cultured human vascular endothelial cells acquire adhesiveness for neutrophils after stimulation with interleukin 1, endotoxin, and tumor-promoting phorbol diesters. *J. Immun.* **136**, 649–654.

SHIELDS, J. M. & HASTON, W. S. (1985). Behaviour of neutrophil leucocytes in uniform concentrations of chemotactic factors: contraction waves, cell polarity and persistence. *J. Cell Sci.* **74**, 75–93.

SHIELDS, J. M., HASTON, W. S. & WILKINSON, P. C. (1984). Invasion of collagen gels by mouse lymphoid cells. *Immunology* **51**, 259–268.

SHOWELL, H. J., FREER, R. J., ZIGMOND, S. H., SCHIFFMANN, E., ASWANIKUMAR, S., CORCORAN, B. & BECKER, E. L. (1976). The structure–activity relations of synthetic peptides as chemotactic factors and inducers of lysosomal enzyme release for neutrophils. *J. exp. Med.* **143**, 1154–1169.

SMITH, C. W., HOLLERS, J. C., PATRICK, R. A. & HASSETT, C. (1979). Motility and adhesiveness in human neutrophils. Effects of chemotactic factors. *J. clin. Invest.* **63**, 221–229.

SNYDERMAN, R., ed. (1984). Regulation of leukocyte function. *Contemp. Topics Immunobiol.* **14**, 1–410.

SULLIVAN, S. J., DAUKAS, G. & ZIGMOND, S. H. (1984). Asymmetric distribution of the chemotactic peptide receptor on polymorphonuclear leukocytes. *J. Cell Biol.* **99**, 1461–1467.

WALTER, R. J., BERLIN, R. D. & OLIVER, J. M. (1980). Asymmetric Fc receptor distribution on human PMN oriented in a chemotactic gradient. *Nature, Lond.* **286**, 724–725.

WEISS, P. (1934). In vitro experiments on the factors determining the course of the outgoing nerve fiber. *J. exp. Zool.* **68**, 393–448.

WILKINSON, P. C. (1982*a*). Visual observations of chemotaxis and chemotropism in mouse macrophages. *Immunobiology* **161**, 376–384.

WILKINSON, P. C. (1982*b*). *Chemotaxis and Inflammation*. 2nd edn. Edinburgh: Churchill-Livingstone.

WILKINSON, P. C. (1986). The locomotor capacity of human lymphocytes and its enchancement by cell growth. *Immunology* **57**, 281–289.

WILKINSON, P. C. & HASTON, W. S. (1988). Chemotaxis: an overview. *Meth. Enzym.* (in press).

WILKINSON, P. C. & HIGGINS, A. (1987*a*). OKT3-activated locomotion of human blood lymphocytes: a phenomenon requiring contact of T cells with Fc receptor bearing cells. *Immunology* **60**, 445–451.

WILKINSON, P. C. & HIGGINS, A. (1987*b*). Cyclosporin A inhibits mitogen-activated but not phorbol-ester activated locomotion of human lymphocytes. *Immunology* **61**, 311–316.

WILKINSON, P. C. & LACKIE, J. M. (1983). The influence of contact guidance on chemotaxis of human neutrophil leukocytes. *Expl Cell Res.* **145**, 255–264.

WILKINSON, P. C., LACKIE, J. M., FORRESTER, J. V. & DUNN, G. A. (1984). Chemokinetic accumulation of human neutrophils on immune-complex-coated substrata: analysis at a boundary. *J. Cell Biol.* **99**, 1761–1768.

WILKINSON, P. C., MICHL, J. & SILVERSTEIN, S. C. (1980). Receptor distribution in locomoting neutrophils. *Cell Biol. Int. Rep.* **4**, 736.

WILKINSON, P. C., PARROTT, D. M. V., RUSSELL, R. J. & SLESS, F. (1977). Antigen-induced locomotor responses in lymphocytes. *J. exp. Med.* **145**, 1158–1168.

WILKINSON, P. C., SHIELDS, J. M. & HASTON, W. S. (1982). Contact guidance of human neutrophil leukocytes. *Expl Cell Res.* **140**, 55–62.

WILLIAMS, L. T., SNYDERMAN, R., PIKE, M. C. & LEFKOWITZ, R. J. (1977). Specific receptor sites for chemotactic peptides on human polymorphonuclear leukocytes. *Proc. natn. Acad. Sci., U.S.A.* **74**, 1204–1208.

ZIGMOND, S. H. (1974). Mechanisms of sensing chemical gradients by polymorphonuclear leukocytes. *Nature, Lond.* **249**, 450–452.

ZIGMOND, S. H., LEVITSKY, H. I. & KREEL, B. J. (1981). Cell polarity: an examination of its behavioural expression and its consequences for polymorphonuclear leukocyte chemotaxis. *J. Cell Biol.* **89**, 585–592.

ZIGMOND, S. H. & SULLIVAN, S. J. (1979). Sensory adaptation of leukocytes to chemotactic peptides. *J. Cell Biol.* **82**, 517–527.

J. Cell Sci. Suppl. 8, *121–140 (1987)*

CELL MOTILITY AND THE PROBLEM OF ANATOMICAL HOMEOSTASIS*

ALBERT K. HARRIS

Department of Biology, University of North Carolina at Chapel Hill, Chapel Hill, NC 27599-3280, USA

SUMMARY

The locomotion of tissue cells need not be invasive or disrupt normal tissue geometry, as occurs in cancer. The normal relationship between anatomical structure and cell locomotion is exactly the reverse, with motility serving to create and maintain the structures of the body. This relationship is most extreme in sponges, where time-lapse films show that the cells move about continually in patterns that restructure these animals' simple anatomy. The cells choose their position according to their differentiated cell type, which is the opposite of what is usually assumed to occur in development and has important implications for the functional significance of histotypic cell sorting.

A particular type of cellular force that seems to be important in morphogenesis is the traction that all motile tissue cells exert. This traction can be studied by culturing cells on very thin sheets of silicone rubber, so that the locations and variations in the cellular forces are made visible by the wrinkles they produce in the rubber substratum. One finding has been that the traction forces exerted by untransformed fibroblasts are very much stronger than is needed for their own locomotion, but are well adapted for the function of rearranging and aligning collagen fibres to form structures like ligaments, tendons and muscles. These forces are found to be greatly weakened by neoplastic transformation, however, suggesting that malignant invasiveness results from some sort of deflection of cell traction forces from their proper morphogenetic functions, so as to produce uncontrolled invasion.

To explain how motile cells create and maintain structures, as well as how their locomotion sometimes becomes perverted into the form of cancerous invasiveness, what seems to be needed is an extension of the concept of homeostasis to apply to the control of geometric relations between cells. This task may not be easy; one obstacle is the widespread belief that asymptotic stability implies the minimization of free energy. Instead, I suggest that stability results from balance of opposing forces within tissues, and that genes control which anatomical shapes will exist by determining the rules by which the relative strengths of these forces vary as functions of shape: to control shape, one must control the way forces vary with shape.

INTRODUCTION: CELL MOTILITY IN RELATION TO ANATOMICAL STRUCTURE

The motility of the body's component cells can be either destructive or constructive. Cell motility is destructive when it takes the form of malignant invasiveness and disrupts the proper geometric arrangements of cells into tissues and organs. But this same motility is constructive when it creates these anatomical structures during embryonic development, and also when it serves to maintain their geometry during subsequent life, despite damage and turnover. We should very much like to understand both the constructive and the destructive effects of cell motility, and it is to be expected that the study of the one should aid our

*This was the Cancer Research Campaign Lecture.

understanding of the other. This will be especially true if, as seems likely, malignancy results from normal cellular maintenance and repair mechanisms that have somehow escaped their normal controls.

Among the obstacles to understanding these problems is the tendency to think of morphogenesis as having ceased at the end of embryonic development, or at least by the time growth is completed. In actual fact, many parts of the body continue throughout life to replace, rearrange and repair their component cells and molecules; their morphogenesis is continual, since it is by means of this continual renewal and rearrangement (rather than simply by inertia) that the structures are maintained. To mention one example, it has been found that the collagen molecules that make up the periodontal ligament (which holds the teeth in the mouth) turn over constantly throughout life with a half-life of only about one day (Sodek, 1977). There are many other examples, including the continuous replacement by lateral migration of the epithelial cells that line the intestine, reorganization of capillary networks, and a continual breakdown and re-formation of the bones of the skeleton itself. Probably, if we could make time-lapse films of the cell movement within our body, as we can do with sponges, we would be shocked by the amount of cell movement and wonder how it is possible for the geometry of our body to be maintained in spite of it.

The major theme of this article is that it is not *in spite of* the movements and turnover that anatomical structure is maintained; it is actually *by means of* these movements that anatomy maintains itself. Cell locomotion itself should not be considered as equivalent to invasiveness, or as inherently disruptive to tissue architecture. Controlled locomotion is a necessary part of the maintenance of our anatomy. We therefore need to think of anatomical shapes as being less like those of an inert statue, and more like the shapes formed by water shooting up in a fountain. The external shape of a statue is, of course, very much more similar to that of the human body; but this shape has been imposed by external forces, rather than arising from the properties of the material itself. In contrast, the shapes taken by the water of a fountain reflect properties of the water itself, and it is not in spite of the water's continuous movement that these shapes are maintained, but precisely by means of this movement.

When a biological property is maintained relatively unchanged, despite disturbances, it is said to be in homeostasis. Physiologists have developed the concept of homeostasis to a high degree of sophistication over the past century, with Bernard and Cannon having been the major contributors (see Langley, 1973). It has even become part of our collective 'common sense' as biologists that, when one encounters a constancy of some property like body temperature or blood pH, one should seek explanations in terms of negative feedback and countervailing influences, the relative strengths of which vary as functions of whatever physiological variable is being kept constant. Unfortunately, however, when the variable being kept constant happens to be a geometric or mechanical one (the shape of an organ, perhaps, or the relative positions of some cells) it has not been usual to think of this as being a case of homeostasis, or to ask what the counter-balanced forces or the feed-back cycles that function to maintain tissue geometry might be.

There are some exceptions to this general lack of attention to anatomical homeostasis: the Chalone hypothesis, for example, seeks to explain the constancy of size in the liver, skin and other organs in terms of negative feedback by hormone-like substances (Bullough, 1975; see also Lord *et al.* 1978); there is also the theory that bone mass, shape and internal structure may be controlled by electrical fields (whether piezoelectric or electro-osmotic), which the bones themselves generate when strained (Bassett, 1971; Currey, 1984). Thoma's (1893) comparable work on the control of arterial pathways and diameters by physical tensions and blood flow-rates, however, is seldom even cited.

Likewise, in modern technology, it is much more usual for homeostatic servo-mechanisms to be used to control quantitative variables, rather than geometric or structural ones. Lest this imbalance suggests some inherent limitation to the capacities of negative feed-back (rather than limitations of human imagination), and as an example of the general sort of mechanisms we need to look for, let me interject the interesting example of the 'quartz–halogen' lamp (Dettingmeijer *et al.* 1975) (see Fig. 1). These are incandescent light-bulbs whose tungsten filaments are heated to such high temperatures that the housings would melt were they made of glass rather than quartz; the hotter filaments produce a brighter light, but at the cost of considerable evaporation of tungsten atoms from the filament. Halogen gasses are included in the bulb in order to react with the free tungsten atoms, and because the

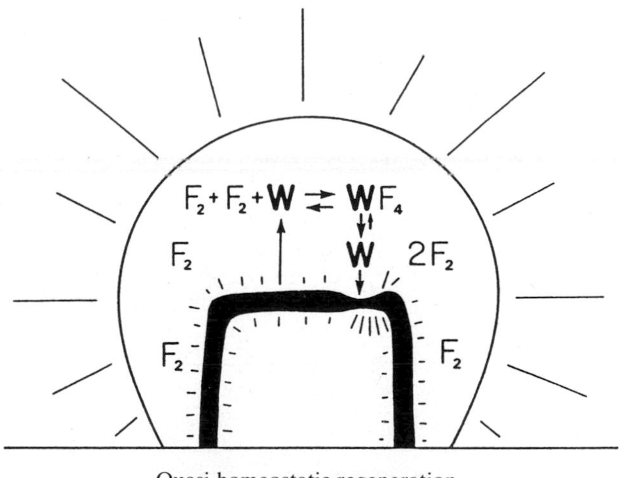

Fig. 1. Diagram of the principle of operation of a quartz–halogen lamp as an illustration of geometric homeostasis achieved by means of a continuous expenditure of energy and a recycling of material. The intense heating of the filament by an electric current causes evaporation of tungsten atoms from the filament, but these react with halogen gas to form a tungsten halide, which is then itself broken down by heat to redeposit tungsten onto the filament. Ideally, this redeposition is concentrated on the thinnest parts of the filament, where it is hottest.

resulting tungsten halides are themselves broken down by high temperatures, tungsten metal is continuously redeposited back onto the filament. The most truly homeostatic feature is the tendency for this deposition to be concentrated wherever the filament is hottest (since the highest temperatures will be produced where the filament is thinnest, this effect can tend to even out filament diameter). Unfortunately, this last effect is seldom achieved.

The development of the concept of contact inhibition by Abercrombie & Heaysman (1953, 1954) can (and, I think, should) be regarded as having been the crucial first step towards understanding how the motility of our component cells can be homeostatically controlled in such a way as to permit renewal and repair of tissues, whilst blocking invasiveness. But now we need to go still further towards understanding how cell behaviour and interaction can bring into existence and maintain those complex spatial arrangements of cells and matrix that constitute anatomy.

SPONGES: AN EXTREME CASE OF PERPETUAL MORPHOGENESIS

Both fresh-water and marine sponges, at least those of the majority morphological type called 'leuconoid', can be cultured in thin spaces between microscope coverslips, slides or Petri dishes (Ankel & Eigenbrodt, 1950). The sponges obligingly adapt their anatomy to these 'sandwich cultures' (Fig. 2), so that one can observe the movements of their component cells, much as one observes the behaviour of ants living in colonies between parallel sheets of plate glass. By this and similar methods, the behaviour of cells within living sponges has been studied extensively by Weissenfels (1981), Harrison (1972) and more recently by Calhoun Bond (1986) in my own laboratory.

Time-lapse films of sponges growing between coverslips and slides show that their component cells are continually moving about (Fig. 3). The most active are the several classes of mesenchymal cells in the sponge interior; these carry the spicules (skeletal elements) from place to place, here installing and joining them into skeletal supports, there moving other spicules to new locations. The special type of epithelial cell peculiar to sponges (called 'pinacocytes') also shows active movement and locomotion; sheets of these cells form the sponge's surface layer, including what one might call the floor, by which the sponge adheres to the substratum. As Bond (1986) has shown, these floor pinacocytes actually exert a substantial traction force on the external substratum, and the net result of this traction is that the entire sponge crawls laterally; in aquaria, for example, one finds sponges climbing the glass walls at speeds of the order of 1 mm per day.

Individual pinacocytes move around within their sheets; not infrequently some of these cells detach themselves from the edge of the sponge and crawl around for a few minutes on their own before rejoining it. Water is sucked into the sponge through many small pores in the pinacocyte layer; these pores run through and between the pinacocytes themselves, so that the diameters and number of these incurrent pores are a constant function of the cells' motile activity and the constriction of these pores.

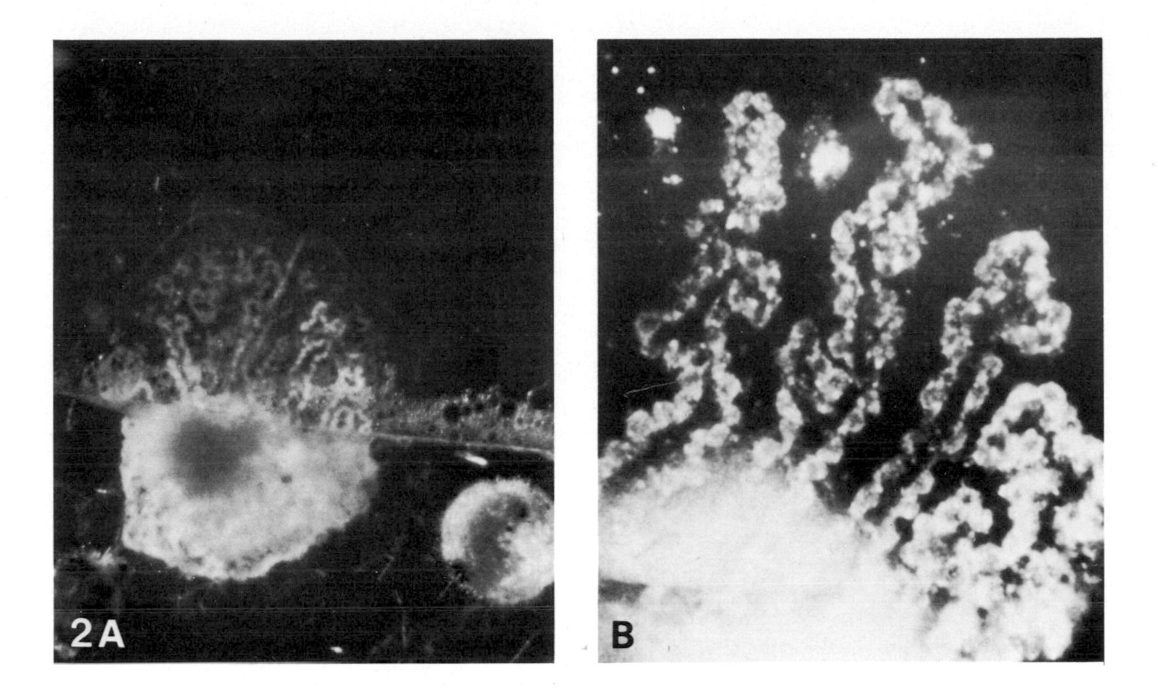

Fig. 2. Photographs of living fresh-water sponges (Ephydatia) living in 'sandwich cultures' between coverslips. A. Low magnification; sponge extending under coverslip at top. Thicker region of sponge at bottom, flanked by two gemmules. B. Higher-magnification view of choanocyte chambers and excurrent canals from the same species. This is a single frame from a time-lapse film taken by fluorescence microscopy; the choanocytes appear white because of the fluorescent plastic beads that they have filtered out of the water.

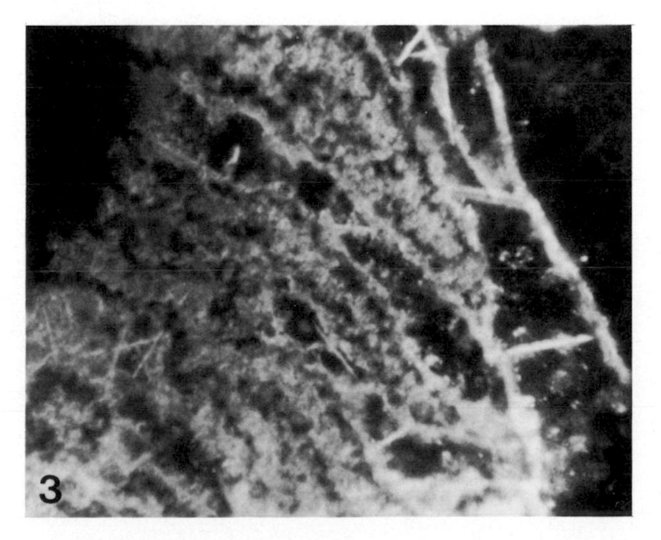

Fig. 3. Single frame from a time-lapse film showing movements and anatomical rearrangements inside a living *Ephydatia* sponge.

Other pinacocytes (whether these are interchangeable with those forming the outer layer seems not to be known) arrange themselves into a branching network of excurrent canals, which conduct the water away from clusters of the flagellated cells called choanocytes.

The choanocytes are the third major cell type and are the ones that do the actual pumping of water. It is these cells that filter food from the water; one might even paraphrase the cliché about the egg and the chicken by saying that the rest of the sponge is just the choanocytes' way of channelling water past themselves most efficiently (as well as affording themselves some degree of protection). Groups of choanocytes spontaneously arrange themselves into rosettes (or hollow balls), with their flagella all pointing inwards; the beating of these flagella pulls water through narrow spaces between adjacent choanocytes and produces a pressure that pushes the water out of the sponge through the tubular excurrent ducts made of pinacocytes (mentioned above), to which these hollow clusters of choanocytes spontaneously connect themselves.

From my observations of food particles and fluorescent plastic beads being filtered out of water by sponges in sandwich cultures, it appears that the water reaches the choanocytes by flowing directly through the space (called the 'mesohyl') where the mesenchymal cells, spicules and collagen are located. Text illustrations of leuconoid sponges always show 'incurrent ducts' (see Hyman, 1940), but these seem to be imaginary. The true situation is apparently analogous to the way air reaches the fire in an ordinary wood stove, i.e. by coming through the surrounding room. The water is then sucked between adjacent choanocytes, which take up the fluorescent beads as the water goes by. The beating of the chanocyte flagella then pushes the water out of the excurrent canals, while it simultaneously creates a suction in the mesohyl space, so that water is drawn into this space through pores in the surrounding sheet of pinacocytes.

Time-lapse films of sponges cultured in these 'sandwich' chambers show very extensive and continuous rearrangements of cells, spicules, choanocyte chambers, excurrent canals, and the 'spongin' collagen matrix. Pronounced waves of contractility sweep repeatedly through all the tissues and the shapes of the chambers and canals change radically from hour to hour. When initially shown such films, people usually assume that the subject matter must be the fabled reaggregation of dissociated sponge cells, as was originally observed by H. V. Wilson (1908), late of my department. They are surprised to be told that these are not reaggregating or otherwise experimentally treated sponges; this is just the way their component cells behave all the time. These ordinary day-to-day movements of cells within sponges are at least as rapid, active and extensive as one sees in time-lapse films of reaggregation.

In effect, sponges are always in a perpetual state of spontaneous anatomical reorganization. Thus, Wilson's remarkable reaggregation phenomenon should apparently be regarded as the imposition of a somewhat more extreme version of events that are normally going on all the time inside sponges. As Wilson pointed out, sponges living under poor conditions frequently form one or another sort of 'reduction body'. In the case of fresh-water sponges, these are special well-organized spherical structures called 'gemmules'. The reorganization of a functioning sponge from the cells of a gemmule or other reduction bodies is a normal equivalent of the reaggregation phenomenon. Nor are sponges unique in this respect: fresh-water ectoproct bryozoans (such as *Pectinatella*) also reorganize their anatomies from cells stored in special reduction bodies called 'statoblasts'.

WHAT IS THE FUNCTIONAL SIGNIFICANCE OF HISTOTYPIC CELL SORTING?

The constant renewal of sponge anatomy by cell motility may have important implications for the whole phenomenon of histotypic cell sorting, including that of vertebrate cells. Let us look at the problem very abstractly. The central task of metazoan development is to put the correct differentiated cell types into the proper geometric locations relative to one another. Logically, there are two extreme alternative ways to get the right cell types in the right places. The first alternative is *to have position control differentiation*, so that the specialized cells simply develop where they ought to be, and then stay there. The second alternative is exactly the reverse: *to have differentiation control position*, by which I mean the inclusion among the differentiated characteristics of whatever behaviour or properties will make the cells move spontaneously to their correct relative positions.

The first of these two extreme alternatives (position determining differentiation) is the common-sense one; it is also the one posited by the conceptual system called 'positional information'. Many cases are definitely known in which position controls determination and subsequent cytodifferentiation.

The second of these alternatives (differentiation determining position) may well be counterintuitive and seem impractical to the point of absurdity. But this absurdity seems not to deter the sponge cells, because it is apparent from the time-lapse films of their perpetual reorganizations that it is the second of these alternatives that the sponges are actually using to create and maintain their humble anatomies. Their cells choose position on the basis of their differentiated state, rather than the other way around, and they do so constantly.

What I am led to suggest is that the morphogenesis of all metazoans should be regarded as employing some mixture of these two stratagems for getting the right cell types into the right geometric locations: either having position control differentiation, or having differentiation control position. In the case of sponges, a rough estimate might be that they are using 90 % in the second stratagem and only 10 % in the first; in the case of our own anatomies, the estimated percentages might be approximately the reverse. Histotypic cell sorting, then, would represent the cells' capacity for this second stratagem being forced to operate in isolation from their capacity for the first. Any behaviour or property (and not just selective adhesiveness), which has the effect of moving cells to certain relative geometric positions (according to their differentiated cell type), should likewise cause cell sorting. But

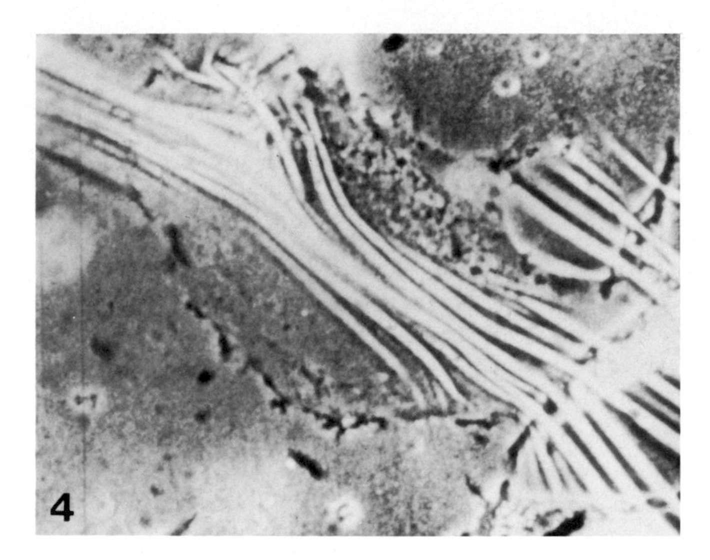

Fig. 4. A single frame from a time-lapse film showing a chick heart fibroblast crawling on the surface of a thin sheet of silicone rubber. The traction forces are made visible by the wrinkles they form in the rubber substratum. Notice how these wrinkles begin behind the leading margin of the cell where the ruffling activity is concentrated. The cell is crawling toward the upper right.

what kind of cellular behaviour and what forces would have the ability to rearrange cells, spicules and matrix into their proper geometric patterns?

CELL TRACTION AS A MORPHOGENETIC FORCE

The silicone rubber substratum technique was originally invented as a means of studying the mechanism of locomotion in tissue cells. In this technique, liquid silicone fluid is cross-linked by brief exposure to a flame, so as to form a layer of silicone rubber only about 1 μm thick. This layer coats the fluid's surface. Tissue culture cells are then plated out directly onto the surface of this rubber layer; the cells adhere to the rubber, spread on it and crawl about, just as they would on a glass or polystyrene surface. The rubber layer, however, is sufficiently weak and elastic to be visibly distorted by the propulsive forces exerted by the individual cells. These cellular forces produce complex patterns of wrinkles in the rubber substrata; the wrinkles are easily observed by phase-contrast microscopy, and provide information about where, and in what directions, the cellular forces are exerted (Fig. 4).

This method does not lend itself to quantification of the forces exerted, partly because of the difficulty of making two sheets of rubber with exactly the same elasticity, but even more because of the mathematically complex relationship between tensile stress and wrinkle size and number. The method can, however, yield unambiguous information about which cell types exert stronger forces than others, or whether a given experimental treatment causes a strengthening or a weakening of these forces. Changes in the forces exerted are most clearly seen when the wrinkling patterns are recorded by time-lapse cinemicrography.

The cells whose motility has been most intensively studied using this technique are those generalized mesenchymal cells called fibroblasts. These cells exert strong centripetal forces on the silicone rubber substrata; bipolar fibroblasts, for example, will pull rubber in from both directions toward their centre. The result is that the rubber sheet becomes thrown into 'compression wrinkles' directly beneath the cell body, but stretched into 'tension wrinkles' that radiate outward beyond the cell margins (Fig. 5). The latter type of wrinkle, especially, can often extend beyond the cell for many hundreds of μm, and sometimes a mm or more.

These pulling forces, which fibroblasts and other tissue cells exert, have been given the name 'traction'. The locations and directions in which a given cell exerts its traction are found to be correlated with the ruffling and blebbing activities along the cell margins, as well as with the direction in which the different parts of the cell margins spread outwards over the substratum. Traction is concentrated in those regions directly behind (centripetal to) the particular parts of the cell margin where the plasma membrane is undergoing its most active ruffling movements. The direction in which the traction force is exerted is rearward or centripetal; in other words, the direction of traction tends to approximate the predominant direction of ruffle backfolding.

We should definitely not conclude, however, that the ruffles or other protrusions from the cell surface play a direct role in the exertion of the traction force; in particular, there is no indication of the cell margin reaching out, attaching, and then pulling back on the substratum, intuitively attractive as such a scenario might be.

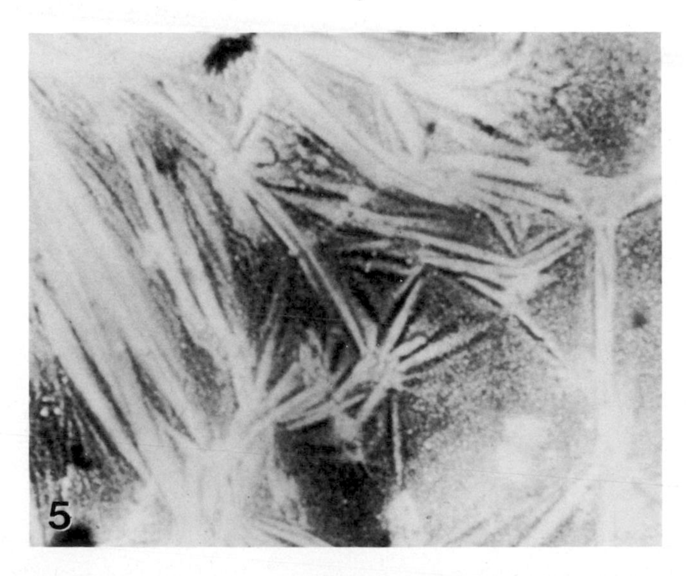

Fig. 5. A single frame from a time-lapse film showing chick heart fibroblasts at low magnification compressing a sheet of silicone rubber. Within an hour of the time this picture was taken, the entire area of rubber visible in this field had been compressed to a small wrinkled mass and pulled out of the field of view at the upper left.

Low-magnification observations might suggest such a cycle; but when filmed at high magnification, the ruffles themselves do not appear to exert any appreciable forces on the substratum, neither to pull it nor to push it, nor usually even to touch it. On the basis of the locations where the wrinkles appear in the rubber substrata, cell traction is exerted 5–10 μm or more behind the ruffling margins, in the area where dark contact areas and points are seen by interference reflection microscopy (fortunately, the optical properties of the silicone rubber are similar enough to those of glass to permit observation of contacts by interference reflection). Moreover, this traction seems to be exerted as a steady shearing force, one that can vary over time but without any apparent element of oscillation or pulsatory quality. It is not unusual for opposite sides of a single cell to exert traction in opposite directions; all sides towards the middle.

Spread fibroblasts remain in a state of tensile stress, stretched taut between their adhesions to the substratum, through which they continue to transmit a pulling force. If one or more of the cell margins happens to break its adhesions to the rubber substratum, and this is not infrequent, the tension is released and the wrinkles in the rubber re-expand and disappear within one or two seconds. In such cases, it is not unusual to see a partially detached fibroblast pulled bodily sideways by the elastic re-expansion of the rubber; the cell is pulled away from the sites of its newly broken adhesions at speeds of 10 $\mu m\, s^{-1}$ or more (enough to produce blurred exposures in films). The continued existence of the wrinkles in the rubber substrata depends on the continuing exertion of the contractile forces by the cells; the wrinkles in the rubber are not some kind of 'footprint' left by the motile cells. The only exceptions to this rule are when so much tension has been exerted that the rubber sheet has actually been torn, or when cells have held the rubber continuously in a highly wrinkled state for several days and deposited a layer of collagen fibres on its surface, which can effectively lock some of the wrinkles in place.

I conclude from these and other observations that these traction forces that distort silicone rubber substrata are the same as those that cause cell spreading and locomotion, and that they are also probably equivalent to the forces that move adherent particles centripetally across cell surfaces. They seem also to be the same as the forces responsible for the condensation or compression of fibrin and collagen substrata around cultured cells. It was once generally accepted that this condensation of extracellular matrix around cells was a shrinkage of the matrix itself, stimulated in some way by uptake of water or by other biochemical effects of growing cells; considerable evidence against that type of explanation was accumulated by Stopak & Harris (1982), who showed that those cell lines that exerted the weakest traction on rubber substrata also produced the least compression of collagen gels, regardless of the cells' growth rate or metabolic activity.

Comparisons of the amounts of distortion produced by cells, both on silicone rubber substrata and in gels of re-precipitated rat-tail tendon collagen (Fig. 6), show very large differences in tractional strength between different classes of differentiated cells and also between normal cells and their transformed equivalents (Harris *et al.* 1981). Blood platelets exert the strongest traction, followed by fibroblasts. Epithelial

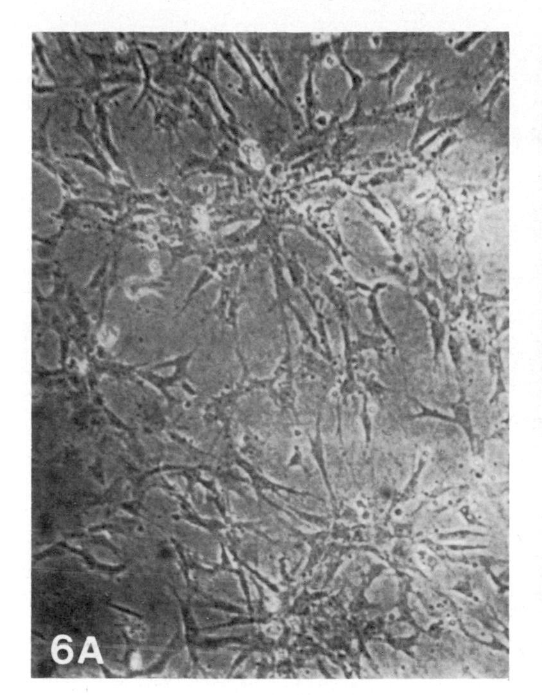

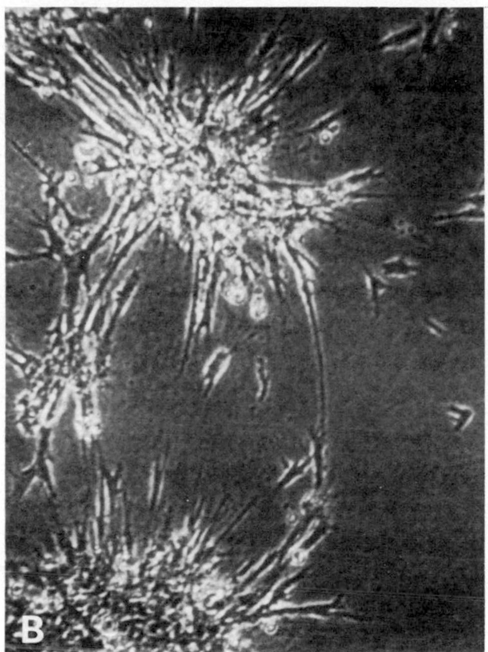

Fig. 6. A,B. The cumulative effect of fibroblast traction in mechanically reorganizing a gel of reprecipitated rat-tail tendon collagen. Individual frames from a continuous time-lapse film; 36 h separates the two time points. Note how the population density of cells becomes progressively more uneven, due to the cells' traction pulling more cells and matrix into tight concentration.

cells are considerably weaker, macrophage traction is barely detectable, and no visible distortion of the rubber is caused by either polymorphonuclear leucocytes or nerve growth cones.

Transformed fibroblasts exert traction on the rubber substrata in the same pattern as do normal fibroblasts, but this traction is very much weaker; the wrinkles produced are smaller and fewer. The systematic comparison by Steinberg *et al.* (1980) of the population densities required to produce a certain degree of collagen gel distortion confirmed that transformed cells are characteristically weaker than normal cells. Using reverse transformation of CHO cells by dibutyryl cyclic AMP, Leader *et al.* (1983) showed that these cells exert much weaker traction in the transformed state, compared with the reverse transformed state. The transformed cells' adhesions to the substrata were also found to be larger in total area, but weaker in total strength. Most recently, Danowski & Harris (1986) found that phorbol ester tumour promotors cause an immediate weakening of fibroblast traction, combined with more gradual changes in cell morphology and adhesion to the substratum. In this case, cells temporarily in a transformed state show decreased adhesion to hydrophilic surfaces but an increased ability to attach to hydrophobic surfaces.

When fibroblasts are explanted from embryos into tissue culture, however, their tractional strength undergoes an increase in strength. This occurs between 3 and 4 days after initial explantation and is accompanied by a conversion of their substratum adhesions to the tight, focal adhesion type. We believe that this increase in the force of the cells' traction corresponds to the increased development of actomyosin stress fibres by such cells and is a response of normal fibroblasts to trauma; as such, it would be equivalent to conversion of the cells to 'myofibroblasts', as described by Gabbiani *et al.* (1973).

Our studies of fibroblast traction were undertaken on the assumption that the only biological function of these forces was to propel the cells exerting the forces from one place to another. The observations described above raised several paradoxes, however: one paradox was that the more motile cells, such as macrophages, leucocytes and transformed fibroblasts, were the ones that exerted the weakest traction forces; another was that fibroblast traction was so strong as to produce large-scale rearrangements in collagen matrices. These rearrangements can easily extend for centimetres. So not only does fibroblast traction seem to be wastefully strong, it seems to pose some danger of disrupting the normal mechanisms that arrange collagen and other matrix materials into their correct geometric patterns within the body.

Stopak and I proposed a simple solution for both these puzzles (Harris *et al.* 1981; Stopak & Harris, 1982), which was that fibroblast traction is itself the principal mechanism for arranging collagen fibres into their correct anatomical patterns. In other words, the traction exerted by macrophages and leucocytes actually is intended to move those cells from place to place; but the much stronger traction that fibroblasts exert has a quite different function; fibroblast traction is intended primarily to distort and rearrange the collagen in their vicinity. Whatever displacement of the fibroblasts might result from their traction would be a secondary effect. When placed on an abnormal, rigid substratum such as glass, fibroblasts will still exert traction, but now the only visible effect of that traction will be a rather inefficient locomotion.

Stopak & Harris (1982) were also able to produce evidence that fibroblast traction can produce several important kinds of morphogenesis; these include the alignment of collagen into ligaments and tendons, as well as the compaction of collagen into sheets much like organ capsules, perichondria and certain dermal structures. Subsequently, Stopak showed that rat tendon collagen, covalently labelled with fluorescein and injected into developing chick limb buds, is subjected to forces that compress and rearrange this collagen so that it becomes part of whichever of the chick's anatomical structures form at the site of the injection (Stopak *et al.* 1985). Although there was no way of observing whether it was cell traction that generated the forces responsible for this *in vivo* remodelling of collagen, the results were those to be expected of traction. A series of mathematical and computer simulations have been started to determine what net geometric consequences are to be expected from traction and other cellular forces, as well as whether these correspond to actual anatomical structure (Oster *et al.* 1983). These continue to be encouraging and it has been possible to show that fibroblast traction can generate periodic spacing of cells and matrix (Harris *et al.* 1984).

ASYMPTOTIC STABILITY AND THE ENERGY MINIMIZATION FALLACY

Although it is well known that our body temperature normally gravitates to about 37 °C, no one concludes that this temperature therefore must represent some kind of state of minimum free energy; nor do people draw such conclusions from other cases of physiological homeostasis. However, when it comes to tissue geometry and to the tendency of cells to sort out into different patterns, this minimization-of-free-energy interpretation has many militant advocates. Their misinterpretation of thermodynamics represents, therefore, a formidable obstacle to any effort to understand the generation and maintenance of tissue geometry in terms of homeostatic mechanisms. Imagine what the effect on the progress of physiology would have been if people had believed that the constancy of body temperature or blood pressure required (or even implied) that the stable states had to minimize free energy.

Of course, there really are many cases in which systems gravitate to certain configurations that do minimize either potential energy or one of the forms of free energy; the latter constitute much of the subject matter in thermodynamics courses, which appears to be the source of this fallacy. When the only stable systems people are told about are those that minimize free energy, it is only natural for them to draw conclusions. The pair of physical analogies illustrated in Fig. 7 are intended to clarify this issue.

In the first of the two examples, a motor boat propels itself upstream against a current, with this current becoming progressively stronger upstream; the boat thus

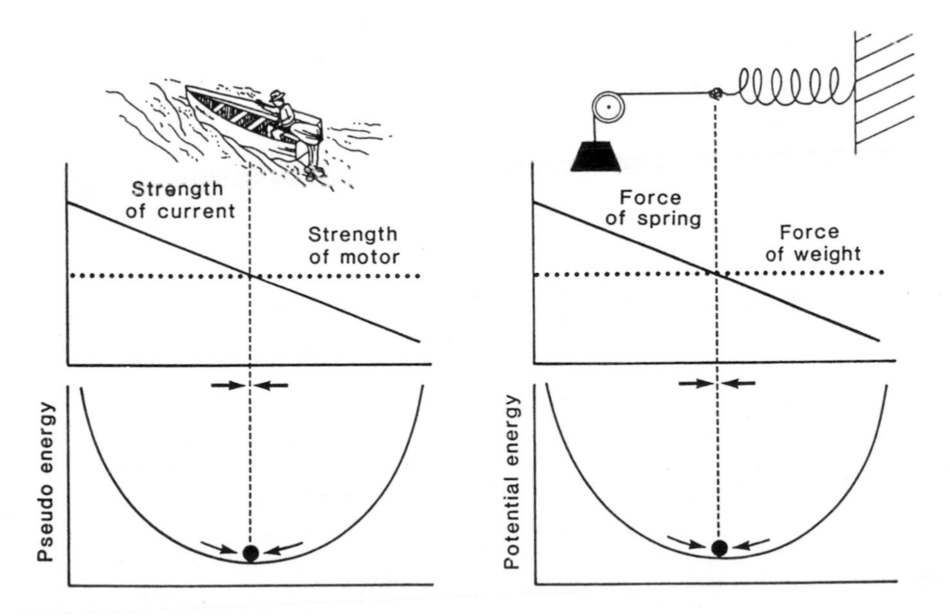

Fig. 7. Diagrammatic illustration of the relationship between force balance, energy minimization and the achievement of an asymptotically stable configuration. On the left side, a boat is propelled by a constant force up a river whose current becomes progressively stronger the farther upstream the boat progresses. On the right, a weight falls until the elastic pull of a spring exactly balances its weight. In both cases, a state of asymptotic stability is reached, but only the situation on the right minimizes energy.

gravitates to a stable, stationary position at which the strength of its motor is exactly counterbalanced by that of the current.

In the second example, the gravitational pull on a weight stretches a spring until the elastic pull of the spring exactly counterbalances the gravitational pull. This configuration is then stable and will spontaneously restore itself if disturbed.

The point of these two examples is that both gravitate to a certain configuration, but neither potential energy nor free energy is minimized in the first example, while in the second potential energy really is minimized. The difference is that the forces exerted by gravity and the spring happen to be conservative forces and do not expend energy in the static situation; in contrast, the forces exerted by the river current and the boat's motor would not be conservative forces, so it would not even make a great deal of sense to speak of the potential energy. The property of gravitating to some particular configuration depends on the balance between opposing forces, the crucial aspect being the rules by which the opposing forces vary as functions of position. The question of energy minimization, on the other hand, depends on whether the opposing forces happen to be conservative or not. These are completely different questions. Stability does not imply the minimization of energy, neither does it imply that the forces responsible have to be conservative.

In both our imaginary examples, the state of force-balance is what is called 'asymptotically stable' Hirsch & Smale (1974), in that the system will gravitate to it from either direction. Both also possess what Rene Thom (1975) meant by 'structural stability', which sounds as if it had something specifically to do with the involvement of physical structures, but actually refers to the fact that the qualitative behaviour of the system is relatively insensitive to qualitative changes in the variables (like the absolute strength of the boat's motor, or that of the current). As long as these qualitative changes are not too large, the qualitative result is the same. Notice that the laws by which the forces vary have been chosen to be the same in both these examples; even though the physical cause of the forces could hardly be more different, the same laws govern how the forces vary as functions of position. Which configurations will be stable does not depend on the physical causes of the forces, it depends on the rules by which the forces vary as functions of configuration. The same rules generate the same geometries.

THE CAUSATION OF SHAPE BY PHYSICAL FORCES

The relationship between physical forces and the shapes they create is not simple or free of logical pitfalls. As part of what must be the greatest single biological treatment of this topic, D'Arcy Thompson (1942) catalogued many examples in which cells or organisms take on shapes resembling those of soap bubbles and liquid droplets. Although Thompson was rather non-committal in his interpretations, the conclusion often drawn from such similarities is that the same physical force (i.e. surface tension) must be shaping cells and organisms. I suggest, however, that we should conclude only that the forces that shape the cells happen to obey rules rather similar to those obeyed by surface tension. Forces that obey the same rules will create

Fig. 8. A mass of swarming bees, which collectively behave much like a liquid droplet with a 'surface tension'.

and maintain the same shapes; their physical causation need not have anything in common.

Fig. 8 shows a mass of swarming bees suspended from my laboratory window; notice how much this mass resembles the shape to be expected of a liquid droplet. Because the individual bees tend to crawl from the surface of the mass into its interior, the net result is as if the surface were contractile and tended to minimize its area. When sugar/water was sprayed on the mass, the bees became more willing to remain at the surface; so the effect was equivalent to a surfactant.

A comparable example is the tendency of aggregates of dissociated embryonic cells to round up, as if they collectively possessed a surface tension. One hypothesis is that the cells tend to maximize their areas of contact with one another, with the minimization of the area of the exposed surface being a secondary consequence. A rather different mechanism, which would have exactly the same net effect, would be for the cell cortices to contract actively (as by actomyosin filaments), but for this cortical contractility to be inhibited over those parts of the cells' surfaces that lie directly adjacent to another cell; this would mean that the strongest cortical contractility would be in those areas directly exposed to the medium. In that case, the minimization of exposed area would be the primary cause, while the maximization of contact area would be the secondary effect. Note that if the sum of exposed surface area and contacted surface area is a constant, then minimization of the first will equal the maximization of the latter.

The preceding examples are meant to illustrate that it is the rules obeyed by forces that determine what shapes these forces will create and render stable. Surface tension contracts the surfaces of liquids with a force that is isotropic and (usually) homogeneous; any other forces that contract a flexible surface (or resist its expansion) isotropically and homogeneously will generate this same range of shapes. The force need not tend to minimize energy or have any other specific property. Physical similarities and analogies to inorganic shape can be helpful when they show us some of the shapes that can be rendered stable by forces obeying certain combinations of rules; but these same analogies can also be very misleading. We must avoid the conclusion that similar shapes imply causation by the same forces; but it is still more important to realize that the range of geometric shapes that can be generated and rendered asymptotically stable (even by quite simple combinations of force-rules) is not limited just to that paltry range of shapes that liquid surface tension can create. Thus, in the attempt to explain morphogenesis in terms of physical forces, we need not feel ourselves limited to those few organisms whose contours happen to mimic soap bubbles. Other force-rules can create other shapes, and the range of variation that can be achieved has only started to be explored by advanced mathematics and computer simulation.

A good example of the dependence of shape on the rules obeyed by forces is the familiar (but odd) behaviour of elongate rubber balloons when these are partly inflated. Such balloons develop a fat end and a thin end, with such different tensions in the two parts of their surfaces as to make it seem almost impossible that the air pressure is the same in both places (as it is). Not only this effect, but also the greater pressure required to initiate the inflation than to continue it, turn out to result from a subtle non-linearity in the elasticity of rubber (see Chater & Hutchinson, 1984). If stress in rubber happened instead to be exactly (linearly) proportional to strain, then neither effect would occur. So imagine what would happen if you could make a balloon out of a material whose rules of contractility could be changed at will; when the elasticity was non-linear (as in actual rubber) the balloon would adopt one set of shapes; but if the elasticity were then made linear, the forces would cease to be balanced and the balloon would jump to some new shape. The same rules produce the same shapes; different rules (can) produce different shapes; a large enough change in the rules obeyed by forces will produce 'spontaneous' jumps to new shapes.

Of course, we want to explain anatomical shapes in terms of the actual forces (such as traction) that create and maintain them; but to achieve this goal, we must not be distracted from also asking what it is about these forces that decides which particular shapes they will create and maintain. My suggested answer is that the shape forces produce is determined by the rules by which the strengths of the forces vary as functions of the existing geometry. Consider how the homeostasis of body temperature depends on having the rates of heat production and heat dissipation vary as functions of the existing temperature to the body. Likewise, in the earlier examples of the boat on the river and the weight hanging from the spring, the property of gravitating to one configuration in preference to others, depended on having the relative strengths of the opposing pairs of forces vary as functions of geometry. The same was true of the quartz–halogen lamp and we ought to expect similar principles to apply to cellular forces.

If we extrapolate to the problem of how to cause some anatomical structure to have this same kind of stability, the requirements seem to be these; first, you need physical forces that have sufficient strength to change the geometry of the system, as well as other forces that can resist or counterbalance these; second, you need the relative strengths of the forces to vary as functions of the existing geometry. The forces that can change geometry must themselves vary in strength as functions of the same geometrical properties that they change. Only if the forces vary as functions of geometry can they be stably counterbalanced when the right geometry exists, but not otherwise (Fig. 9).

It is essential to realize, however, that variations in the relative strengths of forces can occur for several different kinds of reasons. The change can be because of what amounts to leverage, as when the net force exerted perpendicular to a stretched sheet varies locally in proportion to the curvature. Or, alternatively, you can have actual inhibitions or stimulations of the force generators themselves. For example, suppose that crowding cells together weakens their traction; this will tend to even out their distribution. Conversely, the increased strength of fibroblast traction that occurs in response to trauma (as well as explantation) seems well designed as a homeostatic mechanism (Fig. 10) for constricting sites of injury, either for closing surface

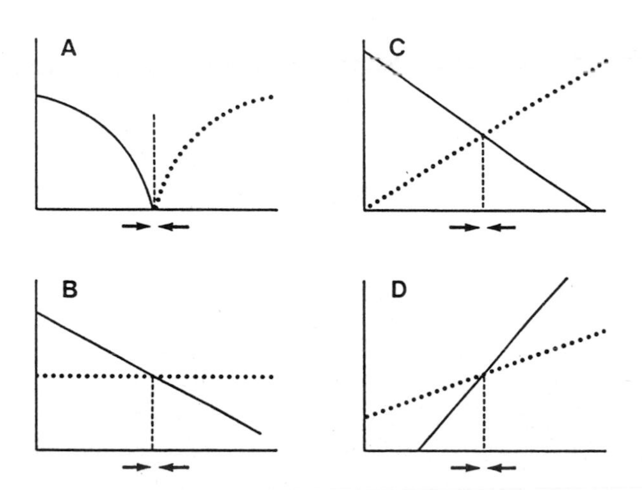

Fig. 9. Stability results from a balance of opposing forces. At which point the stability will occur depends on the rules by which the forces vary, in this case as functions of position. If the continuous lines represent the strengths of forces acting towards the right, while the dotted lines represent the strengths of forces acting towards the left, then for each of these four combinations of force-rules, asymptotic stability will occur at the points towards which the arrows point. Notice how different the rules can be and still produce the same result.

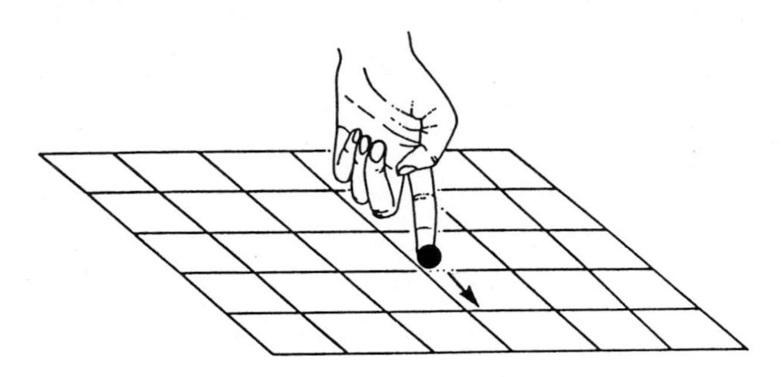

Two kinds of causality

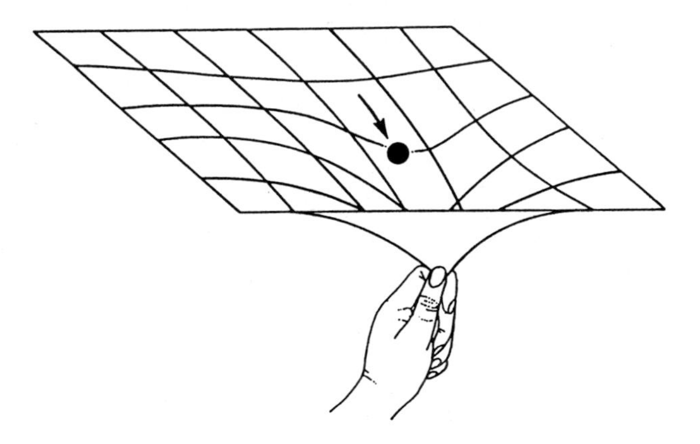

Fig. 10. Two fundamentally different ways of causing a certain combination of variables to come into existence: either (top) by imposing some outside force on the system, or (bottom) by changing the rules of interaction among the component parts, so that the desired combination of variables will arise spontaneously. The bottom sketch is meant to represent the kind of geometric homeostasis discussed in this paper.

wounds or for bringing torn tissues back together in the case of sprains or broken bones.

We should also realize that the absolute strengths of opposing forces will not need to fall to zero in order to achieve a stable balance. For example, in the case of the original observations of contact inhibition, Abercrombie & Heaysman (1953) reported that cell motility was reduced, but by no means completely stopped, in cells having many contacts; such cells reduced their movement only by about half. Others have sometimes concluded that contact inhibition could not be enough to control cell invasiveness. But, depending on what other controlling or countervailing effects are acting, an inhibition by half may be all that is needed. The forces acting on a soap film do not become zero when the stable shape is achieved; they merely become equal and opposite.

Conversely, we also need to bear in mind that no new forces need to come into existence in order to shift a state of force balance; an existing force may instead become (relatively) stronger, or its opposing force could become weaker. The crucial thing is the rule by which the opposing forces vary; if you change this rule, the forces will shift the geometry to a new balance; and if you change the rule too much, the old state can cease to be stable at all, so that the components jump (spontaneously) to some new and perhaps very different configuration. By saying 'spontaneously', I mean that forces unrelated to those actually causing the change will become able to initiate it. Unless the experimental biologist consciously prepares his mind for such effects, he will have little chance of escaping the worst misinterpretations.

These considerations should also be relevant to the problem of invasive locomotion by neoplastic cells. To the extent that structural cells of our body are continually using their motility and traction for purposes of renewal and repair, it is not the motility of malignant cells that we should view as abnormal. What is wrong is that their propulsive forces somehow fail to obey the proper rules.

CONCLUSIONS

The constant renewal and repair of body structures, in sponges and also in higher animals, seems to require the equivalent of homeostatic mechanisms for arranging cells, collagen and other materials into their correct geometric arrangements. By using rubber and collagen substrata, it has been shown that fibroblasts exert shearing forces (traction) of sufficient strength to achieve large-scale geometric rearrangements of cells and matrix. It is a mistake to think that the tendency of a system to gravitate homeostatically to some particular configuration should require or imply energy minimization; the actual requirement is balance between opposing forces, the relative strengths of which need to vary as functions of the geometric properties to be controlled.

I am indebted to my collaborators David Stopak, Patricia Greenwell, Calhoun Bond, Mark Leader, Barbara Danowski, John Dmytryk and Sally Gewalt. I also thank Susan Whitfield for preparation of illustrations and Elizabeth Harris for help with the manuscript.

REFERENCES

Abercrombie, M. A. & Heaysman, J. E. M. (1953). Observations on the social behavior of cells in tissue culture. I. Speed of movement of chick heart fibroblasts in relation to their mutual contacts. *Expl Cell Res.* **5**, 111–131.

Abercrombie, M. A. & Heaysman, J. E. M. (1954). Observations on the social behavior of cells in tissue culture. II. 'Monolayering' of fibroblasts. *Expl Cell Res.* **6**, 293–306.

Ankel, W. E. & Eigenbrodt, H. (1950). Uber die Wuchsform von Spongilla in sehr flachen Raumen. *Zool. Anz.* **145**, 195–204.

Bassett, C. A. L. (1971). Biophysiological principles affecting bone structure. In *The Biochemistry and Physiology of Bone* (ed. G. H. Bourne), vol. 3, pp. 1–76. New York: Academic Press.

Bond, C. (1986). Locomotion of entire sponges is a result of amoeboid locomotion of their component cells. *Am. Zool.* **26**, 14A.

Bullough, W. S. (1975). Mitotic control in adult mammalian tissues. *Biol. Rev.* **50**, 99–127.

Chater, E. & Hutchinson, J. W. (1984). Mechanical analogs of coexistent phases. In *Phase Transformations and Material Instabilities in Solids* (ed. M. E. Gurtin), pp. 21–36. Orlando: Academic Press.

Currey, J. (1984). *The Mechanical Adaptations of Bones*. Princeton: Princeton University Press.

DANOWSKI, B. A. & HARRIS, A. K. (1986). A time lapse study of phorbol ester effects on the contractile and adhesive properties of fibroblasts in tissue culture. *J. Cell Biol.* **103**, 428a.

DETTINGMEIJER, DITTMER, G., KLOPFER, A. & SCHRODER (1975). Regenerative chemical changes in tungsten-halogen lamps. *Phillips tech. Rev.* **35**, 302–306.

GABBIANI, G., MAJNO, G. & RYAN, G. B. (1973). The fibroblast as a contractile cell: the myofibroblast. In *Biology of Fibroblasts* (ed. E. Kulonen & S. Pikkarainen), pp. 139–154. New York: Academic Press.

HARRIS, A. K., STOPAK, D. & WARNER, P. (1984). Generation of spatially periodic patterns by a mechanical instability: a mechanical alternative to the Turing model. *J. Embryol. exp. Morph.* **80**, 1–20.

HARRIS, A. K., STOPAK, D. & WILD, P. (1981). Fibroblast traction as a mechanism for collagen morphogenesis. *Nature, Lond.* **290**, 249–251.

HARRISON, F. W. (1972). The nature and role of the basal pinacoderm of *Corvomeyenia carolinensis* Harrison (Porifera: Spongillidae). A histochemical and developmental study. *Hydrobiology* **39**(4), 495–508.

HIRSCH, M. W. & SMALE, S. (1974). *Differential Equation, Dynamical Systems and Linear Algebra*. New York: Academic Press.

HYMAN, L. H. (1940). *The Invertebrates*, vol. I. *Protozoa through Ctenophora*. New York: McGraw-Hill.

LEADER, M., STOPAK, D. & HARRIS, A. K. (1983). Increased contractile strength and tightened adhesions result from reverse transformation of CHO cells by dibutyryl cyclic adenosine monophosphate. *J. Cell Sci.* **64**, 1–11.

LANGLEY, L. L. (1973). *Homeostasis: Origins of the Concept*. Stroudsburg, Penn.: Dowden, Hutchinson & Ross.

LORD, B. I., POTTEN, C. S. & COLE, R. J. (1978). *Stem Cells and Tissue Homeostasis*. Cambridge University Press.

OSTER, G. F., MURRAY, J. D. & HARRIS, A. K. (1983). Mechanical aspects of mesenchymal morphogenesis. *J. Embryol. exp. Morph.* **78**, 83–125.

SODEK, J. (1977). A comparison of the rates of synthesis and turnover of collagen and non-collagen proteins in adult rat periodontal tissues and skin using a microassay. *Archs Oral Biol.* **22**, 655–665.

STEINBERG, B. M., SMITH, K., COLLOZO, M. & POLLACK, R. (1980). Establishment and transformation diminish the ability of fibroblasts to contract a native collagen gel. *J. Cell Biol.* **87**, 304–308.

STOPAK, D. & HARRIS, A. K. (1982). Connective tissue morphogenesis by fibroblast traction. I. Tissue culture observations. *Devl Biol.* **90**, 383–398.

STOPAK, D., WESSELLS, N. K. & HARRIS, A. K. (1985). Morphogenetic rearrangement of injected collagen in developing chicken limb buds. *Proc. natn. Acad. Sci. U.S.A.* **82**, 2804–2808.

THOM, R. (1975). *Structural Stability and Morphogenesis: An Outline of a General Theory of Models*. Reading, Mass.: W. A. Benjamin.

THOMA, R. (1893). *Untersuchungen uber die Histogenese und Histomechanik des Gefasssystems*. Stuttgart: Verlag Ferdinand Enke.

THOMPSON, D'A. W. (1942). *On Growth and Form*. Cambridge University Press.

WILSON, H. V. (1908). On some phenomena of coalescence and regeneration in sponges. *J. exp. Zool.* **5**, 245–258.

WEISSENFELS, N. (1981). Bau und Funktion des susswasserschwamms Ephydatia fluviatilis L. (Porifera). VIII. Die Entstehung und Entwicklung der Kragengeisselkammern und ihre Verbindung mit dem ausfuhrenden Kanalsystem. *Zoomorphologie* **98**, 35–45.

J. Cell Sci. Suppl. 8, 141–163 (1987)

QUALITATIVE AND QUANTITATIVE ANALYSIS OF TUMOUR INVASION *IN VIVO* AND *IN VITRO*

MARC M. MAREEL[1,*], FRANS M. VAN ROY[2], LUDWINE M. MESSIAEN[1], ERWIN R. BOGHAERT[1] AND ERIK A. BRUYNEEL[1]

[1]*Laboratory of Experimental Cancerology, Department of Radiotherapy and Nuclear Medicine, University Hospital* and [2]*Laboratory of Molecular Biology (F.M.V.R.), State University Ghent, B-9000 Ghent, Belgium*

SUMMARY

Qualitative and quantitative methods for the analysis of invasion in 'natural' and in experimental tumours *in vivo* and *in vitro* are reviewed. In human tumours the functional consequences of invasion were evaluated histologically through staging on the basis of depths of invasion and through the presence of tumour cells inside vessels. Antibodies against components of the basement membrane have facilitated the definition of minimal invasion. With new probes derived from oncogene research the search for molecular differences between invasive and non-invasive parts of the tumour has begun. Since the same methods as those used for analysis of natural tumours also apply to experimental tumours *in vivo*, the major advantage of the latter is the possibility of manipulation. We have described a new mesenterium assay that may permit the selection of invasive cells from non-invasive ones in transfection experiments. Invasion relative to growth as a function of time was quantified in the kidney invasion test. In three-dimensional confrontations between embryonic chick heart fragments and invasive cells, we have used both a subjective grading and a qualitative computer-assisted image analysis of serial histological sections to score invasion. In two-dimensional confrontations supplementary methods could be applied, since such confrontations permitted direct observations on living cultures. In a variety of natural and experimental tumours, ultrastructural analysis, transmigration in two-compartment chambers, and release of metabolic label have demonstrated the role of motility and of lytic activity in tumour invasion.

INTRODUCTION

Abercrombie & Heaysman (1976) published an analysis of invasion *in vitro*. This paper contains most of the elements and caveats of invasion analysis. 'A tumour–host complex': explants of sarcoma cells were put next to explants of chick heart cells and the confronting populations were studied before and after junction. 'Controls': to check the tumour specificity of the sarcoma behaviour, two populations of non-malignant cells were confronted. 'Readability': coverslip cultures permitted direct observation under the microscope. 'Complementary methods of analysis': filming was used with its specific advantages and limitations, and so was analysis of fixed cultures, both methods giving complementary information. 'Artifacts': safeguards were provided to avoid false images of invasion, in this case, cells released from one explant, floating through the medium, and settling onto the other explant. 'Quantification': measurements of intercellular distances and counts of cells were

* Author for correspondence.

made and treated for statistical purposes. 'Caution against generalization': three types of sarcoma were included in the experiments, showing great variability in their invasive behaviour and possibly using multiple mechanisms that were considered to be not mutually exclusive. 'Relevance': because of the artificial character of the host and of the experimental situation *per se*, the invasive behaviour *in vitro* of the three types of sarcoma cells was compared with their local destruction and the formation of metastasis after injection into syngeneic mice.

Ten years later, we discuss how qualitative and quantitative analysis of invasion in both 'natural' human tumours and in experimental tumours *in vivo* and *in vitro* has advanced, and how our concepts about tumour-invasion mechanisms have evolved. We shall concentrate on the value of the methods of analysis more than on the relevance of the experimental techniques. For previous reviews the reader is referred to Poste (1982), Mareel (1983), Easty & Easty (1984) and Mareel *et al.* (1986).

HUMAN TUMOURS

Limited possibilities for the manipulation of human tumours and the relatively poor readability of biopsy specimens have led to the development of experimental assays of invasion. Despite these limitations, however, valuable information has been gained from careful morphological and biochemical analyses of human tumours by old and new methods.

Staging

Invasion is routinely mentioned in the protocol of the surgical pathologist and interpreted by the clinical oncologist as a hallmark of tumour malignancy. More detailed analyses through staging of a series of tumours were made to serve prognosis, to evaluate clinical therapeutic trials, and to decide about safe but minimally mutilating treatment. Using 'spot' roentgenograms Gold *et al.* (1972) distinguished between slightly and highly invasive mammary carcinomas and found a worse prognosis for the latter, regardless of the size of the tumour. Carcinomas of the uterine cervix that had invaded less than 3 mm beneath the basement membrane, as judged from histological sections, were safely treated by limited resection, whereas invasion up to the 5 mm level necessitated more extensive surgery (Leman *et al.* 1976; Hasumi *et al.* 1980). With invasion deeper than 5 mm, nodal metastases were found and their number increased with depth of invasion, worsening the prognosis (Inoue, 1984). Histopathological staging of malignant tumours has been based primarily on their depth of invasion. For epithelial tumours the disposition of various layers of tissues in the invaded organ served as landmarks for the depth of invasion. Examples are shown in Fig. 1. The six levels of invasion used for bladder cancer as compared to the three levels of invasion used for colorectal cancer suggest that the consequences of the depth of invasion *per se* for tumour progression are different for different organs. For mesenchymal tumours the above mentioned landmarks do not exist, so that staging on the basis of depth of invasion remains difficult (for

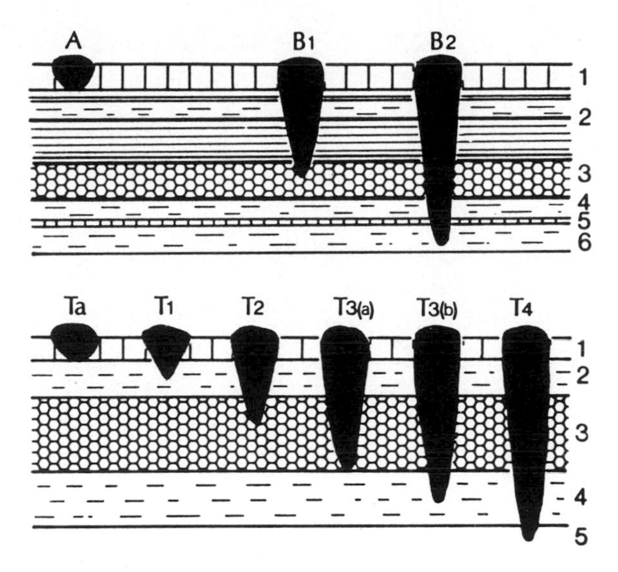

Fig. 1. Staging of carcinomas according to their depth of invasion. Top: colorectal carcinoma; modification of Dukes' (1932) original staging. 1, Mucosa; 2, lamina propria, muscularis mucosae and submucosa; 3, muscularis propria; 4, subserosa; 5, serosa; 6, perirectal tissue. Bottom: urinary bladder carcinoma; modification of Jewett & Strong's (1946) original classification. 1, Epithelium; 2, lamina propria; 3, muscularis; 4, perivesical tissue; 5, prostate or other extravesical structures. Schematic drawings modified after UICC TNM-Atlas (ed. B. Spiessl, O. Scheibe & G. Wagner), Springer-Verlag, Berlin, Heidelberg, New York (1982).

discussion, see Willis, 1960; Galli, 1984). As a consequence, prognosis is uncertain, and malignancy has to be evaluated from the clinical course of the disease.

Invasion into specific structures

Invasion of tumour cells into lymph vessels and blood vessels (intravasation) is the first step in the metastatic cascade (Poste *et al.* 1980), although this step is not sufficient for metastasis (Tarin *et al.* 1984). Histopathological evidence of invasion of the vasculature has been associated with a worse prognosis in a number of carcinomas (Van Nagell *et al.* 1978; Talbot *et al.* 1981; Weigand *et al.* 1982; Hanson *et al.* 1985). Factors influencing correlations between histological analysis and prognosis were the stringency of the definition of vessel invasion and the interpretation of histological changes in the vasculature in terms of loss of their transport function. The latter illustrates, again, the difficulty in interpreting static histological pictures in functional terms.

Minimal invasion

Transition of a neoplasm from the non-invasive to the invasive state is a crucial phase in tumour progression both clinically and biologically. When epithelial tumours start to invade, they have to cross or to push forward their basement membrane. Using sera from patients with bullous pemphigoid and indirect immunofluorescence, Rubio & Biberfeld (1975) demonstrated a continuous basement membrane in normal cervical epithelium, in dysplasia and carcinoma *in situ*; discontinuities in the basement membrane were seen in invasive squamous carcinoma. Use of antisera against laminin, a non-collagenous basement membrane glycoprotein (Foidart *et al.* 1980), or against type IV collagen has demonstrated the presence of a defective basement membrane in invasive carcinomas of the breast (Albrechtsen *et al.* 1981), the colorectum (Burtin *et al.* 1982; Forster *et al.* 1984), the skin (Kallioinen *et al.* 1984) and the endometrium (Faber *et al.* 1986). Such changes in the immunohistochemical aspects of the basement membrane distinguished benign tumours from invasive ones and marked the early stages (*in situ* carcinoma with microinvasion) of invasion (Barsky *et al.* 1983). One exception may be the follicular carcinoma of the thyroid, where an intact laminin coverage was described around follicular carcinomas that were invasive and metastatic (Miettinen & Virtanen, 1984). The discontinuities in basement membrane laminin associated with invasive carcinomas are probably not due to loss of laminin synthesis by the carcinoma cells, since intracytoplasmic staining was observed in these cells (Albrechtsen *et al.* 1981) and since carcinoma cells cultured *in vitro* were shown to produce laminin (Foidart *et al.* 1980). An interesting possibility is that the laminin secreted by malignant cells differs structurally from that of normal cells (Ohno *et al.* 1986) and is no longer able to assemble into a continuous basement membrane. If the basement membrane serves as a scaffold for epithelial organization, abnormal assembly of the scaffold might permit migration of cells into the underlying stroma. Defective assembly of laminin and of other components of the extracellular matrix is an alternative to the commonly suggested lytic breakdown as an explanation for the creation of space for the invading cells.

Probes for invasive cells

Oncogene research (see recent review by Bishop, 1987) has provided interesting new probes for the investigation of invasion in sections from natural tumours. Thor *et al.* (1984) used a broadly active *ras*-group-specific monoclonal antibody raised against a synthetic peptide reflecting sequences of the human T24 *ras* gene product p21. Immunocytochemical analysis with this antibody of colon carcinomas showed that the majority of cells scored positive, whereas a minority of positive cells was found in benign tumours and in healthy colon mucosa. In three cases a correlation could be made between depth of invasion and *ras* p21 expression: a low number of positive cells in normal mucosa, intermediate numbers in superficially invasive and high numbers in deeply invasive carcinomas. Similar immunohistochemical studies on human prostatic and gastric carcinomas yielded a good correlation between *ras* oncogene expression, increased tumour grading and bad prognosis (Viola *et al.* 1986; Tahara *et al.* 1986). Gallick *et al.* (1985) analysed lyophilized tissue extracts using another broadly active *ras*-specific antibody with immunoblotting and immunoprecipitation techniques. They were not able to demonstrate a correlation between various stages of colon carcinoma (see Fig. 1) and the ratio of *ras* p21 in tumour over adjacent normal tissue. Using DNA-mediated gene transfer Fujita *et al.* (1984)

found no apparent correlation between the degree of invasiveness and the presence of an active Ha-*ras* oncogene in urinary tract tumours. The discrepancy in the conclusions from these studies may be due either to the different methods for probing the oncogene and the oncogene product or to inherent biological variations in the expression or activation of oncogenes in various tumours, even if of similar origin. The problem of oncogene implication in tumour invasion is a matter of debate (see review by Mareel & Van Roy, 1986); further investigations on human tumour biopsies with more appropriate probes and with new methods of distinguishing between actively invading and resting cells are warranted.

The present review of some methods for the analysis of invasion in human tumours is intended to show that, whenever material from the natural situation can solve our problem, we should avoid turning exclusively to experimental assays.

EXPERIMENTAL TUMOURS *IN VIVO*

The invasive capabilities of cell populations have been investigated through transplantation into syngeneic or immunodeficient animals in various ways distinguished by the organization and volume of the inoculum used and by the injection sites (Mareel *et al.* 1987). The latter is worth consideration, since clearcut differences in invasiveness of cells from the same stock injected at different sites have been reported from various laboratories (Gao *et al.* 1984; Cajot *et al.* 1986; Walsh *et al.* 1986). For the majority of the experimental tumours the methods used to score invasion can also be applied to natural tumours, so that the only advantage of experimental tumours is that they are amenable to manipulation.

A new mesenterium assay

In combination with transfection experiments (Van Roy *et al.* 1986; Mareel & Van Roy, 1986), we needed an assay to select a minority of invasive cells from a population of mostly non-invasive cells. Therefore, we had to confront the cells with a tissue or an artificial substrate that retained the invasive cells but not the others and that permitted retrieval of the invasive cells. For bacterial invasion, Isberg & Falkow (1985) had solved the problem as follows. Mixtures of non-invasive (*Escherichia coli*) and invasive (*E. coli* infected with chromosomal DNA from *Yersinia pseudotuberculosis*) bacteria were seeded on monolayers of H.Ep.2 cells. After binding and entry of invasive bacteria, the monolayers were washed and incubated with gentamicin. This antibiotic was unable to penetrate into the cells and, therefore, selectively killed bacteria that had not invaded.

Attempts with various assays *in vitro* failed to isolate invasive mammalian cells, at least in our hands (Mareel & Van Roy, 1986; see also Poste *et al.* 1980). For isolation *in vivo*, we needed a rapid test that did not implicate expansion of the cell population before retrieval. Long-term passage *in vivo*, as needed for tumour formation, *per se* may lead to acquisition of invasiveness (De Baetselier *et al.* 1984; Cuzin *et al.* 1985; Van Roy *et al.* 1986; our unpublished results with four other cell families). Data from the literature (Buck, 1973; Sträuli *et al.* 1983; Müller-Glauser *et al.* 1985) indicated that, after intraperitoneal (i.p.) injection, invasive cells entered into the mesenterium within a few days. We, therefore, tested whether an invasive subpopulation could be retrieved from the mesenterium, using our low invasive (Rat2/800 C6) and highly invasive (Rat2TD2A) derivatives of the thymidine kinase-deficient Fischer rat cell line Rat2 (Topp, 1981). Colony-forming efficiencies on tissue culture plastic were similar for Rat2/800 C6 and for Rat2TD2A cells. After i.p. injection both types of cells produced tumours invading the mesenterium (Fig. 2) as well as other abdominal organs, with marked differences in survival time; about 28 days for Rat2TD2A cells; about 100 days for Rat2/800 C6 cells. In the chick heart organ culture assay, described below, RAT2TD2A cells were invasive, whereas Rat2/800 C6 cells were not invasive. However, testing 10 other Rat2/800 clones showed one clone to have become invasive, suggesting some phenotype instability in Rat2 derivatives in agreement with the results *in vivo*. Because of their thymidine kinase deficiency, both cell types could be selected from mesenterial cells through culturing in the presence of bromodeoxyuridine (BrdUrd; $100\,\mu g\,ml^{-1}$). Since Rat2/800 C6 cells were transfected with a plasmid encoding resistance to genetecin, they could be selected from Rat2TD2A cells and from mesenterial cells through culture in presence of this antibiotic (G418; $600\,\mu g\,ml^{-1}$). Obviously, when the reliability of the assay has been established, a simple selection marker will be sufficient.

Preliminary experiments resulted in the following protocol. A total of 2×10^6 cells suspended in 0·2 ml serum-free culture medium were injected i.p. into syngeneic rats. After 2–4 days, pieces of mesenterium were dissected from the abdomen under sterile conditions, washed consecutively in culture medium containing 2500 i.u.

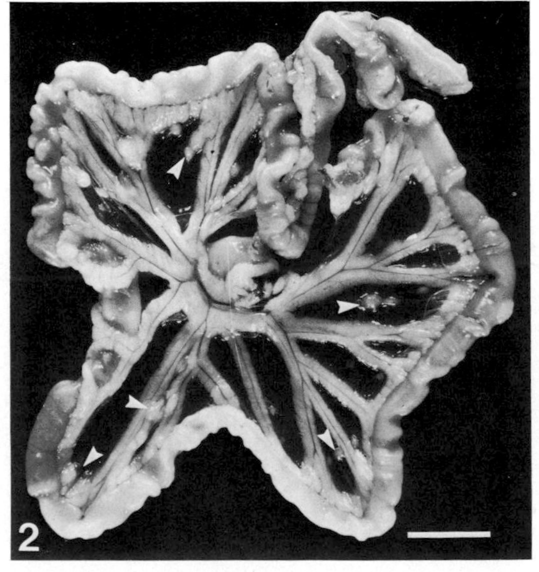

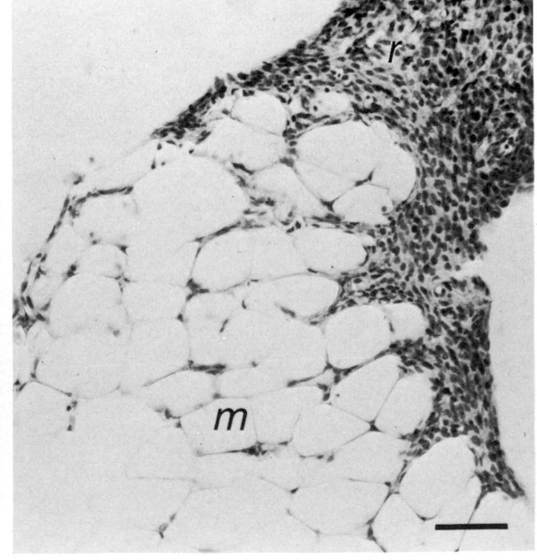

Fig. 2. Macrograph (left) and micrograph (right) of Rat2TD2A nodules (arrowheads and *r*) in the mesenterium (*m*) of a Fischer rat killed 15 days after i.p. injection of 2×10^6 cells. Bars: 10 mm (left), 50 μm (right).

penicillin and 1000 μg streptomycin ml^{-1}, and in Moscona's solution, and then incubated for about 30 min at 37 °C with 10 ml trypsin (0·25 % in Moscona's solution) whilst stirring. Cell suspensions were centrifuged, resuspended in 2×5 ml culture medium and seeded onto 25 cm^2 tissue culture plastic substrata with either 100 μg ml^{-1} BrdUrd or 600 μg ml^{-1} G418. Cultures were fixed and stained after about 2 weeks for counting the number of colonies. Results of three experiments with varying ratios of coinjected Rat2TD2A and Rat2/800 C6 cells are shown in Table 1. The high invasive Rat2TD2A cells scored higher in this assay than the low invasive Rat2/800 C6 cells in all but one culture. Two problems remain to be solved. First, there were large variations in the absolute numbers of colonies cultured from individual animals. This was most probably due to variations in dissociation of the mesenteria during trypsinization, and to variations in the size and origin of the mesenterial pieces. We are trying to solve this problem by dissociation to completion using other enzyme mixtures, and by dissection of the whole mesenterium, including the pancreatic region where invasion is most frequently seen. Second, cells cultured after dissociation of the mesenterium may either have invaded into, or have attached to, the mesothelial basement membrane. Observations *in vivo* with human and experimental tumours (Kiyasu *et al.* 1981; Sträuli *et al.* 1983; Parsons *et al.* 1983; Kimura *et al.* 1985) and *in vitro* (Niedbala *et al.* 1985) showed that retraction of mesothelial cells preceded attachment of injected cells to the submesothelial layers. Afterwards invasive cells rapidly proceeded by translocation of single cells into the inner mesenterial layers, or slowly, by expansion of surface nodules. Retraction of mesothelial cells was not caused specifically by invading graft cells, since it also occurred after injection of cell-free media (Kimura *et al.* 1985). We can, therefore, not exclude the possibility that invasive cells as well as non-invasive ones will attach to the mesenterium after i.p. injection. We are now searching for a treatment that, like gentamicin in the experiments with bacteria (Isberg & Falkow, 1985), eliminates attached cells whilst preserving cells that have invaded into the inner layers of the mesenterium. Provided the above mentioned problems are solved, the mesenterium

Table 1. *Retrieval of low invasive Rat2/800 C6 and of highly invasive Rat2TD2A cells from the mesenterium after i.p. injection of a total number of 2×10⁶ cells into syngeneic Fischer rats*

Time after injection (days)		Number of colonies (n/n)*		
	Ratio coinjected Rat2TD2A:Rat2/800 C6:	1:1	1:10	1:100
2		1/0;21/0;0/0	n.d.;6/0;8/0	n.d.;n.d.;0/0
3		0/0;73/1;4/0	9/0;2/0;2/0	1/0;3/0;0/6
4		n.d.;n.d.;20/0	n.d.;n.d.;46/0	n.d.;n.d.;53/10

* Number of Rat2TD2A colonies plus Rat2/800 C6 colonies (resistant to BrdUrd) over number of Rat2/800 C6 (resistant to G418) in three separate experiments.
n.d., not determined.

assay, as well as its use for selection in transfection experiments, might determine the proportion of invasive cells in heterogeneous populations and the speed of invasion of particular cell types into the mesenterium.

The kidney invasion test

Numerical macroscopic evaluation of invasion was carried out by Distelmans *et al.* (1985) and by Boghaert *et al.* (1987) using the kidney invasion test (KIT), a test derived from the subrenal capsule assay. Tumour fragments or cells aggregated on collagen sponge were implanted under the renal capsule of syngeneic mice. After various periods of incubation the kidney was removed, hemi-sectioned and the total tumour thickness (T) and the invasive part (I) were measured. I was the thickness of the part of the tumour that extended beyond the extrapolated upper renal margin. Considering the possibility that tumour growth influenced invasion either directly or indirectly, the invasion rate (I_r) was calculated as $I_r = I/T \times 100$. The necessity to control macroscopic findings by histology was illustrated by a benign tumour where I, as determined macroscopically, was due to expansive growth rather than to invasion (Fig. 3). A study of I_r as a function of time with invasive MO_4 cell implants showed that invasion and growth followed different courses (Fig. 4). From histology, the interpretation of the I_r curve was as follows. In the first phase the rate of invasion into the parenchyma exceeded growth towards the periphery of the kidney, resulting in a rapid increase of I_r. In the second phase the growth of the tumour into the renal parenchyma and its growth towards the periphery had equal speeds, leading to a flattening of the curve. Finally, rapid peripheral growth of the tumour dominated, resulting in a downward slope of the parabola. Comparison of three other invasive cell types in the KIT (Mareel *et al.* 1987) showed clear-cut differences in the shape of their I_r curves, so that the KIT results with the expression of I_r as a function of time may permit the characterization *in vivo* of the invasiveness of cell lines. I_r curves showed the complex relationship between tumour growth and invasion. We have shown (Mareel, 1982) that, at least *in vitro*, invasion can occur in the absence of cell proliferation. On the other hand, it is hardly conceivable that the multiplication of cells that have invaded would be without an effect on invasion, be it only as an increased amount of space required to harbour the daughter cells.

Fig. 3. Photomicrographs of haematoxylin and eosin-stained sections from mouse kidneys that received implants of Rat11P cells (A), of EL4 cells (B), and of MO_4 cells (C), under their capsula (*c*). Lines along which invasion (*i*), and total tumour thickness (*t*) were measured to calculate the invasion rate ($I_r = I/T \times 100$) are shown in the left-hand photographs. At the right-hand side, details (boxed in) of the frontier between the tumour and the renal parenchyma (*r*) are shown. Mice were killed after 16 days (A), 14 days (B), and 13 days (C). Rat11P cells are from a subcloned cell line originally established from an RIIIMMTV-induced Balb/c mouse mammary tumour (Sonnenberg *et al.* 1986); they do not invade into the renal parenchyma but show expansive growth. MO_4 cells are derived from an immortalized C3H mouse cell line after transformation with Kirsten-MSV (Billiau *et al.* 1973); they are invasive. EL4 cells are derived from a chemically induced mouse lymphoma (ATCC TIB 39); they grow under the renal capsule, but do not invade. Bars: 300 μm (left), 50 μm (right).

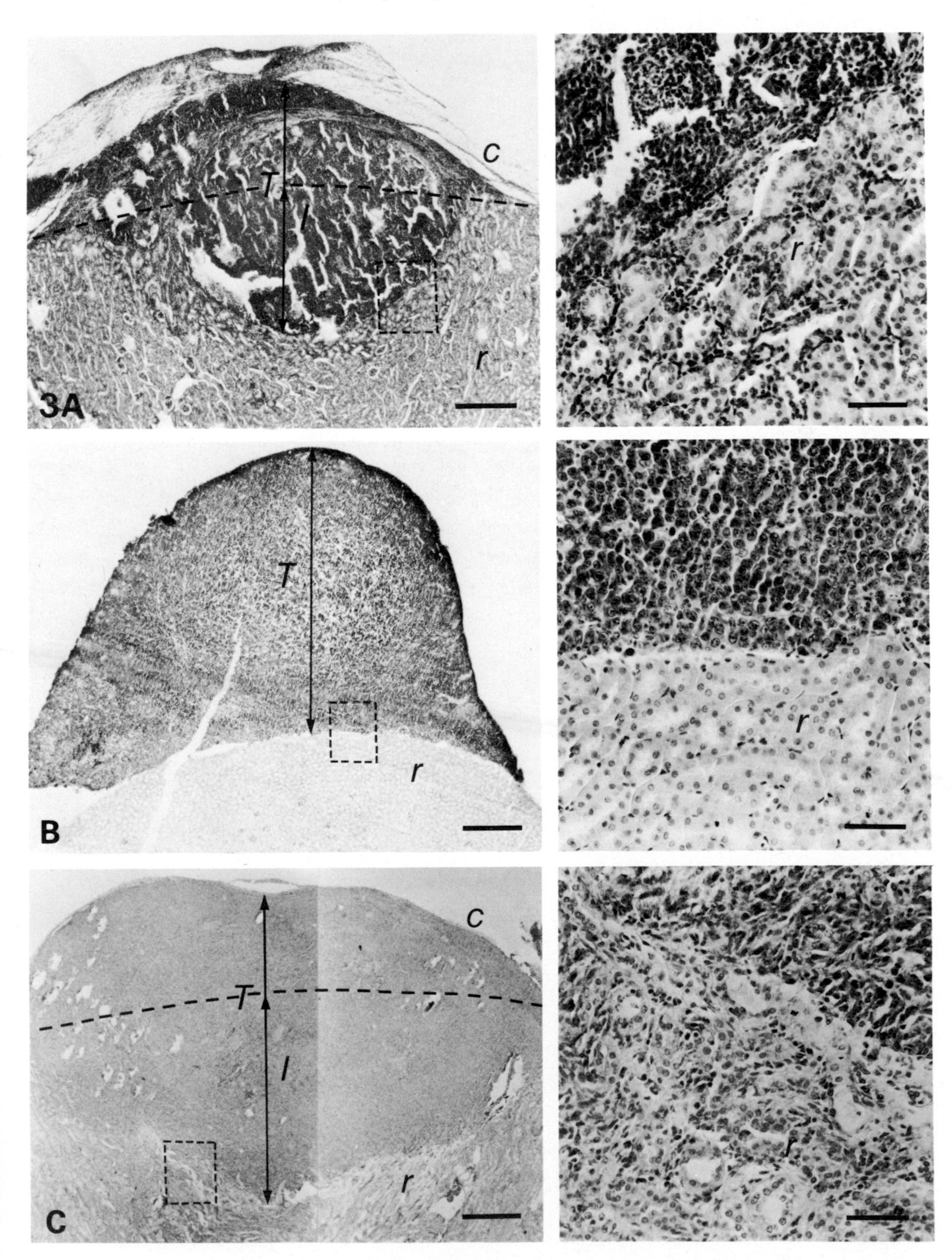

3A
c
T
I
r
r
B
T
r
r
C
c
T
I
r
r

Variations in the mode of invasion

Several authors (e.g. see Easty & Easty, 1974; Walsh *et al.* 1986; Bjerkvig *et al.* 1986) have called attention to differences in the mode of invasion (Fig. 5). Natural landmarks for measuring the depth of invasion are frequently missing, when cell suspensions are injected into animals. In this case, remnants of host tissue between the invasive part of the tumour will influence our decision about qualitative and

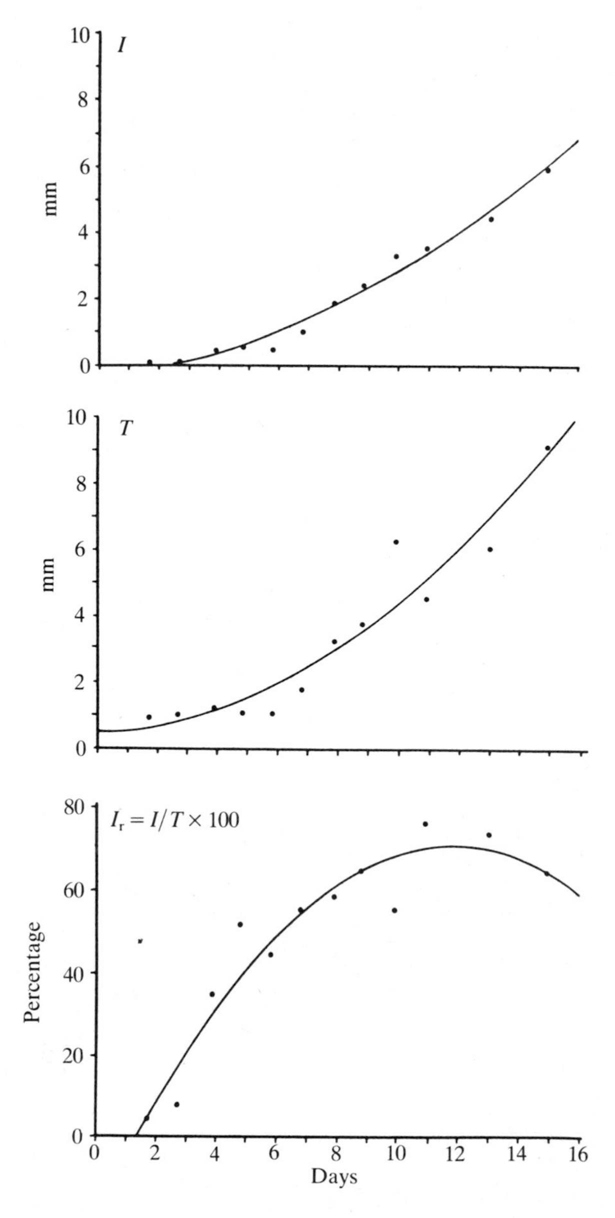

Fig. 4. Examples of invasion (I), total tumour thickness (T), and invasion rate ($I_r = I/T \times 100$) plotted in function of time after implantation of MO_4 cells under the renal capsule of syngeneic C3H mice.

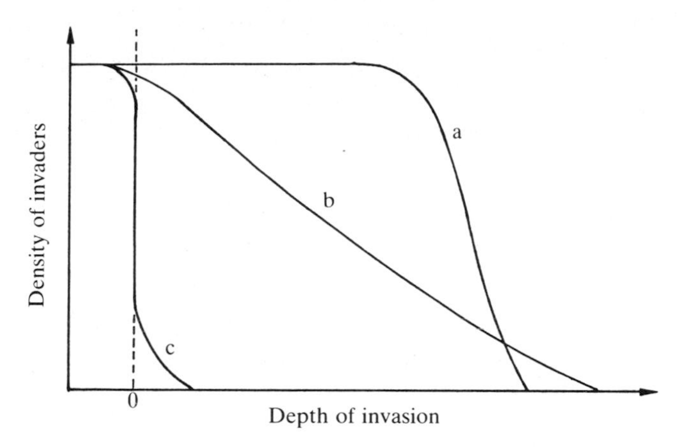

Fig. 5. Theoretical curves showing the relationship between depth of invasion (abscissa) and number of invaded cells per unit area (ordinate): diffuse or solitary invasion (curve a), regional or massive invasion (curve b), minimal invasion (curve c). The broken vertical line is the extrapolated frontier between the original tumour and the normal tissue. Modified from Easty & Easty (1974), and from Walsh *et al.* (1986).

quantitative aspects of invasion. Invasion by solitary cells, without extensive proliferation of the invaders (also called 'diffuse' invasion) will leave large amounts of host tissue, so that estimation of the depth of invasion will be relatively easy. In case of the progression of a broad front of invasion accompanied by progressive replacement of the invaded tissue (also called 'massive' or 'regional' invasion), the depth of invasion will be difficult to evaluate and, sometimes, the distinction between expansive growth and massive invasion will be difficult. Suh & Weiss (1984) have published an interesting example of a kinetic reconstruction based on static pictures from routine pathology specimens to discriminate between expansive growth and active cell movement in invasion. These authors made 'density maps' of an invasive cutaneous melanoma. An abrupt transition from 'saturation density' to 'zero' was consistent with expansive growth; a gradual transition was consistent with invasion by active movement.

OBSERVATIONS *IN VITRO*

Most assays for invasion *in vitro* consist of confrontations of potentially invasive cells with normal cells or tissues. When considering methods of analysis two groups of assays have to be distinguished. Three-dimensional confrontations were analysed mainly by the same methods as natural tumours, namely histology and electron microscopy (for review, see Mareel, 1982); the main advantage of such assays is the possibility of manipulating the process of invasion (e.g. see Bracke *et al.* 1986; Bolscher *et al.* 1986) and not improved possibilities for analysis. Two-dimensional confrontations, such as the one described in the Introduction, have allowed direct observations, for example by time-lapse cinematography. It should be noted that three-dimensional confrontations mimic the natural situation more closely than two-dimensional confrontations, and, therefore, may be more relevant to invasion *in vivo*.

Three-dimensional confrontations

Invasive cells have been confronted with fragments of normal tissues from various origins in various culture systems (e.g. see Mareel, 1983). Most methods of analysis in these assays were not quantitative, although attempts were made to obtain rankings of invasion on the basis of subjective observations. For example, Schleich *et al.* (1976) classified invasion of cells into fragments of human decidua graviditatis in organ culture as absent (−), questionable (±), detectable (+), moderate (++) and intense (+++).

We have scored invasion in confrontations of cells with fragments of embryonic chick heart in organ culture using consecutive serial histological sections stained with haematoxylin/eosin, or with an antiserum against chick heart (Mareel *et al.* 1981). All sections from each culture were examined by at least two independent observers and invasion was scored on the basis of occupation and/or replacement of the heart tissue by the confronting cells according to a grading system (Fig. 6). This subjective score was kept relatively crude, because further refinement led to frequent disagreement between different experienced observers. As staging of natural tumours served prognosis and planning of treatment, so our grading of invasion *in vitro* served the purpose of a number of investigations, including the search for anti-invasive agents (Mareel & De Mets, 1984) and for genes implicated in invasion (Mareel & Van Roy, 1986; Van Roy *et al.* 1986). The same grading system permitted an estimation of the rate of invasion by examination of a number of cultures after various periods of incubation. For example, when malignant MO_4 mouse cells were confronted with chick heart at 28 °C instead of 37 °C, invasion was arrested for about 10 days. Later, invasion started and we gained the impression that the rate of this delayed form of invasion was the same as at 37 °C where invasion started after the first day. This impression was confirmed by plotting relative numbers of cultures with distinct grades of invasion as a function of time (Fig. 7).

Fig. 6. Illustration of subjective grades of invasion through photomicrographs of sections from confrontations of embryonic chick heart (*h*) with MCF-7 human mammary carcinoma cells (A), with Rat2/800 C8 Fischer rat cells (B), with HBL-100 human breast cells (C), and with FR-BPV1-TD3 Fischer rat cells (D). Confronting pairs were fixed after 4 days (D), 7 days (A and C), and 14 days (B). Sections were stained with haematoxylin/eosin (left column) and with an antiserum against chick heart (right column). Grade 0 (not illustrated): no confronting cells were left; grade I (A): confronting cells surrounded the heart fragment with a thin layer of fibroblastic cells (arrowhead) separating them from the core of cardiac muscle (*h*); grade II (B): confronting cells surrounded the heart fragment and were apposed to the cardiac muscle (*h*); grade III (C): confronting cells occupied and/or replaced less than half of the heart tissue (*h*); grade IV (D): confronting cells occupied and/or replaced more than half of the heart tissue (*h*). Grading was scored after examination of all sections, whereas photomicrographs show two consecutive representative sections. Grades III and IV are typical of cells that proved to be invasive *in vivo*. Bars, 50 μm.

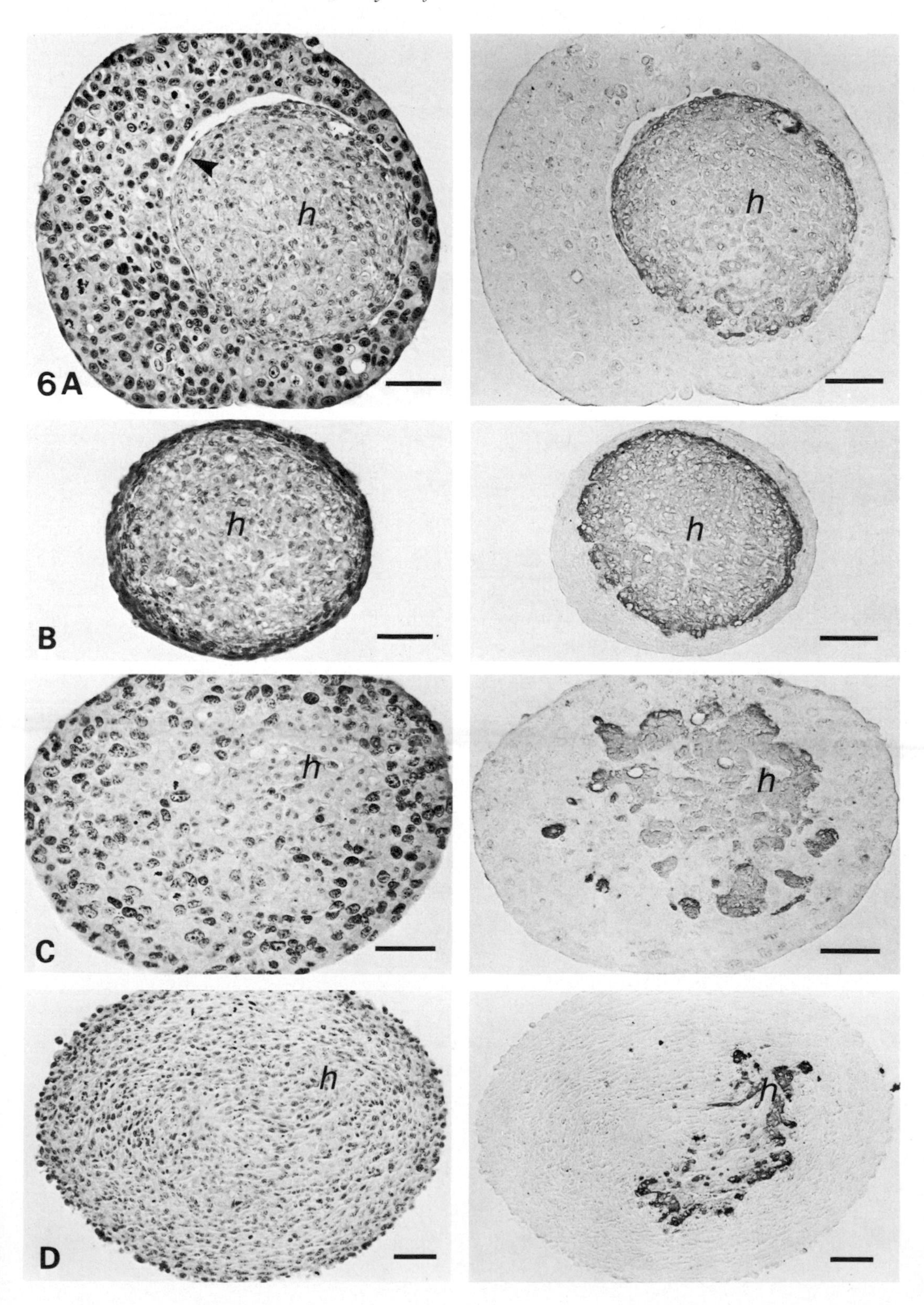
h
6A
h
h
B
h
h
C
h
h
D
h

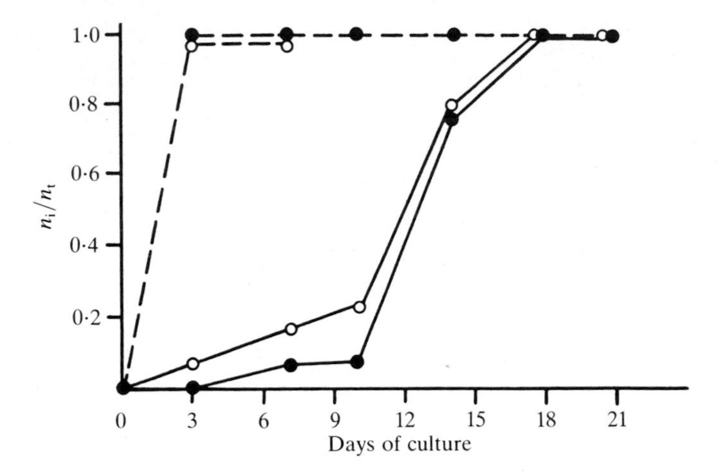

Fig. 7. Invasion of parental (○) and of cloned (●) malignant MO_4 mouse cells into embryonic chick heart in organ culture at 37 °C (---) and at 28 °C (——). Ordinate, number of cultures showing at least grade III over total number examined.

Computer-assisted image analysis was used to quantify the invasion of MO_4 cells in the chick heart assay (De Neve *et al.* 1985). The question was asked how progressive occupation of the heart tissue by MO_4 cells and how progressive degeneration of the heart tissue would be revealed by individual histological sections. The reasoning was that the disposition of MO_4 cells and heart tissue had a high probability of representing progressive occupation when: (1) the border between the MO_4 cell population and the heart tissue was irregular; (2) strands of MO_4 cells indented the heart tissue; (3) islands of MO_4 cells or single MO_4 cells were present inside the heart tissue; (4) these three features became more obvious with increasing time of incubation. On the basis of this reasoning, occupation was measured through the length of lines, parallel to the direction of invasion, connecting MO_4 cell areas or not (for details, see De Neve *et al.* 1985). Summation for all sections resulted in an index of occupation (*Occ*). Measurement of the amount of immunoreactive heart material in comparison with the amount at the onset of confrontation resulted in a ratio of degeneration (*D*). A complex combination of occupation and degeneration ($I = Occ + D$) resulted in a qualitative aspect of invasion, that was unique in as much as it was based on quantitative data. Fig. 8 shows an example of two types of invasion. During MO_4 cell invasion, occupation and degeneration occurred together; during *ras*-transfected Rat2 cell invasion, occupation preceded degeneration, the latter being minimal at the end of the period of observation. Expression of a complex process such as invasion according to two crude phenotypic aspects illustrates that our conclusions are to a large extent determined by our methods of analysis.

To avoid time-consuming histology, Waller *et al.* (1986) suggested quantifying invasion by measuring the number of radioactively labelled cells trapped on fragments of normal tissue in suspension culture. This assay measured one step of invasion, namely attachment of cells to normal tissue, but provided no information about further steps that might be more invasion-specific than attachment.

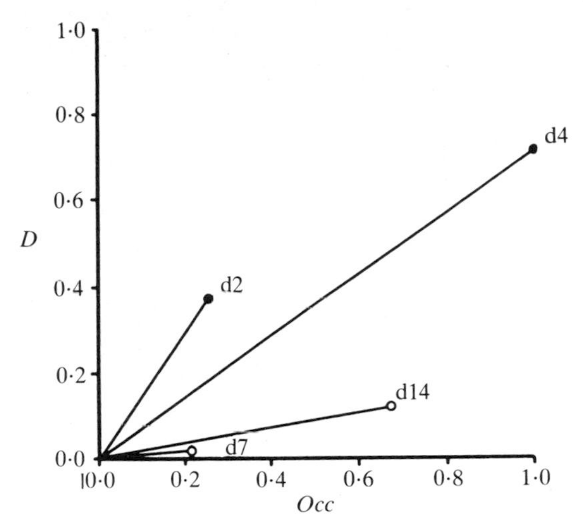

Fig. 8. Graphic representation on the basis of computer-assisted image analysis of invasion of MO_4 mouse cells (●) and of *ras*-transfected Rat2 cells (○) into embryonic chick heart in culture after 2 and 4 days (d2, d4) and after 7 and 14 days (d7, d14). Ordinate, ratio of degeneration (*D*); abscissa, index of occupation (*Occ*).

Two-dimensional confrontations

Time-lapse cinematography has been carried out with lateral confrontations of invasive cells and non-invasive cells (Abercrombie & Heaysman, 1976; Easty *et al.* 1982), with cells seeded on monolayers or on cell-free substrata coated with components of the extracellular matrix (Zamora *et al.* 1980), and with cells invading into thin membranous tissues (Sträuli *et al.* 1981). These observations strongly suggested a rôle in invasion for cell motility, including on the spot pseudopodial activity as well as translocation (for review, see Haëmmerli, 1986). Recent observations in our laboratory (P. Coopman, personal communication) suggested that a detailed analysis of the pseudopodial activity of cells encountering laterally components of the extracellular matrix may be relevant for their invasiveness or non-invasiveness.

Quantitative analysis of invasion of MB6A lymphosarcoma cells and of TA3 mammary carcinoma cells into hepatocyte monolayers was carried out by Roos & Van de Pavert (1982) and by Middelkoop *et al.* (1982) using thin sections from fixed cultures. They counted: (1) cells in contact with hepatocytes (interacting tumour cells); (2) cells completely surrounded by hepatocytes (infiltrated tumour cells); and (3) cells that invaginated hepatocytes but were not completely surrounded. The final score expressed various ratios between these numbers of cells. A more direct method used combined differential interference contrast and interference reflection microscopy to follow the relative vertical positions of lymphoma cells seeded onto monolayers of 10 T1/2 fibroblastic mouse embryo cells (Verschueren *et al.* 1987). The number of lymphoma cells underlying unit areas of 10 T1/2 cells was used as a quantitative index of invasion. Apart from measuring invasion the method was able to select a minority of invasive cells from a large population of non-invasive cells. One limitation is, however, that this method might be applicable only to leucocytes (H. Verschueren, personal communication; our unpublished results). Another method for quantifying invasion of cells into monolayers was suggested by Elvin *et al.* (1985). The functional integrity of an MDCK cell monolayer was monitored by measuring the transepithelial resistance with an adapted voltage clamp device. Changes in the resistance after addition of invasive cells were used as an index of the extent of monolayer disruption. We have not been able to repeat these experiments because none of our invasive cells tested was able to attach to or to penetrate into confluent monolayers of the MDCK cells available in our laboratory. In lateral confrontations of sheets of human head and neck cancer cells, explanted in a central hole made in a sheet of normal buccal mucosa, measurements of areas covered by the two partners and of the cell-free space between them resulted in a quantitative estimation of two phenomena possibly related to invasion: (1) inhibition of inward migration of normal cells representing wound healing; (2) retraction of the inner edge of the normal epithelium upon contact with the cancer cells (Easty *et al.* 1982).

Ultrastructural analysis

In both two-, and three-dimensional assays, scanning electron microscopy (Sträuli *et al.* 1981; Gao *et al.* 1982; Kramer *et al.* 1982; Roos & Van de Pavert, 1982; Wang & Nicolson, 1983; Steinsvag, 1985; Paku *et al.* 1986), transmission electron microscopy (Maignan, 1979; Nicolson, 1982; Bogenman *et al.* 1983; Bjerkvig *et al.* 1986) and high-voltage electron microscopy (Parsons *et al.* 1982; Sacks *et al.* 1984) were used for the analysis of invasion. It should be noted that these methods of analysis were also applied to human (McNutt, 1976; Genadry *et al.* 1978) and to experimental (Dingemans *et al.* 1978; Carr *et al.* 1980; De Bruyn & Cho, 1982; Crissman *et al.* 1985) tumours *in vivo*. Most of these observations have concentrated on the multifarious extensions produced by invasive cells penetrating into the normal tissue, and on the interactions of these extensions with the extracellular matrix. Amongst these investigations we found only one attempt to quantify the lamellar activity of invasive cells. Using scanning electron micrographs, Steinsvag (1985) calculated the size of cellular processes, dividing their square length by the diameter of their neck, and called this value the lamellar index. Lamellar index ratios expressed differences between the indices for processes pointing towards the normal tissue and for those pointing towards other malignant cells. The experiments of Steinsvag (1985), with brain tumour cells confronting fragments of normal brain in organ culture, confirmed earlier conclusions from malignant MO_4 cells confronting chick heart fragments (Bruyneel & Mareel, 1981); namely, that the extension of processes was triggered by contact with the normal tissue. Whether these phenomena are specific for invasive cells and do not occur with confronting non-invasive cells remains to be examined.

From ultrastructural observations, Bruyneel & Mareel (1981) proposed a sequence of events during the invasion of MO_4 cells into chick heart (Fig. 9). (1) Confronting MO_4 cells attached to the outer layers of the heart fragment *via* cell surface

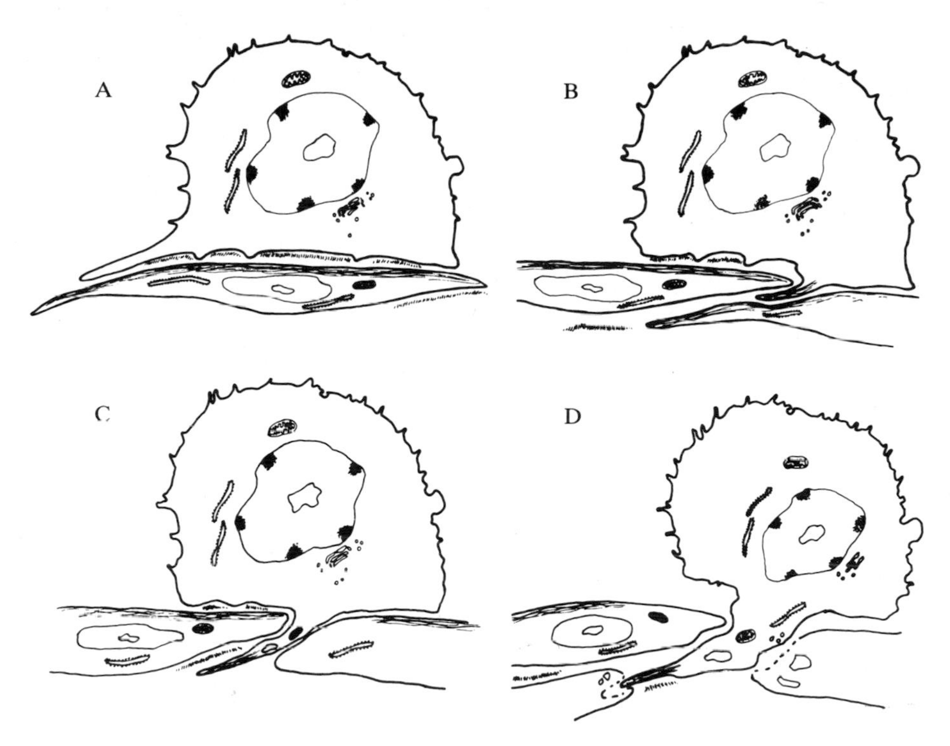

Fig. 9. Schematic drawing of the early steps of invasion of malignant MO_4 mouse cells into embryonic chick heart in organ culture. A. Attachment; B, anchorage; C, penetration; D, destruction. Reproduced from Bruyneel & Mareel (1981) with permission.

glycoproteins or *via* interposition of extracellular matrix components. (2) MO_4 cells extended cytoplasmic processes that anchored between peripheral cells of the heart fragment. (3) Penetration by larger parts of the cytoplasm followed anchorage. (4) Finally, degenerative alterations of the heart tissue were interpreted as destruction by invasive cells. Using a series of manipulations we were able to arrest the process after each of the first two steps, but not after the third one. In Liotta's three-step hypothesis (Liotta, 1986), based on both ultrastructural and biochemical analysis, steps three and four have been reversed. (1) Attachment is mediated by laminin (or other attachment factors) forming a bridge between the cell surface laminin receptor and type IV collagen. (2) Tumour cell-associated proteases cause local degradation of the matrix and the attachment factors. (3) Tumour cells locomote into the area of modified extracellular matrix, probably under the influence of chemotactic factors. Liotta further suggested that continued invasion takes place by cyclic repetition of these three steps. The latter hypothesis sounds more realistic than the former (Bruyneel & Mareel, 1981) in three ways. (1) Locomotion follows destruction, providing space for invading cells. (2) Destruction involves the extracellular matrix earlier than the host cells. (3) Cyclic repetition of the steps accounts for the progressive character of invasion.

Transmigration in two-compartment assays

Quantitative evaluation of invasion by counting cells that had migrated through a biological membrane in a two-compartment chamber was first described by Hart & Fidler (1978), using the chick chorioallantoic membrane to separate the two compartments. The membrane that has been most frequently used in recent experiments is the denuded human amnion (Russo *et al.* 1982; Siegal *et al.* 1982; Thorgeirsson *et al.* 1984; Hendrix *et al.* 1985; Cresson *et al.* 1986; Mignatti *et al.* 1986); cells that had transmigrated were estimated from direct cell counts or from cell-associated radioactivity. In other experiments (Smith *et al.* 1985) histological analysis of cellular invasion into the amnion was used rather than cell counting. In our experience with this assay (unpublished results) histology represented a more realistic evaluation of invasion and was less subject to pitfalls than cell counts. However, histology as a method of analysis lacks quantification.

Release assays

Invasive cells have been seeded on a number of labelled substrata: ^{45}Ca-labelled mouse calvaria (Tsao *et al.* 1981), L-[^{3}H]leucine-, $^{35}SO_4$-, [^{35}S]methionine-, [^{3}H]proline-, and [^{3}H]fucose-labelled subendothelial matrix (Nicolson, 1982; Kramer *et al.* 1982; Laug *et al.* 1983), [^{3}H]proline-labelled smooth muscle cell-derived extracellular matrix (Bogenman *et al.* 1983), and ^{125}I-labelled bovine lens capsule (Starkey *et al.* 1984) amongst others. Destruction of the matrix by the confronting cells was estimated from measurements of radioactivity in the culture medium, sometimes in combination with electrophoresis of the released molecules. More such metabolic and biochemical methods, which cover particular aspects of invasion, need to be developed to improve our understanding of the molecular mechanisms of invasion.

CONCLUSION

During the last 10 years a number of new methods have been developed for the analysis of invasion. Since we are ignorant of the molecular mechanisms of tumour invasion, these methods of analysis rely on phenotypic aspects of invasion. Many of them (e.g. histology, immunocytochemistry, electron microscopy) are applicable to both human and experimental tumours, whereas others (e.g. microcinematography, metabolic labelling) are restricted to experimental situations. From multiple observations by a variety of methods the following picture of invasion has emerged. Invasive cells attach to the host tissue through interaction of cell surface exposed glycoconjugates (e.g. N-linked glycopeptides) with components of the extracellular matrix (e.g. laminin). Thin extensions, possibly dependent upon focal reorganization of the actin cytoskeleton, permit invasive cells to anchor in small intercellular spaces resulting from the retraction of host cells. Lytic factors (e.g. proteases) produced or induced by invasive cells create space for migration in the host tissue. This migration is directional, possibly involving chemotactic factors and an intact cytoplasmic microtubule complex. Molecular events turning a non-invasive cell into an invasive one are being intensely searched for at this moment. It is clear that the success of this search will depend to a large extent upon the reliability of our methods for defining the non-invasive *versus* the invasive state of a cell population.

The authors thank J. Roels van Kerckvoorde for preparing the illustrations and G. Matthys-De Smet for typing the manuscript. Work in the authors' laboratories is supported by grants from the N.F.W.O. (no. 3.0032.87), the A.S.L.K. Kankerfonds, the Centrum voor Gezwelziekten, and the Sport Vereniging tegen Kanker, Belgium. F.V.R. is a Research Associate of the NFWO. L.M. and E.B. are supported by research grants from the IWONL and from the Belgisch Werk tegen Kanker, respectively.

REFERENCES

ABERCROMBIE, M. & HEAYSMAN, J. E. M. (1976). Invasive behavior between sarcoma and fibroblast populations in cell culture. *J. natn. Cancer Inst.* **56**, 561–570.

ALBRECHTSEN, R., NIELSEN, M., WEWER, U., ENGVALL, E. & RUOSLAHTI, E. (1981). Basement membrane changes in breast cancer detected by immunohistochemical staining for laminin. *Cancer Res.* **41**, 5076–5081.

BARSKY, S. H., SIEGAL, G. P., JANNOTTA, F. & LIOTTA, L. A. (1983). Loss of basement membrane components by invasive tumors but not by their benign counterparts. *Lab. Invest.* **49**, 140–147.

BILLIAU A., SOBIS, H., EYSSEN, H. & VAN DEN BERGHE, H. (1973). Non-infectious intracisternal A-type particles in a sarcoma-positive, leukemia-negative mouse cell line transformed by murine sarcoma virus (MSV). *Arch. ges. Virusforsch.* **43**, 345–351.

BISHOP, J. M. (1987). The molecular genetics of cancer. *Science* **235**, 305–311.

BJERKVIG, R., LAERUM, O. D. & MELLA, O. (1986). Glioma cell interactions with fetal rat brain aggregates in vitro and with brain tissue in vivo. *Cancer Res.* **46**, 4071–4079.

BOGENMANN, E., MARK, C., ISAACS, H., NEUSTEIN, H. B., DE CLERCK, Y. A., LAUG, W. E. & JONES, P. A. (1983). Invasive properties of primary pediatric neoplasms in vitro. *Cancer Res.* **43**, 1176–1186.

BOGHAERT, E. R., DISTELMANS, W., VAN GINCKEL, R. & MAREEL, M. M. (1987). Numerical evaluation of the kidney invasion test. *Invasion Metast.* (in press).

BOLSCHER, J. G. M., SCHALLIER, D. C. C., SMETS, L. A., VAN ROOY, H., COLLARD, J. G., BRUYNEEL, E. A. & MAREEL, M. M. K. (1986). Effect of cancer-related and drug-induced alterations in surface carbohydrates on the invasive capacity of mouse and rat cells. *Cancer Res.* **46**, 4080–4086.

BRACKE, M. E., VAN CAUWENBERGE, R. M.-L., STORME, G. A., COOPMAN, P., VAN LAREBEKE, N. & MAREEL, M. M. (1986). Action mechanisms of anti-invasive agents. *Anticancer Res.* **6**, 1273–1278.

BRUYNEEL, E. & MAREEL, M. (1981). Early activities of invasive malignant cells in vitro. *Arch. Geschwulstforsch.* **51**, 34–39.

BUCK, R. C. (1973). Walker 256 tumor implantation in normal and injured peritoneum studied by electron microscopy, scanning electron microscopy, and autoradiography. *Cancer Res.* **33**, 3181–3188.

BURTIN, P., CHAVANEL, G., FOIDART, J. M. & MARTIN, E. (1982). Antigens of the basement membrane and the peritumoral stroma in human colonic adenocarcinomas: an immunofluorescence study. *Int. J. Cancer* **30**, 13–20.

CAJOT, J. F., SORDAT, B. & BACHMANN, F. (1986). Human primary colon carcinomas xenografted into nude mice. II. Modulation of tumor plasminogen activator activity by the host tissue environment. *J. natn. Cancer Inst.* **77**, 1099–1107.

CARR, J., CARR, I., DREHER, B. & BETTS, K. (1980). Lymphatic metastasis: invasion of lymphatic vessels and efflux of tumour cells in the afferent popliteal lymph as seen in the Walker rat carcinoma. *J. Path.* **132**, 287–305.

CRESSON, D. H., BECKMAN, W. C., TIDWELL, R. R., GERATZ, J. D. & SIEGAL, G. P. (1986). In vitro inhibition of human sarcoma cells' invasive ability by bis(5-amidino-2-benzimidazolyl)-methane – a novel esteroprotease inhibitor. *Am. J. Path.* **123**, 46–56.

CRISSMAN, J. D., HATFIELD, J., SCHALDENBRAND, M., SLOANE, B. F. & HONN, K. V. (1985). Arrest and extravasation of B16 amelanotic melanoma in murine lungs. A light and electron microscopic study. *Lab. Invest.* **53**, 470–478.

CUZIN, F., MENEGUZZI, G., BINETRUY, B., CERNI, C., CONNAN, G., GRISONI, M. & DE LAPEYRIERE, O. (1985). Stepwise tumoral progression in rodent fibroblasts transformed with bovine papilloma virus type 1 (BPV1) DNA. In *Papillomaviruses: Molecular and Clinical Aspects* (ed. P. M. Howley & T. R. Broker), pp. 473–486. New York: Alan R. Liss.

DE BAETSELIER, P., ROOS, E., BRYS, L., REMELS, L., GOBERT, M., DEKEGEL, D., SEGAL, S. & FELDMAN, M. (1984). Nonmetastatic tumor cells acquire metastatic properties following somatic hybridization with normal cells. *Cancer Metast. Rev.* **3**, 5–24.

DE BRUYN, P. P. H. & CHO, Y. (1982). Vascular endothelial invasion via transcellular passage by malignant cells in the primary stage of metastases formation. *J. Ultrastruct. Res.* **81**, 189–201.

DE NEVE, W. J., STORME, G. A., DE BRUYNE, G. K. & MAREEL, M. M. (1985). An image analysis system for the quantification of invasion in vitro. *Clin. exp. Metast.* **3**, 87–101.

DINGEMANS, K. P., ROOS, E., VAN DEN BERGH WEERMAN, M. A. & VAN DE PAVERT, I. V. (1978). Invasion of liver tissue by tumor cells and leukocytes: comparative ultrastructure. *J. natn. Cancer Inst.* **60**, 583–598.

DISTELMANS, W., VAN GINCKEL, R., VANHERCK, W. & DE BRABANDER, M. (1985). The kidney invasion test: an assay allowing macroscopic quantification of malignant invasion in vivo. *Invasion Metast.* **5**, 170–184.

DUKES, C. E. (1932). The classification of cancer of the rectum. *J. Path. Bact.* **35**, 323–332.

EASTY, D. M. & EASTY, G. C. (1974). Measurement of the ability of cells to infiltrate normal tissues in vitro. *Br. J. Cancer* **29**, 36–49.

EASTY, G. C. & EASTY, D. M. (1984). In vivo and in vitro models of invasion. In *Invasion. Experimental and Clinical Implications* (ed. M. M. Mareel & K. C. Calman), pp. 24–62. Oxford, New York, Tokyo: Oxford University Press.

EASTY, G. C., HAEMMERLI, G., EASTY, D. M. & STRÄULI, P. (1982). Interactions between normal epithelial and squamous carcinoma cells in monolayer culture. *Cancer Res.* **42**, 4248–4255.

ELVIN, P., WONG, V. & EVANS, C. W. (1985). A study of the adhesive, locomotory and invasive behaviour of Walker 256 carcinosarcoma cells. *Expl Cell Biol.* **53**, 9–18.

FABER, M., WEWER, U. M., BERTHELSEN, J. G., LIOTTA, L. A. & ALBRECHTSEN, R. (1986). Laminin production by human endometrial stromal cells relates to the cyclic and pathologic state of the endometrium. *Am. J. Path.* **124**, 384–398.

FOIDART, J. M., BERE, E. W., YAAR, M., RENNARD, S. I., GULLINO, M., MARTIN, G. R. & KATZ, S. I. (1980). Distribution and immunoelectron microscopic localization of laminin, a noncollagenous basement membrane glycoprotein. *Lab. Invest.* **42**, 336–342.

FORSTER, S. J., TALBOT, I. C. & CRITCHLEY, D. R. (1984). Laminin and fibronectin in rectal adenocarcinoma: relationship to tumour grade, stage and metastasis. *Br. J. Cancer* **50**, 51–61.

FUJITA, J., YOSHIDA, O., YUASA, Y., RHIM, J. S., HATANAKA, M. & AARONSON, S. A. (1984). Ha-*ras* oncogenes are activated by somatic alterations in human urinary tract tumours. *Nature, Lond.* **309**, 464–466.

GALLI, S. J. (1984). Uncertainty of histologic classification of experimental tumors (technical comment). *Science* **226**, 352–353.

GALLICK, G. E., KURZROCK, R., KLOETZER, W. S., ARLINGHAUS, R. B. & GUTTERMAN, J. U. (1985). Expression of p21 ras in fresh primary and metastatic human colorectal tumors. *Proc. natn. Acad. Sci. U.S.A.* **82**, 1795–1799.

GAO, J., XUE, K., BAOGUI, L. & DONG, H. (1984). Site-dependence of invasiveness of ECA109 human oesophageal carcinoma cells in nude mice. *Clin. exp. Metast.* **2**, 205–212.

GAO, J., YOUNG, G., XUE, K., LI, B. & SUN, Y. (1982). Characteristics of invasiveness of human nasopharyngeal carcinoma cells in organ culture, as observed by scanning electron microscopy. *Path. Res. Pract.* **174**, 325–341.

GENADRY, R., OLSON, J., PARMLEY, T. & WOODRUFF, J. D. (1978). The morphology of the earliest invasive cell in low genital tract epidermoid neoplasia. *Obstet. Gynec., N.Y.* **51**, 718–722.

GOLD, R. H., MAIN, G., ZIPPIN, C. & ANNES, G. P. (1972). Infiltration of mammary carcinoma as an indicator of axillary node metastasis. A preliminary report. *Cancer* **29**, 35–40.

HAEMMERLI, G. (1986). The role of cell motility in tumor invasion. In *Proteinases in Inflammation and Tumor Invasion* (ed. H. Tschesche), pp. 245–260. Berlin, New York: Walter de Gruyter.

HANSON, M. B., VAN NAGELL, J. R., POWELL, D. E., DONALDSON, E. S., GALLION, H., MERHIGE, M. & PAVLIK, E. J. (1985). The prognostic significance of lymph-vascular space invasion in stage I endometrial cancer. *Cancer* **55**, 1753–1757.

HART, I. R. & FIDLER, I. J. (1978). An in vitro quantitative assay for tumor cell invasion. *Cancer Res.* **38**, 3218–3224.

HASUMI, K., SAKAMOTO, A. & SUGANO, H. (1980). Microinvasive carcinoma of the uterine cervix. *Cancer* **45**, 928–931.

HENDRIX, M. J. C., GEHLSEN, K. R., WAGNER, H. N., RODNEY, S. R., MISIOROWSKI, R. L. & MEYSKENS, F. L. (1985). In vitro quantification of melanoma tumor cell invasion. *Clin. exp. Metast.* **3**, 221–233.

INOUE, T. (1984). Prognostic significance of the depth of invasion relating to nodal metastases, parametrial extension, and cell types. *Cancer* **54**, 3035–3042.

ISBERG, R. R. & FALKOW, S. (1985). A single genetic locus encoded by Yersinia pseudotuberculosis permits invasion of cultured animal cells by *Escherichia coli* K-12. *Nature, Lond.* **317**, 262–264.

JEWETT, H. J. & STRONG, G. H. (1946). Infiltrating carcinoma of the bladder: relation of depth of penetration of the bladder wall to incidence of local extension and metastases. *J. Urol.* **55**, 366–372.

KALLIOINEN, M., AUTIO-HARMAINEN, H., DAMMERT, K., RISTELI, J. & RISTELI, L. (1984). Discontinuity of the basement membrane in fibrosing basocellular carcinomas and basosquamous carcinomas of the skin: an immunohistochemical study with human laminin and type IV collagen antibodies. *J. invest. Derm.* **82**, 248–251.

KIMURA, A., KOGA, S., KUDOH, H. & ITSUKA, Y. (1985). Peritoneal mesothelial cell injury factors in rat cancerous ascites. *Cancer Res.* **45**, 4330–4333.

KIYASU, Y., KANESHIMA, S. & KOGA, S. (1981). Morphogenesis of peritoneal metastasis in human gastric cancer. *Cancer Res.* **41**, 1236–1239.

KRAMER, R. H., VOGEL, K. G. & NICOLSON, G. L. (1982). Solubilization and degradation of subendothelial matrix glycoproteins and proteoglycans by metastatic tumor cells. *J. biol. Chem.* **257**, 2678–2686.

LAUG, W. E., DE CLERCK, Y. A. & JONES, P. A. (1983). Degradation of the subendothelial matrix by tumor cells. *Cancer Res.* **43**, 1827–1834.

LEMAN, M. H., BENSON, W. L., KURMAN, R. J. & PARK, R. C. (1976). Microinvasive carcinoma of the cervix. *Obstet. Gynaec.* **48**, 571–578.

LIOTTA, L. A. (1986). Tumor invasion and metastases – Role of the extracellular matrix: Rhoades memorial award lecture. *Cancer Res.* **46**, 1–7.

MAIGNAN, M. F. (1979). Etude ultrastructrale des interactions entre des cellules normales ou malignes et le sac vitellin de Rat, explanté in vitro. *Biol. Cell* **35**, 229–232.

MAREEL, M. M. K. (1982). The use of embryo organ cultures to study invasion in vitro. In *Tumor Invasion and Metastasis* (ed. L. A. Liotta & I. R. Hart), pp. 207–230. The Hague, Boston, London: Martinus Nijhoff.

MAREEL, M. M. (1983). Invasion in vitro: methods of analysis. *Cancer Metast. Rev.* **2**, 201–218.

MAREEL, M. M., BRACKE, M. E. & BOGHAERT, E. R. (1986). Tumour invasion and metastasis: therapeutic implications? *Radiother. Oncol.* **6**, 135–142.

MAREEL, M. M., DE BRUYNE, G. K., VANDESANDE, F. & DRAGONETTI, C. (1981). Immunohistochemical study of embryonic chick heart invaded by malignant cells in three-dimensional culture. *Invasion Metast.* **1**, 195–204.

MAREEL, M. M. & DE METS, M. (1984). Effect of microtubule inhibitors on invasion and on related activities of tumor cells. *Int. Rev. Cytol.* **90**, 125–168.

MAREEL, M. M. & VAN ROY, F. M. (1986). Are oncogenes involved in invasion and metastasis? *Anticancer Res.* **6**, 419–436.

MAREEL, M., VAN ROY, F., MESSIAEN, L., BRACKE, M., BOGHAERT, E. & COOPMAN, P. (1987). Investigation of tumour-invasion mechanisms. In *Methodological Surveys in Biochemistry and Analysis*, vol. 17 (ed. E. Reid, G. M. W. Cook & J. P. Lurio). New York: Plenum (in press).

MCNUTT, N. S. (1976). Ultrastructural comparison of the interface between epithelium and stroma in basal cell carcinoma and control human skin. *Lab. Invest.* **35**, 132–142.

MIDDELKOOP, O. P., ROOS, E. & VAN DE PAVERT, I. V. (1982). Infiltration of lymphosarcoma cells into hepatocyte cultures: inhibition by univalent antibodies against liver plasma membranes and lymphosarcoma cells. *J. Cell Sci.* **56**, 461–470.

MIETTINEN, M. & VIRTANEN, I. (1984). Expression of laminin in thyroid gland and thyroid tumors: an immunohistologic study. *Int. J. Cancer* **34**, 27–30.

MIGNATTI, P., ROBBINS, E. & RIFKIN, D. B. (1986). Tumor invasion through the human amniotic membrane: requirement for a proteinase cascade. *Cell* **47**, 487–498.

MÜLLER-GLAUSER, W., HAEMMERLI, G. & STRÄULI, P. (1985). Ultrastructural evidence for contacts between migrating L5222 rat leukemia cells and extracellular matrix components of the rat mesentery. *Cell Biol. Int. Rep.* **9**, 447–461.

NICOLSON, G. L. (1982). Metastatic tumor cell attachment and invasion assay utilizing vascular endothelial cell monolayers. *J. Histochem. Cytochem.* **30**, 214–220.

NIEDBALA, M. J., CRICKARD, K. & BERNACKI, R. J. (1985). Interactions of human ovarian tumor cells with human mesothelial cells grown on extracellular matrix. *Expl Cell Res.* **160**, 499–513.

OHNO, M., MARTINEZ-HERNANDEZ, A., OHNO, N. & KEFALIDES, N. A. (1986). Laminin M is found in placental basement membranes, but not in basement membranes of neoplastic origin. *Conn. Tiss. Res.* **15**, 199–207.

PAKU, S., WERLING, H. O., AULENBACHER, P., PAWELETZ, N. & SPIESS, E. (1986). Invasive activities of metastasizing and nonmetastasizing tumor cell variants in vitro. II. Studies on confrontations with aorta, vein, ductus thoracicus, diaphragm, and lung. *Anticancer Res.* **6**, 17–26.

PARSONS, D. F., MARKO, M., BRAUN, S. J. & WANSOR, K. J. (1982). Ascites tumor invasion of mouse peritoneum studied by high-voltage electron microscope stereoscopy. *Cancer Res.* **42**, 4574–4583.

PARSONS, D. F., MARKO, M. & WANSOR, K. J. (1983). Inflammation with restricted lysosomal proteolysis during early ascites carcinoma invasion of mouse parietal peritoneum. A medium and high-voltage electron microscopic and cytochemical study. *Tissue & Cell* **15**, 499–507.

POSTE, G. (1982). Methods and models for studying tumor invasion. In *Tumor Invasion and Metastasis* (ed. L. A. Liotta & I. R. Hart), pp. 147–172. The Hague, Boston, London: Martinus Nijhoff.

POSTE, G., DOLL, J., HART, I. R. & FIDLER, I. J. (1980). In vitro selection of murine B16 melanoma variants with enhanced tissue-invasive properties. *Cancer Res.* **40**, 1636–1644.

ROOS, E. & VAN DE PAVERT, I. V. (1982). Effect of tubulin-binding agents on the infiltration of tumour cells into primary hepatocyte cultures. *J. Cell Sci.* **55**, 233–245.

RUBIO, C. A. & BIBERFELD, P. (1975). The basement membrane of the uterine cervix in dysplasia and squamous carcinoma: an immunofluorescent study with antibodies to basement membrane antigen. *Acta path. microbiol. scand. sect. A* **83**, 744–748.

RUSSO, R. G., THORGEIRSSON, U. & LIOTTA, L. A. (1982). In vitro quantitative assay of invasion using human amnion. In *Tumor Invasion and Metastasis* (ed. L. A. Liotta & I. R. Hart), pp. 173–187. The Hague, Boston, London: Martinus Nijhoff.

SACKS, P. G., WANSOR, K. J. & PARSONS, D. F. (1984). Organ-cultured epithelial tissue as an in vitro model for invasion: quantitation and high-voltage electron microscopy of tumor cell attachment. *Cancer Res.* **44**, 3063–3074.

SCHLEICH, A. B., FRICK, M. & MAYER, A. (1976). Patterns of invasive growth in vitro. Human decidua graviditatis confronted with established human cell lines and primary human explants. *J. natn. Cancer Inst.* **56**, 221–237.

SIEGAL, G. P., THORGEIRSSON, U. P., RUSSO, R. G., WALLACE, D. M., LIOTTA, L. A. & BERGER, S. L. (1982). Interferon enhancement of the invasive capacity of Ewing sarcoma cells in vitro. *Proc. natn. Acad. Sci. U.S.A.* **79**, 4064–4068.

SONNENBERG, A., DAAMS, H., CALAFAT, J. & HILGERS, J. (1986). *In vitro* differentiation and progression of mouse mammary tumor cells. *Cancer Res.* **46**, 5913–5922.

SMITH, H. S., LIOTTA, L. A., HANCOCK, M. C., WOLMAN, S. R. & HACKETT, A. J. (1985). Invasiveness and ploidy of human mammary carcinomas in short-term culture. *Proc. natn. Acad. Sci. U.S.A.* **82**, 1805–1809.

STARKEY, J. R., HOSICK, H. L., STANFORD, D. R. & LIGGITT, H. D. (1984). Interaction of metastatic tumor cells with bovine lens capsule basement membrane. *Cancer Res.* **44**, 1585–1594.

STEINSVAG, S. K. (1985). Interaction between glioma cells and normal brain tissue in organ culture studied by scanning electron microscopy. *Invasion Metast.* **5**, 255–269.

STRÄULI, P., HAEMMERLI, G., TSCHENETT, C. & KRSTIC, R. V. (1981). Different modes of mesenteric infiltration displayed by two rat leukemias. *Virchows Arch. Cell Path.* **35**, 93–108.

STRÄULI, P., IN-ALBON, A. & HAEMMERLI, G. (1983). Morphological studies on V2 carcinoma invasion and tumor-associated connective tissue changes in the rabbit mesentery. *Cancer Res.* **43,** 5403–5410, 1983.

SUH, O. & WEISS, L. (1984). The development of a technique for the morphometric analysis of invasion in cancer. *J. theor. Biol.* **107**, 547–561.

TAHARA, E., YASUI, W., TANIYAMA, K., OCHIAI, A., YAMAMOTO, T., NAKAJO, S. & YAMAMOTO, M. (1986). Ha-*ras* oncogene product in human gastric carcinoma: correlation with invasiveness, metastasis or prognosis. *Jap. J. Cancer Res.* **77**, 517–522.

TALBOT, I. C., RITCHIE, S., LEIGHTON, M., HUGHES, A. O., BUSSEY, H. J. R. & MORSON, B. C. (1981). Invasion of veins by carcinoma of rectum: method of detection, histological features and significance. *Histopathology* **5**, 141–163.

TARIN, D., VASS, A. C. R., KETTLEWELL, M. G. W. & PRICE, J. E. (1984). Absence of metastatic sequelae during long-term treatment of malignant ascites by peritoneo-venous shunting. *Invasion Metast.* **4**, 1–12.

THOR, A., HORAN HAND, P., WUNDERLICH, D., CARUSO, A., MURARO, R. & SCHLOM, J. (1984). Monoclonal antibodies define differential ras gene expression in malignant and benign colonic diseases. *Nature, Lond.* **311**, 562–565.

THORGEIRSSON, U. P., TURPEENNIEMI-HUJANEN, T., NECKERS, L. M., JOHNSON, D. W. & LIOTTA, L. A. (1984). Protein synthesis but not DNA synthesis is required for tumor cell invasion in vitro. *Invasion Metast.* **4**, 73–83.

TOPP, W. C. (1981). Normal rat cell lines deficient in nuclear thymidine kinase. *Virology* **113**, 408–411.

TSAO, S. W., BURMAN, J. F., EASTY, D. M., EASTY, G. C. & CARTER, R. L. (1981). Some mechanisms of local bone destruction by squamous carcinomas of the head and neck. *Br. J. Cancer* **43**, 392–401.

VAN NAGELL, J. R., DONALDSON, E. S., WOOD, E. G. & PARKER, J. C. (1978). The significance of vascular invasion and lymphocytic infiltration in invasive cervical cancer. *Cancer* **41**, 228–234.

VAN ROY, F. M., MESSIAEN, L., LIEBAUT, G., GAO, J., DRAGONETTI, C. H., FIERS, W. C. & MAREEL, M. M. (1986). Invasiveness and metastatic capability of rat fibroblast-like cells before and after transfection with immortalizing and transforming genes. *Cancer Res.* **46**, 4787–4795.

VERSCHUEREN, H., DEKEGEL, D. & DE BAETSELIER, P. (1987). Development of a monolayer invasion assay for the discrimination and isolation of metastatic lymphoma cells. *Invasion Metast.* (in press).

VIOLA, M. V., FROMOWITZ, F., ORAVEZ, S., DEB, S., FINKEL, G., LUNDY, J., HAND, P., THOR, A. & SCHLOM, J. (1986). Expression of *ras* oncogene p21 in prostatic cancer. *New Engl. J. Med.* **314**, 133–137.

WALLER, C. A., BRAUN, M. & SCHIRRMACHER, V. (1986). Quantitative analysis of cancer invasion in vitro: comparison of two new assays and of tumour sublines with different metastatic capacity. *Clin. exp. Metast.* **4**, 73–89.

WALSH, J. W., ZIMMER, S. G., OELTGEN, J. & MARKESBERY, W. R. (1986). Invasiveness in primary intracranial tumors: part 1. *Neurosurgery* **19**, 185–200.

WANG, T. Y. & NICOLSON, G. L. (1983). Metastatic tumor cell invasion of brain organ tissue cultured on cellulose polyacetate strips. *Clin. exp. Metast.* **1**, 327–339.

WEIGAND, R. A., ISENBERG, W. M., RUSSO, J., BRENNAN, M. J., RICH, M. A. & THE BREAST CANCER PROGNOSTIC STUDY ASSOCIATES (1982). Blood vessel invasion and axillary lymph node involvement as prognostic indicators for human breast cancer. *Cancer* **50**, 962–969.

WILLIS, R. A. (1960). *Pathology of Tumours*. London: Butterworths.

ZAMORA, P. O., DANIELSON, K. G. & HOSICK, H. L. (1980). Invasion of endothelial cell monolayers on collagen gels by cells from mammary tumor spheroids. *Cancer Res.* **40**, 4631–4639.

J. Cell Sci. Suppl. 8, 165–180 (1987)
Printed in Great Britain

FOETAL-TO-ADULT TRANSITIONS IN FIBROBLAST PHENOTYPE: THEIR POSSIBLE RELEVANCE TO THE PATHOGENESIS OF CANCER

S. L. SCHOR

Department of Cell and Structural Biology, Manchester University, Manchester M13 9PL, England

AND A. M. SCHOR

CRC Department of Medical Oncology, Christie Hospital, Wilmslow Road, Manchester M20 9BX, England

SUMMARY

We have previously shown that the migration of foetal, adult and transformed fibroblasts into three-dimensional collagen gels is differentially affected by plating cell density. We now present data indicating that the migration of these fibroblasts is also differentially affected by local cell density in microdomains of the gel surface. In this article we discuss the possible biochemical and behavioural mechanisms that may contribute to the different migratory phenotypes expressed by foetal, adult and transformed fibroblasts; these include: (1) cell-induced alterations in the orientation and or packing density of collagen fibres in the gel; (2) deposition of specific matrix macromolecules by the fibroblasts; (3) social interactions between the cells; and (4) secretion of soluble factors affecting cell migration. We show that foetal fibroblasts secrete a migration stimulating factor (MSF) not produced by adult cells. Incubation of adult fibroblasts in the presence of MSF induces these cells to express a foetal-like migratory phenotype. Foetal fibroblasts undergo a spontaneous foetal-to-adult transition in migratory phenotype after prolonged passage *in vitro*; this transition is accompanied by a cessation in MSF production. MSF appears to promote fibroblast migration at high cell density by stimulating the deposition of hyaluronic acid in the extracellular matrix.

Recent studies have indicated that skin fibroblasts from cancer patients display certain behavioural abnormalities characteristic of transformed and/or foetal cells. In this regard, we have shown that skin fibroblasts from cancer patients commonly express a foetal-like phenotype with respect to migratory behaviour and secretion of MSF: it is of interest to note that these cancer patient fibroblasts are indistinguishable from normal adult cells in other respects, such as morphology in confluent culture. On the basis of these observations, we suggest that: (1) fibroblasts in certain individuals fail to undergo normal foetal-to-adult transitions in a number of phenotypic characteristics; and that (2) the disruption in epithelial–mesenchymal interactions caused by the continued presence of these foetal-like fibroblasts in the adult significantly increases the risk of cancer development.

INTRODUCTION

Epithelial and mesenchymal tissues are commonly found in close anatomical proximity. Signals arising from the mesenchyme exert a profound influence upon the proliferation, differentiation and morphogenesis of the associated epithelium, both during normal development (Sawyer & Fallon, 1983) and in the adult organism (Hill & Mackenzie, 1984; Cuhna *et al.* 1985); conversely, the epithelium influences various important aspects of mesenchyme function, e.g. the deposition of matrix macromolecules and secretion of matrix degrading enzymes (Cummings *et al.* 1981; Johnson-Wint & Gross, 1984). The nature of this 'dynamic reciprocity' whereby the epithelium and mesenchyme influence each other in a self-regulating fashion has been discussed by Bissell *et al.* (1982). Both soluble factors (i.e. paracrine mechanisms) and matrix macromolecules are involved in mediating epithelial–mesenchymal interactions (Bissell *et al.* 1982; Trelstad, 1984; Lawrence, 1985; Gurdon, 1987).

A number of workers have proposed that a disruption in normal epithelial–mesenchymal interactions in the adult might be involved in the genesis of various proliferative disorders, including neoplasia (Cunha *et al.* 1985; Rubin, 1985). This suggestion is supported by the report of Saiag *et al.* (1985), which indicates that the abnormalities in epithelial proliferation and differentiation associated with psoriasis are caused by aberrant fibroblasts in the underlying dermal tissue. It is consequently of interest to note that fibroblasts from cancer patients have been reported to display a number of the aberrant phenotypic characteristics commonly associated with transformed and/or foetal cells.

In this article we: (1) review our data indicating that foetal and adult fibroblasts display different migratory phenotypes on collagen gels; (2) discuss the biochemical mechanisms that may be responsible for these behavioural differences; (3) document the expression of foetal phenotypic characteristics by fibroblasts derived from cancer patients; and (4) discuss the possible involvement of foetal-like fibroblasts in the pathogenesis of epithelial tumours.

DIFFERENCES IN THE MIGRATORY PHENOTYPE OF FOETAL AND ADULT FIBROBLASTS

Fibroblasts are a rather poorly defined group of cells, identified *in vivo* by their location in connective tissues and *in vitro* by such non-specific characteristics as spindle-shaped morphology, the presence of vimentin intermediate filaments and the synthesis of interstitial collagens and fibronectin. Transformed fibroblasts differ from their normal counterparts in a number of behavioural and biochemical characteristics, e.g. ability to form colonies in semi-solid medium (Cameron & Pool, 1981).

We have previously reported that fibroblast migration into three-dimensional collagen gels is influenced by plating density (Schor *et al.* 1985*a*). In our standard migration assay, fibroblasts are plated on the surface of collagen gels at defined low and high densities (i.e. 10^3 and $2{\cdot}5\times10^4$ cells cm^{-2}) and the cultures incubated for 4 days. The percentage of cells found within the gel matrix is then determined by viewing cultures under phase optics and counting fibroblasts on and within the gel in rectangular areas of the gel delimited by a photographic graticule (Schor, 1980). Results obtained with three representative (normal adult, foetal and transformed) fibroblast lines are shown in Fig. 1. These data reveal a differential effect of cell density on fibroblast migration, i.e. the adult fibroblast line migrated to a relatively greater extent at low density, the foetal line migrated to approximately the same extent at both plating densities, while the transformed line migrated to a relatively greater extent at high density. In order to express this effect of cell density on fibroblast migration in quantitative terms, we have defined a 'cell density migration index' or CDMI as follows:

$$\text{CDMI} = \log (\% \text{ low density}/\% \text{ high density}) ,$$

where '% low density' refers to the percentage of cells within the gel matrix in cultures plated at 10^3 cells cm^{-2} and '% high density' is the corresponding value for cells plated at $2{\cdot}5 \times 10^4$ cells cm^{-2} (Schor *et al.* 1985*a*). It should be noted that the logarithm is employed in the definition of the CDMI to facilitate graphical representation of the data. According to this definition, cells that display a pattern of migration similar to that of the adult line shown in Fig. 1 will have positive CDMI values, cells behaving like the foetal line will have CDMI values near zero, while cells behaving like the transformed line will have negative CDMI values.

The results obtained in migration assays performed with a large number of fibroblast lines confirm that the CDMI may be used to distinguish between adult, foetal and transformed fibroblasts (Fig. 2); we found that adult and transformed

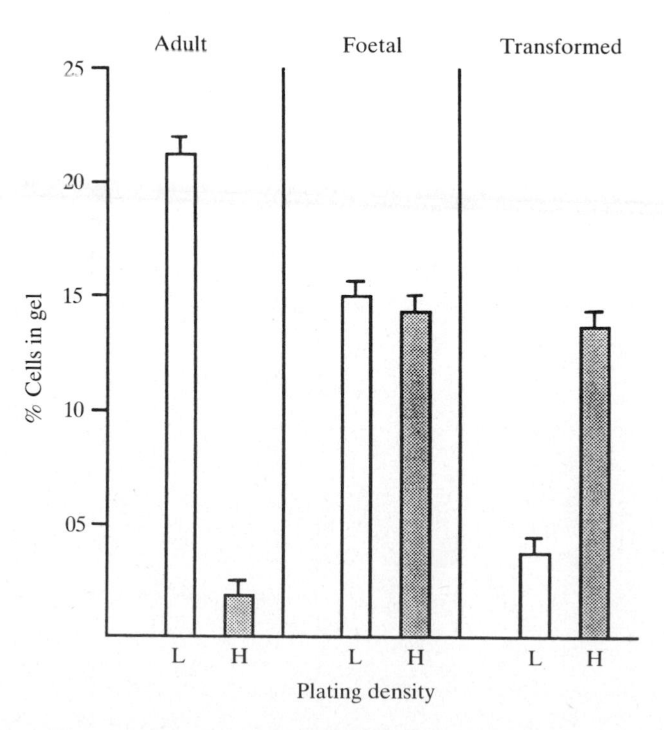

Fig. 1. Migratory behaviour of representative adult (ratio 10·5, CDMI 1·02), foetal (ratio 1·07, CDMI 0·03) and transformed (ratio 0·26, CDMI −0·58) fibroblast lines. Data are given regarding the % of cells within the gel matrix in cultures plated at low density (L) and high density (H). The ratio of %L/%H and the calculated CDMI are also indicated.

fibroblasts display completely non-overlapping distribution profiles of CDMI values, while foetal cells form a distinct group lying intermediate between the two. Inspection of Fig. 2 indicates that over 90% of the adult fibroblasts examined had CDMI values greater than +0·4, while over 90% of the foetal fibroblasts had CDMI values less than +0·4; on the basis of these results, we empirically define a CDMI above +0·4 as adult-like and one falling below this point as foetal-like. The CDMI thus provides a convenient and novel behavioural marker of 'foetalness', which can be used to assess the phenotype of fibroblasts cultured *in vitro*.

THE PRESENCE OF ABERRANT FIBROBLASTS IN CANCER PATIENTS

We have reported that tumour-derived fibroblasts obtained from approximately 50% of patients with cancer of the breast express a foetal-like migratory phenotype (Durning *et al.* 1984). Ostensibly normal skin fibroblasts obtained from these

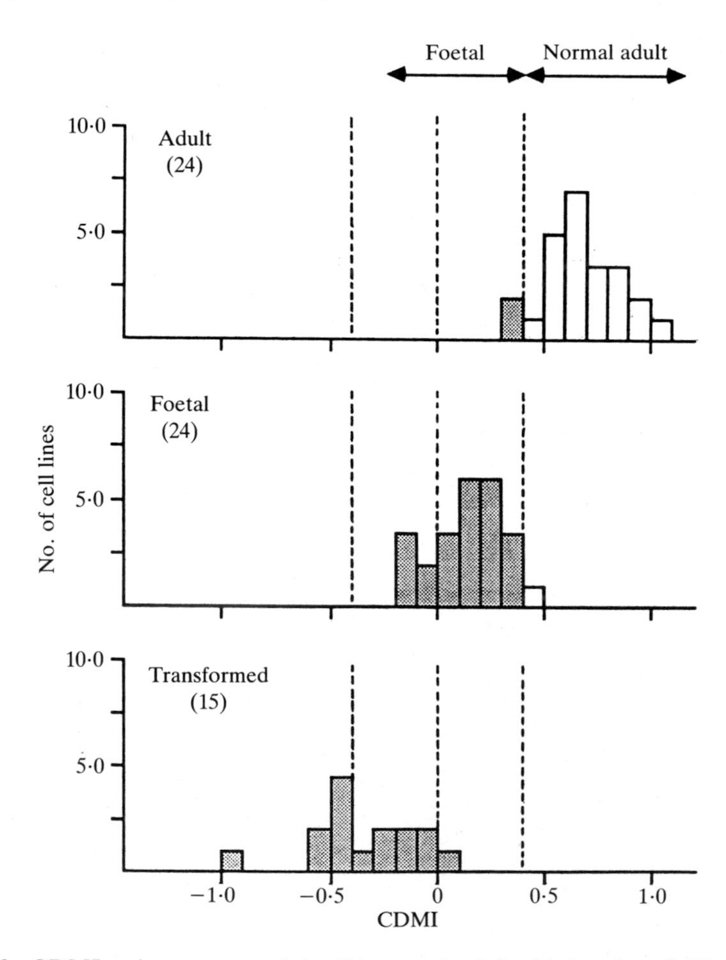

Fig. 2. CDMI values expressed by 24 normal adult, 24 foetal and 15 transformed fibroblast lines. CDMIs greater than +0·4 are displayed as open bars, while those less than +0·4 are shaded.

patients also displayed foetal-like migratory behaviour, thus indicating the systemic nature of this behavioural abnormality. Similar observations were made with skin fibroblasts obtained from patients with a variety of other types of carcinoma, as well as tumours of mesenchymal origin (Schor *et al.* 1985*b*).

These results are consistent with a growing body of data indicating that fibroblasts obtained from cancer patients may display a number of phenotypic abnormalities generally associated with foetal and/or transformed cells; these include increased agglutinability with concanavalin A (Chaudhuri *et al.* 1975), criss-crossed pattern of growth, decreased serum requirement for growth and anchorage-independent growth (Azzarone *et al.* 1976, 1981; Pfeffer *et al.* 1976; Danes, 1980), prolonged lifespan *in vitro* (Azzarone *et al.* 1984; Wynford-Thomas *et al.* 1986), abnormalities in the organization and metabolism of actin (Kopelovich *et al.* 1977; Antecol *et al.* 1986), decreased ability to contract a fibrin clot (Curatolo *et al.* 1982), ability to form colonies on contact-inhibited epithelial cell monolayers (Azzarone *et al.* 1984), the formation of nodules in immunosuppressed mice (Smith *et al.* 1976) and karyotypic abnormalities (Lynch *et al.* 1984). The fibroblasts examined in these studies were obtained both from the primary tumour and from apparently normal skin at a distant site from the tumour.

CORRELATION BETWEEN GENETIC SUSCEPTIBILITY TO BREAST CANCER AND THE PRESENCE OF ABERRANT FIBROBLASTS

The systemic expression of a foetal-like migratory phenotype by skin fibroblasts from a significant proportion of cancer patients suggested that genetic factors may be involved in controlling the expression of this abnormality. With this possibility in mind, we embarked on a study designed to examine the migratory behaviour of skin fibroblasts in breast cancer patients believed to have a genetically determined predisposition for the disease.

Epidemiological data clearly indicate that genetic factors are involved in determining susceptibility to certain rare cancer syndromes, such as adenomatosis of the colon and rectum. It is considerably more difficult to demonstrate the involvement of hereditary factors in the more common types of cancer (e.g. carcinoma of the breast or bronchus), owing to the significant predicted occurrence of random familial clustering. Lynch *et al.* (1984) operationally defined hereditary breast cancer by the presence of two or more affected individuals within the modified nuclear pedigree in association with at least one of the following additional features: (1) evidence for a vertical mode of transmission, (2) bilaterality, (3) early age at onset, and (4) the presence of certain types of second malignancies, e.g. ovarian carcinoma. In a recent survey we reported that 8·9% of breast cancer patients in our Manchester study group fulfilled these criteria of putative hereditary disease (Haggie *et al.* 1985), a value in close agreement with that previously reported by Lynch *et al.* (1984).

Data comparing the migratory phenotype of fibroblasts obtained from patients with sporadic and hereditary breast cancer are presented in Fig. 3. Fibroblasts obtained from 13/23 (56%) of the sporadic breast cancer patients and 16/18 (89%)

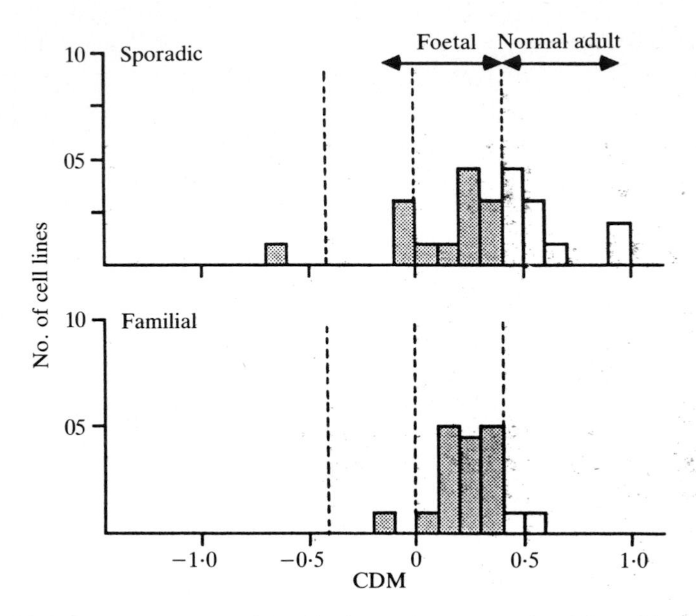

Fig. 3. CDMI values expressed by fibroblasts from sporadic (23) and hereditary breast (18) cancer patients.

of the hereditary breast cancer patients expressed CDMI values falling within the foetal range. The high incidence of foetal-like fibroblasts in patients with sporadic breast cancer suggests that hitherto unrecognized genetic factors may be operative in determining disease susceptibility in this group of patients.

Pedigree data collected from families displaying a high incidence of breast cancer suggest that susceptibility to the disease is transmitted as an autosomal dominant trait (Lynch *et al.* 1984). This is consistent with the observation that unaffected daughters of patients with hereditary breast cancer have a 50 % cumulative lifetime risk of developing the disease themselves (Ottman *et al.* 1983). We have examined the migratory behaviour of skin fibroblasts from 15 apparently normal first-degree relatives of patients fulfilling Lynch's criteria of hereditary breast cancer; these consisted of 2 brothers, 1 sister, 8 daughters and 4 sons. Normal age-matched controls for the patients ($n = 12$) were healthy women with no family history of breast cancer. Our data indicate that an aberrant migratory phenotype was expressed by fibroblasts obtained from a significant proportion (10/15 or 67 %) of clinically unaffected first-degree relatives (males and females) of patients with hereditary breast cancer. This finding clearly argues in favour of the interpretation that expression of this abnormality by skin fibroblasts precedes the appearance of a clinically recognizable epithelial tumour and does not result as a secondary consequence of fibroblast interaction with tumour cells. Indeed, the continued expression of foetal CDMI values by these fibroblasts after prolonged passage *in vitro* (Schor *et al.* 1985*b*, 1986) indicates that this aberrant mode of behaviour is a stable phenotypic characteristic of the cells and is independent of factors present in the *in vivo* environment.

MECHANISMS RESPONSIBLE FOR THE DIFFERENT CDMI VALUES EXPRESSED BY ADULT, FOETAL AND TRANSFORMED FIBROBLASTS

The CDMI is a measure of the effect of plating density on cell migration. Cells plated at the low density (10^3 cells cm^{-2}) remain sparsely distributed over the gel surface during the 4-day incubation period, whilst cells plated at high density ($2{\cdot}5\times10^4$ cells cm^{-2}) form a confluent layer immediately following cell attachment and spreading (i.e. 1–2 h after plating). In our standard migration assay, cells are plated in such a fashion as to achieve a uniform distribution over the gel surface. Data providing some insight into the mechanisms by which cell density influences fibroblast migration have been obtained by deliberately plating cells in a non-homogeneous fashion so that very different local densities are established in microdomains of the gel surface. This is achieved by dropping the plating inoculum slowly in the centre of the gel and then allowing the fibroblasts to attach with minimal agitation. The cell density in each microdomain of the gel surface in which cells are counted in the migration assay may be calculated knowing the optical magnification and the area of the rectangular field defined by the graticule. Data collected using this approach are shown in Fig. 4 for late-passage WI-38 cells (displaying an adult CDMI) and its virally transformed counterpart, SV WI-38. These data indicate that fibroblast migration is influenced by cell density in microdomains of a given gel in the same manner as previously reported for gels homogeneously plated at different densities (e.g. as shown in Fig. 1). Such a finding suggests that the mechanisms mediating this phenomenon are operative in the microenvironment of the cell and are not determined by the mean cell density in the culture.

The data presented in Figs 1, 2 and 4 indicate that at high cell density foetal and transformed fibroblasts migrate to a greater extent than do adult cells, whilst the

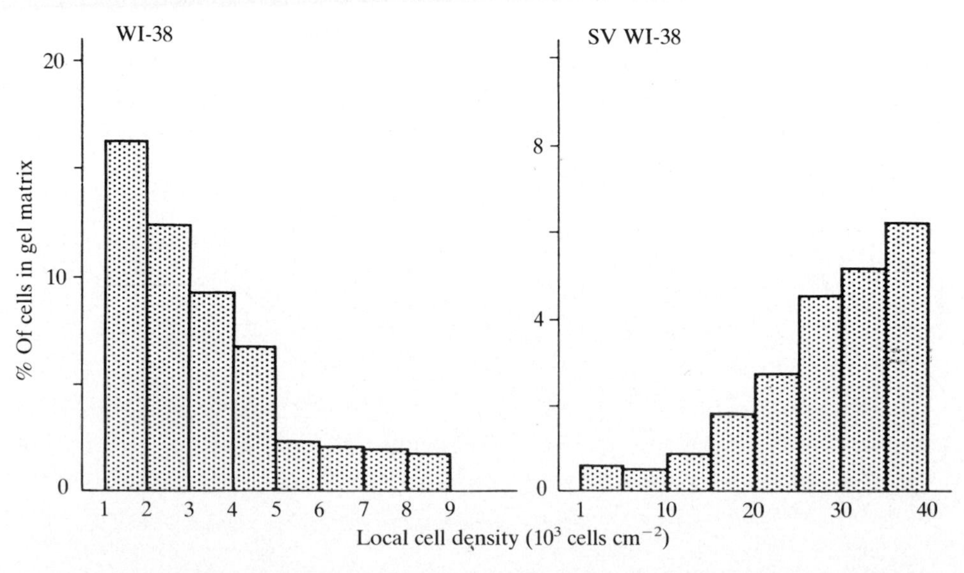

Fig. 4. The effect of local cell density on the migration of WI-38 (normal) and SV WI-38 (transformed) fibroblasts.

opposite situation prevails at low cell density. This differential effect of cell density may be mediated by a number of mechanisms, including: (1) cell-induced alterations in the orientation and/or packing density of collagen fibres in the gel; (2) deposition of specific matrix components by the fibroblasts; (3) social interactions between the cells; and (4) secretion of soluble factors.

Alterations in the orientation and/or packing density of collagen fibres

The contraction of connective tissue during wound healing is attributed to the activity of dermal fibroblasts. Normal fibroblasts plated within a three-dimensional collagen matrix exert a tractional force on the collagen fibres. This force is directly proportional to cell number and results in a marked contraction of free-floating gels (Bell *et al.* 1979; Allen & Schor, 1983). Neonate foreskin fibroblasts plated on the gel surface produce a similar compaction of collagen fibres in the superficial region of the gel (Grinnell & Lamke, 1984). Other stromal cells that have a contractile function *in vivo*, such as smooth muscle cells and pericytes, are also able to compact collagen gels (Schor & Schor, 1986). In contrast, transformed fibroblasts exert little tractional force on the collagen fibres and consequently compact the gels significantly less than do their normal counterparts (Steinberg *et al.* 1980). We have previously demonstrated that fibroblast migration into the collagen matrix is impeded at high concentrations of collagen (Schor *et al.* 1982). The different effects of normal and transformed fibroblasts on collagen fibre packing may contribute to the opposing effects of cell density on the migration of these cells; i.e. normal adult fibroblasts at high density would be expected to contract the superficial region of the gel to a greater extent than transformed cells and thereby inhibit their own migration into the gel matrix.

We have examined the ability of foetal fibroblasts and the foetal-like fibroblasts of breast cancer patients to contract floating collagen gels and compared these results with those obtained with normal adult and transformed cells (Table 1). Our results confirm the above-mentioned reports that normal adult fibroblasts contract collagen gels to a significantly greater extent than do transformed cells and further indicate that foetal fibroblasts and the foetal-like fibroblasts of breast cancer patients are indistinguishable from normal adult fibroblasts by this criterion. It therefore seems unlikely that a differential contraction and/or reorganization of collagen fibres is responsible for the distinctive CDMI values expressed by foetal and normal adult fibroblasts.

Deposition of specific matrix components

Fibroblasts cultured *in vitro* deposit a complex extracellular matrix containing collagens, fibronectin, hyaluronic acid and proteoglycans, as well as other macromolecular constituents. The synthesis of fibronectin by normal fibroblasts is density-dependent, with significantly greater quantities deposited by cells at high density compared to low density (Mautner & Hynes, 1977). We have previously shown that the migration of normal adult fibroblasts into collagen gels is inhibited by exogenous fibronectin (Schor *et al.* 1981). These observations suggest a possible mechanism

Table 1. *The contraction of free-floating collagen gels by different types of human fibroblasts*

Cell type	Gel diameter	% Contraction
Normal adult		
FSF37	16·1	49·7
NSF11	15·8	50·1
NSF41	14·9	53·4
Foetal		
FS6	15·5	51·6
FS8	14·1	55·9
FS10	16·0	50·0
Breast cancer		
BSF7	17·2	46·3
BSF11	14·9	53·4
BSF14	15·1	52·8
Transformed		
SV-WI38	29·9	6·6
HT-1080	30·8	3·8

Cells were suspended in collagen gelling solution and 2 ml of this used to cast gels in plastic tissue culture dishes (32 mm internal diameter) with a final concentration of 5×10^5 cells per gel. Gels were allowed to set for 2 h, then overlaid with growth medium containing 15 % calf serum and rimmed to produce free-floating cultures. Gel diameter was measured after 3 days incubation.

whereby the migration of normal adult fibroblasts is reduced at high density; i.e. the elevated amounts of fibronectin produced by normal adult fibroblasts under such conditions would inhibit their migration into the gel. In contrast to normal adult cells, transformed fibroblasts synthesize greatly reduced levels of fibronectin, even in confluent cultures (Hynes *et al.* 1979), and their migration is stimulated by exogenous fibronectin (Ali & Hynes, 1978; Schor *et al.* 1981).

Recent reports have indicated that fibronectin is actually a complex family of closely related molecules and that there are differences in amino acid composition and glycosylation in the fibronectins synthesized by normal adult, foetal and transformed fibroblasts (Castellani *et al.* 1986). Such variations in molecular fine structure, especially as they influence the cell-binding and collagen-binding domains, may have differential effects upon fibroblast migration.

Hyaluronic acid is another major constituent of the extracellular matrix that has been shown to stimulate cell migration into collagen gels (Bernanke & Markwald, 1979). Foetal and transformed fibroblasts synthesize more hyaluronic acid than normal adult fibroblasts, which may contribute to the elevated levels of migration displayed by these cells in high density culture (Schor *et al.* unpublished data).

The relative synthesis of types I and III collagens is regulated by cell density, with greater amounts of type I collagen produced in sparse cultures and the reverse situation applying in dense cultures (Abe *et al.* 1979). The consequences of these cell density-related changes in collagen biosynthesis on fibroblast migration are unknown and currently under study. In this context, it should be noted that foetal fibroblasts synthesize more type III collagen than type I (Epstein, 1974).

Social interactions amongst fibroblasts

When migrating normal fibroblasts collide, they exhibit a transient paralysis and soon start movement in the opposite direction, a phenomenon termed 'contact inhibition of cell movement' (Abercrombie, 1970). In confluent cultures, normal fibroblasts make contact with neighbouring cells at various points around their periphery and do not therefore display significant migratory activity. In contrast, transformed fibroblasts do not display contact inhibition of cell movement. These differences in social interactions may contribute to the relatively low level of migration seen in confluent cultures of normal adult cells and the elevated levels of migration in similar cultures of transformed cells. Foetal fibroblasts are similar to normal adult cells in that they display contact inhibition of cell movement (Abercrombie *et al.* 1968).

Foetal and normal adult fibroblasts differ with respect to the orientation cells adopt in confluent culture. As can be seen in Fig. 5, normal adult skin fibroblasts form a characteristic swirl pattern of parallel aligned cells, while foetal fibroblasts exhibit a considerable degree of overlapping similar to that shown by transformed cells. The foetal-like fibroblasts of breast cancer patients form parallel arrays of aligned cells in confluent culture and in this sense are indistinguishable from normal adult cells.

Secretion of soluble factors capable of affecting cell migration

We have recently reported (Schor *et al.* 1987*a*) that conditioned medium (CM) from foetal fibroblasts stimulates the migration of normal adult fibroblasts in high-density culture to the elevated levels characteristically achieved by foetal cells

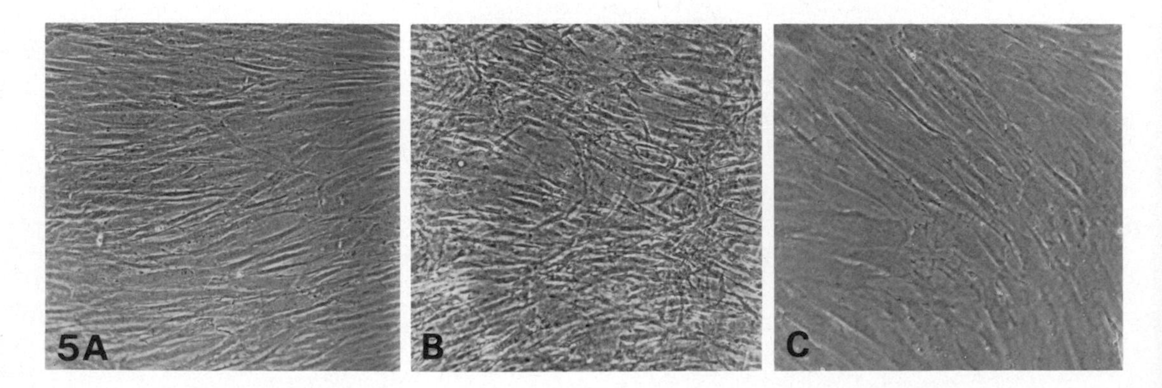

Fig. 5. Confluent cultures of normal adult fibroblasts (A), foetal fibroblasts (B), and breast cancer patient fibroblasts (C) growing on the surface of collagen gel substrata. Phase optics: ×266.

Table 2. *The effects of foetal and adult conditioned medium (CM) on fibroblast migration at different plating densities*

Target cell	CM	% Of cells within gel matrix	
		Low density	High density
Adult	None	21·2	2·9
	Foetal	19·8	14·1
	Adult	27·0	4·1
Foetal	None	15·2	12·9
	Foetal	12·9	10·5
	Adult	13·7	12·6

Adult and foetal fibroblasts were plated on collagen gel substrata at low and high cell densities in growth medium containing 5 % calf serum and 25 % of the indicated CM. Cultures were incubated for 4 days and the % of cells within the gel matrix then measured. Foetal CM stimulates the migration of adult fibroblasts plated at high cell density.

(Table 2); foetal CM has no effect on the already elevated level of migration achieved by adult fibroblasts in low-density culture. Exposure of adult fibroblasts to foetal CM therefore has the overall effect of inducing them to express CDMI values falling within the foetal range. In contrast, adult CM has no effect on foetal or adult fibroblast migration at either low or high density, suggesting that adult fibroblasts do not produce an inhibitor of cell migration.

The CM obtained from the foetal-like fibroblasts of cancer patients also contains migration-stimulating activity with similar characteristics to that found in foetal CM. Initial biochemical characterization of the migration stimulating factor (MSF) in foetal and cancer patient fibroblast CM indicates that it is trypsin-sensitive, heat-labile, non-dialysable and sensitive to alkylation/reduction (Schor *et al.* 1987*a*). FPLC gel filtration data indicate that MSF in both foetal and cancer patient fibroblast CM is found in a single peak with an estimated M_r of approximately 55×10^3 (Schor *et al.* unpublished data).

Preliminary investigations indicate that the stimulatory effect of foetal fibroblast CM on the migration of adult target cells is completely inhibited by *Streptomyces* hyaluronidase at 10 units ml^{-1}. These data suggest that the primary effect of the foetal migration factor may be to stimulate hyaluronic acid synthesis by the adult fibroblasts, which in turn stimulates cell migration. This conclusion is supported by direct measurement of hyaluronic acid biosynthesis by adult fibroblasts exposed to foetal CM (Schor *et al.* unpublished data) and is consistent with the growing body of data indicating that many well-characterized peptide growth and/or transforming factors (e.g. EGF, TGF-beta) exert a primary effect on matrix biosynthesis (Ignotz & Massague, 1986).

Taken together, these data lend strong support to the view that the differences in CDMI values expressed by foetal and adult fibroblasts results principally from the production of a migration-stimulating peptide factor by the foetal cells. Data relating to the purification and further biochemical characterization of this factor will be published.

POSSIBLE ROLE OF ABERRANT FIBROBLASTS IN THE PATHOGENESIS OF EPITHELIAL CANCERS

The existence of aberrant fibroblasts in apparently normal skin of cancer patients and their unaffected first-degree relatives is a rather unexpected finding, the interpretation of which remains unclear. The majority of previous studies in this area have dealt with skin fibroblasts derived from patients with relatively rare cancer syndromes in which the involvement of genetic factors in determining disease susceptibility is unambiguous (e.g. familial polyposis coli). As a consequence of the well-recognized genetic nature of these conditions, the aberrant skin fibroblasts have tended to be viewed as a convenient cell type with which to demonstrate genomic abnormalities also expressed by the relevant target epithelial population, but have not generally been considered to contribute directly to the carcinogenic process themselves (Kopelovich, 1982).

We have presented an alternative, but not mutually exclusive, interpretation, which stems from an appreciation of the important role played by epithelial–mesenchymal interactions in the control of cell behaviour (Schor *et al.* 1987*b*). According to this view, aberrations expressed solely by fibroblasts are postulated to influence the development of an epithelial tumour. More specifically, we suggest that: (1) foetal fibroblasts undergo programmed transitions in phenotype during the course of normal development; (2) these foetal-to-adult transitions do not occur in certain individuals; and (3) the resultant dysfunction in normal epithelial–mesenchymal interactions puts the affected individual at an elevated risk of developing cancer.

Foetal fibroblasts undergo phenotypic transitions during normal development

We have demonstrated that the migration of foetal and adult fibroblasts is differentially affected by cell density. These results imply that foetal fibroblasts undergo a transition in migratory phenotype during the course of normal development. This suggestion is supported by our observation (Schor *et al.* 1985*a*) that cloned foetal lines undergo a spontaneous and stable transition to expression of CDMI values falling within the normal adult range after 50–55 population doublings in tissue culture (i.e. approximately 3/4 of their *in vitro* lifespan). This foetal-to-adult transition is accompanied by a cessation in the production of MSF (Table 3).

Foetal and adult fibroblasts differ from each other by a number of other criteria; these include the ability to form colonies in semi-solid medium (Nakano & Ts'O, 1981), the production of various growth and transforming factors (Clemmons, 1983; Lawrence *et al.* 1984; Eisinger *et al.* 1985), the production of an epithelial cell scatter factor (Stoker & Perryman, 1986), and the synthesis of particular isoforms of matrix macromolecules (Matsura & Hakomori, 1985; Castellani *et al.* 1986). Programmed foetal-to-adult transitions in these characteristics occur at various times during development, including the neonatal period, and are believed to play an important role in the control and integration of tissue interactions (Caplan *et al.* 1983).

These foetal-to-adult transitions do not occur in certain individuals

The aberrant phenotypic characteristics displayed by cancer patient fibroblasts have generally been discussed in terms of cell transformation. Foetal fibroblasts, however, display many of the phenotypic characteristics used to define transformation (as indicated in the preceding section), thus lending support to the view that the aberrant fibroblasts of cancer patients should properly be thought of as foetal-like. In this context, it may be noted that Bartal *et al.* (1986) reported that monoclonal antibody VIF3 specifically recognizes a determinant present on foetal fibroblasts, but not normal adult cells; immunolocalization studies revealed that this antibody also stained a subset of apparently foetal-like fibroblasts associated with *all* the carcinomas they examined. Chiquet-Ehrismann *et al.* (1986) demonstrated that the newly described matrix macromolecule tenascin is found in various foetal connective tissues, but is generally absent from adult tissue; interestingly, tenascin was consistently demonstrated in the stroma associated with mammary carcinomas.

The disruption in epithelial–mesenchymal interactions produced by the presence of aberrant fibroblasts plays a causative role in cancer development

Direct experimental support of this hypothesis has been provided by the studies of Sakakura (1983), who observed that implantation of foetal (but not adult) fibroblasts into the adult rat mammary gland induced the hyperplastic growth of the normal glandular epithelial elements and rendered them more sensitive to overt neoplastic transformation by carcinogenic agents. Subsequent work revealed that foetal fibroblasts produce a soluble factor that promotes the proliferation and inhibits the differentiation of normal adult mammary epithelial cells (Taga *et al.* 1983).

Possible clinical implications

The central point of our hypothesis is that the expression of certain abnormalities by fibroblasts may be causally related to the development of epithelial tumours.

Table 3. *The effects of pre- and post-transition foetal CM on the migration of adult fibroblasts*

Target cell	Source of CM	% Of cell within gel matrix
Adult	None	5·8
	Pre-transition foetal	17·3
	Post-transition foetal	5·0

Adult fibroblasts were plated at high cell density in growth medium containing 5 % calf serum and 25 % of the indicated CM. Cultures were incubated for 4 days and the % of cells within the gel matrix then measured. CM obtained from foetal fibroblasts expressing foetal CDMI values (i.e. pre-transition cells) contained migration stimulating activity, whilst CM from foetal cells expressing adult CDMI values (i.e. post-transition cells) was devoid of this activity.

Should this indeed prove to be the case, such a paradigm has far reaching clinical implications for population screening and for the development of novel preventative or therapeutic agents targeted at stromal fibroblasts rather than the neoplastic epithelial cells.

This work has been entirely supported by generous research grants from the Cancer Research Campaign. The authors thank Mr G. Rushton for excellent technical assistance.

REFERENCES

ABE, S., STEINMANN, B. U., WAHL, L. M. & MARTIN, G. R. (1979). High cell density alters the ratio of type III to I collagen synthesis by fibroblasts. *Nature, Lond.* **279**, 442–444.

ABERCROMBIE, M. (1970). Contact inhibition in tissue culture. *In Vitro* **6**, 126–142.

ABERCROMBIE, M., LAMONT, D. M. & STEPHENSON, E. M. (1968). The monolayering in tissue culture of fibroblasts from different sources. *Proc. R. Soc. Lond.* B **170**, 349–360.

ALLEN, T. D. & SCHOR, S. L. (1983). The contraction of collagen matrices by dermal fibroblasts. *J. Ultrastruct. Res.* **83**, 205–219.

ALI, I. U. & HYNES, R. O. (1978). Effects of LETS glycoprotein on cell motility. *Cell* **14**, 439–446.

ANTECOL, M. H., DARVEAU, A., SONENBERG, N. & MUKHERJEE, B. B. (1986). Altered biochemical properties of actin in normal skin fibroblasts from individuals predisposed to dominantly inherited cancers. *Cancer Res.* **46**, 1867–1873.

AZZARONE, B., MAREEL, M., BILLARD, C., SCEMANA, P., CHAPONNIER, C. & MACIERA-COEHLO, A. (1984). Abnormal properties of skin fibroblasts from patients with breast cancer. *Int. J. Cancer* **33**, 759–764.

AZZARONE, B., PEDULLA, D. & ROMANZI, C. A. (1976). Spontaneous transformation of human skin fibroblasts derived from neoplastic patients. *Nature, Lond.* **262**, 74–75.

AZZARONE, B., ROMANZI, C. A. & MACIEIRA-COELHO, A. (1981). Human skin fibroblasts from patients with mammary tumours; Differences in growth properties. *Cancer Detect. Prevent.* **4**, 249–259.

BARTAL, A. H., LICHTIG, C., CORDON-CARDO, C., FEIT, C., ROBINSON, E. & HIRSHAUT, Y. (1986). Monoclonal antibody defining fibroblasts appearing in fetal and neoplastic tissues. *J. natn. Cancer Inst.* **76**, 415–419.

BELL, E., IVARSSON, B. & MERRILL, C. (1979). Production of tissue-like structure by contraction of collagen lattices by human fibroblasts of different proliferative potential. *Proc. natn. Acad. Sci. U.S.A.* **76**, 1274–1278.

BERNANKE, D. H. & MARKWALD, R. R. (1979). Effects of hyaluronic acid on cardiac cushion tissue cells in collagen matrix cultures. *Tex. Rep. Biol. Med.* **39**, 271–285.

BISSELL, M., HALL, H. G. & PARRY, G. (1982). How does the extracellular matrix direct gene expression? *J. theor. Biol.* **99**, 31–68.

CAMERON, I. L. & POOL, T. B. (1981). *The Transformed Cell.* New York: Academic Press.

CAPLAN, A. I., FISZMAN, M. Y. & EPPENBERGER, H. M. (1983). Molecular and cell isoforms during development. *Science* **221**, 921–927.

CASTELLANI, P., SIRI, A., ROSELLINI, C., INFUSINI, E., BORSI, L. & ZARDI, L. (1986). Transformed cells release different fibronectin variants than do normal cells. *J. Cell Biol.* **103**, 1671–1678.

CHAUDHURI, S., KOPROSKA, I. & ROWINSKI, J. (1975). Different agglutinability of fibroblasts underlying various precursor lesions of human uterine cervical carcinoma. *Cancer Res.* **35**, 2350–2354.

CHIQUET-EHRISMANN, R., MACKIE, E., PEARSON, C. A. & SAKAKURA, T. (1986). Tenascin: An extracellular matrix protein involved in tissue interactions during fetal development of oncogenesis. *Cell* **47**, 131–139.

CLEMMONS, D. R. (1983). Age-dependent production of a competence factor by human fibroblasts. *J. cell. Physiol.* **114**, 61–67.

CUHNA, G. R., BIGSBY, R. M., COOKE, P. S. & SUGIMURA, Y. (1985). Stromal–epithelial interactions in adult organs. *Cell Differ.* **17**, 137–148.

Cummings, E. G., Bringas, P., Grodin, M. S. & Slavkin, H. (1981). Epithelial-directed mesenchyme differentiation *in vitro*. *Differentiation* **20**, 1–9.

Curalto, L., Borgia, R., Donati, M. B. & Morasca, L. (1982). Fibrin clot retractile activity of fibroblast-like cells from normal individuals and cancer patients. *Cell Biol. Int. Rep.* **6**, 609–618.

Danes, B. S. (1980). Heritable colonic cancer syndromes: Induction of anchorage independent growth in dermal cultures derived from patients with adenomatosis of the colon and rectum. *Oncology* **37**, 386–389.

Durning, P., Schor, S. L. & Sellwood, R. A. S. (1984). Fibroblasts from patients with breast cancer show abnormal migratory behaviour *in vitro*. *Lancet* **I**, 890–892.

Eisinger, M., Marko, O., Ogata, S. I. & Old, L. J. (1985). Growth regulation of human melanocytes: Mitogenic factors in extracts of melanoma, astrocytoma and fibroblast lines. *Science* **229**, 984–986.

Epstein, E. H. (1974). $[\alpha 1(III)]_3$ human skin collagen. Release by pepsin digestion and preponderance in fetal life. *J. biol. Chem.* **249**, 3225–3231.

Grinnell, F. & Lamke, C. R. (1984). Reorganization of hydrated collagen lattices by human skin fibroblasts. *J. Cell Sci.* **66**, 51–63.

Gurdon, J. (1987). Embryonic induction – molecular prospects. *Development* **99**, 285–306.

Haggie, J., Birch, J. M., Schor, S. L., Howell, A. & Sellwood, R. A. S. (1985). Prevalence of a family history in premenopausal patients with cancer of the breast. *Proc. Biennial Breast Cancer Research Conference*, London, p. 110.

Hill, M. W. & Mackenzie, I. C. (1984). The influence of differing connective tissue substrates on the maintenance of adult stratified squamous epithelia. *Cell Tiss. Res.* **237**, 473–478.

Hynes, R. O., Destree, A. T., Perkins, M. E. & Wagner, D. D. (1979). Cell surface fibronectin and oncogenic transformation. *J. supramolec. Struct.* **11**, 95–104.

Ignotz, R. A. & Massague, J. (1986). Transforming growth factor beta stimulates the expression of fibronectin and collagen and their incorporation into the extracellular matrix. *J. biol. Chem.* **261**, 4337–4345.

Johnson-Wint, B. & Gross, J. (1984). Regulation of connective tissue collagenase production: Stimulators from adult and fetal epidermal cells. *J. Cell Biol.* **98**, 90–96.

Kopelovich, L. (1982). Hereditary adenomatosis of the colon and rectum: Relevance to cancer promotion and cancer control in humans. *Cancer Genet. Cytogenet.* **5**, 333–351.

Kopelovich, L., Conlon, S. & Pollack, R. (1977). Defective organization of actin in cultured skin fibroblasts. *Proc. natn. Acad. Sci. U.S.A.* **74**, 3019–3022.

Lawrence, D. A. (1985). Transforming growth factors – An overview. *Biol. Cell* **53**, 93–98.

Lawrence, D. A., Pircher, C. K. M. & Jullien, P. (1984). Normal embryo fibroblasts release transforming growth factor in latent form. *J. cell. Physiol.* **121**, 184–188.

Lynch, H. T., Albano, W. A., Heieck, J. J., Mulcahy, G. M., Lynch, J. F., Layton, M. A. & Danes, B. S. (1984). Genetics, biomarkers and control of breast cancer: A review. *Cancer Genet. Cytogenet.* **13**, 43–92.

Matsura, H. & Hakomori, S. I. (1985). The oncofetal domain of fibronectin defined by a monoclonal antibody FDC-6: Its presence in fetal and tumor tissues and its absence in those from normal tissue and plasma. *Proc. natn. Acad. Sci. U.S.A.* **83**, 6517–6521.

Mautner, V. & Hynes, R. O. (1977). Surface distribution of LETS protein in relation to the cytoskeleton of normal and transformed fibroblasts. *J. Cell Biol.* **75**, 743–768.

Nakano, S. & Ts'o, P. O. (1981). Cellular differentiation and neoplasia: Characterization of subpopulations of cells that have neoplasia-related growth properties in Syrian hamster embryo cell cultures. *Proc. natn. Acad. Sci. U.S.A.* **78**, 4995–4999.

Ottman, R., Pike, M. C., King, M.-C. & Henderson, B. E. (1983). Practical guide for estimating risk of familial breast cancer. *Lancet* **II**, 556–558.

Pfeffer, L., Lipkin, M., Stutman, O. & Kopelovich, L. (1976). Growth abnormalities of cultured skin fibroblasts derived from individuals with hereditary adenomatosis of the colon and rectum. *J. cell. Physiol.* **89**, 29–38.

Rubin, H. (1985). Cancer as a dynamic developmental disorder. *Cancer Res.* **45**, 2935–2942.

Saiag, P., Coulomb, B., Lebreton, C., Bell, E. & Dubertret, L. (1985). Psoriatic fibroblasts induce hyperproliferation of normal keratinocytes in a skin equivalent model *in vitro*. *Science* **230**, 669–672.

SAKAKURA, T. (1983). Epithelial–mesenchymal interactions in mammary gland development and its perturbation in relation to tumorigenesis. In *Understanding Breast Cancer* (ed. M. A. Rich, J. C. Hager & P. Furmanski), pp. 261–284. New York: Marcel Dekker.

SAWYER, R. H. & FALLON, J. F. (1983). *Epithelial–Mesenchymal Interactions in Development*. New York: Praeger.

SCHOR, A. M. & SCHOR, S. L. (1986). The isolation and culture of endothelial cells and pericytes from the bovine retinal microvasculature. A comparative study with large vessel vascular cells. *Microvasc. Res.* **32**, 21–38.

SCHOR, S. L. (1980). Cell proliferation and migration within three-dimensional collagen gels. *J. Cell Sci.* **41**, 159–175.

SCHOR, S. L., HAGGIE, J. A., DURNING, P., HOWELL, A., SMITH, L., SELLWOOD, R. A. S. & CROWTHER, D. (1986). Occurrence of a fetal fibroblast phenotype in familial breast cancer. *Int. J. Cancer* **37**, 831–836.

SCHOR, S. L., SCHOR, A. M. & BAZILL, G. W. (1981). The effects of fibronectin on the migration of human foreskin fibroblasts and Syrian hamster melanoma cells into three-dimensional gels of native collagen fibres. *J. Cell Sci.* **48**, 301–314.

SCHOR, S. L., SCHOR, A. M., DURNING, P. & RUSHTON, G. (1985*b*). Skin fibroblasts obtained from cancer patients display foetal-like behaviour on collagen gels. *J. Cell Sci.* **73**, 235–244.

SCHOR, S. L., SCHOR, A. M., HOWELL, A. & CROWTHER, D. (1987*b*). Hypothesis: Persistent expression of fetal phenotypic characteristics by fibroblasts is associated with an increased susceptibility to neoplastic disease. *Expl Cell Biol.* **55**, 11–17.

SCHOR, S. L., SCHOR, A. M., RUSHTON, G. & MCCORMICK, L. (1987*a*). Fetal and cancer patient fibroblasts secrete a soluble migration stimulating factor not produced by normal adult cells. *Cell Biol. Int. Rep.* **11**, 231.

SCHOR, S. L., SCHOR, A. M., RUSHTON, G. & SMITH, L. (1985*a*). Adult, foetal and transformed fibroblasts display different migratory phenotypes on collagen gels: Evidence for an isoformic transition during foetal development. *J. Cell Sci.* **73**, 221–234.

SCHOR, S. L., SCHOR, A. M., WINN, B. & RUSHTON, B. (1982). The use of three-dimensional collagen gels for the study of tumour cell invasion *in vitro*: Experimental parameters influencing cell migration into the gel matrix. *Int. J. Cancer* **29**, 57–62.

SMITH, H. S., OWENS, R. B., HILLER, A. J., NELSON-REES, W. A. & JOHNSTON, J. O. (1976). Biology of cell in tissue culture. I. Characterization of cells obtained from osteogenic sarcoma. *Int. J. Cancer* **17**, 219–234.

STEINBERG, B. M., SMITH, K., COLOZZO, M. & POLLACK, R. (1980). Establishment and transformation diminish the ability of fibroblasts to contract a native collagen gel. *J. Cell Biol.* **87**, 304–308.

STOKER, M. & PERRYMAN, M. (1986). An epithelial scatter factor released by embryo fibroblasts. *J. Cell Sci.* **77**, 209–224.

TAGA, M., SAKAKURA, T. & OKA, T. (1983). Identification and partial purification of mesenchyme derived growth factor that stimulates the proliferation and inhibits the terminal differentiation of mammary epithelium in culture. *J. Cell Biol.* **97**, 317a.

TRELSTAD, R. L. (1984). *Role of the Extracellular Matrix in Development*. New York: Academic Press.

WYNFORD-THOMAS, D., SMITH, P. & WILLIAMS, E. D. (1986). Prolongation of fibroblast life span associated with epithelial rat tumor development. *Cancer Res.* **46**, 3125–3127.

J. Cell Sci. Suppl. 8, 181–197 (1987)

MECHANISMS OF TUMOUR CELL METASTASIS

ROGER W. PARISH, CHRISTIAN SCHMIDHAUSER, THOMAS SCHMIDT AND ROBERT K. DUDLER

Plant Biology Institute, University of Zürich, Zollikerstrasse 107, CH-8008 Zürich, Switzerland

SUMMARY

Abercrombie and his colleagues have accumulated evidence that changes in the heterotypic contact-inhibition response are largely responsible for the invasiveness of cells, at least in culture. We have identified a 37 000 M_r protein on the surface of mouse fibrosarcoma cells that is involved in their *in vitro* invasion. Blocking this protein with specific antibodies inhibits the invasion of chicken heart fibroblasts by the tumour cells and normal heterotypic contact inhibition is restored. These results are presented in the general framework of metastatic mechanisms and we review a selection of more recent studies aimed at describing the metastatic phenotype in molecular terms.

INTRODUCTION

Primary solid tumours are benign and it is the appearance of the metastatic phenotype that eventually kills the host. An understanding of the mechanisms leading to uncontrolled cell proliferation will presumably arise from the study of oncogenes. However, the biochemical changes critical for the development of metastatic potential are poorly understood. Whether oncogene activation also directs such changes is at present unclear (see below).

Attempts to recognize mechanisms required for metastasis are generally based on analysis of the sequence of events involved (Liotta *et al.* 1986). The metastatic cascade includes:

(1) Release from the primary tumour.

(2) Invasion of the epithelial basement membrane to reach the interstitial stroma.

(3) Invasion of the basement membrane and endothelial layer of the blood vessel wall (intravasation).

(4) Dissemination *via* the blood or lymphatics.

(5) Arrest in capillaries of another organ by adherence to endothelial cell luminal surfaces and/or exposed basement membranes.

(6) Penetration of the vascular endothelium and/or its underlying basal lamina (extravasation).

(7) Proliferation in the parenchyma of the organ.

The term 'invasion' has been used in two contexts. First, to describe cell infiltration of the extracellular matrix. The basal membrane, for example, represents a type of matrix that is normally impermeable to large proteins, but becomes permeable to cell movement during tissue healing, remodelling, inflammation and neoplasia (Liotta *et al.* 1986). The *in vitro* systems used to study this type of invasion do not include cells additional to those of the tumour under examination. The second type of invasion, so-called cellular invasion, relates to the contact interactions between moving cells (Heaysman, 1978; Abercrombie, 1979; Paddock & Dunn, 1986). The behaviour of two cell types during and following collision *in vitro* can be related to their metastatic potential *in vivo* (see below).

This paper summarizes a selection of the more recent studies on the metastatic cascade. It is not our aim to review the field, but a number of reviews covering earlier work are cited. Our own interests concern the cell contact-related invasive behaviour. However, we present our results in the general framework of metastatic mechanisms.

Metastasis also implies the cells are able to evade the host defences. The mechanisms involved are unknown, although both decreased and increased expression of the major histocompatibility complex antigens have been invoked (Hart, 1985). The greatly reduced expression of the major histocompatibility complex found in many primary tumours suggests therapeutic approaches. Immunization with parental tumour cells in which these antigens have been induced (e.g. by transfection or interferon treatment) can afford protection against the untreated tumour cells (Tanaka *et al.* 1986). These immunological aspects are not covered here.

EXPRESSION OF THE METASTATIC PHENOTYPE

Role of oncogenes

Do oncogenes influence not only cell proliferation but also the development of the malignant phenotype? Results to date are preliminary and contradictory.

Greig *et al.* (1985) transfected NIH 3T3 cells with the c-Ha-*ras* 1 gene and found that, in the mouse, both tumorigenicity was accelerated and metastatic potential was enhanced. However, under specific conditions (e.g. inoculation in the foot pad), non-transfected NIH 3T3 cells were also metastatic. The transformed cells formed lung metastases irrespective of the site of implantation. The interpretation is that the normal cell population contains a subpopulation of cells expressing malignant properties, transfection with c-Ha-*ras* 1 accelerating the formation of metastases. Growth of transformed cells was faster *in vivo*, although their proliferative capacity was the same as non-transformed cells *in vitro*. Moreover, the culture history of the NIH 3T3 cells was found to influence their tumorigenicity.

These results underline the difficulties associated with studying immortalized cell lines and of correlating *in vivo* and *in vitro* findings.

Bradley *et al.* (1986) found that NIH 3T3 cells transformed with a wide variety of either normal or activated mammalian *ras* genes, when injected into the tail vein of nude mice, formed approximately equal numbers of lung metastases. Non-transfected cells failed to metastasize. The authors conclude that mutation or overexpression of *ras* switches on the phenotype required for metastases in NIH 3T3 cells. Moreover, they cite unpublished experiments in which first-passage rat embryo cells could be converted to the metastatic phenotype within 3·5 generations of a *myc* and *ras* transfection.

Nevertheless, it would be premature to contend that rapid transformation of cells to a metastatic phenotype is simply dependent on the appropriate activation of oncogenes. Olsson & Forchhammer (1984) induced the expression of the metastatic phenotype in a stable, non-metastatic mouse tumour following demethylation of the DNA with 5 -azacytidine. The presence of proteins specific for the metastatic cells indicates that gene activation may have occurred. The results imply that the genetic bases for tumorigenicity and metastatic activity do at least differ partly from one another.

Identification of genes bestowing the metastic phenotype

Approaches that were successful in identifying oncogenes are now being applied to the search for genes conferring metastatic potential on tumorigenic cells. Bernstein & Weinberg (1985) transfected EJ-Ha-*ras* oncogene-transformed NIH 3T3 mouse fibroblasts with genomic DNA isolated from nine metastatic human cell lines. Cells transformed with *ras* and inoculated intramuscularly, subcutaneously, intraperitoneally or in the foot pad did not have a significantly high rate of metastases formation in immunocompetent mice. Tail vein injection resulted in a 50% rate of metastasis. When DNA from a human cervical carcinoma was transfected into the *ras*-transformed cells, one of the resulting colonies yielded lung metastases after subcutaneous injection. Second-round transfection of DNA isolated from these metastases increased the frequency of metastases formation. A human DNA fragment that remained associated with the metastatic phenotype through the two cycles of DNA passage has not been identified. However, the results indicate that the expression of a single gene may suffice, suggesting that only a small number of steps are required for tumorigenic cells to become metastatic. Alternatively, the transfected gene(s) may confer protection against the immune system. In fact, there was uniform metastatic spread of the *ras*-transformed NIH 3T3 cells in immunoincompetent (irradiated) nude mice but not in immunocompetent, histocompatible animals.

Recently, Kerbel *et al.* (1987) found that the process of calcium phosphate-mediated DNA transfection itself can lead to heritable changes in the malignant behaviour of transfected tumour cells. These changes are observed at high frequency and may be a function of the extent of genetic instability of the cell line transfected. The results raise doubts about the interpretation of transfection experiments in the study of tumour progression and metastasis since they show that products of a transferred gene may not be responsible for the observed phenotype of transfectants.

Antioncogenes

Malignancy can be suppressed when malignant and non-malignant cells are fused (Stanbridge, 1976; Harris, 1986), suggesting that tumours may arise as a consequence of recessive mutations in somatic cells. Such recessive cancer genes or antioncogenes (so named because of the antioncogenic effect of the presence of one allele) have also been identified through the study of heriditary cancer (Knudson, 1986). (Harris (1986) argued that no cellular genes acting to produce tumours in a genetically dominant fashion have been found.) Antioncogenes differ from oncogenes in being inactive in malignant cells and cancer occurs when no normal copy is present. The normal alleles are probably important tissue-regulation genes, perhaps regulating the expression of one or more oncogenes and/or growth factors. Their role in metastasis is unknown.

ADHESIVE PROPERTIES OF METASTATIC CELLS

Adhesion to the vascular endothelium

The first barrier to cells that are disseminated throughout the vascular system is the endothelial lining of capillaries (Weiss, 1976; Fidler, 1978). Tumour cells must adhere to the endothelium before passing through it. Auerbach & Joseph (1984) postulated that capillary endothelial cells differ in their surface antigens, the differences reflecting their developmental history. The distinct organ-associated antigens on their surfaces would determine the tumour types that recognize and adhere to them. This would explain the preferential metastasis of tumours to various organs in the body (Weiss, 1976; Fidler, 1978; Fidler & Hart, 1982). To examine the role of differential tumour cell adhesion in preferential metastasis, Alby & Auerbach (1984) used endothelial cells from mouse brain capillaries or ovaries in an *in vitro* assay system for adhesion. They found that ovary-derived teratoma cells and a testicular teratoma with ovary seeding properties adhered preferentially to ovary endothelial cells. On the other hand, glioma cells, an endothelioma and a bladder tumour line adhered preferentially to the brain endothelial cells. Hence, cell surface differences that can be distinguished by tumour cells are present on endothelial cells derived from different sources.

At present, too few endothelial cell types are available for study to validate the model. However, lymphocyte homing studies demonstrate clearly the importance of endothelial cell specificity in regulating the extravasation of circulating cells (Chin *et al.* 1983). Lymphocyte adherence to and penetration through specialized endothelial cells depend on the presence of specific adherence molecules on the endothelial cells. Moreover, there is organ specificity in this lymphocyte–endothelial cell interactive system (Gallatin *et al.* 1983).

Adhesion to the basement membrane

Adhesion of tumour cells to the subendothelial matrix might also be expected to be a prerequisite for extravasation (Kramer & Nicolson, 1979). Many metastatic cells bind preferentially to basement membrane (type IV) collagen using laminin as an attachment protein (Terranova *et al.* 1986).

Vollmers & Birchmeier (1983) have selected monoclonal antibodies that block the adhesion of mouse B16 melanoma cells to tissue culture dishes. The antibodies recognized antigens on the B16 cells but not on normal mouse cells. The monoclonal antibodies, when either preabsorbed by the melanoma cells or injected intraperitoneally before tumour cells, were found to abolish lung colonization by tail-vein-injected B16 lines.

Such results raise hopes that identification of molecules involved in endothelial or matrix adhesion will open the way to clinical treatment with antibodies. Unfortunately, tumour cells appear to have a variety of molecules that can assist adhesion, and inhibition of one such molecule with antibodies may simply select for cells with alternative adhesion mechanisms. Clearly, the heterogeneity and plasticity of metastasizing cells is an enigma facing any antigen-directed treatment.

Adhesion in the primary tumour

Certain cell adhesion molecules (CAMS) have been identified. N-CAM, the adhesion molecule from nerve tissue, is implicated in nerve fasciculation, nerve-muscle binding, the development of retinal layers in organ culture, and early embryonic events (Edelman, 1985). Transformation of a rat cerebellar cell line with Rous sarcoma virus resulted in decreased N-CAM expression coupled with a decrease in cell–cell adhesion (Greenberg *et al.* 1984). The loss of a specific adhesion system would be expected to facilitate the detachment of tumour cells from the primary tumour and surrounding tissue. Unfortunately, the significance of the results is uncertain, since a chemically transformed cerebellar cell line had high levels of N-CAM.

Role of carbohydrate moieties

Cell surface carbohydrates appear to be involved in cell adhesiveness and recognition of target organs. The attachment and spreading of cells *in vitro* is modified by treatments with neuraminidase (Dennis *et al.* 1982), glycosidases and lectins (Grimstad *et al.* 1984). Cell surface lectins that aggregate liver-metastasizing tumour cells have been found on normal hepatocytes (Springer *et al.* 1983).

Highly branched and sialylated N-linked oligosaccharides are commonly found in malignant and transformed cells and result in altered lectin-binding characteristics (Nicolson, 1982). A direct correlation between sialylation of galactose and *N*-acetylgalactosamine residues and metastatic capacity has been reported (Yogeeswaran & Salk, 1981; Altvogt *et al.* 1983). Swainsonine, a drug that inhibits Golgi α-mannosidase II and causes the formation of complex high mannose, hybrid-type oligosaccharides, reduced by 80% the ability of tail-vein-injected B16 murine melanoma cells to colonize lungs (Humphries *et al.* 1986). The treated cells were cleared from the lungs at a greater rate than the control cells, suggesting that tumour retention (adhesion) by the target organ was altered. These results suggest that the specific structure of the carbohydrate (orientation and/or structure) is essential for successful colonization of target organs.

TUMOUR CELL INVASION OF BASEMENT MEMBRANES

Since basement membranes line most blood vessels, thereby creating a physical barrier to the passage of cells, metastatic cells must be able to degrade as well as bind to these membranes (Jones & De Clerck, 1982). The constitution of basement membranes is at least partly known and the levels of relevant digestive enzymes produced by tumour cells have been intensively studied. Furthermore, a variety of *in vitro* systems using reconstituted basement membrane-like matrices or isolated basement membranes have been employed to study directly this aspect of the invasive capacity of tumour cells.

The matrix-invasiveness or the metastatic potential of many tumours has been correlated with an increased production of proteolytic enzymes (Mullins & Rohrlicht, 1983). These include plasminogen activators (Dano *et al.* 1985), lysosomal hydrolases (Sloane & Honn, 1984) and collagenases (Liotta *et al.* 1982). Specific inhibitors of proteinases block tumour invasion *in vitro* and *in vivo* (Rossman & Troll, 1980).

Mignatti *et al.* (1986) found that invasion of the human amniotic membrane by mouse B16/BL6 melanoma cells (selected for metastatic potential) was prevented by inhibitors of collagenase and plasmin as well as anti-urokinase antibodies. Production of serine proteinases appeared to trigger an amplification mechanism, which resulted in the sequential generation of plasmin and collagenase. The crucial step appeared to be the activation of procollagenase.

Heparanases also assist tumour cells to invade the extracellular matrix (Nakajima *et al.* 1983; Nicolson *et al.* 1985). Certain sulphated polysaccharides inhibit the binding of lymphocytes to high endothelial venules and the passaging of lymphocytes through lymphoid organs (Brenan & Parish, 1986). Rat lung metastasis resulting from intravenous injection of mammary adenocarcinoma cells was significantly reduced by sulphated polysaccharides (e.g. heparin, fucoidan) (Coombe *et al.* 1987). The antimetastatic effect was independent of the ability of the polysaccharides to block coagulation. C. R. Parish *et al.* (unpublished) have shown that the inhibitory effect of the sulphated polysaccharides on metastasis was correlated with their inhibition of tumour cell-derived heparanases.

Although there is often a positive correlation between the ability of tumour cells to invade the extracellular matrix *in vitro* and their metastatic behaviour *in vivo*, it must be stressed that this type of invasiveness represents only a limited part of metastatic formation. Terranova *et al.* (1986) examined the properties of tumour cells able to penetrate a model basement membrane–stromal matrix consisting of laminin and type IV collagen reconstructed onto a disk of type I collagen. Some properties of cells derived from two tumour lines, selected for their ability to migrate through the matrix, were determined. When compared with the parent cells, the selected cells had a higher level of attachment to type IV collagen (40 and 55 %), bound more laminin (3- and 5-fold) and degraded collagen at a faster rate (2- and 2·5-fold). Moreover, when returned to the assay chambers, they penetrated new barriers 4- and 6-fold better than the parental population. Four cell lines selected in this way were examined for their ability to produce lung metastases after injection in the tail vein of mice. One of the lines produced about three times as many metastases as the parental line, whereas increases with the other three lines were between 25 and 100 %. Significantly, a second round of selection produced only moderate increases in metastatic activity, indicating that this type of invasiveness accounts for only a part of metastatic behaviour.

Primary human breast cancer cells could invade a denuded human amniotic basement membrane and were diploid (Smith *et al.* 1985). However, malignant effusion-derived cell cultures were aneuploid.

CELLULAR INVASION BY TUMOUR CELLS

Cellular invasion or cellular infiltration involves cell locomotion and cell–cell contact and is clearly important in both embryonic development and cancer metastasis. A number of methods have been developed to study cellular invasion both *in vitro* and *in vivo* (see Mareel *et al.* 1979, 1987; Kieler, 1984). There is, however, no quantitative measure of cellular invasion *in vivo* and histological descriptions must suffice. Invasion in culture can be readily described, but its relevance to invasion *in vivo* is uncertain. Nevertheless, there is considerable evidence that the contact interactions between moving cells in culture result in patterns that mimic aspects of certain fundamental biological processes, including malignant invasion (Abercrombie, 1979).

Contact inhibition and cellular invasion

Abercrombie and his colleagues (Abercrombie, 1979; Abercrombie & Heaysman, 1953, 1954, 1976; Abercrombie & Turner, 1978; Abercrombie *et al.* 1957, 1968; Heaysman, 1970, 1978; Stephenson & Stephenson, 1978; Paddock & Dunn, 1986) have used the confronted explant assay for assessing cellular invasion. In this method, two foci of cells (explants) are placed about 1 mm apart and the behaviour of cells is observed when the outgrowths (outwanderings) have met. Cellular invasion by metastatic cells, a distinct feature of their behaviour *in vivo*, can be observed in this culture system. Normal cells are not invasive in the assay. The general conclusion of many experiments is that changes in the normal contact inhibition response are the most important single factor in determining invasiveness. Since there has been some confusion in the literature about contact inhibition, it would be instructive to quote Abercrombie (1979). He wrote: "The term contact inhibition refers to the phenomenon of a cell ceasing to continue moving in the same direction after contact with another cell. It is not always operative .... Contact inhibition is observed as one or both colliding cells stopping and perhaps immediately turning aside. Stopping does not usually occur immediately after contact has been made". Effective cell contact is crucial for contact inhibition, since even small amounts of collagen between cells results in anomalous results.

The outward radial migration of cells from an explant reflects their mutual, homotypic contact inhibition. The homotypic contact inhibition of malignant cells is generally lower than that of non-malignant cells and the outward drive of the former is not so powerful. Whether this is related to their invasiveness is not clear. Standardized normal fibroblasts have been used as the control explant. Chicken heart fibroblasts have usually been chosen, although they can be interchanged with other fibroblasts.

Following confluence between the explants of the two different cell populations, one of three patterns ensues. First, a very high degree of obstruction with no cellular infiltration occurs. Such is the case when normal fibroblasts (e.g. from mouse muscle) are confronted with the standard chicken heart fibroblasts. The radial displacement of both cell types is greatly repressed and cells then move into the cell free space at the sides of the region of junction. Time-lapse filming indicates that the high heterotypic contact inhibition between the two non-malignant explants is responsible for the high degree of mutual obstruction. Stephenson & Stephenson (1978) reported invasion of human skin fibroblasts by chicken heart fibroblasts. However, contact inhibition between the two fibroblast populations was not defective and invasion was by diffusion-like movements into free space. It was assisted by the abandonment of territory by retreating human cells.

Second, infiltration or mixing of both cell populations may occur. Such behaviour, so-called reciprocal invasion, is observed when one of the explants consists of tumour cells that are invasive *in vivo*. Filming has indicated, for example, that the invasion of fibroblast populations by human melanoma cells is due to defective non-reciprocal heterologous contact inhibition (Stephenson & Stephenson, 1978). Fibroblasts were contact-inhibited by collision of their leading edges with those of the melanoma cells. However, reciprocal invasion of the melanoma cells by the fibroblasts did occur and may have been due to diffusion-like movement of the fibroblasts into free space.

Third, malignant tumour cells occupy territory held by the normal fibroblasts but not *vice versa* and some infiltration usually occurs (non-reciprocal invasion). The non-reciprocal invasion of chicken heart fibroblasts by a mouse fibrosarcoma (FS9) has recently been studied in detail using film analysis of single cell collisions (Paddock & Dunn, 1986). The invasive behaviour of the FS9 cells was not simply due to suppression or failure of the contact inhibition response. Following collision with the fibroblasts, FS9 cells showed contact promotion of locomotion, a reduced lateral displacement and a tendency to turn towards the point of initial marginal contact. Hence, FS9 cells showed an active invasory response. Moreover, after colliding with FS9 cells, the chicken heart fibroblasts showed higher levels of contact inhibition and greater lateral displacement than were induced by homotypic collisions. This response would function to increase the invasiveness of FS9 cells.

In addition to a failure of heterotypic contact inhibition, cell adhesion may be involved in tumour cell invasion *in vitro*. Homotypic adhesion could prevent penetration by a second cell population and strong heterotypic adhesion could obstruct the invading cells. However, since adhesion is by definition reciprocal it can hardly account for non-reciprocal invasion (Abercrombie, 1979).

Abercrombie (1979) formulated the concept of non-reciprocity (Heaysman, 1970) to explain invasion, invoking the presence of separate emittors and receptors. In this model, a tumour that induces strong contraction of a fibroblast would be a strong emittor but, when not itself inhibited by the fibroblast, it would be a weak receptor. In reciprocal inhibition, both cells would have emittors and receptors for each other.

The positive correlation between infiltration and occupation of territory by tumour cells in culture and their invasivity *in vivo* is encouraging. However, the contact responses are only observable in culture and it is difficult to be certain of their significance for pattern formation *in vivo*.

Identification of a surface protein that influences cell invasion in vitro

There is considerable evidence that changes in the surface of tumour cells are involved in the acquisition of the metastatic phenotype (Nicolson, 1982); however, the precise nature of these changes is not known. Moreover, it is not clear whether the same surface components are consistently involved or whether metastatic potential can be achieved by a variety of different combinations.

We wished to identify cell surface changes associated with the invasive behaviour (i.e. reduced heterotypic contact inhibition) in the confronted explant system. Our simple working hypothesis was that tumour cells become invasive as a result of either the acquisition or the loss of one or more surface proteins. We decided to use antibodies to detect and block relevant antigens, as such models have been successfully employed to study cell adhesion systems (Gerisch, 1986; Edelman, 1985).

We selected the chemically induced mouse fibrosarcoma (FS9) for our studies, a tumour showing non-reciprocal invasion in the confronted explant assay (Abercrombie, 1979; Paddock & Dunn, 1986). As a control we chose the non-invasive L929 mouse tumour cell line, which has the same haplotype as FS9.

We initially purified plasma membranes from the two cell types, which were then used as a source of surface antigens. Sodium dodecyl sulphate–PAGE showed some differences in the pattern of proteins associated with the plasma membrane of FS9 and L929 cells, in particular a $37\times10^3 M_r$ protein (denoted gp37) was prominent in FS9 membranes and either absent or only weakly detectable in L929 cells (Steinemann *et al.* 1984*a*). This appeared to be a glycoprotein, since following oxidation it was reduced with borohydride. Polyclonal antibodies directed against a variety of plasma membrane proteins in both cell types were obtained. The antibodies recognizing epitopes present on both cell types were removed by absorbing the antiserum directed against FS9 plasma membranes with L929 cells and *vice versa*. Western blotting showed that the preabsorbed FS9 antiserum mainly contained antibodies that recognized gp37. A $55\times10^3 M_r$ protein was the major antigen recognized after the L929 antiserum had been preabsorbed by FS9 cells.

The effects of the FS9 and L929 specific antisera on the invasion of chicken heart fibroblasts by FS9 cells in the confronted explant assay were examined. Fab fragments were first prepared from the antisera to avoid cell agglutination and surface deformation by divalent antibodies (Gerisch, 1986). The Fabs specific for FS9 membranes completely inhibited the invasion of the fibroblasts by FS9 cells at concentrations above $0{\cdot}8\,mg\,ml^{-1}$. Control Fabs or those specific for L929 cells had no effect.

Since the inhibitory Fabs were largely directed against gp37, it appeared that blocking this antigen was sufficient to prevent FS9 cell invasion. However, the Fabs did bind weakly to a number of other antigens specific for FS9 plasma membranes. Consequently, we produced a variety of monoclonal antibodies (mAbs) directed against FS9 plasma membrane antigens (Steinemann *et al.* 1984*b*). We selected mAbs that preferentially bound to FS9 rather than L929 cells. Western blotting identified the mAbs directed against gp37. Fabs prepared from a gp37-specific mAb (DD9, Fig. 1) inhibited FS9 invasion of fibroblasts at concentrations as low as 1 $\mu g\,ml^{-1}$ (Fig. 2). Two other mAbs recognizing different surface antigens specific for FS9 cells failed to influence invasion.

Immunofluorescence studies confirmed the presence of gp37 on the surface of FS9 cells (Steinemann *et al.* 1984*b*). The protein does not appear to be excreted by the cells, the low levels in the medium being sedimentable and presumably attached to shedded membranes or cell debris. Using specific mAbs we have shown that gp37 is

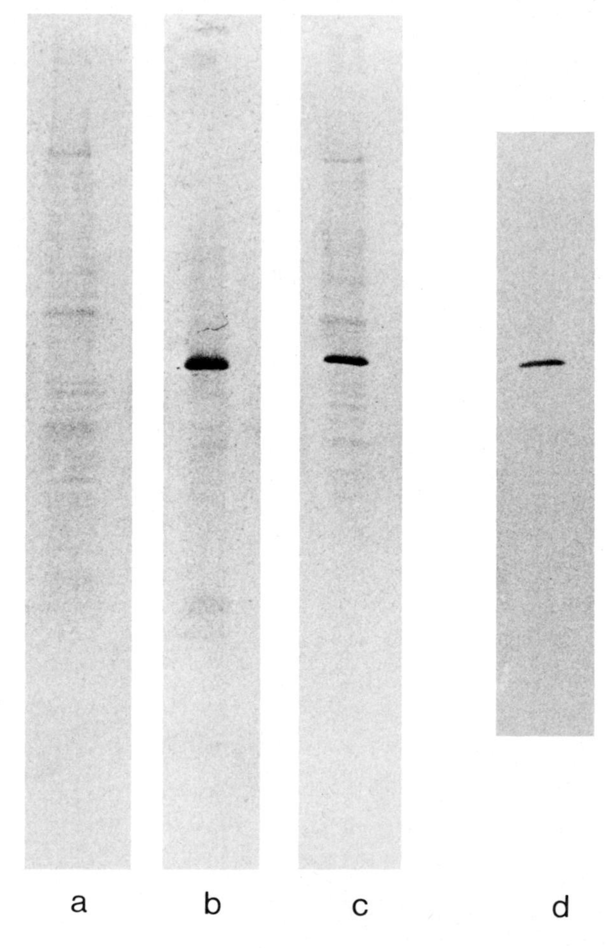

Fig. 1. Identification of gp37 using the monoclonal antibody DD9. Crude membranes or purified gp37 separated on SDS–PAGE gels were electroblotted and the filters incubated with DD9 antibody. Lane a, L929 cell membranes; lane b, FS9 fibrosarcoma membranes; lane c, MM96 human melanoma membranes; lane d, gp37 purified by immunoaffinity chromatography and gel elution.

not the 37K ($37 \times 10^3 M_r$) envelope glycoprotein of Rous sarcoma virus and is not a histocompatibility antigen. It is not related to the major excretable protein (MEP) or mitogen-releasable proteins (MRP), which have similar molecular weights and are excreted by transformed cells (see Steinemann *et al.* 1984*b*).

gp37 binds to concanavalin A. Following tunicamycin treatment of FS9 cells a 35K antigen appears in Western blots. This antigen does not bind to a concanavalin A affinity column (L. Catanzariti, Diplomarbeit, University of Zurich, 1985). We tentatively conclude that gp37 is *N*-glycosylated, but have not been able to determine whether *O*-sugars are present. Apparently, the mAb (DD9) does not bind to the *N*-sugars.

We are currently pursuing four lines of research:

(1) *Time-lapse filming of FS9–chicken heart fibroblast single cell collisions.* Preliminary experiments (in collaboration with Dr G. Dunn) indicate that gp37-specific Fab causes FS9 cells to become contact inhibited following heterotypic collisions with fibroblasts. Instead of showing contact promotion, the Fab-treated FS9 cells retreat from the fibroblasts following collision.

(2) *Cloning the gp37 gene.* We have used the mAb DD9 to purify gp37 (Fig. 1d). The first 28 N-terminal amino acids have been sequenced. A data bank search detected no known proteins with a similar sequence. We are using oligonucleotides to screen bacteriophage λ gt_{10} cDNA libraries for the relevant gene. We have synthesized a 16-amino acid peptide corresponding to the N-terminal sequence of gp37 and used it to obtain polyclonal antibodies specific for gp37 (Ingrid Siefert, Diplomarbeit, Universities of Zürich and Freiburg i. Breisgau, 1987). These antibodies and the mAbs are being used to screen a λgt_{11} expression library for the gene. Once the gene is obtained, transformation experiments can be used to discover whether introducing the protein into non-invasive cells is sufficient to make them invasive *in vitro* and *in vivo*. Mechanisms by which the gene is regulated can also be studied. Moreover, knowledge of the amino acid sequence will provide information about the structure/function of gp37 and its relationship to other proteins.

(3) *Ubiquity of gp37.* gp37 is not restricted to FS9 cells and we have found a variety of cell lines, including human tumours (Fig. 1c), that carry the antigen. There is a positive correlation between the presence of gp37 and invasion in the confronted explant assay. This invasion was consistently inhibited by gp37-specific Fabs.

(4) *Localization of gp37 in normal tissues.* Immunohistochemical methods have to date failed to detect the antigen in normal mouse tissues. A role for gp37 in embryo development, when specific cellular invasion is occurring, could be envisaged. Hence, we are screening mouse embryo tissue for the antigen.

Since so little is known about the mechanisms by which cells regulate movement and how cell contact influences these mechanisms, we can only speculate on the reasons why gp37 facilitates cellular invasion. According to the concept of non-reciprocity (Heaysman, 1970), FS9 cells are strong emittors and so gp37 may be part of the emission mechanism. Its presence may prevent the information deriving from cell contact from being translated into cell movement. Fab binding to gp37 may

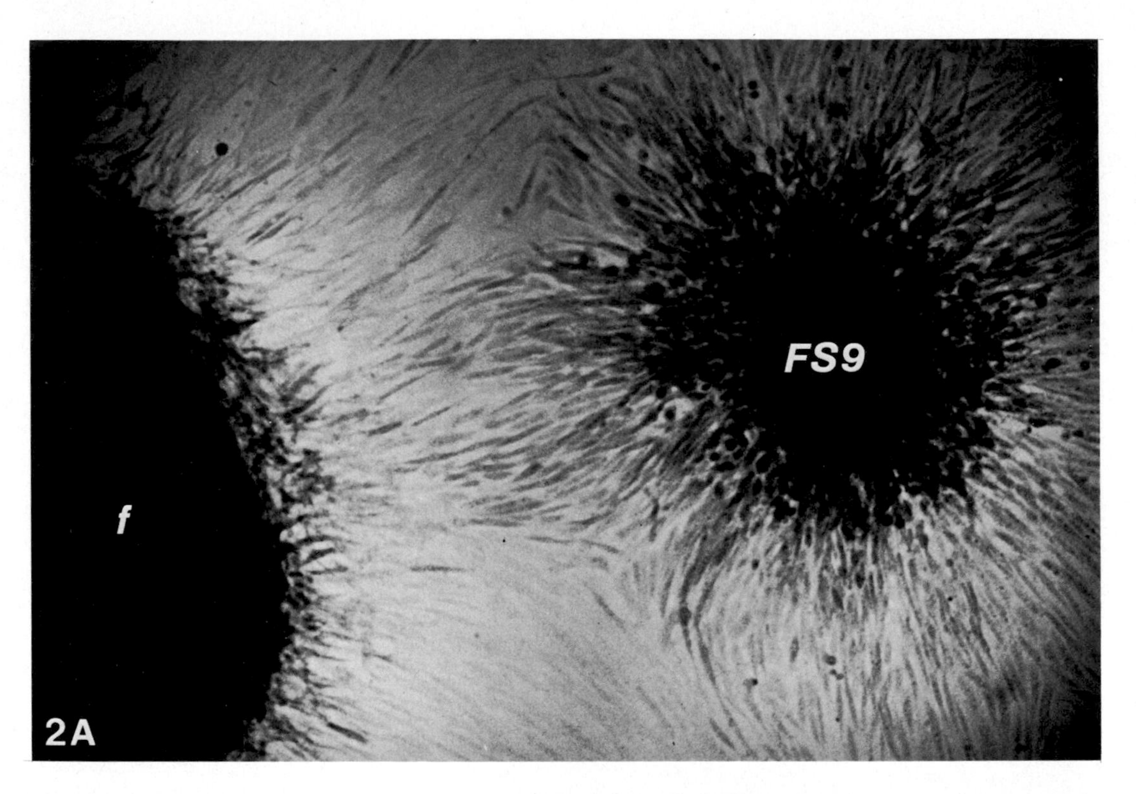
FS9
f
2A

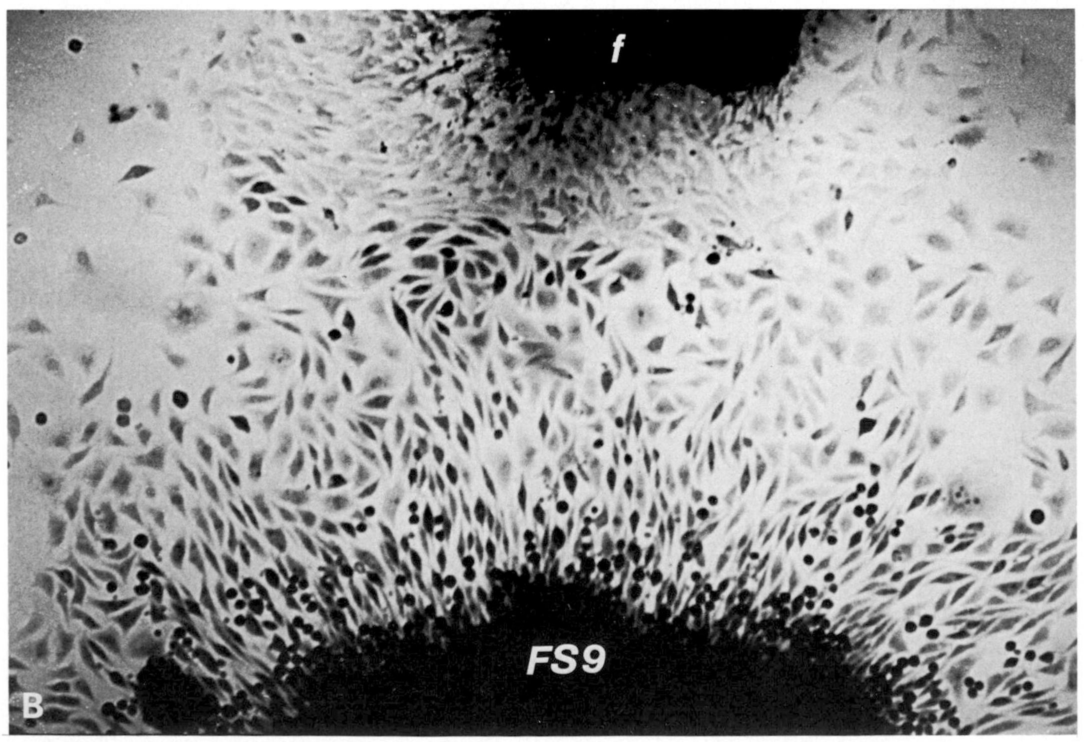
f
FS9
B

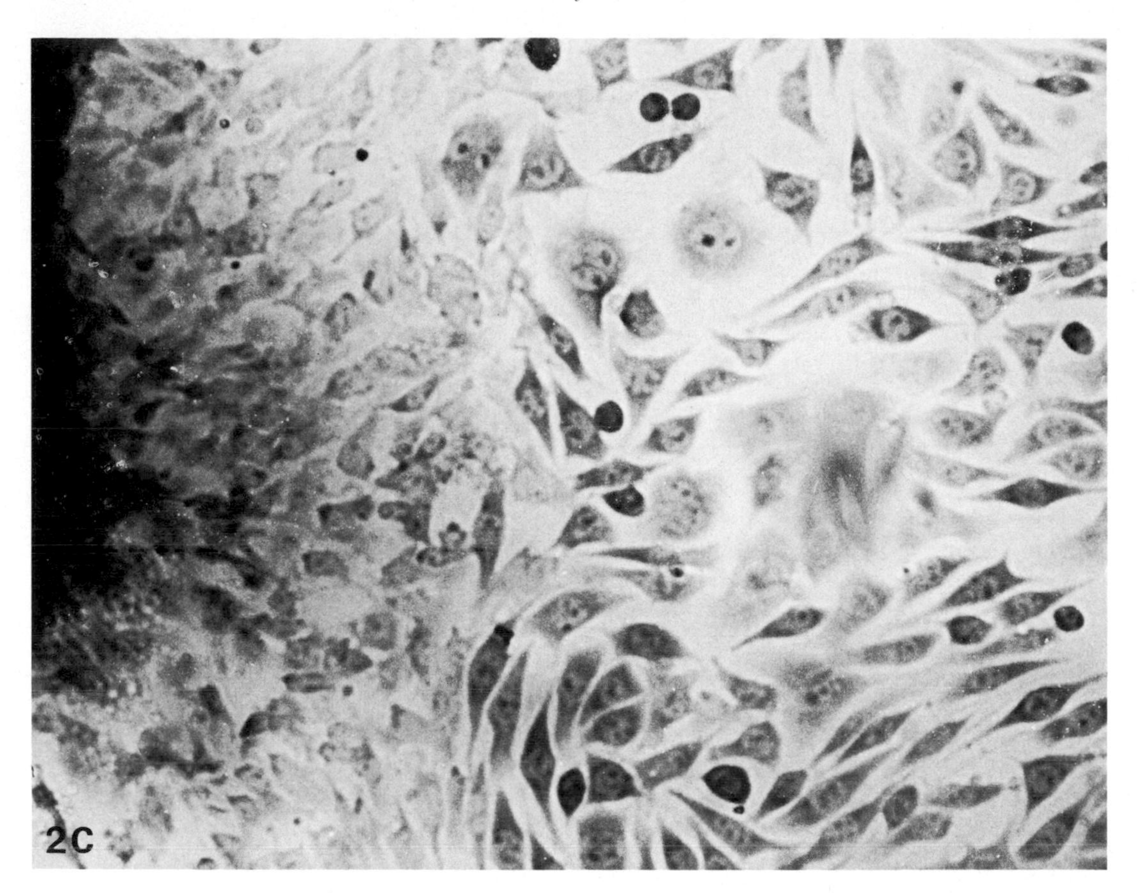

Fig. 2. The effects of Fab derived from the gp37-specific monoclonal antibody DD9 on the invasiveness of FS9 fibrosarcoma cells and chicken heart fibroblasts (*f*). The two explants were confronted on acid-washed coverslips. DMEM containing 10 % FCS was used as medium and cells were fixed 1 day after confluence of the two cell populations. A. Control (from Steinemann *et al.* 1984*a*). B. Fab (0·1 mg ml^{-1}). C. Fab (0·1 mg ml^{-1}), the FS9 explant is on the right (out of the picture).

change its conformation and 'uncouple it' from the regulatory system, i.e. block its inhibitory effect. The transient association of specific receptors on adjacent cells may induce cell withdrawal and, if gp37 itself can act as a receptor positively coupled to the regulatory system, its levels on the cell surface may be so high that insufficient molecules are bound to activate the contact inhibition machinery. In such a case, Fab binding might simulate heterotypic cell contact, although this implies Fab would permanently activate the withdrawal mechanism. However, no aberrant FS9 cell behaviour is observed. If contact involves local biochemical changes in the cell (e.g. in phosphatidylinositol metabolism) that trigger contact-inhibition behaviour, gp37 may interfere with the detection of such changes (e.g. by raising basal levels). A further possibility is that gp37 inhibits invasion-blocking mechanisms of the chicken heart fibroblasts. However, it is difficult to reconcile these ideas with the contact-promoting behaviour of FS9 cells.

EMBRYONIC DEVELOPMENT

Vertebrate embryonic development involves dramatic changes in the relative position of single cells, cell masses and extracellular domains. Both types of invasion discussed above are presumably involved in these changes and may employ mechanisms similar or identical to those bestowing metastatic potential on tumour cells. Cell surface proteins (Edelman, 1985) and the extracellular matrix (see below) have been implicated in embryonic cell migration and pattern formation.

Virtually all migrating mesenchymal cells synthesize sulphated macromolecules during active translocation. On the basis of studies of cardiac mesenchymal cell migration, Fundenburg & Markwald (1986) have presented a 'substratum conditioning' model for cell movement. Mesenchymal cells migrate on and through a scaffold of collagen fibrils *in situ*, translocation probably being the accumulative result of synchronous series of attachment–detachment events. The model proposes that chondroitin sulphate proteoglycans secreted by the cells mask the substratum and prevent static cycles of reattachment at the same site. This would provide for directed and sustained cell movement, migration of the population ultimately being inhibited.

In avian embryos, sclerotome cells radiate from the somites towards the notochord to occupy the perichordal space. Neural crest cells (NC), however, do not enter the perichordal space (Newgreen *et al.* 1986). *In vitro* experiments showed that the notochord prevented NC, but not sclerotome cells, from occupying adjacent collagen gel and fibronectin-rich extracellular matrix substrates. The inhibition of NC was a local phenomenon, occurring close to the notochord and not requiring direct contact. (It was not absolute, as NC prevented from moving elsewhere could approach the notochord.) The notochord avoidance by NC was abolished by including testicular hyaluronidase and chondroitinase ABC in the culture medium, suggesting differential responses to the extracellular material (e.g. chondroitin sulphate proteoglycan) may be responsible for the distribution of NC and sclerotome cells. Other aspects of sclerotome and NC mesenchyme cell morphogenesis cannot, however, be explained by such cell–extracellular matrix interactions.

CONCLUSIONS

Comparative studies on metastatic and non-metastatic tumour cells have pinpointed a variety of properties that may be required at specific points in the metastatic cascade. These changes are complex; however, the underlying mechanisms may be associated with the activation (or repression) of only a few genes. Hopes that DNA transfection experiments will identify such regulatory genes must be tempered by the discovery that the transformation process itself can alter the metastatic properties of neoplastic cells (Kerbel *et al.* 1987). Identification of genes regulating the invasion-like behaviour of embryonic cells may provide the long-awaited breakthrough. This will require the development of suitable *in vitro* systems, even though extrapolation to the *in vivo* situation can be tenuous. The cellular collisions studied by Abercrombie and his colleagues are, for technical reasons, only easily observable in sparse culture. Nevertheless, the confronted explant assay has convincingly shown a correlation between the lack of heterotypic contact inhibition *in vitro* and invasive behaviour *in vivo*. The reasons why the 37K tumour cell protein influences cellular invasion in culture are quite unknown, as is the relevance of this protein to metastasis. However, it has provided us with a 'tool' for dissecting the molecular mechanisms responsible for such invasion.

This work was supported by the Schweizerische Krebsliga.

REFERENCES

ABERCROMBIE, M. (1979). Contact inhibition and malignancy. *Nature, Lond.* **281**, 259–262.

ABERCROMBIE, M. & HEAYSMAN, J. E. M. (1953). Observations on the social behaviour of cells in tissue culture. I. Speed of movement of chick heart fibroblasts in relation to their mutual contacts. *Expl Cell Res.* **5**, 111–131.

ABERCROMBIE, M. & HEAYSMAN, J. E. M. (1954). Social behaviour of cells in tissue culture. II. Monolayering of fibroblasts. *Expl Cell Res.* **6**, 293–306.

ABERCROMBIE, M. & HEAYSMAN, J. E. M. (1976). Invasive behaviour between sarcoma and fibroblast populations in cell culture. *J. natn. Cancer Inst.* **56**, 561–570.

ABERCROMBIE, M., HEAYSMAN, J. E. M. & KARTHAUSER, H. M. (1957). Social behaviour of cells in tissue culture. III. Mutual influence of sarcoma cells and fibroblasts. *Expl Cell Res.* **13**, 276–291.

ABERCROMBIE, M., LAMONT, D. M. & STEPHENSON, E. M. (1968). The monolayering in tissue culture of fibroblasts from different sources. *Proc. R. Soc. Lond.* B **170**, 349–360.

ABERCROMBIE, M. & TURNER, A. A. (1978). Contact reactions influencing cell locomotion of mouse sarcoma in culture. *Med. Biol.* **56**, 299–303.

ALBY, L. & AUERBACH, R. (1984). Differential adhesion of tumor cells to capillary endothelial cells *in vitro*. *Proc. natn. Acad. Sci. U.S.A.* **81**, 5739–5743.

ALTVOGT, P., FOGEL, M., CHEINGSONG-POPOV, R., DENNIS, J., ROBINSON, P. & SCHIRRMACHER, V. (1983). Different patterns of lectin binding and cell surface sialylation detected on related high- and low-metastatic tumor lines. *Cancer Res.* **43**, 5138–5144.

AUERBACH, R. & JOSEPH, J. (1984). In *The Biology of Endothelial Cells* (ed. E. A. Jaffe), pp. 394–400. The Hague: Nijhoff.

BERNSTEIN, S. C. & WEINBERG, R. A. (1985). Expression of the metastatic phenotype in cells transfected with human metastatic tumor DNA. *Proc. natn. Acad. Sci. U.S.A.* **82**, 1726–1730.

BRADLEY, M. O., KRAYNAK, A. R., STORER, R. D. & GIBBS, J. B. (1986). Experimental metastasis in nude mice of NIH 3T3 cells containing various *ras* genes. *Proc. natn. Acad. Sci. U.S.A.* **83**, 5277–5281.

BRENAN, M. & PARISH, C. R. (1986). Modification of lymphocyte migration by sulphated polysaccharides. *Eur. J. Immun.* **16**, 423–430.

CHIN, Y.-H., CAREY, G. D. & WOODRUFF, J. J. (1983). Lymphocyte recognition of lymph node high endothelium. IV. Cell surface structure mediating entry into lymph nodes. *J. Immun.* **129**, 1911–1916.

COOMBE, D. R., PARISH, C. R., RAMSHAW, I. A. & SNOWDEN, J. M. (1987). Analysis of the inhibition of tumour metastasis by sulphated polysaccharides. *Int. J. Cancer* **39**, 82–88.

DANO, K., ANDREASEN, P. A., GRONDAHL-HANSEN, J., KRISTENSEN, B., NIELSEN, L. S. & SKRIVER, L. (1985). Plasminogen activators, tissue degradation and cancer. *Adv. Cancer Res.* **44**, 146–239.

DENNIS, J., WALLER, C., TIMPL, R. & SCHIRRMACHER, V. (1982). Surface sialic acid reduces attachment of metastatic tumour cells to collagen type IV and fibronectin. *Nature, Lond.* **300**, 274–276.

EDELMAN, G. M. (1985). Cell adhesion and the molecular process of morphogenesis. *A. Rev. Biochem.* **54**, 135–169.

FIDLER, I. J. (1978). Tumor heterogeneity and the biology of cancer invasion and metastasis. *Cancer Res.* **38**, 2651–2660.

Fidler, I. J. & Hart, I. R. (1982). Biological diversity in metastatic neoplasms: Origins and implications. *Science* **217**, 998–1003.

Funderburg, F. M. & Markwald, R. R. (1986). Conditioning of native substrates by chondroitin sulfate proteoglycans during cardiac mesenchymal cell migration. *J. Cell Biol.* **103**, 2475–2487.

Gallatin, W. M., Weissman, I. L. & Butcher, E. C. (1983). A cell-surface molecule involved in organ-specific homing of lymphocytes. *Nature, Lond.* **304**, 30–34.

Gerisch, G. (1986). Inter-relation of cell adhesion and differentiation in *Dictyostelium discoideum*. *J. Cell Sci. Suppl. 4*, 201–219.

Greenberg, M. E., Brackenbury, R. & Edelman, G. M. (1984). Alteration of neural cell adhesion molecule (N-CAM) expression after neuronal cell transformation by Rous sarcoma virus. *Proc. natn. Acad. Sci. U.S.A.* **81**, 969–973.

Greig, R. G., Koestler, T. F., Trainer, D. L., Corwin, S. P., Miles, L., Kline, T., Sweet, R., Yokoyama, S. & Poste, G. (1985). Tumorigenic and metastatic properties of "normal" and *ras*-transformed NIH/3T3 cells. *Proc. natn. Acad. Sci. U.S.A.* **82**, 3698–3701.

Grimstad, I. A., Varani, J. & McCoy, J. P. (1984). Contribution of α-D-galactopyranosyl end groups to attachment of highly and low metastatic murine fibrosarcoma cells to various substrates. *Expl Cell Res.* **155**, 345–358.

Harris, H. (1986). Malignant tumours generated by recessive mutations. *Nature, Lond.* **323**, 582–583.

Hart, I. R. (1985). Molecular basis of tumour spread. *Nature, Lond.* **315**, 274–275.

Heaysman, J. E. M. (1970). Non-reciprocal contact inhibition. *Experientia* **26**, 1344.

Heaysman, J. E. M. (1978). Contact inhibition of locomotion: a reappraisal. *Int. Rev. Cytol.* **55**, 49–66.

Humphries, M. J., Matsumoto, K., White, S. L. & Olden, K. (1986). Oligosaccharide modification by swainsonine treatment inhibits pulmonary colonization by B16-F10 murine melanoma cells. *Proc. natn. Acad. Sci. U.S.A.* **83**, 1752–1756.

Jones, P. A. & De Clerck, Y. A. (1982). Extracellular matrix destruction by invasive tumor cells. *Cancer Metast. Rev.* **1**, 289–317.

Kerbel, R. S., Waghorne, E., Man, M. S., Elliott, B. & Breitman, M. L. (1987). Alteration of the tumorigenic and neoplastic properties of neoplastic cells is associated with the process of calcium phosphate-mediated DNA transfection. *Proc. natn. Acad. Sci. U.S.A.* **84**, 1263–1267.

Kieler, J. v. F. (1984). Invasiveness of transformed bladder cells. *Cancer Metast. Rev.* **3**, 265–296.

Knudson, A. G. (1986). Genetics of human cancer. *A. Rev. Genet.* **20**, 231–251.

Kramer, R. H. & Nicolson, G. L. (1979). Interactions of tumor cells with vascular endothelial cell monolayers: A model for metastic invasion. *Proc. natn. Acad. Sci. U.S.A.* **76**, 5704–5708.

Liotta, L. A., Thorgeirsson, V. P. & Garbisa, S. (1982). Role of collagenases in tumor cell invasion. *Cancer Metast. Rev.* **1**, 277–288.

Liotta, L. A., Rao, D. N. & Wewer, U. M. (1986). Biochemical interactions of tumor cells with the basement membrane. *A. Rev. Biochem.* **55**, 1037–1057.

Mareel, M. M., Kint, J. & Meyvisch, C. (1979). Methods of study of the invasion of malignant C3H-mouse fibroblasts into embryonic chick heart *in vitro*. *Virchows Arch. B Cell Path.* **30**, 95–111.

Mareel, M. M., van Roy, F. M., Messian, L. M., Boghaert, E. R. & Bruyneel, E. A. (1987). Qualitative and quantitative analysis of tumour invasion *in vivo* and *in vitro*. *J. Cell Sci. Suppl. 8*, 141–163.

Mignatti, P., Robbins, E. & Rifkin, D. B. (1986). Tumor invasion through the human amniotic membrane: Requirement for a proteinase cascade. *Cell* **47**, 487–498.

Mullins, D. E. & Rohrlich, S. T. (1983). The role of proteinases in cellular invasiveness. *Biochim. biophys. Acta* **895**, 177–214.

Nakajima, M., Irimura, T., Di Ferrante, D., Di Ferrante, N. & Nicolson, G. L. (1983). Heparan sulphate degradation: relation to tumor invasion and metastatic properties of mouse B16 melanoma sublines. *Science* **220**, 611–613.

Newgreen, D. F., Scheel, M. & Kastner, V. (1986). Morphogenesis of sclerotome and neural crest in avian embryos. *In vivo* and *in vitro* studies on the role of notochordal extracellular material. *Cell Tiss. Res.* **244**, 299–313.

NICOLSON, G. L. (1982). Organ colonization and the cell surface properties of malignant cells. *Biochim. biophys. Acta* **695**, 113–176.

NICOLSON, G. L., NAKITIMA, M. & IRIMURA, T. (1985). In *Mechanisms of Cancer Metastasis: Potential Therapeutic Implications* (ed. K. V. Honn, W. F. Powers & B. F. Sloane), pp. 275–297. The Hague: Nijhoff.

OLSSON, L. & FORCHHAMMER, J. (1984). Induction of the metastatic phenotype in a mouse tumor model by 5-azacytidine, and characterization of an antigen associated with metastatic activity. *Proc. natn. Acad. Sci. U.S.A.* **81**, 3389–3393.

PADDOCK, S. W. & DUNN, G. A. (1986). Analysing collisions between fibroblasts and fibrosarcoma cells: Fibrosarcoma cells show an active invasionary response. *J. Cell Sci.* **81**, 163–187.

ROSSMAN, T. G. & TROLL, W. (1980). Protease inhibitors in carcinogenesis: possible sites of action. In *Carcinogenesis*, vol. 5, *Modifiers of Chemical Carcinogenesis* (ed. T. J. Slaga), pp. 127–143. New York: Raven Press.

SLOANE, B. F. & HONN, K. V. (1984). Cysteine proteinases and metastasis. *Cancer Metast. Rev.* **3**, 249–263.

SMITH, H. S., LIOTTA, L., HANCOCK, M. C., WOLMAN, S. R. & HACKETT, A. J. (1985). Invasiveness and ploidy of human mammary carcinomas in short-term culture. *Proc. natn. Acad. Sci. U.S.A.* **82**, 1805–1809.

SPRINGER, G. F., CHEINGSONG-POPOV, R., SCHIRRMACHER, V., DESAI, P. R. & TEGTMEYER, H. (1983). Proposed molecular basis of murine tumor cell–hepatocyte interaction. *J. biol. Chem.* **258**, 5702–5706.

STANBRIDGE, E. J. (1976). Suppression of malignancy in human cells. *Nature, Lond.* **260**, 17–20.

STEINEMANN, C., FENNER, M., BINZ, H. & PARISH, R. W. (1984*a*). Evidence that the invasive behaviour of mouse sarcoma cells is inhibited by blocking a 37,000 dalton plasma membrane glycoprotein with Fab. *Proc. natn. Acad. Sci. U.S.A.* **81**, 3747–3750.

STEINEMANN, C., FENNER, M., PARISH, R. W. & BINZ, H. (1984*b*). Studies of the invasiveness of the chemically induced mouse sarcoma FS9. I. Monoclonal antibodies to a 37,000 dalton membrane glycoprotein inhibit invasion of fibroblasts *in vitro*. *Int. J. Cancer* **34**, 407–414.

STEPHENSON, E. M. & STEPHENSON, N. G. (1978). Invasive locomotory behaviour between malignant human melanoma cells and normal fibroblasts filmed *in vivo*. *J. Cell Sci.* **31**, 380–418.

TANAKA, K., HAYASHI, H., HAMADA, C., KHOURY, G. & JAY, G. (1986). Expression of major histocompatibility complex I antigens as a strategy for the potentiation of immune recognition of tumor cells. *Proc. natn. Acad. Sci. U.S.A.* **83**, 8723–8727.

TERRANOVA, V. P., HUJANEN, E. S., LOEB, D. M., MARTIN, G. R., THORNBURG, L. & GLUSHKO, V. (1986). Use of a reconstituted basement membrane to measure cell invasiveness and select for highly invasive tumor cells. *Proc. natn. Acad. Sci. U.S.A.* **83**, 465–469.

VOLLMERS, H. P. & BIRCHMEIER, W. (1983). Monoclonal antibodies inhibit the adhesion of mouse B16 melanoma cells *in vitro* and block lung metastasis *in vivo*. *Proc. natn. Acad. Sci. U.S.A.* **80**, 3729–3733.

WEISS, L., ed. (1976). *Fundamental Aspects of Metastasis*. Amsterdam: North Holland.

YOGEESWARAN, G. & SALK, P. L. (1981). Metastatic potential is positively correlated with cell surface sialylation of cultured murine tumor cell lines. *Science* **212**, 1514–1516.

J. Cell Sci. Suppl. 8, 199–209 (1987)
Printed in Great Britain © *The Company of Biologists Limited 1987*

ACTIVATION OF KERATINOCYTE FIBRONECTIN RECEPTOR FUNCTION DURING CUTANEOUS WOUND HEALING

FREDERICK GRINNELL, KEN-ICHI TODA
AND AKIRA TAKASHIMA

Department of Cell Biology and Anatomy, University of Texas Health Science Center, Dallas, TX 75235, USA

SUMMARY

Keratinocytes freshly isolated from unwounded skin could not attach and spread on fibronectin (FN)-coated culture dishes and could not bind and phagocytose FN-coated beads. These adhesive functions were activated, however, in keratinocytes that were isolated from healing wounds. Moreover, adhesiveness of basal keratinocytes to FN substrata was activated during epidermal cell or explant culture. Activation was specific for attachment to FN compared to other adhesion ligands, and occurred even when epidermal cells were cultured on collagen, basement membrane matrix, or lectin-coated substrata. Biochemical studies showed that keratinocytes have a $140\times10^3 M_r$ FN receptor analogous to the fibroblast receptor for FN, and that this receptor is expressed in activated keratinocytes but not in keratinocytes freshly isolated from unwounded skin. The absence of FN receptors from keratinocytes in unwounded skin is not surprising since the basal keratinocytes of the epidermis are attached to a basement membrane containing laminin and type IV collagen. During wound repair, however, these cells migrate over or through a FN-coated matrix. Consequently, expression of FN receptors may be an essential feature of healing. Believing that FN is the required substratum for keratinocyte migration during wound healing, we have initiated clinical studies to determine if topical application of FN is useful as a therapy for non-healing cutaneous ulcers.

INTRODUCTION

In recent years, research concerning cell–substratum adhesion has focused on the identification of extracellular ligands that mediate adhesion and on the cell surface receptors with which these ligands interact (reviewed by Grinnell, 1978; Yamada, 1983). To understand the physiological functions and specificity of adhesive interactions, however, it will be necessary to analyse the topographical distribution and temporal expression of adhesion ligands and their receptors *in situ*. Consequently, we have become interested in the wound-repair process, since this involves changes in cell adhesion and motility as well as changes in the extracellular matrices with which the cells interact (Grinnell, 1984). For instance, basal keratinocytes in unwounded skin exist as stationary cells attached to a basement membrane that contains laminin and type IV collagen (Katz, 1984). But during wound repair, these cells migrate over or through a fibronectin (FN)-coated matrix (Grinnell *et al.* 1981; Clark *et al.* 1982) in the absence of laminin and type IV collagen (Stanley *et al.* 1981). In this brief review, we describe our recent findings on the adhesion of keratinocytes to FN and other adhesion ligands and on the modulation of keratinocyte adhesiveness that occurs during wound healing.

RESULTS

In vitro *activation of keratinocyte FN receptor function*

Several years ago it was suggested that laminin was the adhesion ligand specific for epidermal cells (Terranova *et al.* 1980; Kleinman *et al.* 1981), but other studies did not support this idea (Gilchrest *et al.* 1982; Stenn *et al.* 1983). Subsequently, we and others examined the adhesive properties of cultured human epidermal cells and found that FN was indeed an adhesion ligand for these cells that promoted not only cell attachment and spreading, but also, phagocytosis and motility (Takashima & Grinnell, 1984, 1985; O'Keefe *et al.* 1985; Clark *et al.* 1985). Moreover, FN also promoted the migration of corneal epithelial cells (Nishida *et al.* 1985).

In the course of our experiments, we found that epidermal cells freshly isolated from human skin, unlike cultured cells, were unable to attach to FN substrata in short-term (45 min) assays (Takashima & Grinnell, 1985). Subsequently, we studied the onset of FN adhesion function during epidermal cell culture. After different periods of culture, cells were harvested using the same combination of dispase and trypsin treatments used to harvest cells from skin. Then, the adhesiveness of the harvested, cultured cells was tested in short-term assays on FN-coated substrata (Fig. 1). In contrast to freshly isolated cells or cells from 2- or 4-day cultures, about 25 % of the cells harvested from 7-day cultures were able to attach, and 75 % of the attached cells were spread. Adhesiveness to FN reached its maximal level in cells harvested from 10-day cultures. The activated epidermal cells were found to be basal keratinocytes, on the basis of indirect immunofluorescence staining with bullous pemphigoid (BP) serum. It should be noted that the onset of adhesiveness to FN occurred similarly in medium that contained complete serum or FN-depleted serum. Therefore, the activation effect was not simply a consequence of increasing the level of exogenous FN in the medium to which the cells were exposed.

To test whether the activation of keratinocyte FN receptor function was a consequence of dissociated cell culture, studies were performed with epidermal explant cultures. Skin explants were maintained for 9 days, during which time extensive outgrowth of epidermal cells occurred. Then the cells from the central explant region and the migration region were harvested separately and tested for adhesion (Table 1). Consistent with the above results, keratinocytes that had migrated out of the skin explants were enhanced markedly in their attachment and spreading on FN substrata compared with non-motile keratinocytes that remained behind.

Activation of keratinocyte adhesion to FN in vivo

We also analysed the activation of FN receptor function during wound healing *in vivo* (Takashima *et al.* 1986). In these studies, rabbit ear epidermal cells were transplanted onto full-thickness wound beds that had been prepared on the backs of

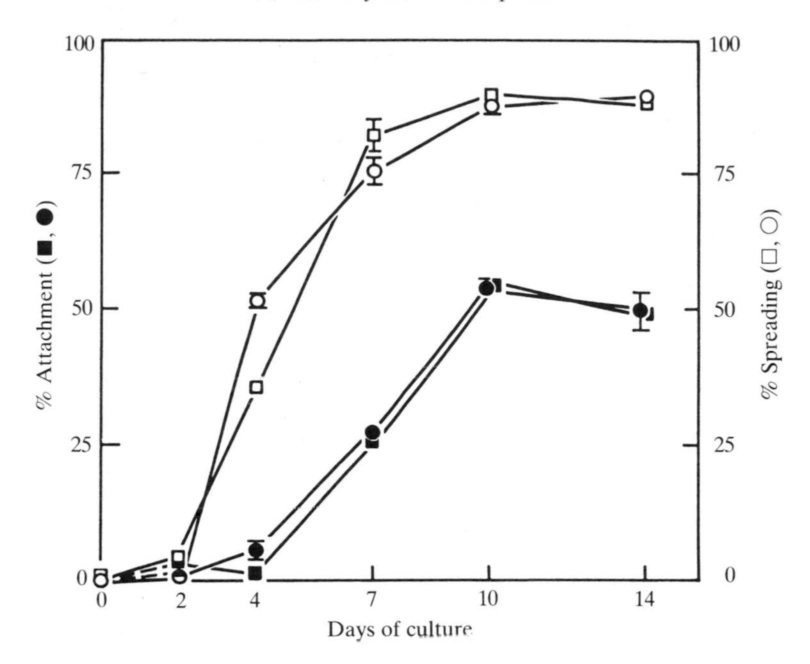

Fig. 1. Initiation of FN-mediated cell attachment and spreading during cell culture. Human epidermal cells were freshly isolated or cultured in medium with complete serum or FN-depleted serum. At the times indicated, the cells were harvested by treatment with dispase and trypsin, after which attachment and spreading on FN substrata were measured in 45-min assays. Data shown are the means ± S.D. from duplicate experiments. For details see Takashima & Grinnell (1985). (■, □) Control serum; (●, ○) pFN-depleted serum.

the same rabbits (Fig. 2). At various times after transplantation, biopsy samples were taken from the wound beds, and cells harvested from the biopsies were tested for adhesion to FN. Keratinocytes in the biopsy samples were identified by indirect immunofluorescence staining with anti-keratin antibodies (Fig. 3). It was found that keratinocytes harvested from 3-day grafts were able to attach and spread on FN substrata (Fig. 3A,B), unlike keratinocytes freshly harvested from ear skin (Fig. 3C,D).

Quantification of the results (Fig. 4) showed that there was a dramatic increase in the ability of keratinocytes to attach and spread on FN substrata, and this activity

Table 1. *Plasma FN-mediated attachment and spreading of cells in explant cultures*

Cells	% Attachment	% Spreading
Central explant region	9·4 ± 1·3	2·5 ± 0·5
Migrating region	44·7 ± 0·1	70·0 ± 2·0

Skin explants were cultured for 9 days. Incisions were made along the edges of the explant, after which the samples were treated with dispase. The migratory and central explant regions were separated and then subjected to trypsin to prepare single cell suspensions. Attachment and spreading on FN substrata were measured after 45 min. Data shown are the means and S.D. from duplicate experiments. Details are given by Takashima & Grinnell (1985).

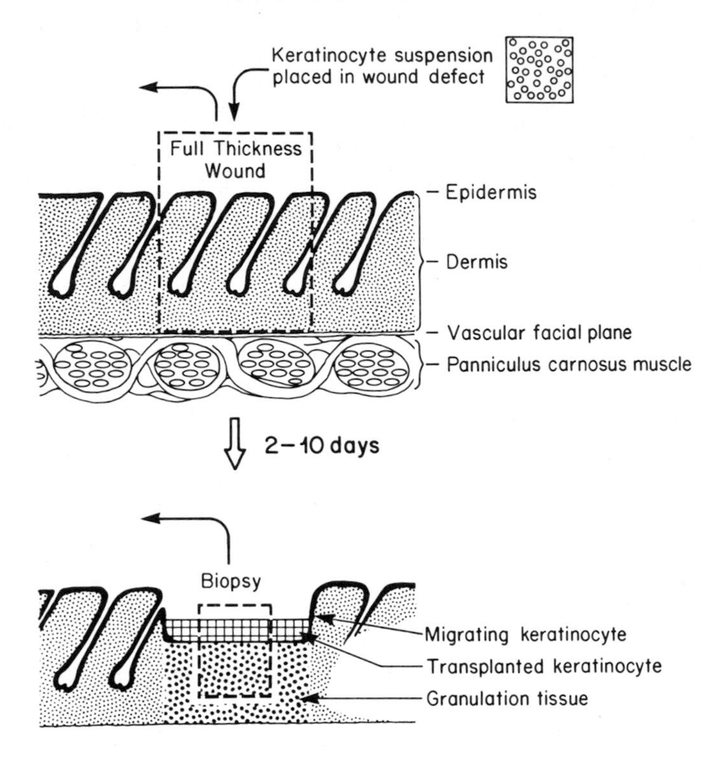

Fig. 2. Autotransplantation model to study re-epithelialization of full-thickness wounds. Rabbit ear epidermal cells were transplanted onto full-thickness wound beds that had been prepared on the backs of the same rabbits. At various times after transplantation, biopsy samples were taken from the wound beds, and cells harvested from the biopsies were tested for attachment and spreading on FN substrata in 2-h assays. For details see Takashima *et al.* (1986).

reached a maximum in cells isolated from the graft bed 3 days after transplantation. A similar activation occurred in the ability of cells to bind and phagocytose FN-coated beads. Subsequently, FN receptor function returned towards the resting level in cells isolated around the same time that the epidermis was reconstituted. These results led us to suggest that activation of keratinocyte FN receptor function might be necessary for migration of keratinocytes through the wound matrix.

Specificity of keratinocyte adhesion to FN

One explanation for the activation of keratinocyte adhesion to FN was a general increase in cell adhesiveness. To test this possibility, we studied the ability of freshly isolated and cultured cells to attach to substrata other than FN (Toda & Grinnell, 1987). The other substrata tested were laminin and type IV collagen-containing basement membrane matrix produced by HR-9 cells, collagen (95 % type I), and the lectins concanavalin A and wheat-germ agglutinin. Freshly isolated epidermal cells were able to attach to basement membrane matrix, collagen and lectins (Table 2). It could be concluded, therefore, that these cells had adhesion receptors for ligands

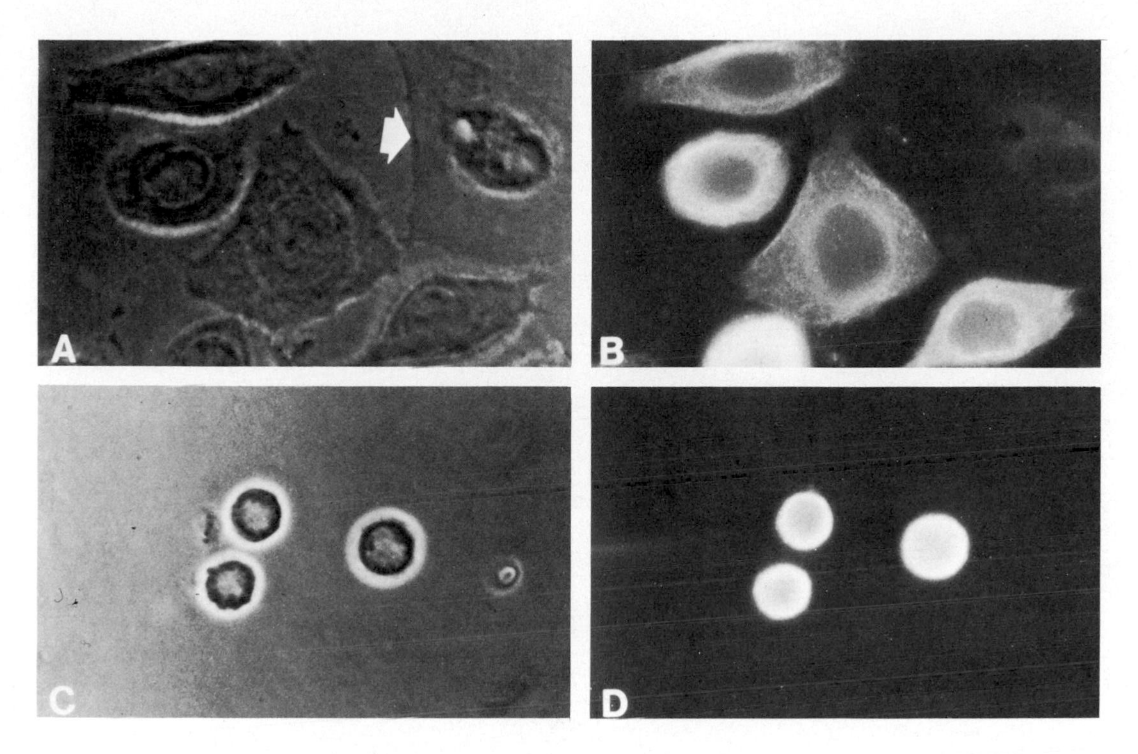

Fig. 3. Antibody identification of cells attached to FN substrata (see Fig. 2). A,B. Cells harvested 3 days after transplantation; C,D. Cells freshly isolated from rabbit ear skin. At the end of adhesion assays, cells were fixed, permeabilized and processed for indirect immunofluorescence with anti-keratin antibodies. Most cells harvested from the 3-day transplant sites were keratinocytes that spread well on the dishes (A,B). Non-keratinocytes were detected by the lack of keratin staining (A, arrow). Freshly isolated keratinocytes attached to the dishes loosely and did not spread (C,D). ×700. For details see Takashima *et al.* (1986).

other than FN. Significantly, however, no spreading of the attached cells was observed on any of the adhesion ligands.

About 28 % of the cells in the freshly isolated epidermal preparations were basal keratinocytes. Of the cells that attached to basement membrane matrix and collagen-coated substrata, however, about 80 % were BP-positive (Table 2). Therefore, more than 90 % of the basal cells in the preparation had attached to these substrata. The selective attachment of basal keratinocytes to collagen substrata was also found by others (Stanley *et al.* 1980). The lectin-coated substrata, on the other hand, were not selective for basal keratinocytes since the percentage of basal cells that attached to these substrata was the same as the percentage of these cells in the epidermal preparation (Table 2).

The adhesiveness of cultured epidermal cells to substrata other than FN also was tested (Fig. 5). Unlike cell attachment to FN-coated substrata, there was little change in the ability of cultured cells to attach to collagen or lectin-coated substrata. That is, the extent of cell attachment measured with freshly isolated cells (Fig. 5, day

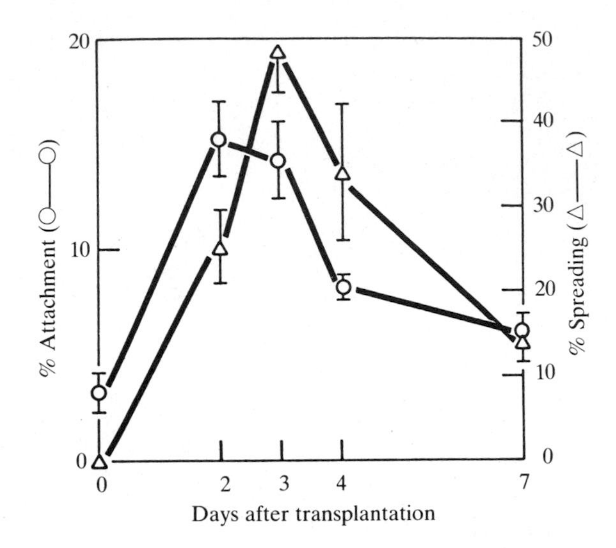

Fig. 4. Attachment and spreading activity of freshly isolated and transplanted keratinocytes (see Fig. 2). Data shown are the means ± S.D. from duplicate experiments. For details see Takashima *et al.* (1986).

0) was similar to the extent of cell attachment measured with cells harvested from 9-day cultures or 22-day cultures. Similar results were obtained for cell attachment to basement membrane matrix. Since there was an increase in cell attachment to FN-coated substrata but not to the other ligand-coated substrata, we concluded that the activation of cell attachment to FN was specific.

In addition to the selective activation of FN attachment activity, we observed a coordinated pattern of cell spreading activation that was independent of the substratum (Fig. 6). That is, freshly isolated cells did not spread on any of the adhesion ligands tested, but more than 50% of the cells harvested from 4-day cultures were able to spread. With cells that were harvested from 9-day cultures, about 80% of the cells that attached were observed to spread. On the basis of the

Table 2. *Adhesion of freshly isolated epidermal cells to various substrata*

Adhesion test substratum	% Attachment	% Spreading	Identity of attached cells	
			% Keratin-positive	% BP-positive
Plastic	2·1 ± 1·0	0	n.d.	n.d.
FN	1·3 ± 0·9	0	n.d.	n.d.
Collagen	39·4 ± 5·8	0	88·4 ± 5·6	77·8 ± 4·6
HR-9 BM	31·9 ± 6·8	0	92·3 ± 6·9	83·1 ± 11·8
ConA	66·2 ± 7·9	0	83·2 ± 11·2	29·9 ± 4·1
WGA	52·1 ± 3·6	0	85·1 ± 9·1	31·1 ± 4·9

Freshly isolated epidermal cells were incubated for 45 min on the substrata indicated (6 dishes per substratum). Duplicate samples were used to determine cell attachment and spreading, keratin-positive cells, and BP-positive cells. Data shown are the averages and S.D. from four separate experiments. Details are given by Toda & Grinnell (1987). BM, basement membrane; ConA, concanavalin A; WGA, wheat-germ agglutinin.

simultaneous onset of cell spreading activity that was independent of the ligand on the substratum, it seemed likely this was a general activation process.

Samples from the experiments with cultured cells were also analysed to determine the percentage of attached cells that were basal keratinocytes. Most of the cells harvested from 22-day cultures that attached to FN and collagen substrata were basal

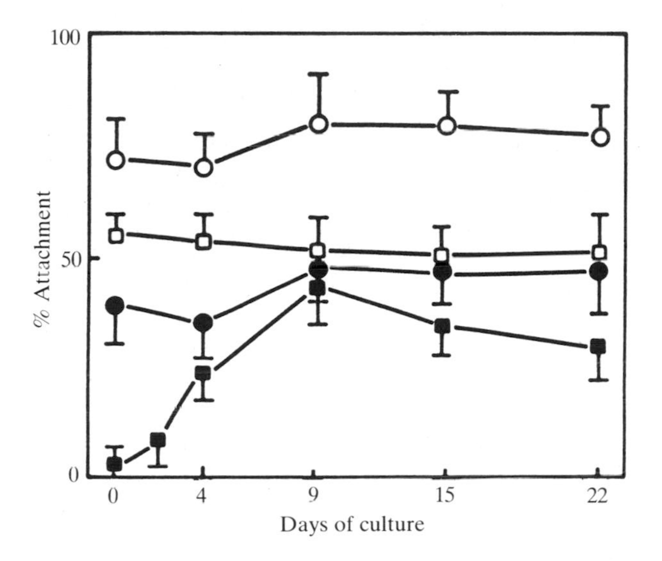

Fig. 5. Attachment of freshly isolated and cultured epidermal cells to various substrata. Human epidermal cells, freshly isolated or cultured on plastic for the times indicated, were harvested and incubated for 45 min on the substrata shown (6 dishes per experiment). Data shown are for cell attachment and are the averages and S.D. from four separate experiments. For details see Toda & Grinnell (1987). (○) ConA; (□) WGA; (●) collagen; (■) FN. See Table 2 for abbreviations.

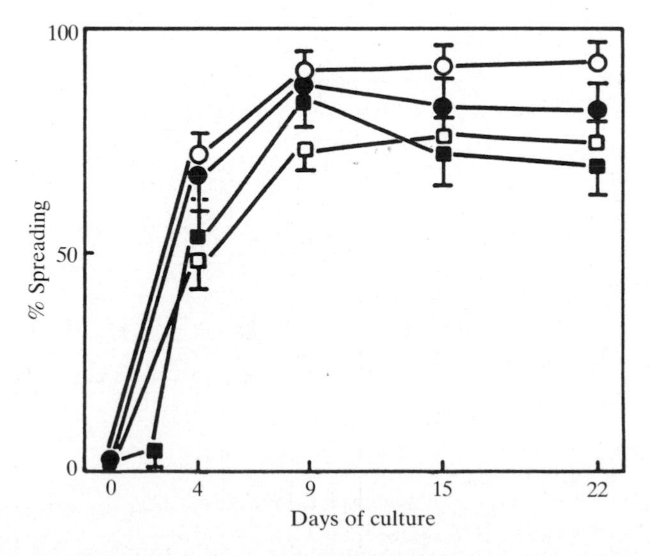

Fig. 6. Spreading of freshly isolated and cultured epidermal cells on various substrata. Same as Fig. 5 except the data shown are for cell spreading.

cells (80–90%), but basal cells accounted for only about 50% of the epidermal cells in these cultures. It could be concluded, therefore, that cultured basal cells attached selectively to FN and collagen-coated substrata.

As already mentioned above, keratinocyte adhesiveness to FN was activated if FN-depleted serum was used in the cell cultures. We also measured keratinocyte adhesion to FN, collagen and basement membrane matrix after culturing cells on these substrata. The chemical composition of the substratum on which the cells were cultured, however, did not appear to affect the subsequent adhesiveness of the cells (Table 3).

Analysis of keratinocyte FN receptors

To learn more about the mechanisms underlying activation of keratinocyte adhesion to FN, we analysed keratinocyte FN receptors (Toda *et al.* 1987). In the presence of the peptide Gly-Arg-Gly-Asp-Ser-Pro-Cys, which is known to compete for the FN cell-binding domain (Pierschbacher & Ruoslahti, 1984; Yamada & Kennedy, 1984), we found that keratinocyte adhesion to FN but not to collagen was inhibited. Also, keratinocyte adhesion to FN but not to collagen was inhibited by polyclonal antibodies to the $140\times10^3 M_r$ FN receptors of Chinese hamster ovary cells (Brown & Juliano, 1986). Consequently, it seems likely that the keratinocyte FN receptor is similar to the fibroblast FN receptor that has been described by others (Neff *et al.* 1982; Pytela *et al.* 1985; Brown & Juliano, 1985) and called integrin (Tamkun *et al.* 1986; and see Buck & Horwitz, this volume).

The molecular composition of keratinocyte receptors was analysed in two ways. First, metabolically radiolabelled, cultured keratinocytes were extracted with detergent, and the extracts were chromatographed on antibody columns prepared with non-immune IgG or anti-$140\times10^3 M_r$ FN receptor IgG. The results of these studies showed that a single cellular component (molecular mass about 140×10^3) bound to the immune column (Toda *et al.* 1987). Also, the non-immune and immune IgGs were used to immunoprecipitate cell extracts prepared from freshly isolated and cultured keratinocytes. A polypeptide of approximately $140\times10^3 M_r$

Table 3. *Adhesion of epidermal cells cultured on plastic, FN, collagen and HR-9 basement membrane substrata*

Cell culture substratum	Adhesion test substratum: Fibronectin % Att.	Fibronectin % Sp.	Collagen % Att.	Collagen % Sp.	HR-9 BM % Att.	HR-9 BM % Sp.
Plastic	44·9 ± 6·9	83·2 ± 4·6	45·4 ± 7·9	86·1 ± 7·7	32·0 ± 4·4	24·2 ± 3·6
FN	46·1 ± 2·0	89·1 ± 5·6	51·0 ± 9·9	71·9 ± 5·4	37·6 ± 4·9	18·7 ± 4·1
Collagen	50·9 ± 5·3	72·1 ± 5·8	45·4 ± 8·9	81·6 ± 3·9	34·8 ± 2·1	24·1 ± 4·7
HR-9 BM	45·1 ± 7·9	74·1 ± 3·6	59·7 ± 6·0	77·4 ± 6·4	29·9 ± 9·5	16·5 ± 7·1

Epidermal cells were cultured on the substrata indicated for 8–11 days (until confluency). The cells were harvested, duplicate samples were incubated for 45 min on the test substrata shown, and cell attachment (Att.) and spreading (Sp.) were determined. Data shown are the averages and S.D. from four separate experiments. Details are given by Toda & Grinnell (1987).

was detected in extracts from cultured cells but not in extracts from freshly isolated cells. It seems likely, therefore, that cultured keratinocytes were activated to express the 140K (K = $\times 10^3 M_r$) FN receptors. Additional evidence favouring this interpretation is that cultured keratinocytes but not freshly isolated keratinocytes were able to absorb the adhesion inhibition activity from the anti-140K FN receptor IgG preparation, and that cultured keratinocytes but not freshly isolated keratinocytes were able to attach to culture dishes coated with the anti-140K FN receptor IgG preparation (Toda *et al.* 1987).

Fibronectin as a therapeutic reagent

On the basis of our studies summarized above and those reported by others, we believe that FN is the matrix component that promotes keratinocyte adhesion and migration during wound repair (cf. Woodley *et al.* 1985). Consequently, one explanation for deficient healing of poorly vascularized wounds is that they lack sufficient FN or that FN in the wounds is degraded. In support of this idea, preliminary studies have shown that topical application of FN can promote healing of corneal ulcers (Nishida *et al.* 1985; Kono *et al.* 1985). To analyse further the possible therapeutic benefit of FN, we have initiated a double-blind, controlled clinical study in which topical FN is being used to treat non-healing decubitus and stasis ulcers. Although insufficient data have been collected to reach general conclusions, one patient who has been treated with topical FN for an extended period of time has shown a dramatic improvement. This patient had bilateral stasis ulcers that had resisted both routine and experimental treatments for more than 5 years. At the end of the 3-week period of the clinical trial, the patient requested continued FN therapy since one of her ulcers was improved. The improved ulcer was the one that had been treated with FN, and subsequently the patient was treated with FN on both ulcers. After 4 months, one ulcer had healed almost completely, and the other was improved more than 50% (Wysocki *et al.* 1987).

DISCUSSION

Cell adhesion during wound repair appears to be a paradigmatic example of how adhesion specificity is determined by the topographical distribution and temporal expression of adhesion ligands and their receptors *in situ*. Keratinocytes from unwounded skin lack FN receptors, but these receptors are expressed transiently during wound repair at the same time as there is a transient change in the extracellular matrix from a laminin and type IV collagen-containing basement membrane to a FN-coated matrix. Thus, the wound-healing situation modulates keratinocyte FN receptor expression.

The precise signal that turns expression of FN receptors on and off during wound healing is unknown. Probably, however, the change in extracellular matrix from laminin and type IV collagen to FN is not the key feature. This can be concluded since epidermal cells cultured on serum-coated plastic, fibronectin, collagen type I and basement membrane matrix were all activated to the same extent in their adhesiveness to FN. More probably, the loss of contact inhibition of the intact epidermal layer has pleotropic effects leading to increased cell motility and division (Rosen & Misfeldt, 1980), and one of these effects is the expression of FN receptors.

Changes in the expression of FN receptors have also been reported during development. In murine erythroleukaemia cells, for instance, it was found that the 140K FN receptors disappeared after dimethyl sulphoxide-induced differentiation of these cells (Patel & Lodish, 1986). Consistent with this finding, reticulocytes but not erythrocytes from peripheral blood express the 140K receptors. Thus, loss of the receptors may be a feature of terminal differentiation during haematopoiesis. In another study, it was found that the 140K FN receptor was present on embryonic chick lung cells, but markedly reduced in differentiated cells except smooth muscle (Chen *et al.* 1986). Future studies will be necessary to determine whether similar molecular mechanisms control developmental changes in FN receptor expression and the modulation of FN receptor expression during wound repair.

We are indebted to Dr William Snell for his helpful comments regarding this manuscript. This research has been supported by a grant from the NIH (GM31321).

REFERENCES

Brown, P. J. & Juliano, R. L. (1985). Selective inhibition of fibronectin mediated cell adhesion by monoclonal antibodies to a cell surface glycoprotein. *Science* **228**, 1448–1451.

Brown, P. J. & Juliano, R. L. (1986). Expression and function of a putative cell surface receptor for fibronectin in hamster and human cell lines. *J. Cell Biol.* **103**, 1595–1603.

Buck, C. A. & Horwitz, A. F. (1987). Integrin, a transmembrane glycoprotein complex mediating cell–substratum adhesion. *J. Cell Sci. Suppl. 8*, 231–250.

Chen, W.-T., Chen, J.-M. & Mueller, S. C. (1986). Coupled expression and colocalization of 140K cell adhesion molecules, fibronectin, and laminin during morphogenesis and cytodifferentiation in chick lung cells. *J. Cell Biol.* **103**, 1073–1090.

Clark, R. A. F., Folkvord, J. M. & Wertz, R. L. (1985). Fibronectin, as well as other extracellular matrix proteins, mediate human keratinocyte adherence. *J. invest. Derm.* **84**, 378–383.

Clark, R. A. F., Lanigan, J. M., DellaPelle, P., Manseau, E., Dvorak, H. F. & Colvin, R. B. (1982). Fibronectin and fibrin provide a provisional matrix for epidermal cell migration during wound re-epithelialization. *J. invest. Derm.* **79**, 264–269.

Gilchrest, B. A., Calhoun, J. K. & Maciag, T. (1982). Attachment and growth of human keratinocytes in a serum-free environment. *J. cell. Phys.* **112**, 197–206.

Grinnell, F. (1978). Cellular adhesiveness and extracellular substrata. *Int. Rev. Cytol.* **53**, 65–144.

Grinnell, F. (1984). Fibronectin and wound healing. *J. cell. Biochem.* **26**, 107–116.

Grinnell, F., Billingham, R. E. & Burgess, L. (1981). Distribution of fibronectin during wound healing *in vivo*. *J. invest. Derm.* **76**, 181–189.

Katz, S. I. (1984). The epidermal basement membrane zone – structure, ontogeny, and role in disease. *J. Am. Acad. Derm.* **11**, 1025–1037.

Kleinman, H. K., Klebe, R. J. & Martin, G. R. (1981). Role of collagenous matrices in the adhesion and growth of cells. *J. Cell Biol.* **88**, 473–485.

Kono, I., Matsumoto, Y., Kano, K., Ishibashi, Y., Narushima, K., Kabashima, T., Tamane, T., Sakurai, T. & Kashiwati, H. (1985). Beneficial effect of topical fibronectin in patients with keratoconjunctivitis sicca of Sjogren's syndrome. *J. Rheumatol.* **12**, 487–489.

Neff, N. T., Lowrey, C., Decker, C., Tovar, A., Damsky, C., Buck, C. & Horwitz, A. F. (1982). A monoclonal antibody detaches embryonic skeletal muscle cells from extracellular matrices. *J. Cell Biol.* **95**, 654–666.

NISHIDA, T., NAKAGAWA, S. & MANABE, R. (1985). Clinical evaluation of fibronectin eyedrops on epithelial disorders after herpatic keratitis. *Ophthalmology* **92**, 213–216.

O'KEEFE, E. J., PAYNE, R. E., RUSSELL, N. & WOODLEY, D. T. (1985). Spreading and enhanced motility of human keratinocytes on fibronectin. *J. invest. Derm.* **85**, 125–130.

PATEL, V. P. & LODISH, H. F. (1986). The fibronectin receptor on mammalian erythroid precursor cells: Characterization and developmental regulation. *J. Cell Biol.* **102**, 449–456.

PIERSCHBACHER, M. D. & RUOSLAHTI, E. (1984). Cell attachment activity of fibronectin can be duplicated by small synthetic fragments of the molecule. *Nature, Lond.* **309**, 30–33.

PYTELA, R., PIERSCHBACHER, M. & RUOSLAHTI, E. (1985). Identification and isolation of a 140 kd cell surface glycoprotein with properties expected of a fibronectin receptor. *Cell* **40**, 191–198.

ROSEN, P. & MISFELDT, D. S. (1980). Cell density determines epithelial migration in culture. *Proc. natn. Acad. Sci. U.S.A.* **77**, 4760–4763.

STANLEY, J. R., FOIDART, J.-M., MURRAY, J. C., MARTIN, G. R. & KATZ, S. I. (1980). The epidermal cell which selectively adheres to a collagen substrate is the basal cell. *J. invest. Derm.* **74**, 54–58.

STANLEY, J. R., ALVAREZ, O. M., BERE, E. W., EAGLSTEIN, W. H. & KATZ, S. I. (1981). Detection of basement membrane zone antigens during epidermal wound healing in pigs. *J. invest. Derm.* **77**, 240–243.

STENN, K. S., MADRI, J. A., TINGHITELLA, T. & TERRANOVA, V. P. (1983). Multiple mechanisms of dissociated epidermal cell spreading. *J. Cell Biol.* **96**, 63–67.

TAKASHIMA, A., BILLINGHAM, R. E. & GRINNELL, F. (1986). Activation of rabbit keratinocyte fibronectin receptor function *in vivo* during wound healing. *J. invest. Derm.* **86**, 585–590.

TAKASHIMA, A. & GRINNELL, F. (1984). Human keratinocyte adhesion and phagocytosis promoted by fibronectin. *J. invest. Derm.* **83**, 352–358.

TAKASHIMA, A. & GRINNELL, F. (1985). Fibronectin-mediated keratinocyte migration and initiation of fibronectin receptor function *in vitro*. *J. invest. Derm.* **85**, 304–308.

TAMKUN, J. W., DESIMONE, D. W., FONDA, D., PATEL, R. S., BUCK, C., HORWITZ, A. F. & HYNES, R. O. (1986). Structure of integrin, a glycoprotein involved in the transmembrane linkage between fibroblasts and actin. *Cell* **46**, 271–282.

TERRANOVA, V. P., ROHRBACH, D. H. & MARTIN, G. R. (1980). Role of laminin in the attachment of PAM212 (epithelial) cells to basement membrane collagen. *Cell* **22**, 719–726.

TODA, K.-I. & GRINNELL, F. (1987). Activation of human keratinocyte fibronectin receptor function in relationship to other ligand–receptor interactions. *J. invest. Derm.* **88**, 412–417.

TODA, K.-I., TUAN, T.-L., BROWN, P. J. & GRINNELL, F. (1987). Fibronectin receptors of human keratinocytes and their expression during cell culture. *J. Cell Biol.* (in press).

WOODLEY, D. T., O'KEEFE, E. J. & PRUNIERAS, M. (1985). Cutaneous wound healing: A model for cell–matrix interactions. *J. Am. Acad. Derm.* **12**, 420–433.

WYSOCKI, A., BERGSTRESSER, P. R., BAXTER, C. R., HOROWITZ, M. S. & GRINNELL, F. (1987). Topical fibronectin therapy for treatment of a patient with chronic stasis ulcers. *Archs Derm.* (in press).

YAMADA, K. M. (1983). Cell surface interactions with extracellular materials. *A. Rev. Biochem.* **52**, 761–799.

YAMADA, K. M. & KENNEDY, D. W. (1984). Dualistic nature of adhesive protein function: Fibronectin and its biologically active peptide fragments can autoinhibit fibronectin function. *J. Cell Biol.* **99**, 29–36.

J. Cell Sci. Suppl. 8, 211–229 (1987)

ADHESION PLAQUES: SITES OF TRANSMEMBRANE INTERACTION BETWEEN THE EXTRACELLULAR MATRIX AND THE ACTIN CYTOSKELETON

KEITH BURRIDGE, LESLIE MOLONY AND THOMAS KELLY

Laboratories for Cell Biology, Department of Cell Biology and Anatomy, The University of North Carolina at Chapel Hill, Chapel Hill, NC 27514, USA

SUMMARY

In this paper we review what is known about the organization of adhesion plaques, the regions where cells in culture adhere most tightly to the underlying substratum. These specialized areas of the plasma membrane serve as attachment sites for stress fibres. A major objective has been to determine how microfilament bundles are anchored at such regions. In their morphology and composition adhesion plaques resemble the adhesions fibroblasts make to the extracellular matrix. Some extracellular matrix components have been identified on the outside face of adhesion plaques. Within the plasma membrane of adhesion plaques, extracellular matrix receptors, such as the fibronectin receptor (integrin), have been identified. This transmembrane glycoprotein complex has been shown to bind the cytoplasmic protein talin, which, in turn, associates with vinculin. These proteins establish a transmembrane chain of attachment between the extracellular matrix and the cytoskeleton, although how the actin filaments interact with these components remains to be determined. Besides having a structural function, adhesion plaques may also be regions where regulatory signals are transmitted across the membrane. Consistent with this idea has been the finding that various tyrosine kinases and a calcium-dependent protease are concentrated at the cytoplasmic aspect of adhesion plaques. Furthermore, several adhesion plaque proteins become phosphorylated during cell transformation by Rous sarcoma virus. In future work it will be important to determine how such modifications affect the interactions of these proteins and the stability of adhesion plaques.

INTRODUCTION

In the fourth paper of their landmark series on the locomotion of fibroblasts in culture, Abercrombie and his colleagues observed electron-dense plaques on the ventral surfaces of cells (Abercrombie *et al.* 1971). The plaques were associated with filaments and corresponded to regions where the plasma membrane came closest to the underlying substratum. On the basis of their observations they suggested that these regions were involved in cell adhesion and were linked to the cells' filamentous system. Subsequent work has confirmed both ideas. The plaques noted by Abercrombie and coworkers have become known variously as adhesion plaques, focal contacts or focal adhesions. We will use these terms synonymously. These structures have generated much interest, both because they are the sites of attachment of stress fibres to the plasma membrane and because they are regions where the cell interacts with the substratum or extracellular matrix. In this paper we will discuss briefly the organization and biology of adhesion plaques. We wish to emphasize that not only are they sites of mechanical linkage between the cytoskeleton, the plasma membrane and the extracellular matrix, but that they are also regions of communication between the external environment and the cell. For a more detailed review of adhesion plaque organization and function, the reader is referred to Burridge (1986).

ADHESION PLAQUES, STRESS FIBRES AND THE EXTRACELLULAR MATRIX

The adhesion plaques first observed by Abercrombie *et al.* (1971) were identified by electron microscopy. Although this continues to be a useful technique for examining their ultrastructure, the study of adhesion plaques has been facilitated by various light-microscopic techniques such as interference reflection and immunofluorescence microscopy. Used with increasing frequency, interference reflection microscopy (IRM) gives an indication of the separation of the cell from the substratum, the most adherent regions appearing black or dark grey (Curtis, 1964). Izzard & Lochner (1976) classified the ventral surface of fibroblasts into three types of region depending on their IRM images. The darkest images, the adhesion plaques or focal contacts, corresponded to a separation of about 10–15 nm between the cell and the substratum. These regions are frequently surrounded by broad, grey areas, which they have named 'close contacts'. Finally, there are regions appearing white by IRM, indicating a separation from the substratum of 100 nm or more, where adhesion appears to be minimal. All three types of region are seen in the cell in Fig. 1.

Many cells in tissue culture develop adhesion plaques. Abercrombie *et al.* (1971) considered they were probably involved in cell migration, but subsequent work has shown that they are more prominent in cells displaying little or no motility (Couchman & Rees, 1979; Kolega *et al.* 1982). Highly motile cells reveal regions of close contact by IRM. Stress fibres, the large bundles of microfilaments anchored at adhesion plaques, similarly, seem to have little to do with generating cell movement (Couchman & Rees, 1979; Herman *et al.* 1981). At first this was a surprising observation given that stress fibres are reminiscent of muscle myofibrils and contain many of the same proteins. It has been suggested that their prominence in cultured cells reflects a very tight adhesion to an inflexible substratum and a resulting isometric tension generated by the contractile proteins within the stress fibres (Burridge, 1981). Cells that migrate rapidly lack stress fibres and adhesion plaques, and appear to have a less highly ordered array of microfilaments.

When studying the migration of cells from an explant, Couchman and colleagues observed that initially the cells lacked both stress fibres and focal adhesions (Couchman & Rees, 1979; Couchman *et al.* 1982). With time both of these developed and there was a decrease in motility. These changes were paralleled by an increase in surface fibronectin. It was found that the appearance of stress fibres and focal adhesions could be induced earlier by addition of fibronectin to the cells. Fibronectin addition can also have dramatic effects on the cytoskeletal organization of virus-transformed cells. As will be discussed below, transformed cells typically have reduced levels of fibronectin and lack both adhesion plaques and stress fibres. When

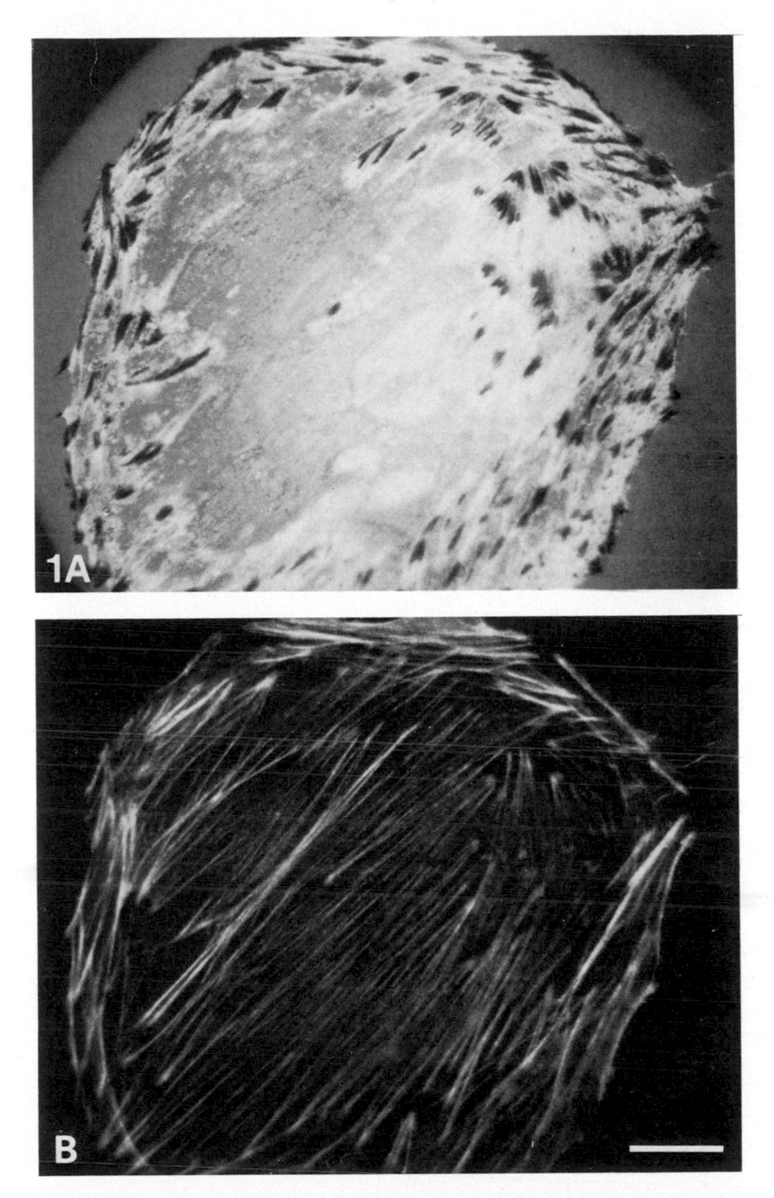

Fig. 1. A cultured BSC-1 cell photographed to show adhesion plaques (A) and stress fibres (B). IRM was used to view the cell in A. The same cell was fixed, permeabilized and stained with rhodamine–phalloidin to reveal the distribution of actin filaments (stress fibres) by immunofluorescence microscopy (B). The darkest regions in the cell in A are adhesion plaques and correspond to the ends of stress fibres seen in B. Large grey areas seen in A are the 'close contacts'. Bar, 20 μm. (Micrographs were kindly provided by C. A. Huff.)

fibronectin is added back to some transformed cells a more normal morphology is restored and the cells develop adhesion plaques and stress fibres (Ali *et al.* 1977; Willingham *et al.* 1977).

Table 1. *Structural proteins in adhesion plaques*

Extracellular face	Transmembrane	Cytoplasmic face
Fibronectin ±	Fibronectin receptor (Integrin)	Actin
		α-Actinin
Heparan sulphate proteoglycan ±	30B6	Fimbrin
	FC1	Vinculin
	HSV D glycoprotein	Talin
		HA1
		$200\times10^3 M_r$
		$82\times10^3 M_r$

The presence of fibronectin depends on the conditions of cell culture. Heparan sulphate proteoglycan has been detected in some adhesion plaques, but how widespread this occurrence is has not been determined. For references see the text.

Stress fibres and adhesion plaques are generally absent from most cells *in situ*, although similar structures are seen at specific locations. For example, the dense plaques of smooth muscle resemble the adhesion plaques of cultured cells, being sites of attachment of actin filaments and regions of adhesion to the extracellular matrix. Adhesion plaques also resemble some types of cell–cell junction, such as the adherens junctions found in epithelial tissues and in cardiac muscle. Analysing the components at these sites, however, indicates that adhesion plaques resemble more closely adhesions to the extracellular matrix than the adhesions made between cells (Geiger *et al.* 1985). For example, both vinculin and talin are found in adhesion plaques and in adhesions to the extracellular matrix, whereas talin appears to be absent from certain cell–cell adhesions, such as the zonula adherens of epithelia and the fascia adherens of cardiac muscle (Geiger *et al.* 1985). When cells in tissue culture interact with glass or plastic substrata, these surfaces are usually covered with adsorbed extracellular matrix components such as fibronectin or vitronectin, and the presence of these appears very important for the formation of adhesion plaques (Woods *et al.* 1986). From these observations we interpret the adhesion plaque of cultured cells as usually being an adhesion to specific extracellular matrix components. In support of this view is the finding that receptors for extracellular matrix components are clustered in adhesion plaques (see below). From this point on, we will consider the adhesion plaque as very closely related, if not equivalent, to an adhesion to the extracellular matrix. Future work may reveal that adhesions to the extracellular matrix can be classified into different types, reflecting the presence of different components. Such a level of analysis has not been achieved.

ORGANIZATION OF ADHESION PLAQUES

We have listed in Table 1 the structural elements concentrated in adhesion plaques. These have been categorized according to their location, on the extracellular face of the plasma membrane, within the membrane or at its cytoplasmic face. A major objective in this area of research has been to identify the critical components and to determine how those on the cytoplasmic side link up with elements in the membrane and thence to the extracellular matrix.

Extracellular components of adhesion plaques

A major component of the extracellular matrix is fibronectin; its relationship to adhesion plaques has been controversial. Some investigators have found it in these structures (Grinnell, 1980; Singer & Paradiso, 1981; Singer, 1982), whereas others have noted it to be absent (Birchmeier *et al.* 1980; Chen & Singer, 1980; Badley *et al.* 1980). The presence or absence of fibronectin in adhesion plaques appears to reflect the conditions of growth: those cells grown in low serum have fibronectin within their adhesion plaques, whereas those grown in high serum clear it from these regions. In part this is due to the fibronectin being less tightly adsorbed to the substratum in the presence of other proteins (Grinnell, 1986).

Many cells in culture secrete fibronectin and, in addition, it is usually present in soluble form in the serum added to cell cultures. Cultured fibroblasts normally develop extensive fibrillar networks of fibronectin on both their dorsal and ventral surfaces (Chen *et al.* 1976). Frequently, when it is on the cell surface, fibronectin is found to co-align with cytoplasmic adhesion plaque proteins, such as vinculin and talin (Burridge & Feramisco, 1980; Singer & Paradiso, 1981; Burridge & Connell, 1983). This supports the idea that adhesion plaques and the adhesions to fibronectin are closely related, if not equivalent, structures.

The properties of fibronectin and its effect on cells have been extensively reviewed (Hynes & Yamada, 1982; Yamada, 1983). For most cells it increases adhesion to the substratum and promotes flattening and the formation of adhesion plaques and stress fibres. When cells are grown in the absence of serum, fibronectin is often added to promote cell adhesion, which is necessary for normal growth (Orley & Sato, 1979; Rizzino & Crowley, 1980; Wolfe *et al.* 1980; Rockwell *et al.* 1980). Although the increased adhesion resulting from added fibronectin is often associated with reduced motility (Couchman *et al.* 1982), in some cases addition of fibronectin has been found to enhance cell migration (Ali & Hynes, 1978). This apparent discrepancy may reflect the properties of different cell types or the fact that adhesion is necessary for migration, but if adhesion becomes excessive it is inhibitory.

Fibronectin has been biochemically dissected into several domains with distinct properties. One of the domains contains a cell-binding sequence that interacts with a specific plasma membrane receptor (see below). The behaviour of cells plated on coverslips coated with this cell-binding domain has been studied (Woods *et al.* 1986). Somewhat surprisingly this fragment of fibronectin will promote cell attachment and even spreading but is not sufficient to induce the formation of adhesion plaques. However, cells plated on the intact fibronectin molecule will form these adhesions, implying that another region in fibronectin is required. This additional region has been identified as a distinct domain that will bind to heparin. Adding a fragment containing both domains or even addition of the two domains as separate fragments will induce formation of adhesion plaques (Woods *et al.* 1986). These results suggest that the induction of adhesion plaques involves the participation of a proteoglycan and requires more than a single type of surface receptor. Related to this, Woods *et al.* (1985) have also demonstrated the presence of a heparan sulphate proteoglycan in the adhesion plaques of some cells. It will be interesting to learn whether this or related proteoglycans are always present in adhesion plaques.

Integral membrane components in adhesion plaques

Although many of the effects of fibronectin on cells have been known for some years, a cellular receptor for fibronectin eluded identification until recently. The discovery of the cellular fibronectin receptor came about from research in two different directions. In the one approach, the cell-binding domain of fibronectin was pared down progressively to a smaller and smaller region until a three-amino-acid sequence (Arg-Gly-Asp) was obtained (Pierschbacher & Ruoslahti, 1984; Yamada & Kennedy, 1984). This short sequence would compete with fibronectin for binding to cells and would detach cells that had been plated on a fibronectin substratum. Affinity chromatography on immobilized fibronectin was used to identify a receptor that could be released by peptides containing this cell-binding peptide (Pytela *et al.* 1985*a*). With mammalian cells this approach revealed a glycoprotein complex with an apparent polypeptide molecular weight of 140 000 on SDS–polyacrylamide gels under reducing conditions. In non-reducing conditions two distinct polypeptide bands were identified. This same approach has been used to identify the receptors for other extracellular matrix proteins (e.g. vitronectin) (Pytela *et al.* 1985*b*), many of which also contain the same Arg-Gly-Asp sequence in their cell-binding domains (reviewed by Ruoslahti & Pierschbacher, 1986).

The fibronectin receptor was also identified independently in several laboratories, using a different strategy employing monoclonal antibodies (Mabs). These Mabs, raised against whole cells, were found to affect cell adhesion (Neff *et al.* 1982; Greve & Gottlieb, 1982). They were shown to interact with a glycoprotein complex with subunits of about 140 000 M_r (Chapman, 1984; Horwitz *et al.* 1984; Knudsen *et al.* 1985; Hasegawa *et al.* 1985; Brown & Juliano, 1985). Isolated by affinity chromatography on these Mabs, the glycoprotein complex was shown to bind to fibronectin in solution (Horwitz *et al.* 1985; Akiyama *et al.* 1986). Most work has been performed using two Mabs, CSAT and JG22E, both of which are specific for the avian fibronectin receptor. Whereas the mammalian receptor appears to be a heterodimer by SDS–polyacrylamide gel electrophoresis (SDS–PAGE), the avian receptor reveals three bands on non-reduced SDS–PAGE (Knudsen *et al.* 1985; Hasegawa *et al.* 1985). The reason for this difference is not clear, but the avian receptor isolated on these antibody columns might be a mixture of two heterodimers that share a common polypeptide recognized by the antibodies. The avian receptor differs from the mammalian in that the same receptor binds not only fibronectin but also several other extracellular matrix components, such as laminin, vitronectin and some types of collagen (Horwitz *et al.* 1985). With mammalian cells distinct receptors generally appear to bind the different extracellular matrix components, although in the case of platelets one receptor, glycoproteins IIb/IIIa, binds several extracellular matrix ligands (Gardner & Hynes, 1985). Cloning and sequencing the genes for some of these receptors indicates a large family of related proteins (reviewed by Hynes, 1987). The name 'integrin' has been proposed for this family of proteins (Tamkun *et al.* 1986; Hynes, 1987; and see Buck & Horwitz, this volume).

The Mabs CSAT and JG22E tend to label migratory cells diffusely, but cells that are more stationary show staining of the adhesion plaques with these antibodies (Damsky *et al.* 1985; Chen *et al.* 1985). By immunofluorescence microscopy the staining of the adhesions is uneven, with most of the stain being concentrated at the periphery, giving rise to an image like the eye of a needle (Fig. 2A). In our laboratory we have raised polyclonal antibodies against two smooth-muscle glycoproteins that appear to be members of the integrin family (Kelly *et al.* 1987). Immunologically these antibodies cross-react with the antigens recognized by the CSAT Mab. Unlike CSAT or JG22E, however, these polyclonal antibodies stain adhesion plaques much more evenly (Fig. 2B). The explanation for this difference may be that the Mabs recognize a single epitope on the proteins that is at or close to the ligand binding site for these receptors. At the centre of adhesion plaques these receptors may be occupied and sterically inaccessible, resulting in a staining pattern that is concentrated at the adhesion plaque periphery. On the other hand, the polyclonal antibodies recognize multiple epitopes on these proteins, particularly in fixed and permeabilized cells. Because most of the antigenic sites on the receptors are not blocked by the presence of extracellular matrix components, these antibodies reveal the presence of the receptors throughout the adhesion plaques.

It is striking that these receptors are clustered within adhesion plaques of chicken embryo fibroblasts even when these plaques lack fibronectin. Since in the avian system this receptor can interact with ligands besides fibronectin, this observation suggests that other extracellular matrix components may be present and important in organizing adhesion plaques. Vitronectin is a possible candidate. It has not been listed in Table 1 because it is not concentrated within these substratum adhesions, but under most culture conditions where serum is used, vitronectin is adsorbed uniformly across the glass or plastic substratum (Neyfakh *et al.* 1983; Hayman *et al.* 1985).

Mab 30B6 binds to another membrane glycoprotein in adhesion plaques of avian cells (Rogalski & Singer, 1985). This glycoprotein shares some characteristics with the avian fibronectin receptor, but the Mab 30B6 stains adhesion plaques more evenly than the Mabs CSAT or JG22E. From our results cited above, however, this would be consistent with 30B6 binding to a different epitope on the same receptor. Further work will be needed to determine whether 30B6 is identifying a novel component in focal contacts.

Two other membrane proteins have been identified in focal contacts, the herpes simplex viral glycoprotein D (Norrild *et al.* 1983) and a component recognized by the Mab FCI (Oesch & Birchmeier, 1982). Since little is known about these they will not be discussed.

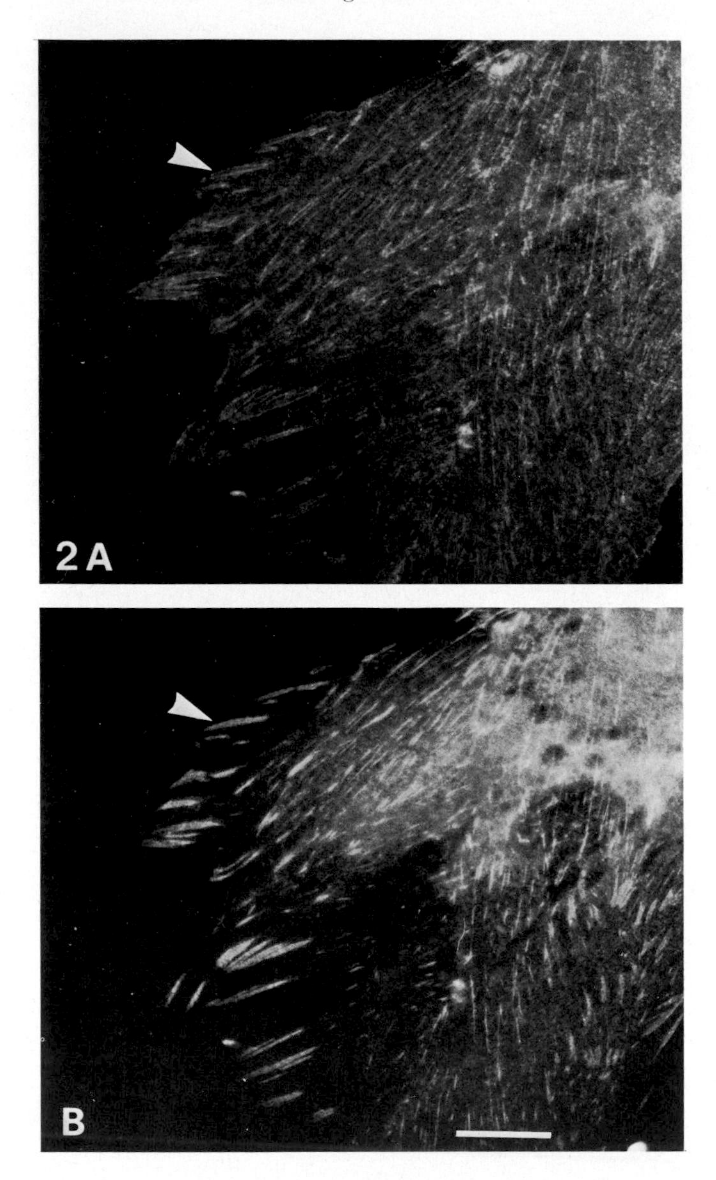

Fig. 2. Distribution of the fibronectin receptor (integrin) in a chicken embryo fibroblast. In A the cell was stained live with the CSAT Mab; in B the same cell was stained after fixation and permeabilization with a polyclonal antibody that binds to the same antigen. Note that in A the antibody labels the adhesion plaques unevenly, concentrating at the periphery, whereas in B the adhesion plaques are more uniformly stained (arrowheads). Bar, 20 μm.

Proteins at the cytoplasmic face of adhesion plaques

Much of the attention focused on adhesion plaques has been aimed at trying to determine how the bundles of actin filaments are attached to the plasma membrane.

This quesion has not been resolved, but several proteins have been identified as candidates for a role in this function. Two proteins that bind to actin filaments, and which are concentrated in adhesion plaques, are α-actinin (Lazarides & Burridge, 1975; Wehland *et al.* 1979) and fimbrin (Bretscher & Weber, 1980). Both proteins crosslink actin filaments *in vitro* and may be important in stabilizing the filaments within a stress fibre. Since they bind to actin they may also function in attachment of the filaments to the membrane. This has been suggested periodically for α-actinin, although evidence against this has also been presented (Burridge & McCullough, 1980). Supporting a possible membrane attachment role for α-actinin are recent experiments indicating that the protein can interact with specific lipids (Burn *et al.* 1985) and also that α-actinin can interact with vinculin (Craig, 1985), itself a protein thought to have a function in attachment to the membrane. If further work substantiates an attachment role for α-actinin, it will be important to explore how this is regulated, since only a fraction of the cell's α-actinin is found in these adhesions and much of the protein is distributed along the stress fibres.

Vinculin and talin are two proteins that have generated much interest as potential links between actin and the adhesion plaque plasma membrane (Geiger, 1979; Geiger *et al.* 1980; Burridge & Feramisco, 1980; Burridge & Connell, 1983; and see Geiger *et al.*, this volume). These two proteins interact (Burridge & Mangeat, 1984) and are generally found co-distributed in fibroblasts, in both adhesion plaques and underlying bundles of fibronectin on the cell surface. How these proteins associate with actin filaments has not been determined, but one mode of interaction with the membrane has been identified. Talin binds to the cytoplasmic domain of the fibronectin receptor (Horwitz *et al.* 1986). It seems probable that vinculin may also interact with membrane proteins directly and this is supported by the fact that in some cells, such as epithelia and cardiac muscle, vinculin is found associated with regions of the plasma membrane in the absence of talin. In some circumstances talin may function independently of vinculin; for example, Kupfer *et al.* (1986) have shown that talin, but not vinculin, concentrates in cytotoxic T lymphocytes at the site of adhesion to a target cell.

For a time vinculin was thought to interact directly with actin, capping the ends of actin filaments or inducing the filaments to form bundles (Jockusch & Isenberg, 1981; Wilkins & Lin, 1982; Burridge & Feramisco, 1982). Further work established that the apparent effects of vinculin on actin were due to contaminants in vinculin preparations (Evans *et al.* 1984; Rosenfeld *et al.* 1985; Schroer & Wegner, 1985; Otto, 1986; Wilkins & Lin, 1986). Because these contaminants flow through a hydroxyapatite column in the first fraction, Wilkins & Lin (1986) have referred to these as the HAI components. Several relatively low molecular weight bands are responsible for this activity, but antibodies raised against these components cross-react with higher molecular weight proteins in immunoblots of whole cells or tissues, suggesting that the low molecular components are proteolytic fragments derived from these larger proteins (Wilkins *et al.* 1986). These antibodies also localize the proteins to adhesion plaques. This result, together with earlier data indicating an interaction with the ends of actin filaments, suggests that the HAI proteins may have a critical role in attachment of actin to the adhesion plaque membrane. In future work it will be important to characterize these proteins and their interactions in detail.

Even less is known about some of the other components that have been identified in adhesion plaques. For example, Maher & Singer (1983) raised an antibody against a 200 000 M_r component from cardiac fascia adherens and this antibody stains adhesion plaques. This protein has not been purified. While screening rabbit sera, Beckerle (1986) discovered one serum that labelled fibroblast adhesion plaques. This serum bound to an 82 000 M_r protein in immunoblots. Preliminary work has indicated that this is a relatively minor component compared with vinculin or talin, possibly indicating a regulatory role rather than a structural one for this protein.

We are confident that many more proteins remain to be identified in adhesion plaques and many of those that have been identified are poorly characterized. Conscious of these deficits, we have tried to represent the better-characterized adhesion plaque components and their interactions in a simple diagram (Fig. 3). On the outside of the plasma membrane, fibronectin is shown interacting with the fibronectin receptor (integrin). The shape of this receptor complex is based on electron microscopy (Molony, unpublished results) and on parallel studies of the platelet fibronectin receptor, glycoprotein IIb/IIIa (Carrell *et al.* 1985). The receptor is shown spanning the membrane and then binding on the cytoplasmic side to talin (Horwitz *et al.* 1986; Tapley *et al.* unpublished data). In turn, talin is shown interacting with vinculin. The shapes of talin and vinculin are based on platinum-shadowed images of these molecules (Milam, 1985; Molony *et al.* 1987). These have revealed that talin is an elongated, flexible molecule at physiological ionic strengths, whereas vinculin has two domains with a globular head and a short extended tail. Although our work has indicated that the head region of vinculin binds to talin, the binding site on talin has not been defined. Recently, we have discovered that talin will dimerize at concentrations above about 0·7 mg ml^{-1} (Molony *et al.* 1987). This has not been indicated in the diagram because we do not know whether this dimerization involves side-to-side or end-on association of the talin molecules. Although not shown, the dimerization would be expected to crosslink the proteins to which talin binds, such as vinculin and the fibronectin receptor, and this may contribute to the stability of adhesion plaques.

In Fig. 3, we have indicated an unidentified protein that may link vinculin to the membrane independently of talin. As mentioned earlier, the existence of such a protein is suggested by finding vinculin associated with some membranes without talin. It is also supported by experiments that showed that fluorescent vinculin would bind back to adhesion plaques in permeabilized fibroblasts and that this was not dependent on talin (Ball *et al.* 1986). Also shown in the diagram is the component(s) HAI capping the end of an actin filament. The shape of this molecule has not been determined and it will be important to discover with what other components it interacts.

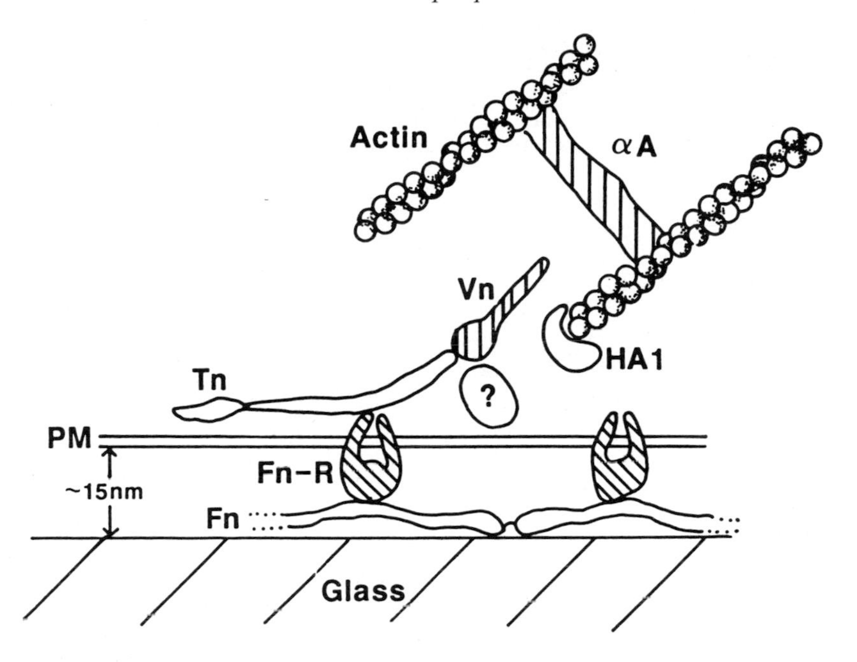

Fig. 3. A diagram of some of the proteins identified in adhesion plaques. The lengths of the proteins are drawn approximately to scale, with the separation of the plasma membrane bilayer (PM) being about 15 nm from the glass substrate. Part of a fibronectin (Fn) dimer is shown adhering to the glass. It should be noted that fibronectin is frequently absent from adhesion plaques although other extracellular matrix components may be present. The fibronectin receptor (Fn-R) (integrin) spans the plasma membrane and binds to talin (Tn) on the cytoplasmic face. In turn, talin binds vinculin (Vn). The shapes of the fibronectin receptor, talin and vinculin are derived from electron microscopy of isolated molecules (Milam, 1985; Molony *et al.* 1987; Molony, unpublished data). A constriction in the talin molecule indicates the site of cleavage by the calcium-dependent protease II. An unidentified protein (?) is shown linking vinculin to the membrane independently of talin. The actin filaments are shown crosslinked by α-actinin (αA) and being capped by the HA1 component(s). The shape of the latter has not been determined. How the actin filaments link to the transmembrane components remains a major unresolved question.

ADHESION PLAQUES AND THE REGULATION OF CELLULAR ACTIVITIES

It is our contention that the adhesion plaque is more than just a structural link between the cytoskeleton, the plasma membrane and the extracellular matrix. Adhesion plaques are sites of communication between the cell and the extracellular environment. It has been known for some time that adequate adhesion is necessary for the growth of many cells in culture. Paradoxically, many agents that promote cell growth and proliferation, such as various hormones, growth factors, tumour promoters and transforming viruses, result in a disruption of these adhesions (reviewed by Burridge, 1986). The reasons for this are not clear. Not only does adhesion permit the growth of many cells, but the type of surface to which the cells adhere can have marked effects on the growth properties, morphology and behaviour

Table 2. *Regulatory proteins in adhesion plaques*

Protein	
$p60^{src}$ (1)	Tyrosine kinases
$p120^{gag\text{-}abl}$ (2)	Tyrosine kinases
$p90^{gag\text{-}yes}$ (3)	Tyrosine kinases
$p80^{gag\text{-}yes}$ (3)	Tyrosine kinases
Calcium-dependent protease II (4)	

(1) Rohrschneider (1980); Nigg *et al.* (1982); Krueger *et al.* (1984); (2) Rohrschneider & Najita (1984); (3) Gentry & Rohrschneider (1984); (4) Beckerle *et al.* (1987).

of these cells. Again this implies the communication of information across the plasma membrane at adhesions to the substratum or extracellular matrix.

Several potential regulatory enzymes have been identified at the cytoplasmic face of adhesion plaques (Table 2). A number of these are tyrosine kinases, the products of various viral oncogenes. Generally, transformed cells are more rounded with few if any adhesion plaques. However, in cells transformed by the appropriate virus, immunofluorescence microscopy has revealed the presence of these tyrosine kinases in those cells sufficiently adherent and spread to retain adhesion plaques (Rohrschneider, 1980; Rohrschneider & Najita, 1984; Gentry & Rohrschneider, 1984; Nigg *et al.* 1982; Krueger *et al.* 1984). These viral oncogenes have normal cellular homologues, but these are expressed at too low a level in fibroblasts for their distribution to have been detected by immunofluorescence microscopy. Elevated levels of phosphotyrosine, however, have been found in the adhesion plaques of non-transformed fibroblasts (Maher *et al.* 1985), suggesting that tyrosine kinases are normally concentrated within these structures.

What are the substrates for these tyrosine kinases within adhesion plaques? Vinculin was the first adhesion-plaque protein found to contain elevated phosphotyrosine levels in cells transformed by Rous sarcoma virus (RSV) (Sefton *et al.* 1981). This result, combined with the localization of the RSV oncogene product, $pp60^{src}$, within adhesion plaques (Rohrschneider, 1980), led to a model that envisaged the phophorylation of vinculin as being a major event in the disruption of adhesion plaques and stress fibres in transformed cells. Appealing though this model was, it has not been supported by subsequent work. A number of groups have examined the level of vinculin phosphorylation in cells infected with viral mutants of RSV that do not result in the transformed phenotype. In several of these studies the level of vinculin phophorylation on tyrosine residues has been found to be elevated, but this has not been accompanied by a loss of stress fibres or adhesion plaques (Rohrschneider & Rosok, 1983; Iwashita *et al.* 1983; Antler *et al.* 1985; Nigg *et al.* 1986; Kellie *et al.* 1986). At present it is not clear whether vinculin phosphorylation has any significance. The level of vinculin phosphorylation is low at best and it is perhaps an inconsequential event reflecting a fortuitous proximity to the kinase.

Recently, talin has also been found to contain phosphotyrosine and to have elevated levels in cells transformed by some of the viruses carrying oncogenes encoding tyrosine kinases (Pasquale *et al.* 1986; DeClue & Martin, 1987). DeClue & Martin (1987) investigated the level of tyrosine phosphorylation in talin in cells infected by several RSV mutants that do not induce a fully transformed morphological phenotype. In these partially transformed cells talin was found to contain elevated phosphotyrosine at levels close to those found in cells fully transformed by the wild-type virus. These authors concluded that elevated phosphotyrosine in talin did not correlate with loss of fibronectin from the cell surface, loss of stress fibres or a rounded morphology (DeClue & Martin, 1987).

The avian fibronectin receptor (integrin) also contains elevated levels of phosphotyrosine in cells transformed by RSV, and certain other viruses (Hirst *et al.* 1986). Two of the receptor polypeptides become phosphorylated. One of these polypeptides has been cloned and sequenced (Tamkun *et al.* 1986) and it was noted that a region of homology existed in the presumptive cytoplasmic domain with a sequence in the epidermal growth factor (EGF) receptor. Interestingly, this sequence in the EGF receptor contains the tyrosine that is autophosphorylated in response to EGF binding. It is this related sequence in the fibronectin receptor that is phosphorylated in cells transformed by RSV. In addition, a synthetic decapeptide corresponding to this region of the cytoplasmic domain has been found to inhibit the binding of talin to the fibronectin receptor in solution (Tapley *et al.* unpublished data; and see Buck & Horwitz, this volume). The fibronectin receptor purified from RSV-transformed cells is phosphorylated on this tyrosine residue and has reduced binding of both talin and fibronectin (Tapley *et al.* unpublished data). It has not been determined, however, whether the decreased affinity for talin and fibronectin is due to this phosphorylation or to some other modification that has not been identified. It is easy to envisage how various modifications of the receptor could destabilize the adhesion plaque and promote its disassembly. It will be important, however, to determine whether phosphorylation of the receptor correlates with the transformed phenotype using the viral mutants mentioned above. In transformed cells there are other important events, which undoubtedly affect the integrity of adhesion plaques. In many transformed cells, for example, there is an increased secretion of proteolytic enzymes and a consequent reduction in fibronectin and other extracellular matrix proteins (Unkeless *et al.* 1973; Chen *et al.* 1984). That this reduction in fibronectin affects adhesion plaques and cytoskeletal organization has been shown by adding fibronectin back to transformed cells. In many cases this addition of exogenous fibronectin will temporarily reverse the transformed phenotype, restoring adhesion plaques, stress fibres and a more normal morphology. It is probable that the disruption of adhesion plaques in transformed cells is due to multiple events and it will be important to determine whether the phosphorylation of any of the focal contact proteins contributes to this process.

One of the isoforms of the calcium-dependent protease (CDPII), another potential regulatory enzyme, has also been identified in adhesion plaques (Beckerle *et al.* 1987). Talin has been found to be a particularly good substrate for this enzyme. Following platelet activation cleavage of the platelet form of talin (P235) occurs as a result of calcium-dependent proteases (Fox *et al.* 1985). The significance of this fragmentation of talin in platelets has not been determined, but it raises the possibility that proteolysis of talin by CDPII in fibroblasts may be important in the disassembly or reorganization of adhesion plaques. We have found that cleavage of talin by CDPII does not separate the vinculin binding site from the fibronectin–receptor binding site, and that this cleavage occurs asymmetrically in the molecule (O'Halloran *et al.* 1985; Beckerle *et al.* 1986; Horwitz *et al.* 1986). The approximate position of the cleavage site in talin is indicated in the diagram, in Fig. 3, by a constriction in the molecule. Although this proteolysis of talin does not appear to affect the binding to vinculin or to the fibronectin receptor, it may affect other talin interactions. We are currently investigating whether it prevents talin dimerization, which might have major consequences on the ability of talin to crosslink and stabilize components in adhesion plaques.

FUTURE DIRECTIONS

In this brief overview we have summarized much of what is known about the structural elements found within adhesion plaques. There are many holes in our current model, indicating that critical components remain to be identified. One of the major questions continues to be: how are the actin filaments of a stress fibre linked to the adhesion plaque membrane? We would not be surprised to find that the filaments are anchored at these sites by more than one set of linker proteins functioning in parallel. It should be remembered that even in the model system of the erythrocyte plasma membrane, actin is linked to the membrane through two different sets of proteins. In the adhesion plaque one transmembrane linkage has been identified to date. This involves the fibronectin receptor, which in avian cells can interact on the outside with several types of extracellular matrix protein besides fibronectin, and which binds talin on the cytoplasmic face of the membrane. We anticipate, however, that this is just the first of several transmembrane links that will be discovered to operate in adhesion plaques.

Several potential regulatory enzymes have been identified in adhesion plaques and we have discussed these enzymes in terms of their modification of various cytoskeletal and membrane proteins. These actions may be involved in regulating the reorganization and disassembly of adhesion plaques and stress fibres; for example, during mitosis or in response to growth factors or transforming viruses. This may be just a small part of the regulatory activity that occurs at these sites. Little is known about the larger question of the signal transduction that occurs at adhesion plaques, and which may also involve enzymes such as the tyrosine kinases that have been identified in these regions. Cells respond in dramatic ways when cultured on different extracellular matrices and cell substrata. Cells that need one set of growth factors when cultured on one substratum may lose this requirement or require different growth factors when cultured on a different substratum (reviewed by Burridge, 1986). Elucidating the signals and second messages generated at adhesion plaques in response to specific extracellular matrix components is an exciting prospect for the future.

We thank our colleagues and collaborators, Mary Beckerle, Clayton Buck, Dorothy Croall and Rick Horwitz, for valuable discussions and gifts of antibodies. We thank Ms Betty Stewart for typing the manuscript and Ms Gina Harrison for help with the illustrations. This work was supported by NIH grant GM 29860.

REFERENCES

Abercrombie, M., Heaysman, J. & Pegrum, S. M. (1971). The locomotion of fibroblasts in culture. *Expl Cell Res.* **65**, 359–367.

Akiyama, S. K., Yamada, S. S. & Yamada, K. M. (1986). Characterization of a 140-kD avian cell surface antigen as a fibronectin-binding molecule. *J. Cell Biol.* **102**, 442–448.

Ali, I. U. & Hynes, R. O. (1978). Effects of LETS glycoprotein on cell motility. *Cell* **14**, 439–446.

Ali, I. U., Mautner, V., Lanza, R. P. & Hynes, R. O. (1977). Restoration of normal morphology, adhesion and cytoskeleton in transformed cells by addition of a transformation-sensitive surface protein. *Cell* **11**, 115–126.

Antler, A. M., Greenberg, M. E., Edelman, G. M. & Hanafusa, H. (1985). Increased phosphorylation of tyrosine in vinculin does not occur upon transformation by some avian sarcoma viruses. *Molec. Cell Biol.* **5**, 263–267.

Badley, R. A., Woods, A., Smith, C. G. & Rees, D. A. (1980). Actomyosin relationships with surface features in fibroblast adhesion. *Expl Cell Res.* **126**, 263–272.

Ball, E. H., Freitag, C. & Gurofsky, S. (1986). Vinculin interaction with permeabilized cells: disruption and reconstitution of a binding site. *J. Cell Biol.* **103**, 641–648.

Beckerle, M. C. (1986). Identification of a new protein localized at sites of cell–substrate adhesion. *J. Cell Biol.* **103**, 1679–1687.

Beckerle, M. C., Burridge, K., DeMartino, G. N. & Croall, D. E. (1987). Colocalization of calcium-dependent protease-II and one of its substrates at sites of cell adhesion. *Cell* (in press).

Beckerle, M. C., O'Halloran, T. & Burridge, K. (1986). Demonstration of a relationship between talin and P235. A major substrate of the calcium-dependent protease in platelets. *J. cell. Biochem.* **30**, 259–270.

Birchmeier, C., Kreis, T. E., Eppenberger, H. M., Winterhalter, K. H. & Birchmeier, W. (1980). Corrugated attachment membrane in WI-38 fibroblasts. Alternating fibronectin fibers and actin-containing focal contacts. *Proc. natn. Acad. Sci. U.S.A.* **77**, 4108–4112.

Bretscher, A. & Weber, K. (1980). Fimbrin, a new microfilament-associated protein present in microvilli and other cell surface structures. *J. Cell Biol.* **86**, 335–340.

Brown, P. J. & Juliano, R. L. (1985). Selective inhibition of fibronectin-mediated cell adhesion by monoclonal antibodies to a cell surface glycoprotein. *Science* **228**, 1448–1451.

Buck, C. A. & Horwitz, A. F. (1987). Integrin, a transmembrane glycoprotein complex mediating cell–substratum adhesion. *J. Cell Sci. Suppl.* *8*, 000–000.

Burn, P., Rotman, A., Meyer, R. K. & Burger, M. M. (1985). Diacylglycerol in large α-actinin/actin complexes and in the cytoskeleton of activated platelets. *Nature, Lond.* **314**, 469–471.

Burridge, K. (1981). Are stress fibers contractile? *Nature, Lond.* **294**, 691–692.

Burridge, K. (1986). Substrate adhesions in normal and transformed fibroblasts: organization and regulation of cytoskeletal, membrane and extracellular matrix components at focal contacts. *Cancer Rev.* **4**, 18–78.

Burridge, K. & Connell, L. (1983). A new protein of adhesion plaques and ruffling membranes. *J. Cell Biol.* **97**, 359–367.

Burridge, K. & Feramisco, J. R. (1980). Microinjection and localization of a 130K protein in living fibroblasts: a relationship to actin and fibronectin. *Cell* **19**, 587–595.

Burridge, K. & Feramisco, J. R. (1982). α-Actinin and vinculin from non-muscle cells: calcium-sensitive interactions with actin. *Cold Spring Harbor Symp. quant. Biol.* **46**, 587–597.

Burridge, K. & Mangeat, P. (1984). An interaction between vinculin and talin. *Nature, Lond.* **308**, 744–746.

Burridge, K. & McCullough, L. (1980). The association of α-actinin with the plasma membrane. *J. supramolec. Struct.* **13**, 53–65.

Carrell, N. A., Fitzgerald, L. A., Steiner, B., Erickson, H. P. & Phillips, D. R. (1985). Structure of human platelet membrane glycoproteins IIb and IIIa as determined by electron microscopy. *J. biol. Chem.* **260**, 1743–1749.

CHAPMAN, A. E. (1984). Characterization of a 140kd cell surface glycoprotein involved in myoblast adhesion. *J. cell. Biochem.* **25**, 109–121.

CHEN, L. B., GALLIMORE, P. H. & MCDOUGALL, J. K. (1976). Correlation between tumor induction and the large external transformation sensitive protein on the cell surface. *Proc. natn. Acad. Sci. U.S.A.* **73**, 3570–3574.

CHEN, W. T., OLDEN, K., BERNARD, B. A. & CHU, F. (1984). Expression of transformation-associated protease(s) that degrade fibronectin at cell contact sites. *J. Cell Biol.* **98**, 1546–1555.

CHEN, W. T., HASEGAWA, E., HASEGAWA, T., WEINSTOCK, C. & YAMADA, K. M. (1985). Development of cell surface linkage complexes in cultured fibroblasts. *J. Cell Biol.* **100**, 1103–1114.

CHEN, W. T. & SINGER, S. J. (1980). Fibronectin is not present in the focal adhesions formed between normal cultured fibroblasts and their substrata. *Proc. natn. Acad. Sci. U.S.A.* **77**(12), 7318–7322.

COUCHMAN, J. R. & REES, D. A. (1979). The behavior of fibroblasts migrating from chick heart explants: changes in adhesion, locomotion and growth, and in the distribution of actomyosin and fibronectin. *J. Cell Sci.* **39**, 149–165.

COUCHMAN, J. R., REES, D. A., GREEN, M. R. & SMITH, C. G. (1982). Fibronectin has a dual role in locomotion and anchorage of primary chick fibroblasts and can promote entry into the division cycle. *J. Cell Biol.* **93**, 402–410.

CRAIG, S. W. (1985). Alpha-actinin, an F-actin cross-linking protein, interacts directly with vinculin and meta-vinculin. *J. Cell Biol.* **101**, 136a.

CURTIS, A. S. G. (1964). The mechanism of adhesion of cells to glass. A study by interference reflection microscopy. *J. Cell Biol.* **20**, 199–215.

DAMSKY, C. H., KNUDSEN, K. A., BRADLEY, D., BUCK, C. A. & HORWITZ, A. F. (1985). Distribution of the cell–substratum attachment (CSAT) antigen on myogenic and fibroblastic cells in culture. *J. Cell Biol.* **100**, 1528–1539.

DECLUE, J. E. & MARTIN, G. S. (1987). Phosphorylation of talin at tyrosine in Rous sarcoma virus-transformed cells. *Molec. cell. Biol.* **7**, 371–378.

EVANS, R. R., ROBSON, R. M. & STROMER, M. H. (1984). Properties of smooth muscle vinculin. *J. biol. Chem.* **259**, 3916–3924.

FOX, J. E. B., GOLL, D. E., REYNOLDS, C. C. & PHILLIPS, D. R. (1985). Identification of two proteins (actin-binding protein and P235) that are hydrolyzed by endogenous Ca^{2+}-dependent protease during platelet aggregation. *J. biol. Chem.* **260**, 1060–1066.

GARDNER, J. M. & HYNES, R. O. (1985). Interaction of fibronectin with its receptor on platelets. *Cell* **42**, 439–448.

GEIGER, B. (1979). A 130K protein from chicken gizzard: its localization at the termini of microfilament bundles in cultured chicken cells. *Cell* **18**, 193–205.

GEIGER, B., TOKUYASU, K. T., DUTTON, A. H. & SINGER, S. J. (1980). Vinculin, an intracellular protein localized at specialized sites where microfilament bundles terminate at cell membranes. *Proc. natn. Acad. Sci. U.S.A.* **77**, 4127–4131.

GEIGER, B., VOLK, T. & VOLBERG, T. (1985). Molecular heterogeneity of adherens junctions. *J. Cell Biol.* **101**, 1523–1531.

GEIGER, B., VOLK, T., VOLBERG, T. & BENDORI, R. (1987). Molecular interactions in adherens-type contacts. *J. Cell Sci. Suppl. 8*, 251–272.

GENTRY, L. E. & ROHRSCHNEIDER, L. R. (1984). Common features of the *yes* and *src* gene products defined by peptide-specific antibodies. *J. Virol.* **51**, 539–546.

GREVE, J. M. & GOTTLEIB, D. I. (1982). Monoclonal antibodies which alter the morphology of cultured chick myogenic cells. *J. cell. Biochem.* **18**, 221–229.

GRINNELL, F. (1980). Visualization of cell–substratum adhesion plaques by antibody exclusion. *Cell Biol. Int. Rep.* **4**, 1031–1036.

GRINNELL, F. (1986). Focal adhesion sites and the removal of substratum-bound fibronectin. *J. Cell Biol.* **103**, 2697–2706.

HASEGAWA, T., HASEGAWA, E., CHEN, W. T. & YAMADA, K. M. (1985). Characterization of a membrane-associated glycoprotein complex implicated in cell adhesion to fibronectin. *J. cell. Biochem.* **28**, 307–318.

HAYMAN, E. G., PIERSCHBACHER, M. D., SUZUKI, S. & RUOSLAHTI, E. (1985). Vitronectin – a major cell attachment-promoting protein in fetal bovine serum. *Expl Cell Res.* **160**, 245–258.

HERMAN, I. M., CRISONA, N. J. & POLLARD, T. D. (1981). Relation between cell activity and the distribution of cytoplasmic actin and myosin. *J. Cell Biol.* **90**, 84–91.

HIRST, R., HORWITZ, A., BUCK, C. & ROHRSCHNEIDER, L. (1986). Phosphorylation of the fibronectin receptor complex in cells transformed by oncogenes that encode tyrosine kinases. *Proc. natn. Acad. Sci. U.S.A.* **83**, 6470–6474.

HORWITZ, A., DUGGAN, K., BUCK, C., BECKERLE, M. C. & BURRIDGE, K. (1986). Interaction of plasma membrane fibronectin receptor with talin – a transmembrane linkage. *Nature, Lond.* **320**, 531–533.

HORWITZ, A., DUGGAN, K., GREGGS, R., DECKER, C. & BUCK, C. (1985). The CSAT antigen has properties of a receptor for laminin and fibronectin. *J. Cell Biol.* **101**, 2134–2144.

HORWITZ, A. F., KNUDSEN, K. A., DAMSKY, C. H., DECKER, C., BUCK, C. A. & NEFF, N. T. (1984). Adhesion-related integral membrane glycoproteins identified by monoclonal antibodies. In *Monoclonal Antibodies and Functional Cell Lines: Progress and Applications* (ed. R. H. Kenneth, K. B. Bechtol & T. S. McKearn), pp. 103–118. New York: Plenum Press.

HYNES, R. O. (1987). Integrins: a family of cell surface receptors. *Cell* **48**, 549–554.

HYNES, R. O. & YAMADA, K. M. (1982). Fibronectins: multifunctional modular glycoproteins. *J. Cell Biol.* **95**, 369–377.

IWASHITA, S., KITAMURA, N. & YOSHIDA, M. (1983). Molecular events leading to fusiform morphological transformation by partial src deletion mutant of Rous sarcoma virus. *Virology* **125**, 419–431.

IZZARD, C. S. & LOCHNER, L. R. (1976). Cell-to-substrate contacts in living fibroblasts: An interference reflexion study with an evaluation of the technique. *J. Cell Sci.* **21**, 129–159.

JOCKUSCH, B. M. & ISENBERG, G. (1981). Interaction of α-actinin and vinculin with actin: opposite effects on filament network formation. *Proc. natn. Acad. Sci. U.S.A.* **78**, 3005–3009.

KELLIE, S., PATEL, B., MITCHELL, A., CRITCHLEY, D. R., WIGGLESWORTH, N. M. & WYKE, J. A. (1986). Comparison of the relative importance of tyrosine-specific vinculin phosphorylation and the loss of surface-associated fibronectin in the morphology of cells transformed by Rous sarcoma virus. *J. Cell Sci.* **82**, 129–142.

KELLY, T., MOLONY, L. & BURRIDGE, K. (1987). Purification of two smooth muscle glycoproteins related to integrin: distribution in cultured chicken embryo fibroblasts. *J. biol. Chem.* **262** (in press).

KNUDSEN, K. A., HORWITZ, A. F. & BUCK, C. A. (1985). A monoclonal antibody identifies a glycoprotein complex involved in cell–substratum adhesion. *Expl Cell Res.* **157**, 218–226.

KOLEGA, J., SHURE, M. S., CHEN, W. T. & YOUNG, N. D. (1982). Rapid cellular translocation is related to close contacts formed between various cultured cells and their substrata. *J. Cell Sci.* **54**, 23–34.

KRUEGER, J. G., GARBER, E. A., CHIN, S. S. M., HANAFUSA, N. & GOLDBERG, A. R. (1984). Size variant pp60^{src} proteins of recovered avian sarcoma viruses interact with adhesion plaques as peripheral membrane proteins: effects on cell transformation. *Molec. cell. Biol.* **4**, 454–467.

KUPFER, A., SINGER, S. J. & DENNERT, G. (1986). On the mechanism of unidirectional killing in mixtures of two cytotoxic T-lymphocytes. *J. exp. Med.* **163**, 489–498.

LAZARIDES, E. & BURRIDGE, K. (1975). α-Actinin: immunofluorescent localization of a muscle structural protein in nonmuscle cells. *Cell* **6**, 289–298.

MAHER, P. A., PASQUALE, E. B., WANG, J. Y. J. & SINGER, S. J. (1985). Phosphotyrosine-containing proteins are concentrated in focal adhesions and intercellular junctions in normal cells. *Proc. natn. Acad. Sci. U.S.A.* **82**, 6576–6580.

MAHER, P. & SINGER, S. J. (1983). A 200-kd protein isolated from the fascia adherens membrane domains of chicken cardiac muscle cells is detected immunologically in fibroblast focal adhesions. *Cell Motil.* **3**, 419–429.

MILAM, L. M. (1985). Electron microscopy of rotary shadowed vinculin and vinculin complexes. *J. molec. Biol.* **184**, 543–545.

MOLONY, L., MCCASLIN, D., ABERNETHY, J., PASCHAL, B. & BURRIDGE, K. (1987). Properties of talin from chicken gizzard smooth muscle. *J. biol. Chem.* **262**, 7790–7795.

NEFF, N. T., LOWREY, C., DECKER, C., TOVAR, A., DAMSKY, C., BUCK, C. & HORWITZ, A. F. (1982). A monoclonal antibody detaches embryonic skeletal muscle from extracellular matrices. *J. Cell Biol.* **95**, 654–666.

NEYFAKH, A. A., TINT, I. S., SVITKINA, T. M., BERSHADSKY, A. D. & GELFAND, V. I. (1983). Visualization of cellular focal contacts using a monoclonal antibody to 80 kd serum protein adsorbed on the substratum. *Expl Cell Res.* **149**, 387–396.

NIGG, E. A., SEFTON, B. M., HUNTER, T., WALTER, G. & SINGER, S. J. (1982). Immunofluorescent localization of the transforming protein of Rous sarcoma virus with antibodies against a synthetic src peptide. *Proc. natn. Acad. Sci. U.S.A.* **79**, 5322–5326.

NIGG, E. A., SEFTON, B. M., SINGER, S. J. & VOGT, P. K. (1986). Cytoskeletal organization, vinculin-phosphorylation, and fibronectin expression in transformed fibroblasts with different cell morphologies. *Virology* **151**, 50–65.

NORRILD, B., VIRTANEN, I., LEHTO, V. P. & PEDERSEN, B. (1983). Accumulation of herpes simplex virus Type I glycoprotein D in adhesion areas of infected cells. *J. gen. Virol.* **64**, 2499–2503.

OESCH, B. & BIRCHMEIER, W. (1982). New surface component of fibroblast's focal contacts identified by a monoclonal antibody. *Cell* **31**, 671–679.

O'HALLORAN, T., BECKERLE, M. C. & BURRIDGE, K. (1985). Identification of talin as a major cytoplasmic protein implicated in platelet activation. *Nature, Lond.* **317**, 449–451.

ORLY, J. & SATO, G. (1979). Fibronectin mediates cytokinesis and growth of rat follicular cells in serum-free medium. *Cell* **17**, 295–305.

OTTO, J. J. (1986). The lack of interaction between vinculin and actin. *Cell Motil. Cytoskel.* **6**, 48–55.

PASQUALE, E. B., MAHER, P. A. & SINGER, S. J. (1986). Talin is phosphorylated on tyrosine in chicken embryo fibroblasts transformed by Rous sarcoma virus. *Proc. natn. Acad. Sci. U.S.A.* **83**, 5507–5511.

PIERSCHBACHER, M. D. & RUOSLAHTI, E. (1984). Cell attachment activity of fibronectin can be duplicated by small synthetic fragments of the molecule. *Nature, Lond.* **309**, 30–33.

PYTELA, R., PIERSCHBACHER, M. D. & RUOSLAHTI, E. (1985*a*). Identification and isolation of a 140 kd cell surface glycoprotein with properties expected of a fibronectin receptor. *Cell* **40**, 191–198.

PYTELA, R., PIERSCHBACHER, M. D. & RUOSLAHTI, E. (1985*b*). A 125/115-kDa cell surface receptor specific for vitronectin interacts with the arginine-glycine-aspartic acid adhesion sequence derived from fibronectin. *Proc. natn. Acad. Sci. U.S.A.* **82**, 5766–5770.

RIZZINO, A. & CROWLEY, C. (1980). Growth and differentiation of embryonal carcinoma cell line F9 in defined media. *Proc. natn. Acad. Sci. U.S.A.* **77**, 457–461.

ROCKWELL, G. A., SATO, G. H. & MCCLURE, D. B. (1980). The growth requirements of SV40 virus-transformed Balb/c-3T3 cells in serum-free monolayer culture. *J. cell. Physiol.* **103**, 323–331.

ROGALSKI, A. A. & SINGER, S. J. (1985). An integral glycoprotein associated with the membrane attachment sites of actin microfilaments. *J. Cell Biol.* **101**, 785–801.

ROHRSCHNEIDER, L. R. (1980). Adhesion plaques of Rous sarcoma virus-transformed cells contain the src gene product. *Proc. natn. Acad. Sci. U.S.A.* **77**, 3514–3518.

ROHRSCHNEIDER, L. R. & NAJITA, L. M. (1984). Detection of the v-*abl* gene product at cell–substratum contact sites in Abelson murine leukemia virus-transformed fibroblasts. *J. Virol.* **51**, 547–552.

ROHRSCHNEIDER, L. & ROSOK, M. J. (1983). Transformation parameters and $pp60^{src}$ localization in cells infected with partial transformation mutants of Rous sarcoma virus. *Molec. cell. Biol.* **3**, 731–746.

ROSENFELD, G. C., HOU, D. C., DINGUS, J., MEZA, I. & BRYAN, J. (1985). Isolation and partial characterization of human platelet vinculin. *J. Cell Biol.* **100**, 669–676.

RUOSLAHTI, E. & PIERSCHBACHER, M. D. (1986). Arg-Gly-Asp: A versatile cell recognition signal. *Cell* **44**, 517–518.

SCHROER, E. & WEGNER, A. (1985). Purification and characterization of a protein from chicken gizzard, which inhibits actin polymerization. *Eur. J. Biochem.* **153**, 515–520.

SEFTON, B. M., HUNTER, T., BALL, E. H. & SINGER, S. J. (1981). Vinculin: A cytoskeletal target of the transforming protein of Rous sarcoma virus. *Cell* **24**, 165–174.

SINGER, I. I. (1982). Association of fibronectin and vinculin with focal contacts and stress fibers in stationary hamster fibroblasts. *J. Cell Biol.* **92**, 398–408.

Singer, I. I. & Paradiso, P. R. (1981). A transmembrane relationship between fibronectin and vinculin (130kd protein): serum modulation in normal and transformed hamster fibroblasts. *Cell* **24**, 481–492.

Tamkun, J. W., DeSimone, D. W., Fonda, D., Patel, R. S., Buck, C., Horwitz, A. F. & Hynes, R. O. (1986). Structure of integrin, a glycoprotein involved in the transmembrane linkage between fibronectin and actin. *Cell* **46**, 271–282.

Unkeless, J. C., Tobia, A., Ossowski, L., Quigley, J. P., Rifkin, D. B. & Reich, E. (1973). An enzymatic function associated with transformation of fibroblasts by oncogenic viruses. I. Chick embryo fibroblast cultures transformed by avian RNA tumor viruses. *J. exp. Med.* **137**, 85–111.

Wehland, J., Osborn, M. & Weber, K. (1979). Cell-to-substratum contacts in living cells: A direct correlation between interference-reflexion and indirect-immunofluorescence microscopy using antibodies against actin and α-actinin. *J. Cell Sci.* **37**, 257–273.

Wilkins, J. A. & Lin, S. (1982). High-affinity interaction of vinculin with actin filaments *in vitro*. *Cell* **28**, 83–90.

Wilkins, J. A. & Lin, S. (1986). A re-examination of the interaction of vinculin with actin. *J. Cell Biol.* **102**, 1085–1092.

Wilkins, J. A., Risinger, M. A. & Lin, S. (1986). Studies on proteins that co-purify with smooth muscle vinculin: identification of immunologically related species in focal adhesions of nonmuscle and Z-lines of muscle cells. *J. Cell Biol.* **103**, 1483–1494.

Willingham, M. C., Yamada, K. M., Yamada, S. S., Pouyssegur, J. & Pastan, I. (1977). Microfilament bundles and cell shape are related to adhesiveness to substratum and are dissociable from growth control in cultured fibroblasts. *Cell* **10**, 375–380.

Wolfe, R. A., Sato, G. H. & McClure, D. B. (1980). Continuous culture of rat C6 glioma in serum-free medium. *J. Cell Biol.* **87**, 434–441.

Woods, A., Couchman, J. R. & Höök, M. (1985). Heparan sulfate proteoglycans of rat embryo fibroblasts. *J. biol. Chem.* **260**, 10 872–10 879.

Woods, A., Couchman, J. R., Johansson, S. & Höök, M. (1986). Adhesion and cytoskeletal organization of fibroblasts in response to fibronectin fragments. *EMBO J.* **5**, 665–670.

Yamada, K. M. (1983). Cell surface interactions with extracellular materials. *A. Rev. Biochem.* **52**, 761–799.

Yamada, K. M. & Kennedy, D. W. (1984). Dualistic nature of adhesive protein function: fibronectin and its biologically active peptide fragments can auto-inhibit fibronectin function. *J. Cell Biol.* **99**, 29–36.

J. Cell Sci. Suppl. 8, 231–250 (1987)

INTEGRIN, A TRANSMEMBRANE GLYCOPROTEIN COMPLEX MEDIATING CELL–SUBSTRATUM ADHESION

CLAYTON A. BUCK
The Wistar Institute, 36th Street at Spruce, Philadelphia, PA 19104, USA
AND A. F. HORWITZ
Department of Biochemistry, University of Pennsylvania Medical School, Philadelphia, PA 19104, USA

SUMMARY

A monoclonal antibody, CSAT, which inhibits the adhesion of chick cells to substrata coated with fibronectin, laminin and vitronectin, has been used to identify a cell surface receptor required for cell–substratum adhesion. This receptor, termed integrin, is found on the ventral surface of cells in close contact adhesion sites, at the periphery of adhesion plaques and beneath stress fibres. It is a heterodimer consisting of non-covalently linked alpha and beta subunits. Integrin binds directly to laminin, fibronectin and vitronectin with dissociation constants in the micromolar range. The binding of integrin to matrix molecules is sensitive to peptides carrying the cell-binding sequence Arg-Gly-Asp and requires heteromeric integrity. Integrin also binds directly to the cytoskeleton-associated protein talin. Thus, integrin has the properties of a transmembrane molecule capable of bringing extracellular matrix and cytoskeleton-associated molecules in proper juxtaposition to form adhesion structures. The integrin beta subunit is phosphorylated following Rous sarcoma virus transformation. Phosphorylation alters the ability of the receptor to bind extracellular matrix molecules as well as talin, suggesting a mechanism for the alteration of cellular adhesive and morphological properties following malignant transformation. A major phosphorylation site is on the cytoplasmic domain of the beta subunit. Synthetic peptides homologous with this region of integrin inhibit integrin–talin binding. The gene for the beta subunit of integrin has been sequenced. Its structure is consistent with the membrane-spanning properties of the receptor. Integrin is structurally and serologically related to adhesion receptors from mammalian tumour cells, fibroblasts, platelets and lymphocytes. It appears to be a member of a supergene family of receptors involved in cellular adhesive interactions. Antibody and peptide inhibition experiments have suggested a role for integrin and integrin-like molecules in cell migration, neurite extension, neural differentiation, histogenesis and embryonic development in *Drosophila*. Thus, integrin appears representative of a set of evolutionarily conserved, biologically important adhesive molecules.

INTRODUCTION

The interaction of cells with their extracellular matrix is basic to such processes as histogenesis, wound healing, metastasis, neuronal organization and angiogenesis, to name but a few. To study the process of cell–matrix adhesion, most investigators have turned to model *in vitro* systems focusing on structures such as adhesion plaques described by Abercrombie *et al.* (1971). At sites of cell–matrix contact, molecules of the extracellular matrix, the surface membrane and cytoskeleton are brought into highly organized juxtaposition. Over the past 15 years, considerable effort has gone into defining the molecular basis of this organization, with various groups focusing their research efforts on one of the three regions involved in adhesive events, i.e. the cell surface, the extracellular matrix or the cytoskeleton.

Our interest has been in the molecules within the surface membrane that serve to coordinate the organization of these adhesive structures. Our working hypothesis has been that a cell surface molecule (or molecules) exists that serves as a bridge spanning the surface membrane, interacting with both the extracellular matrix and elements of the cytoskeletal complex. To search for these molecules, we first developed polyclonal, and later monoclonal, antibodies that could perturb cell–matrix adhesion in a reversible, non-toxic manner and could then be used to identify the cell surface constituents required for adhesion (Wylie *et al.* 1979; Knudsen *et al.* 1981; Neff *et al.* 1982). The monoclonal antibody we have used is designated CSAT (Neff *et al.* 1982). A second monoclonal antibody, which interferes with chick fibroblast adhesion, was independently isolated and characterized by Greve & Gottlieb (1982). This antibody, designated JG22, has properties that appear indistinguishable from those of CSAT. The cell surface complex with which these antibodies react has been called CSAT antigen, 140K complex and integrin. For the sake of clarity, the term integrin will be used here.

RESULTS

The effect of the monoclonal antibody CSAT on the adhesion of chick fibroblasts to fibronectin and laminin is both cell-type- and substratum-dependent. While the antibody interferes with the adhesion of chick tendon fibroblasts to both fibronectin and laminin, it prevents adhesion of chick cardiac fibroblasts to laminin only (Fig. 1), unless the cells are briefly trypsinized prior to plating on fibronectin, at which time the antibody will also prevent adhesion of the cardiac fibroblasts to fibronectin (Decker *et al.* 1984; Horwitz *et al.* 1985). The simplest interpretation of these results is that cells exhibit more than one adhesion mechanism. Chick tendon fibroblasts adhere to both fibronectin and laminin by a CSAT-sensitive mechanism, whereas cardiac fibroblasts adhere to laminin primarily by a CSAT-sensitive mechanism and to fibronectin by at least two different mechanisms, one of which is trypsin-sensitive. Thus, integrin is clearly not the only cell surface molecule involved in cell–matrix adhesion. While early cell adhesion and spreading appear to take place by a CSAT-sensitive mechanism and hence involve integrin, the establishment of mature adhesion plaques requires other molecules (Oesch & Birchmeier, 1982; Rogalski & Singer, 1985) including, in some instances (depending upon the cell type), proteoglycan and proteoglycan receptors (Lark *et al.* 1985; Izzard *et al.* 1986; Rapraeger *et al.* 1986; Singer *et al.* 1987).

The antigen to which the CSAT monoclonal antibody binds is located on the ventral surface of well-spread cells beneath actin-containing stress fibres, at the periphery of adhesion plaques, and in presumptive close contact-like structures (Fig. 2). In double immunofluorescence experiments, it colocalizes with fibronectin, actin, talin and vinculin (Damsky *et al.* 1985; Chen *et al.* 1985*a*,*b*, 1986*a*). Thus, its

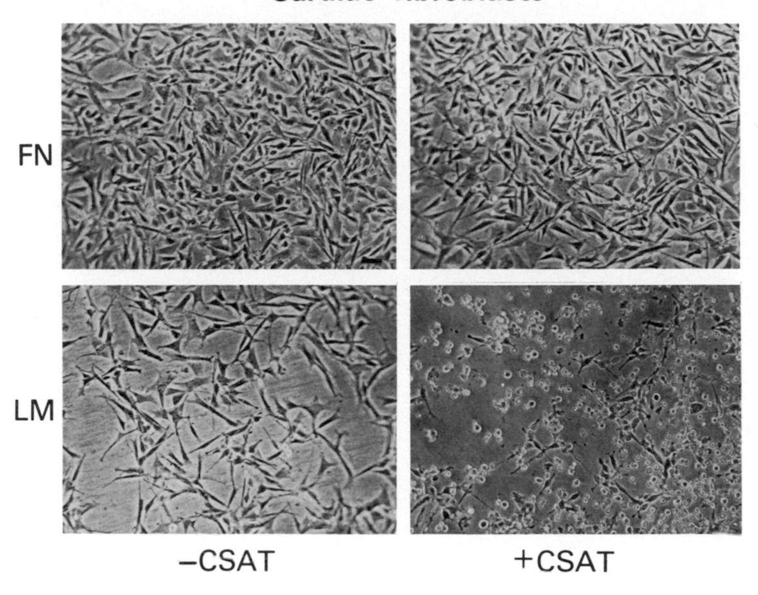

Fig. 1. Effect of CSAT monoclonal antibody on adhesion of chick cardiac fibroblasts to fibronectin and laminin. Chick cardiac fibroblasts were plated onto wells previously coated with fibronectin or laminin and allowed to spread for 2 h. CSAT monoclonal antibody was then added ($40\,\mu g\,ml^{-1}$) and monolayers photographed 2 h later. FN, fibronectin; LM, laminin.

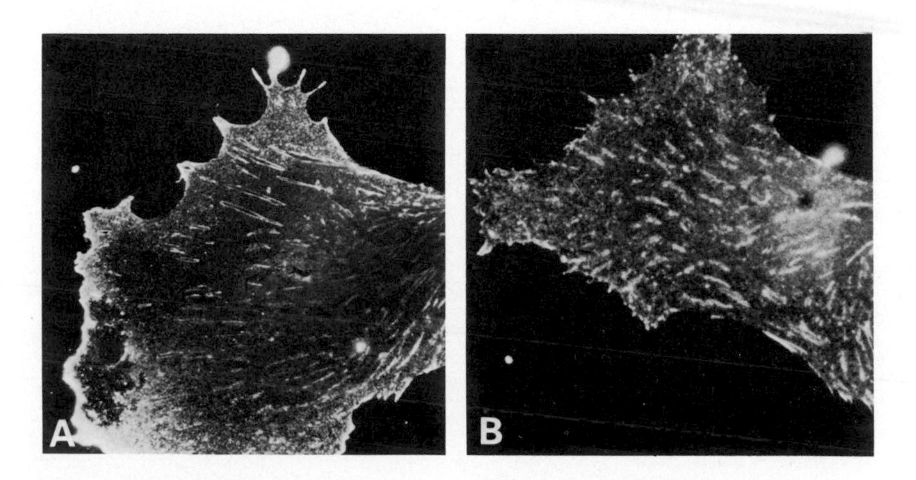

Fig. 2. Distribution of integrin on the ventral surface of chick fibroblasts. Chick tendon fibroblasts were plated on coverslips coated with fibronectin. Integrin was localized by indirect immunofluorescence using a polyclonal anti-integrin serum as the primary antibody. A. Distribution of integrin around the periphery of adhesion plaques forming needle's-eye-like patterns. B. Distribution of integrin in close contact-like regions of initially spreading fibroblasts, note lack of needle's eye pattern.

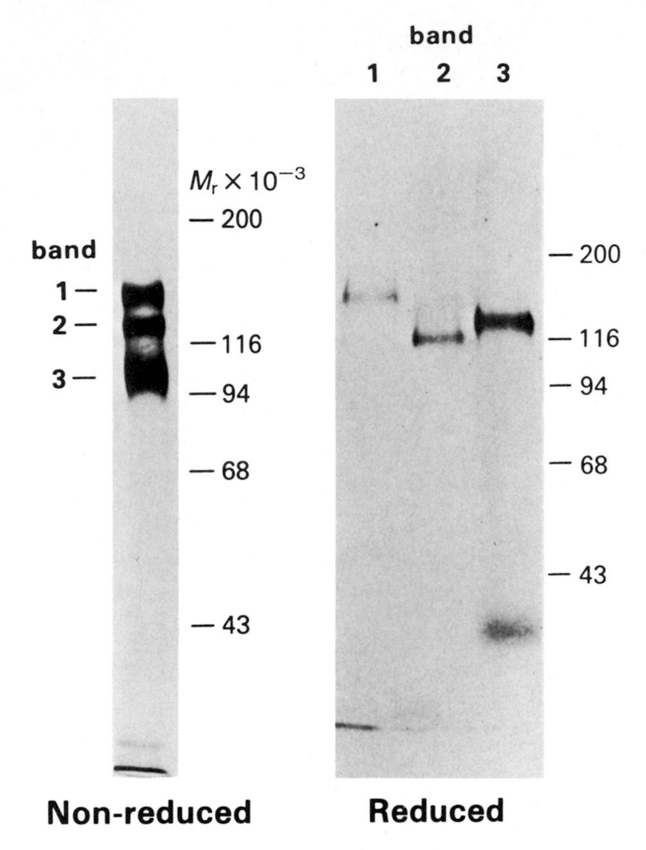

Fig. 3. Autoradiogram of integrin analysed by SDS–PAGE. Monoclonal antibody affinity-purified [^{35}S]integrin was subjected to SDS–PAGE in the presence (reduced) or absence (non-reduced) or beta-mercaptoethanol. Position of M_r standards ($\times 10^{-3}$) shown to the right of each gel.

position in adherent cells is consistent with its serving as a coordinator of cell–matrix adhesion.

The use of monoclonal antibodies has greatly simplified the biochemical characterization of the antigen, due to the ease with which it can be purified by monoclonal antibody affinity chromatography (Neff *et al.* 1982; Greve & Gottlieb, 1982). The antigen purified by this method (or identified by immunoprecipitation) consists of at least three distinct glycoproteins (Fig. 3), which can only be resolved by SDS–PAGE under non-reducing conditions (Knudsen *et al.* 1985; Hasegawa *et al.* 1985). At this point, several obvious questions arise. First, does this complex serve as a receptor for extracellular matrix and cytoskeleton-associated molecules? Second, is the antigen a heteromeric complex, or are these merely different glycoproteins all sharing a common epitope? Third, is heteromeric integrity required for function? In the past few years, we have addressed each of these questions.

The binding properties of the complex have been examined by equilibrium gel filtration (Horwitz *et al.* 1986). Since this method permits the measurement of receptor–ligand interactions in the constant presence of excess ligand, it is possible to

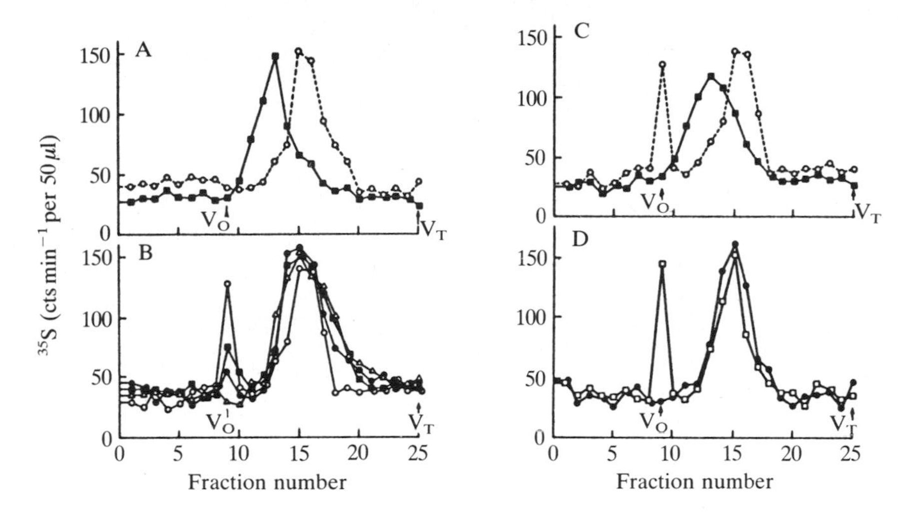

Fig. 4. Equilibrium gel filtration elution profile of integrin in the presence of laminin. ^{35}S-labelled integrin was subjected to equilibrium gel filtration in the presence of: A, CSAT monoclonal antibody; B, laminin; C, laminin plus CSAT monoclonal antibody; D, laminin plus Arg-Gly-Asp-containing peptide. A. (○) Antigen alone; (■) integrin plus monoclonal antibody. B. (△) Integrin in the presence of 25 μg ml^{-1} laminin; (●) integrin plus 100 μg ml^{-1} laminin; (■) integrin plus 200 μg ml^{-1} laminin; (○) integrin plus 400 μg ml^{-1} laminin. C. (○) Integrin plus 400 μg ml^{-1} laminin; (■) integrin plus CSAT monoclonal antibody and 400 μg ml^{-1} laminin. D. (●) Integrin plus 400 μg ml^{-1} laminin and 1 mg ml^{-1} cell-binding tetrapeptide; (□) integrin plus 400 μg ml^{-1} laminin and 1 mg ml^{-1} control peptide.

detect binding that occurs at moderate to low affinities and possesses rapid equilibria. This was necessary in the case of matrix receptor–ligand interactions, as earlier work had shown that fibronectin bound to the surface of cells with an affinity in the micromolar range (Akiyama *et al.* 1985). The results of equilibrium gel filtration of integrin in the presence of laminin and fibronectin are shown in Figs 4 and 5. The change in the elution profile of radioactive integrin in the presence of either ligand indicates that ligand–receptor interaction occurred. The interaction of laminin with integrin could be blocked by the CSAT monoclonal antibody, suggesting that the integrin–laminin interaction monitored by equilibrium gel filtration resembled that which occurred between the cell-associated integrin and laminin (Fig. 4C). Because the complex formed between the monoclonal antibody and the receptor eluted from the gel filtration column in the same position as the fibronectin–receptor complex, it was not possible to determine if the CSAT monoclonal antibody would block fibronectin–integrin binding. However, the interaction of fibronectin with its receptor is sensitive to the fibronectin cell-binding peptide Arg-Gly-Asp (Pytela *et al.* 1985*a*). Therefore, it was possible to determine if this peptide would interfere with fibronectin–integrin binding as measured by gel filtration. Fig. 5B shows that this was indeed the case. In the presence of peptides containing the Arg-Gly-Asp sequence, no complex was formed between fibronectin and integrin. Further, this peptide also competed with laminin for binding to integrin (Fig. 4D). Control

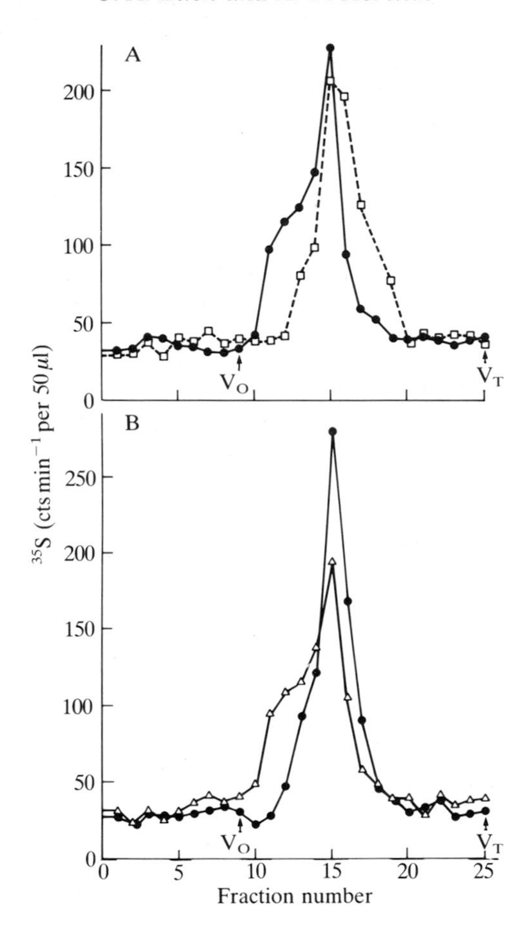

Fig. 5. Equilibrium gel-filtration elution profile of integrin in the presence of fibronectin. [^{35}S]integrin was subjected to equilibrium gel filtration in the presence of: A, fibronectin; or B, fibronectin plus cell-binding tetrapeptide. A. (□) Integrin alone; (●) integrin plus 200 μg ml^{-1} fibronectin. B. (△) Integrin plus 200 μg ml^{-1} fibronectin; (●) integrin plus 200 μg ml^{-1} fibronectin and 1 mg ml^{-1} Arg-Gly-Asp-containing peptide.

experiments showed that a related peptide containing the sequence Arg-Gly-Glu was not able to block either fibronectin or laminin binding to integrin (Horwitz *et al.* 1985). The Arg-Gly-Asp, but not the control peptide, also inhibited chick fibroblast adhesion to both fibronectin and laminin (Horwitz *et al.* 1985). Thus, the interaction between the receptor complex, integrin, and the matrix molecules, fibronectin and laminin, as measured by equilibrium gel filtration, resembled that which occurred between the membrane-bound receptor and the extracellular ligand.

If integrin were to serve as a transmembrane link between the extracellular matrix and the cytoskeleton, it should also bind to either cytoskeletal or cytoskeleton-associated molecules. This was also tested by equilibrium gel filtration (Horwitz *et al.* 1986). It was found that integrin would not bind directly to the cytoskeleton-associated molecules vinculin or alpha actinin. It would, however, bind to talin. The

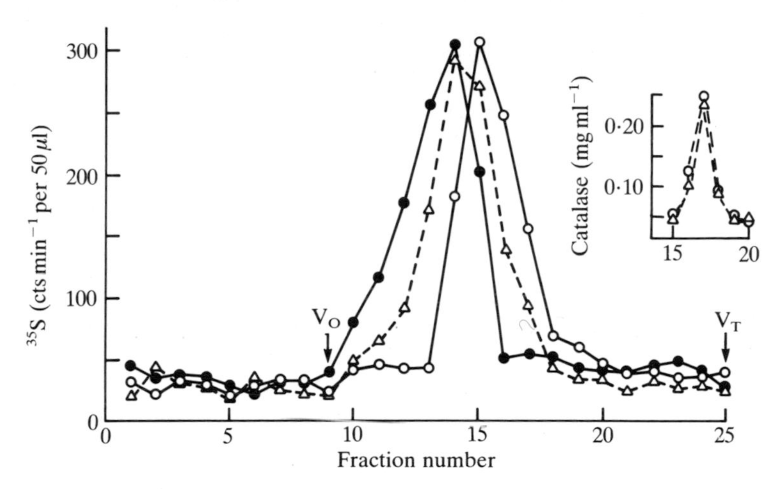

Fig. 6. Equilibrium gel filtration of integrin in the presence of cytoskeleton-associated molecules. [^{35}S]integrin was subjected to equilibrium gel filtration in the presence of 200 μg ml^{-1} vinculin (○); 200 μg ml^{-1} talin (△); 200 μg ml^{-1} talin plus 200 μg ml^{-1} vinculin (●). Inset: profile of internal catalase standard included in all experiments. V_o, void volume; V_t, inclusion volume.

binding of integrin to talin resulted in the formation of a complex of larger Stokes' radius that eluted closer to the void volume of the gel filtration column in the same manner as when integrin bound fibronectin (Fig. 6). The talin–integrin binding was, however, not sensitive to the cell-binding peptide, showing that talin reacted with integrin at a different site from fibronectin.

Talin and vinculin bind to one another, and in some undetermined manner, appear to mediate actin–membrane interactions (reviewed by Burridge, 1987; and see Geiger *et al.* this volume). Thus, while vinculin itself could not bind to integrin, it should bind to a talin–integrin complex if the configuration of the complex is physiologically appropriate. This was indeed the case (Fig. 6). The presence of vinculin in an equilibrium gel filtration column did not change the elution position of integrin. The addition of talin and integrin to the column resulted in the characteristic shift in the elution position of integrin, showing that a complex had been formed. If vinculin was added along with talin, the elution profile of integrin was further shifted towards the void volume of the column (Fig. 6), showing that an even larger molecular complex had been formed presumably due to the addition of vinculin to the talin-integrin complex. These experiments show that the cytoskeleton-associated molecule, talin, binds to integrin at a site on the integrin complex different from that which binds fibronectin. It also shows that talin binds to integrin at a site different from that required for talin–vinculin interactions. Thus, it appears that integrin has all the properties of a transmembrane receptor capable of binding both extracellular matrix molecules and cytoskeleton-associated linking molecules.

Structural information that allows us to gain further insight into the function of different regions of integrin is becoming available as the genes coding for members of the complex are being isolated and sequenced. The gene coding for band 3 of integrin

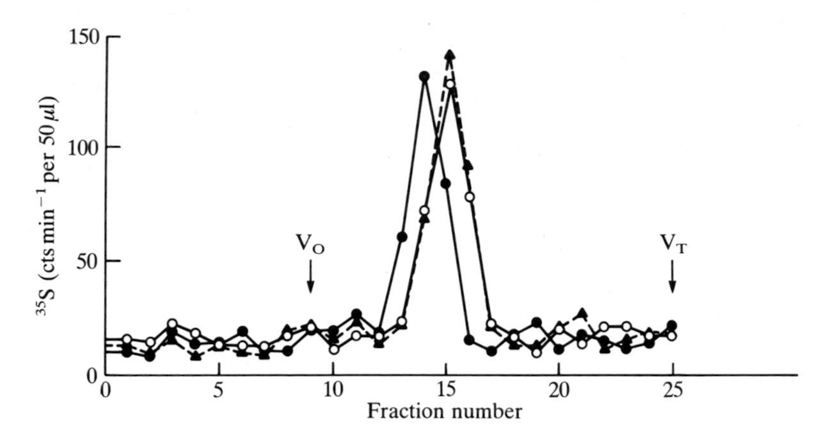

Fig. 7. Effect of a synthetic peptide from the cytoplasmic domain of integrin on talin–integrin binding. [^{35}S]integrin was subjected to equilibrium gel filtration alone, in the presence of talin, or in the presence of talin plus 1 mg ml^{-1} of synthetic peptide from the cytoplasmic domain of integrin corresponding to the tyrosine kinase phosphorylation site on band 3 glycoprotein (10-mer). (▲) Integrin; (●) integrin + 0·4 mg ml^{-1} talin; (○) integrin + 0·4 mg ml^{-1} talin + 1 mg ml^{-1} 10-mer.

has recently been isolated (Tamkun *et al.* 1986). Nucleotide sequence determination shows that this molecule consists of 803 amino acids. It has multiple glycosylation sites, four cysteine-rich repeats in the extracellular domain, a hydrophobic transmembrane domain and a consensus tyrosine kinase phosphorylation site in the 47-amino-acid cytoplasmic domain. The structure of this subunit is consistent with the role of integrin as a transmembrane bridge between the extracellular matrix and the cytoplasm. The role of the cytoplasmic domain in talin binding to integrin has been examined using a synthetic peptide consisting of the amino acids Trp-Asp-Thr-Gly-Glu-Asn-Pro-Ile-Tyr-Lys. This peptide is the equivalent of a tryptic fragment from the consensus tyrosine kinase phosphorylation site. If this region of the molecule is required for integrin–talin binding, this peptide should block the interaction of talin and integrin as measured by equilibrium gel filtration. That this is the case is shown in Fig. 7. This experiment makes two important points. First, talin binds to the cytoplasmic domain of integrin; and second, the tyrosine kinase phosphorylation site is in the region of the molecule involved in talin binding.

The tyrosine kinase phosphorylation site on integrin is of further interest in the light of the fact that it may play an important role in cellular changes noted during malignant transformation. For example, viral transformation leads to alterations in the morphological and adhesive properties of cells. Immunolocalization studies have shown that the distribution of fibronectin receptors including integrin is greatly altered following viral transformation (Hirst *et al.* 1986; Chen *et al.* 1986*b*; Marchisio *et al.* 1987). In addition, pp60 *src* has been localized to adhesion plaques, suggesting that proteins found within this complex may be the targets of *src* kinase. Consistent with this is the observation by Hirst *et al.* (1986) that band 3 glycoprotein of integrin was phosphorylated following viral transformation. In order to determine

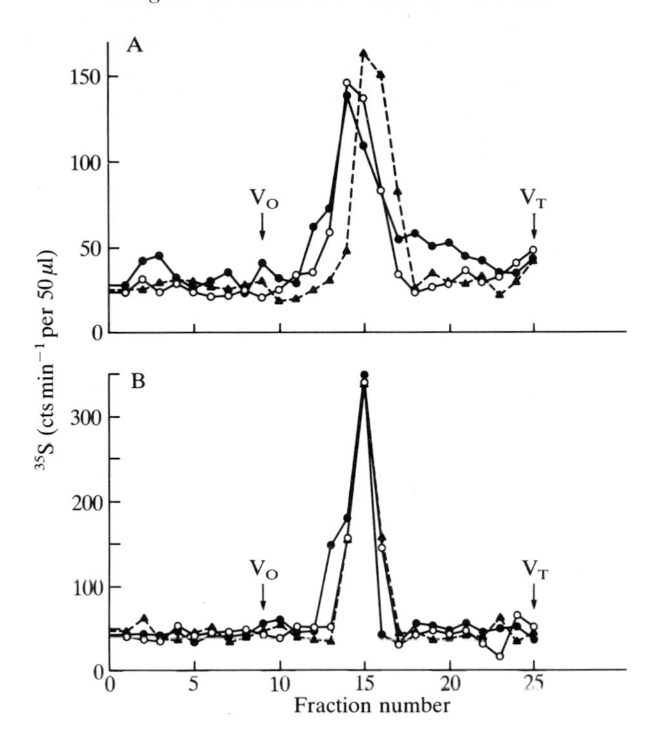

Fig. 8. Effect of the phosphorylation of integrin on its ability to bind fibronectin and talin. Preparations of ^{35}S- and ^{32}P-labelled integrin were mixed and subjected to equilibrium gel filtration in the presence or absence of talin and fibronectin. The column eluates were differentially analysed for either ^{35}S or ^{32}P in a liquid scintillation counter. A. Elution profile of [^{35}S]integrin. B. Elution profile of [^{32}P]integrin. V_o, void volume; V_t, inclusion volume. A. (▲) ^{35}S-labelled non-transformed integrin alone; (○) +0·4 mg ml^{-1} talin; (●) or +0·8 mg ml^{-1} fibronectin.

if phosphorylation results in an altered ability of integrin to bind talin or extracellular matrix molecules, Rous sarcoma virus-transformed chick cells were labelled with ^{32}P and control non-transformed cells were labelled with [^{35}S]methionine. Integrin was isolated from both sets of cells. The ^{32}P- and ^{35}S-labelled integrins were then mixed, and subjected to equilibrium gel filtration in the presence of either fibronectin or talin. The fractions from the column were then analysed in a scintillation counter for ^{32}P and ^{35}S. Fig. 8A shows that the ^{35}S-labelled integrin retained its ability to bind fibronectin and talin. ^{32}P-labelled integrin, on the other hand (Fig. 8B), bound neither fibronectin nor talin suggesting that a reduction of the receptor function of integrin following phosphorylation could, at least partially, contribute to the adhesive and morphological changes noted in transformed cells. While this effect of phosphorylation on adhesion has been observed in the pathological process of malignant transformation, it might well be a mechanism whereby a migrating cell could regulate its interaction with the extracellular matrix or its morphology during normal morphogenetic movements.

We have demonstrated that integrin is a complex of glycoproteins, not merely a single molecule. The question arises as to whether integrin functions as a complex of glycoproteins, or is merely a mixture of antigenically related, but functionally distinct, molecules that are co-purified with the CSAT monoclonal antibody. Biochemically, it has not been possible to separate the integrin complex except under the denaturing conditions of SDS–PAGE (Knudsen *et al.* 1985; Hasegawa *et al.* 1985). We have, however, succeeded in producing a monoclonal antibody specific for the lower molecular weight band 3 of the integrin complex, which is capable of dissociating the complex in such a way as to permit the separation of band 3 from bands 1 and 2 on an antibody affinity column (Buck *et al.* 1986). Using this antibody, we have been able to divide integrin into two fractions under non-denaturing conditions. One fraction enriched in band 3 glycoprotein, and the other enriched in glycoproteins making up SDS–PAGE bands 1 and 2. When each of the fractions was mixed separately with fibronectin and applied to an equilibrium gel filtration column, there was no change in their elution profile from that seen with each fraction chromatographed in the absence of fibronectin (Fig. 9A,B). However, when the two fractions were mixed and applied to the gel filtration column, two changes were noted (Fig. 9C). First, the elution profile of the mixed complex appears different from that of either integrin fraction alone. The profile is sharper than that of the band 1 plus 2 mixture and elutes earlier from the column than band 3 itself, in the precise position of the intact integrin complex. These hydrodynamic changes indicate that the macromolecular complex has been reconstituted, supporting the contention that integrin exists as a complex of glycoproteins. This contention is further strengthened by sucrose density gradient experiments showing that integrin sediments as a complex (Buck *et al.* 1985, 1986; Hasegawa *et al.* 1985). Second, upon mixing the two fractions of integrin glycoproteins, their ability to bind fibronectin was restored. Similarly, they regained their ability to bind talin, which was lost after separation into two fractions (Buck *et al.* 1986). Thus, the ability of integrin to act as a receptor for extracellular matrix molecules and talin requires that its integrity as a heteromer be maintained. This rules out the possibility that each glycoprotein of the integrin complex may have a separate binding function.

Integrin appears to differ from other mammalian extracellular matrix receptors in its ligand specificity (reviewed by Buck & Horwitz, 1987). Integrin has binding activity for more than one matrix molecule, whereas the mammalian receptors described to date are specific for a single matrix molecule. This suggests that either integrin is a single promiscuous receptor, or it is a mixture of receptors each possessing a common subunit. Support for the latter possibility has come from the observation that the epitope for the CSAT monoclonal antibody is located only on integrin band 3 glycoprotein (Buck *et al.* 1986). However, when the issue of receptor promiscuity is explored further by competition experiments, a different conclusion seems likely. For these experiments, we have taken advantage of the fact that vitronectin binds to membrane receptors more tightly than either fibronectin or laminin (Pytela *et al.* 1985*b*). The interaction of vitronectin with integrin is shown in Fig. 10. When vitronectin was mixed with integrin and applied to the equilibrium gel filtration column, most of the vitronectin eluted in the same position as integrin (Fig. 10). Vitronectin–integrin binding is sensitive to both the CSAT monoclonal

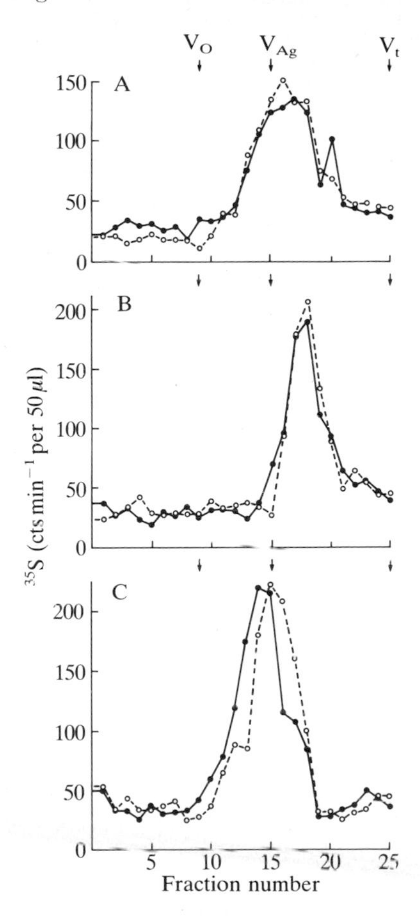

Fig. 9. Fibronectin binding to reconstituted integrin. ^{35}S-labelled integrin was separated into two fractions, one consisting of bands 1 and 2 glycoproteins, and the other consisting of the band 3 glycoprotein. A. Equilibrium gel filtration of bands 1 plus 2 in the presence and absence of fibronectin. B. Equilibrium gel filtration of band 3 in the presence and absence of fibronectin. C. Equilibrium gel filtration of reconstituted integrin (bands 1 plus 2 mixed with band 3) in the presence and absence of fibronectin. (○) Integrin fractions in the absence of fibronectin: (●) integrin fractions in the presence of fibronectin. V_{Ag}, position of antigen elution.

antibody and the Arg-Gly-Asp cell binding peptide (Horwitz & Buck, unpublished) and therefore resembles that of integrin binding to other matrix molecules. The ability of vitronectin to compete with fibronectin or laminin for integrin binding sites was tested by mixing radioactive integrin with either of these matrix molecules in the presence or absence of vitronectin, and subjecting the mixture to equilibrium gel filtration. The presence of vitronectin abolished the ability of integrin to bind either fibronectin or laminin (Fig. 11). By this criterion, integrin would appear to be a promiscuous receptor with respect to the binding of laminin, fibronectin and vitronectin.

To compare further the properties of integrin with those of a mammalian receptor, we have purified a fibronectin receptor from the rat myoblast cell line L6A. The

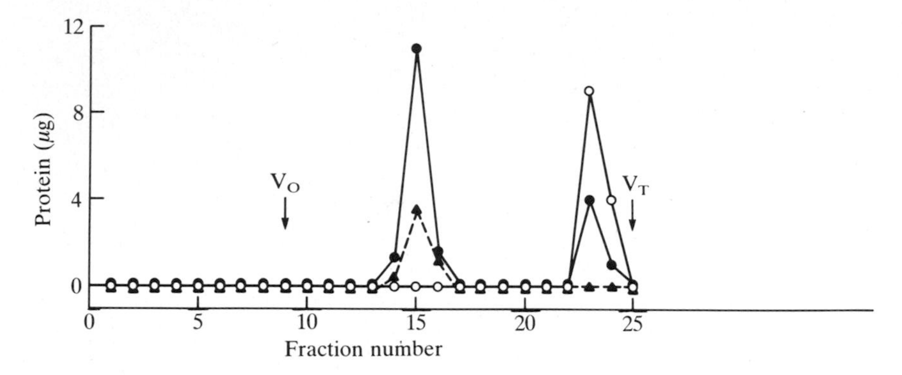

Fig. 10. Integrin–vitronectin binding as measured by equilibrium gel filtration. Vitronectin, integrin or a mixture of vitronectin and integrin was subjected to gel filtration. In this case, gels were not pre-equilibrated with the ligand since vitronectin–integrin binding was more stable than integrin binding to other matrix molecules. Lowry protein analysis was performed on each column fraction to determine the location of each protein or complex. Note the decrease in the amount of protein in the region of free vitronectin and the concomitant increase in protein in the region of integrin elution upon mixing the two molecules. V_o, void volume; V_t, inclusion volume. (▲) Integrin; (○) vitronectin; (●) integrin + vitronectin.

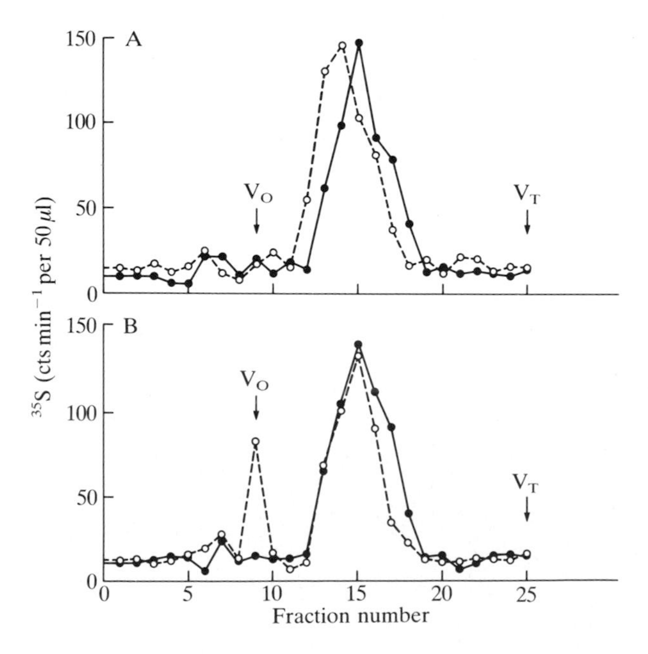

Fig. 11. Vitronectin competes with fibronectin and laminin for binding to integrin. ^{35}S-labelled integrin was subjected to equilibrium gel electrophoresis in the presence of fibronectin, laminin or a mixture of each of these molecules and vitronectin. A. Integrin plus fibronectin (0·8 mg ml^{-1}, (○)) or a mixture of fibronectin and vitronectin (0·8 mg ml^{-1} + 10 μg (●)). B. Integrin plus laminin (0·4 mg ml^{-1} (○)) or a mixture of laminin and vitronectin (0·4 mg ml^{-1} + 10 μg (●)). Note, in each case, the vitronectin prevents the characteristic shift in the elution profile of integrin in the presence of one of the matrix molecules.

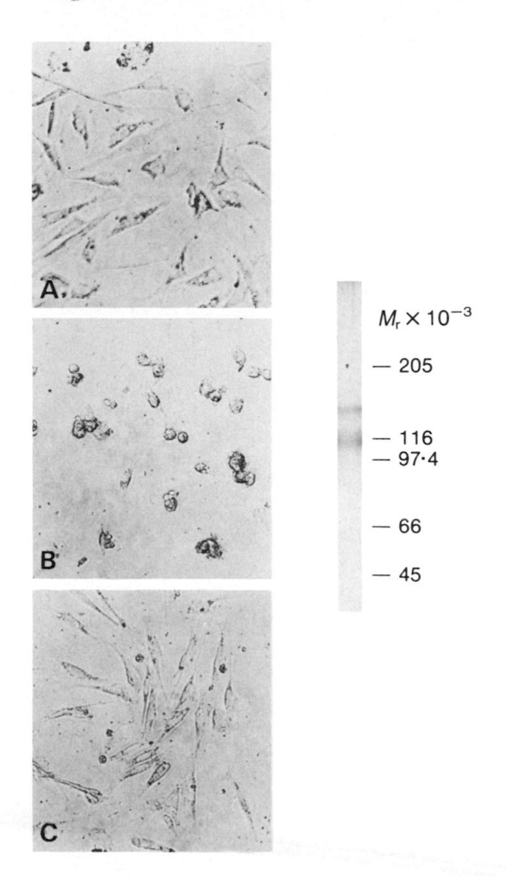

Fig. 12. Fibronectin receptor from rat L6A cells. Silver staining of purified receptor following SDS–PAGE under non-reducing conditions. Antiserum was prepared against this receptor and tested for its effect on L6A cell adhesion. A. Control cells in the presence of pre-immune serum. B. L6A cells 4 h after addition of antisera raised against the rat fibronectin receptor. C. L6A cells exposed to anti-fibronectin receptor that had been mixed with purified receptor. The purified receptor completely blocked the antibody-induced adhesive alterations.

receptor is, as expected, a heterodimer, and antibodies prepared against this receptor will interfere with L6A adhesion to fibronectin-coated tissue culture dishes (Fig. 12). This receptor will bind to fibronectin, but not vitronectin or laminin (Horwitz & Buck, unpublished). The ability of antibodies against integrin to bind to this receptor was determined by immunoblot analysis (Fig. 13). Antibodies against integrin or against band 3 of integrin reacted with the lower molecular weight (beta) band of the L6A fibronectin receptor. There was weak cross-reactivity with the higher molecular weight (alpha) band of the L6A receptor also. The antibody against the rat fibronectin receptor reacted only weakly with integrin and, in this case, it was with the band 2 glycoprotein. These data indicate structural similarities between fibronectin receptors from various species and are consistent with the suggestions that these receptors belong to a single family of cell-surface adhesion molecules

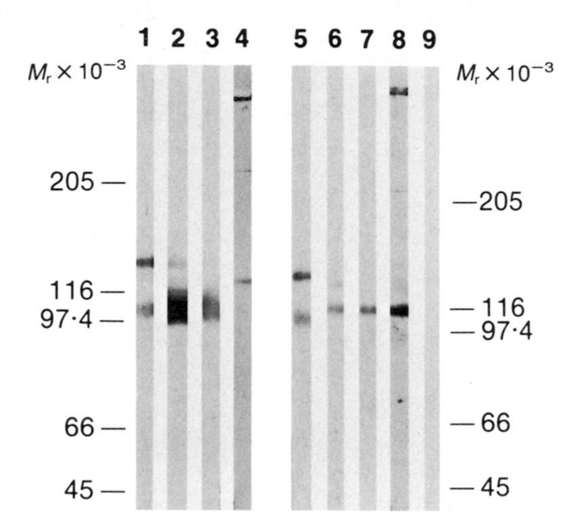

Fig. 13. Immunoblot comparisons of integrin and rat fibronectin receptor. Lanes 1–5, integrin; and lanes 6–9, rat fibronectin receptor. Lanes 1–4, from a different gel from lanes 5–9. Lanes 1 and 5, reacted with a monoclonal antibody specific for band 3 glycoprotein mixed with one specific for band 1 glycoprotein. These serve as internal controls and mark the position of their respective antigens on the gels. Lanes 2 and 3, reacted with a polyclonal antibody raised against integrin. Lanes 3 and 7, reacted with a polyclonal antibody raised against the rat fibronectin receptor. Lane 9, the pre-immune control. Antigen–antibody interactions were detected using antibodies conjugated with alkaline phosphatase.

(Ruoslahti & Pierschbacher, 1986; Leptin, 1986; Hynes, 1987; Hemler *et al.* 1987; Takada *et al.* 1987*a*,*b*).

DISCUSSION AND SPECULATION

Fig. 14 summarizes our current thinking about the general structure and function of integrin. Structurally, we are beginning to view integrin as a heterodimer consisting of an alpha and a beta subunit (reviewed by Buck & Horwitz, 1987). The alpha subunit is composed of a short membrane-spanning peptide disulphide linked to a larger extracellular peptide. The beta subunit is a highly disulphide cross-linked molecule that interacts non-covalently with the alpha subunit to produce a functionally active receptor. Our knowledge of the beta subunit structure comes from actual gene sequence data (Tamkun *et al.* 1986). Our concept of the structure of the alpha subunit is formed predominantly from analogy with the known structure of the mammalian vitronectin and fibronectin receptor (Argraves *et al.* 1986; Suzuki *et al.* 1986) and the fact that it decreases in apparent molecular weight following reduction, suggesting that a small fragment is lost (Knudsen *et al.* 1985; Hasegawa *et al.* 1985). Although as purified by antibody affinity chromatography integrin appears to contain at least three subunits, the molecular weight of the complex as determined hydrodynamically (Buck *et al.* 1985; Hasegawa *et al.* 1985) is between 215 and 230 ($\times 10^3$). This would not accommodate a trimeric structure made up of

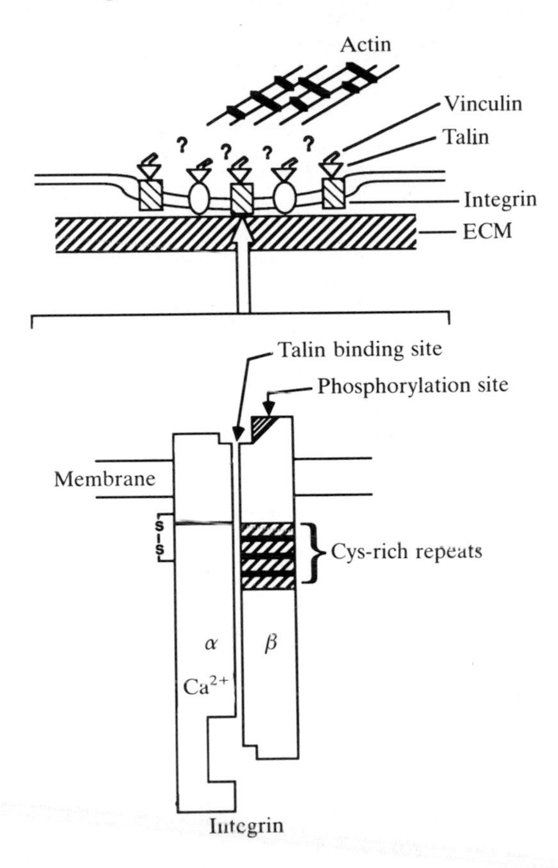

Fig. 14. Schematic drawing of integrin. Top portion showing integrin as a transmembrane bridging molecule between the extracellular matrix (ECM) and the cytoskeleton-associated molecules talin and vinculin. Question marks designate undetermined linkages between vinculin and actin. Lower portion is an enlarged drawing of integrin. The subunits have been labelled α and β to conform to the convention established for other receptors and as suggested by Hynes (1987). Integrin as shown here is a heterodimeric promiscuous receptor capable of binding to more than one extracellular matrix molecule. See the text for detailed discussion of structure.

three glycoproteins with estimated molecular weights of 160, 140 and 110 ($\times 10^3$). The fact that several substratum molecules appear to compete for binding to the same site on integrin suggest that it functions as a promiscuous receptor capable of binding more than one matrix molecule. In this respect, it differs from the mammalian fibronectin and vitronectin receptors (Pytela *et al.* 1985*a*,*b*) and is more like the platelet cytoadhesin IIb/IIIa (Plow *et al.* 1985).

If integrin is, in fact, a promiscuous heterodimer, what about the other glycoproteins that co-purify with it on an antibody affinity column? As pointed out earlier, the CSAT monoclonal antibody reacts with band 3 or the beta subunit of integrin. It is possible that this subunit is a constituent of more than one receptor and that while one combination of alpha and beta subunits come together to form integrin, another alpha-like subunit could combine with the same beta subunit to form a receptor for another group of matrix molecules such as the collagens or proteoglycans. The function of alpha-like subunits remains to be determined.

The discovery of similarities in structure and sensitivity of binding to the fibronectin cell-binding peptide Arg-Gly-Asp have led to the speculation that the cell matrix receptors, lymphoid antigens and platelet cytoadhesions might all be members of a single supergene family (Ruoslahti & Pierschbacher, 1986; Hynes, 1987; Takada *et al.* 1987*a*,*b*; Kishimoto *et al.* 1987; Ginsberg *et al.* 1987). On the basis of careful serological studies, Hemler and his associates (Hemler *et al.* 1987; Takada *et al.* 1987*a*,*b*) have shown that the beta subunit of the VLA group of antigens expressed on mitogen-stimulated T cells (Sanchez-Madrid *et al.* 1982, 1983; Hemler *et al.* 1983; Hemler *et al.* 1985*a*,*b*) and the beta subunit of avian integrin and mammalian fibronectin receptors are antigenically similar. This is consistent with our comparisons of the fibronectin receptor from rat cells and integrin. Thus, one subfamily of receptors defined by a related beta subunit would consist of integrin, the mammalian fibronectin receptors and the VLA antigens. The second subfamily is defined by another common beta subunit, which is associated with LFA-1, Mac-1 and p150,95 (Sanchez-Madrid *et al.* 1983; Springer *et al.* 1985). The alpha subunits of these receptors are different. The third subfamily the cytoadhesins has been defined by Ginsberg *et al.* (1987). It consists of the platelet cytoadhesion (IIb/IIIa) and the mammalian vitronectin receptor. Again, these receptors share a common structurally and antigenically related beta subunit and distinct alpha subunits. The relationship between these receptors is summarized in Table 1, using receptor subunit designations suggested by Hynes (1987). The properties of these receptors are the following. They are heterodimers; some, but not all alpha subunits consist of disulphide-linked heavy and light chains; some, but not all of the receptor–ligand interactions are blocked by the fibronectin cell-binding peptide. All beta subunits contain disulphide cross-linked cysteine-rich repeats. The binding specificities are determined primarily by the alpha subunit. The importance of the alpha subunits is best illustrated in the case of the cytoadhesins (family 3) with gpIIb-IIIa being a promiscuous receptor that binds several ligands and the mammalian vitronectin receptor, which contains a different alpha subunit, being a specific receptor that binds a single ligand only. As the genes for more receptors are isolated and sequenced we will gain further insight into the structural and functional inter-relationships of the members of this supergene family as well as an understanding of how the genes are regulated, the proteins processed and the receptor subunits sorted out and assembled. New additions and combinations will undoubtedly be discovered, which will necessitate refinement of these relationships.

Functionally, integrin is most probably involved in cell motility, morphogenetic movements and the initial establishment of cell–matrix interactions. Its role in development has been demonstrated indirectly by the ability of both CSAT and JG22 monoclonal antibodies as well as Arg-Gly-Asp-containing peptides to interfere with early development in chick embryos (Boucaut *et al.* 1984; Bronner-Fraser, 1985; Duband *et al.* 1986; Jaffredo *et al.* 1986). Also integrin-like molecules termed position-specific (PS) antigens, have been implicated in *Drosophila* development

Table 1. *Supergene family of related receptors*

β Subunit designation	β Subunit source	α Subunit designation	α Subunit source
β_1		α_0	Avian integrin (band 1)
		α_1	VLA 1
	Avian integrin band 3	α_2	VLA 2
	Mammalian fibronectin receptor	α_3	VLA 3 and avian integrin (band 2)
	VLA	α_4	VLA 4
		α_5	VLA 5 and mammalian fibronectin receptor
β_2		α_L	LFA
	LFA-1-Mac-1/p150,95	α_M	Mac-1
		α_X	p150,95
β_3	Cytoadhesin glycoprotein IIIa	α_{IIb}	Cytoadhesin glycoprotein IIb
	Mammalian vitronectin receptor	α_V	Mammalian vitronectin receptor

The supergene family, which includes integrin, is divided into three families each with a common characteristic β subunit, which is found in conjunction with variable alpha subunits. A detailed explanation of the organization of the supergene family is found in the text. The designation of the α and β subunits is as suggested by Hynes (1987). The β subunits are denoted by subscripts. The different α subunits are denoted by subscripts used by the original discoverer (as in the case of the VLA antigens), by subscripts denoting the nature of the ligand (i.e. αIIb, platelet cytoadhesins IIb), or the original cell type from which the receptor was isolated (i.e. α_L, leucocytes). The particular combination of alpha and beta subunits then defines the receptor (i.e. α_3, β_1, integrin and VLA 3).

(Wilcox *et al.* 1984; Wilcox & Leptin, 1985). Here too, the Arg-Gly-Asp peptides have been shown to interfere with morphogenesis (Naidet *et al.* 1987). The apparent evolutionary conservation of integrin-like molecules would argue for its importance in biological systems.

In conclusion, over the past 16 or so years since the description of adhesion plaques, we have made considerable advances in our understanding of the molecules involved in the initial establishment of cell–matrix interactions and coordinating the organization of matrix and cytoskeletal elements. This work has led to the discovery of relationships between unexpected groups of molecules and has begun to lay the ground work for investigations into the mechanisms tissue morphogenesis, metastasis and cellular adhesive interactions involved in various pathological disorders.

We are grateful for the assistance of Ms Marie Lennon in the preparation of the manuscript, Ms Kimberly Duggan for her technical assistance and the preparation of figures, and Mr Jim Averbach for the preparation of drawings. This work was supported by National Institutes of Health grants CA 19144 and CA 10815 to C.A.B., and GM 23244 to A.F.H., and by the H. M. Watts Jr Neuromuscular Disease Research Center (A.F.H.).

REFERENCES

Abercrombie, M., Heaysman, E. M. & Pegrum, S. M. (1971). The locomotion of fibroblasts in culture IV. Electron microscopy of the leading lamella. *Expl Cell Res.* **67**, 359–367.

AKIYAMA, S. K., HASEGAWA, E., HASEGAWA, T. & YAMADA, K. (1985). The interaction of fibronectin fragments with fibroblastic cells. *J. biol. Chem.* **260**, 13256–13260.

ARGRAVES, W. S., PYTELA, R., SUZUKI, S., MILLAN, J. L., PIERSCHBACHER, M. D. & RUOSLAHTI, E. (1986). cDNA sequences from the alpha subunit of the fibronectin receptor predict a transmembrane domain and a short cytoplasmic peptide. *J. biol. Chem.* **261**, 12922–12024.

BOUCAUT, J. C., DARRIEBERE, T., POOLE, T. J., AOYAMA, H., YAMADA, K. M. & THIERY, J. P. (1984). Biologically active synthetic peptides as probes of embryonic development: a competitive peptide inhibition of fibronectin function inhibits gastrulation in an amphibian embryos and neural crest migration in avian embryos. *J. Cell Biol.* **99**, 1822–1830.

BRONNER-FRASER, M. (1985). Alterations in neural crest migration by a monoclonal antibody that affects cell adhesion. *J. Cell Biol.* **101**, 610–617.

BUCK, C. A. & HORWITZ, A. F. (1987). Cell surface receptors for extracellular matrix molecules. *A. Rev. Cell Biol.* **3**, 179–205.

BUCK, C., KNUDSEN, K. A., DAMSKY, C. H., DECKER, C., GREGGS, R. R., DUGGAN, K. E., BOZYCZKO, D. & HORWITZ, A. (1985). Intergral membrane protein complexes in cell–matrix adhesion. In *The Cell in Contact: Adhesions and Junctions as Morphogenic Determinants* (ed. G. M. Edelman & J. P. Thiery), pp. 345–364. New York: Wiley.

BUCK, C. A., SHEA, E., DUGGIN, K. & HORWITZ, A. F. (1986). Integrin (the CSAT antigen): Functionality requires oligomeric integrity. *J. Cell Biol.* **103**, 2421–2428.

BURRIDGE, K. (1987). Substrate adhesions in normal and transformed fibroblasts: Organization and regulation of cytoskeletal, membrane and extracellular matrix components at focal contacts. *Cancer Rev.* **4**, 18–78.

CHEN, W.-T., CHEN, J.-M. & MUELLER, S. C. (1986*a*). Coupled expression and co-localization of 140 K cell adhesion molecules, fibronectin, and laminin during morphogenesis and cytodifferentiation of chick lung cells. *J. Cell Biol.* **103**, 1073–1090.

CHEN, W.-T., GREVE, J. M., GOTTLIEB, D. I. & SINGER, S. J. (1985*a*). Immunocytochemical localization of 140 kD cell adhesion molecules in cultured chicken fibroblasts and in chicken smooth muscle and intestinal epithelial tissues. *J. Histochem. Cytochem.* **33**, 576–586.

CHEN, W.-T., HASEGAWA, E., HASEGAWA, T., WEINSTOCK, C. & YAMADA, K. M. (1985*b*). Development of cell surface linkage complexes in cultured fibroblasts. *J. Cell Biol.* **100**, 1103–1104.

CHEN, W.-T., WONG, J., HASEGAWA, T., YAMADA, S. & YAMADA, K. M. (1986*b*). Regulation of fibronectin receptor distribution by transformation, exogenous fibronectin, and synthetic peptides. *J. Cell Biol.* **103**, 1649–1661.

DAMSKY, C. H., KNUDSEN, K. A., BRADLEY, D., BUCK, C. A. & HORWITZ, A. F. (1985). Distribution of the cell–substratum attachment (CSAT) antigen on myogenic and fibroblastic cells in culture. *J. Cell Biol.* **100**, 1528–1539.

DECKER, C., GREGGS, R., DUGGAN, K., STUBBS, J. & HORWITZ, A. (1984). Adhesive multiplicity in the interaction of embryonic fibroblasts and myoblasts with extracellular matrices. *J. Cell Biol.* **99**, 1398–1404.

DUBAND, J. L., ROCKER, S., CHEN, W. T., YAMADA, K. M. & THIERY, J-P. (1986). Cell adhesion and migration in the early vertebrate embryo: location and possible role of the putative fibronectin receptor complex. *J. Cell Biol.* **102**, 160–178.

GEIGER, B., VOLK, T., VOLBERG, T. & BENDORI, R. (1987). Molecular interactions in adherens-type contacts. *J. Cell Sci. Suppl. 8*, 251–272.

GINSBERG, M. H., LOFTUN, J., PIERSCHBACHER, M. D., RUOSLAHTI, E. & PLOW, E. F. (1987). Immunochemical and N-terminal sequence comparison of two cytoadhesins indicates they contain similar or identical beta subunits and distinct alpha subunits. *J. biol. Chem.* (in press).

GREVE, J. M. & GOTTLIEB, D. I. (1982). Monoclonal antibodies which alter the morphology of culture chick myogome cells. *J. Cell Biochem.* **18**, 221–230.

HASEGAWA, T., HASEGAWA, E., CHEN, W. T. & YAMADA, K. M. (1985). Characterization of a membrane-associated glycoprotein complex implicated in cell adhesion to fibronectin. *J. Cell Biochem.* **28**, 307–318.

HEMLER, M. E., HUANG, C. & SCHWARZ, L. (1987). The VLA protein family. *J. biol. Chem.* **262**, 3300–3309.

HEMLER, M. E., JACOBSON, J. G., BRENNER, M. B., MANN, D. & STROMINGER, J. L. (1985*a*). VLA-1: a T cell surface antigen which defines a novel late stage of human T cell activation. *Eur. J. Immun.* **15**, 502–508.

HEMLER, M. E., JACOBSON, J. G. & STROMINGER, J. L. (1985*b*). Biochemical characterization of VLA-1 and VLA-2 cell surface heterodimers on activated T cells. *J. biol. Chem.* **260**, 15 246–15 252.

HEMLER, M. E., WARE, C. S. & STROMINGER, J. L. (1983). Characterization of a novel differentiation antigen complex recognized by a monoclonal antibody (A-1A5): Unique activation-specific molecular forms on stimulated T cells. *J. Immun.* **131**, 334–340.

HIRST, R., HORWITZ, A., BUCK, C. & ROHRSCHNEIDER, L. (1986). Phosphorylation of the fibronectin receptor complex in cells transformed by onocogenes that encode tyrosine kinases. *Proc. natn. Acad. Sci. U.S.A.* **83**, 6470–6474.

HORWITZ, A., DUGGAN, K., BUCK, C., BECKERLE, K. & BURRIDGE, K. (1986). Interaction of plasma membrane fibronectin receptor with talin–a transmembrane linkage. *Nature, Lond.* **320**, 531–533.

HORWITZ, A., DUGGAN, K., GREGGS, R., DECKER, C. & BUCK, C. (1985). Cell substrate attachment (CSAT) antigen has properties of a receptor for laminin and fibronectin. *J. Cell Biol.* **103**, 2134–2144.

HYNES, R. O. (1987). Integrins: A family of cell surface receptors. *Cell* **48**, 549–554.

IZZARD, C. S., RADINSKY, R. & CULP, L. A. (1986). Substratum contacts and cytoskeletal reorganization of BALB/c 3T3 cells on a cell-binding fragment and heparin-binding fragment of plasma fibronectin. *Expl Cell Res.* **165**, 320–336.

JAFFREDO, T., HORWITZ, A. F., BUCK, C. A., RONG, P. W. & DIETERLEN-LIEVRE, F. (1986). CSAT antibody interferes with *in vivo* migration of somitic myoblast precursors into the body wall. In *The Somites in Developing Embryos* (ed. R. Bellaires & J. W. Lash), pp. 225–236. New York: Plenum.

KISHIMOTO, T. K., O'CONNOR, K., LEE, A., ROBERTS, T. M. & SPRINGER, T. A. (1987). Cloning of the beta subunit of the leukocyte adhesion proteins: homology to an extracellular matrix receptor defines a novel supergene family. *Cell* **48**, 681–690.

KNUDSEN, K. A., HORWITZ, A., & BUCK, C. A. (1985). A monoclonal antibody identifies a glycoprotein complex involved in cell–substratum adhesion. *Expl Cell Res.* **157**, 218–226.

KNUDSEN, K. A., RAO, P., DAMSKY, C. H. & BUCK, C. A. (1981). Membrane glycoproteins involved in cell–substratum adhesion. *Proc. natn. Acad. Sci. U.S.A.* **78**, 6071–6075.

LARK, M. W., LATERRA, J. & CULP, L. A. (1985). Close and local contact adhesions of fibroblasts to a fibronectin-containing matrix. *Fedn Proc. Fedn Am. Socs Exp. Biol.* **44**, 394–403.

LEPTIN, M. (1986). The fibronectin receptor family. *Nature, Lond.* **321**, 728–729.

MARCHISIO, P., CIRILLO, D., TETI, A., ZAMBONIN-ZALLONE, A. & TARONE, G. (1987). Rous sarcoma virus transformed fibroblasts and cells of monocytic origin display a peculiar dot-like organization of cytoskeletal proteins involved in microfilament–membrane interactions. *Expl Cell Res.* **169**, 202–214.

NAIDET, C., SEMERIVA, M., YAMADA, K. & THIERY, J.-P . (1987). Peptides containing the cell-attachment recognition sequence Arg-Gly-Asp prevent gastrulation in *Drosophila* embryos. *Nature, Lond.* **325**, 348–350.

NEFF, N. T., LOWREY, C., DECKER, C., TOVAR, A., DAMSKY, C., BUCK, C. & HORWITZ, A. (1982). A monoclonal antibody detaches embryonic skeletal muscle from extracellular matrices. *J. Cell Biol.* **95**, 654–666.

OESCH, B. & BIRCHMEIER, W. (1982). New surface component of fibroblast focal contacts identified by a monoclonal antibody. *Cell* **31**, 671–679.

PLOW, E. F., PIERSCHBACHER, M. D., RUOSLAHTI, E., MARGUERIE, G. A. & GINSBERG, M. H. (1985). The effect of Arg-Gly-Asp-containing peptides on fibrinogen and von Willerbrand factor binding to platelets. *Proc. natn. Acad. Sci. U.S.A.* **82**, 8057–8061.

PYTELA, R., PIERSCHBACHER, M. D. & RUOSLAHTI, E. (1985*a*). Identification and isolation of a 140 kd cell surface glycoprotein with properties expected of a fibronectin receptor. *Cell* **40**, 191–198.

PYTELA, R., PIERSCHBACHER, M. D. & RUOSLAHTI, E. (1985*b*). A 125/115 kDa cell surface receptor specific for vitronectin interacts with the arginine-glycine-aspartic acid adhesion sequence derived from fibronectin. *Proc. natn. Acad. Sci. U.S.A.* **82**, 5766–5700.

RAPRAEGER, A., JALKANEN, M. & BERNFIELD, M. (1986). Cell surface proteoglycan associates with the cytoskeleton at the basolateral cell surface of mouse mammary epithelial cells. *J. Cell Biol.* **103**, 2683–2696.

ROGALSKI, A. A. SINGER, S. J. (1985). An integral membrane glycoprotein associated with membrane sites of actin with microfilaments. *J. Cell Biol.* **101**, 785–801.

RUOSLAHTI, E. & PIERSCHBACHER, M. D. (1986). Arg-Gly-Asp: A versatile cell recognition signal. *Cell* **44**, 517–518.

SANCHEZ-MADRID, F., KRENSKY, A. M., WARE, C. F., ROBBINS, E., STROMINGER, J. L., BURAKOFF, S. J. & SPRINGER, T. A. (1982). Three distinct antigens associated with human T-lymphocyte mediate cytolysis: LFA-1, LFA-2 and LFA-3. *Proc. natn. Acad. Sci. U.S.A.* **79**, 7489–7493.

SANCHEZ-MADRID, F., NAGY, J. A., ROBBINS, E., SIMON, P. & SPRINGER, T. A. (1983). A human leukocyte differentiation antigen family with distinct alpha subunits and a common beta subunit: the lymphocyte function-associated antigen (LFA-1), the C3bi complement receptor (OKM1/Mac-1), and the p150,95 molecule. *J. exp. Med.* **158**, 1875–1803.

SINGER, I. I., KAWKA, D. W., SCOTT, S., MUMFORD, R. A. & LARK, M. W. (1987). The fibronectin cell attachment sequence Arg-Gly-Asp-Ser promotes focal contact formation during early fibroblast attachment and spreading. *J. Cell Biol.* **104**, 573–584.

SPRINGER, T. A., TEPLOW, D. B. & DREYER, W. J. (1985). Sequence homology of the LFA-1 and Mac-1 leukocyte adhesion glycoproteins and unexpected relation to leukocyte interferon. *Nature, Lond.* **314**, 540–542.

SUZUKI, S., ARGRAVES, W. S., PYTELA, R., ARAI, H., KRUSIUS, T., PIERSCHBACHER, M. D. & RUOSLAHTI, E. (1986). cDNA and amino sequences of the cell adhesive protein receptor recognizing vitronectin reveal a transmembrane domain and homologies with other adhesion protein receptors. *Proc. natn. Acad. Sci. U.S.A.* **83**, 8614–8618.

TAKADA, Y., STROMINGER, J. L. & HEMLER, M. E. (1987*a*). The VLA family of heterodimers are members of a superfamily of molecules involved in adhesion and embryogenesis. *Proc. natn. Acad. Sci. U.S.A.* **84**, 3239–3243.

TAKADA, Y., STROMINGER, C. H. & HEMLER, M. E. (1987*b*). Fibronectin receptor structures within the VLA family of heterodimers. *Nature, Lond.* **326**, 607–609.

TAMKUM, J. W., DESIMONE, D. W., FONDA, D., PATEL, R. S., BUCK, C. A., HORWITZ, A. F. & HYNES, R. O. (1986). Structure of integrin, a glycoprotein involved in the transmembrane linkage between fibronectin and actin. *Cell* **46**, 271–282.

WILCOX, M., BROWN, N., PIOVANT, M., SMITH, R. J. & WHITE, R. A. H. (1984). The *Drosophila* position-specific antigens are a family of cell surface glycoprotein complexes. *EMBO J.* **3**, 2307–2313.

WILCOX, M. & LEPTIN, M. (1985). Tissue-specific modulation of a set of related cell surface antigens in *Drosophila*. *Nature, Lond.* **316**, 351–354.

WYLIE, D. E., DAMSKY, C. H. & BUCK, C. A. (1979). Studies on the function of cell surface glycoproteins. *J. Cell Biol.* **80**, 385–401.

J. Cell Sci. Suppl. 8, 251–272 (1987)
Printed in Great Britain © The Company of Biologists Limited 1987

MOLECULAR INTERACTIONS IN ADHERENS-TYPE CONTACTS

BENJAMIN GEIGER, TALILA VOLK, TOVA VOLBERG AND RONIT BENDORI
Department of Chemical Immunology, The Weizmann Institute of Science, Rehovot 76100, Israel

SUMMARY

Adherens junctions are members of a molecularly and structurally heterogeneous family of cell contacts sharing a common association with the microfilament system. Various topics related to the biogenesis of these cellular contacts and the molecular interactions involved in their formation are discussed. ⅓The role of vinculin, a cytoplasmic 'plaque' component present in all adherens junctions tested to date and its possible interactions with the other junctional domains have been investigated by both biochemical analyses and studies of molecular dynamics in microinjected living cells. The importance of A-CAM, which apparently functions as a 'junctional receptor' is emphasized and its roles in junction formation in cell cultures and in developing embryos are discussed. In addition, its relationship to other Ca^{2+}-dependent cell adhesion molecules (in particular L-CAM) is considered. The evidence indicating that the level of expression of vinculin-specific mRNA is affected by culture conditions and may be markedly modulated by changes in the adhesiveness of the substratum on which the cells grow is reviewed.

INTRODUCTION

Adhesion to exogenous surfaces has many profound effects on the structure and behaviour of metazoan cells. The wide variety of structurally defined cell contacts, the distinct responses of different cells to contact-mediated stimuli and the molecular diversity of cell-adhesion-related molecules, renders it difficult, if not impossible, to provide a unified molecular model for cell adhesion. To illustrate the various levels of complexity of cell contact phenomena a few examples may be outlined. Structural studies, conducted at the light- and electron-microscope levels reveal a multitude of different types of cell contacts, including the major junctional specializations, contacts with the extracellular matrix, etc. Examination of a wide variety of cells *in situ* or in culture reveals remarkable variations in the topology of the various cell contacts, their overall shapes, dimensions and spatial inter-relationships. Temporarily, cell contacts may be constantly modulated, grow, change orientation or fade out. At the molecular level, cell attachments may be mediated by a wide variety of adhesion molecules interacting with a broad spectrum of exogenous surfaces. Finally, cell contacts may play diverse (often conflicting) roles in cell physiology. They are involved in cell locomotion as well as in the extensive spreading and immobilization of cells and they also play a part in the acquisition of cell polarity, transduction of transcellular mechanical forces, formation of permeability barriers, construction of intercellular transport channels, control of cell growth, regulation of differentiation, etc. Needless to say, all these major physiological activities depend on the accurate molecular orchestration of cell contact formation and on the transmembrane transduction of contact-related stimuli into the cell interior.

Attempts to gain an insight into the possible mechanisms of transmembrane signalling in cell contacts have focused considerable attention on those adhesions that are associated with specialized cytoplasmic structures. Among the first contacts of this type to be described were the adherens-type junctions and desmosomes (Farquhar & Palade, 1963) and the focal contacts or adhesion plaques. The latter have been shown, by Abercrombie and co-workers as well as by others (see below), to be associated with bundles of cytoplasmic microfilaments.

The major goal that has guided our studies over the last several years has been to characterize the molecular interactions that occur in these sites subsequent to and as a consequence of contact formation. Following the discovery of vinculin (Geiger, 1979) major efforts were directed toward studies on focal contacts and these studies were extended when it was realized that vinculin is also present in intercellular contacts of the adherens type. In this article we will briefly summarize our current view of the structure, dynamics and regulation of expression of junction-related proteins.

VINCULIN: AN ADHERENS JUNCTION-ASSOCIATED PROTEIN

Adherens junctions are a morphologically diverse group of cell contacts that are associated at their cytoplasmic surfaces with microfilament bundles (Farquhar & Palade, 1963; Geiger *et al.* 1983, 1985*a*,*b*). One of the features common to all adherens junctions studied to date is their association with a cytoplasmic, vinculin-rich plaque (Geiger, 1979, 1982). Thus, the labelling of different cells and tissues with vinculin-specific antibodies has served as a primary tool to identify adherens junctions, localize them, delineate their structure and monitor their assembly (Geiger *et al.* 1981, 1985*a*,*b*).

The most conspicuous vinculin-containing sites in cultured cells (and probably the most extensively studied) are the focal contacts formed with tissue culture substrata. In these areas, which were thoroughly investigated by Abercrombie and co-workers, as well as by many others (e.g. Abercrombie *et al.* 1971; Heaysman & Pegrum, 1973; Abercrombie & Dunn, 1975; Vasiliev & Gelfand, 1981), the ventral cell membrane is closely and firmly attached to the substratum and in its cytoplasmic aspect it is bound to actin filaments (Heath & Dunn, 1978). This apparent transmembrane linkage is demonstrated in Fig. 1, showing the ventral vinculin plaques, which are localized at

Fig. 1. Adherens-type contacts formed by cultured cells. A. Transmission electron micrograph of cultured chick lens cells showing large focal contacts formed with the substratum, as well as subapical adherens-type junctions with neighbouring cells. The inset clearly shows the microfilaments associated with the focal contact and bundles of intermediate filaments, which are particularly enriched in these areas. Bars, $0{\cdot}2\,\mu m$. B,C. Double fluorescent labelling of cultured chick fibroblasts for vinculin (B) and actin (C) showing the typical association of vinculin with the termini of actin stress fibres, corresponding to focal contact areas. Bar, $10\,\mu m$.

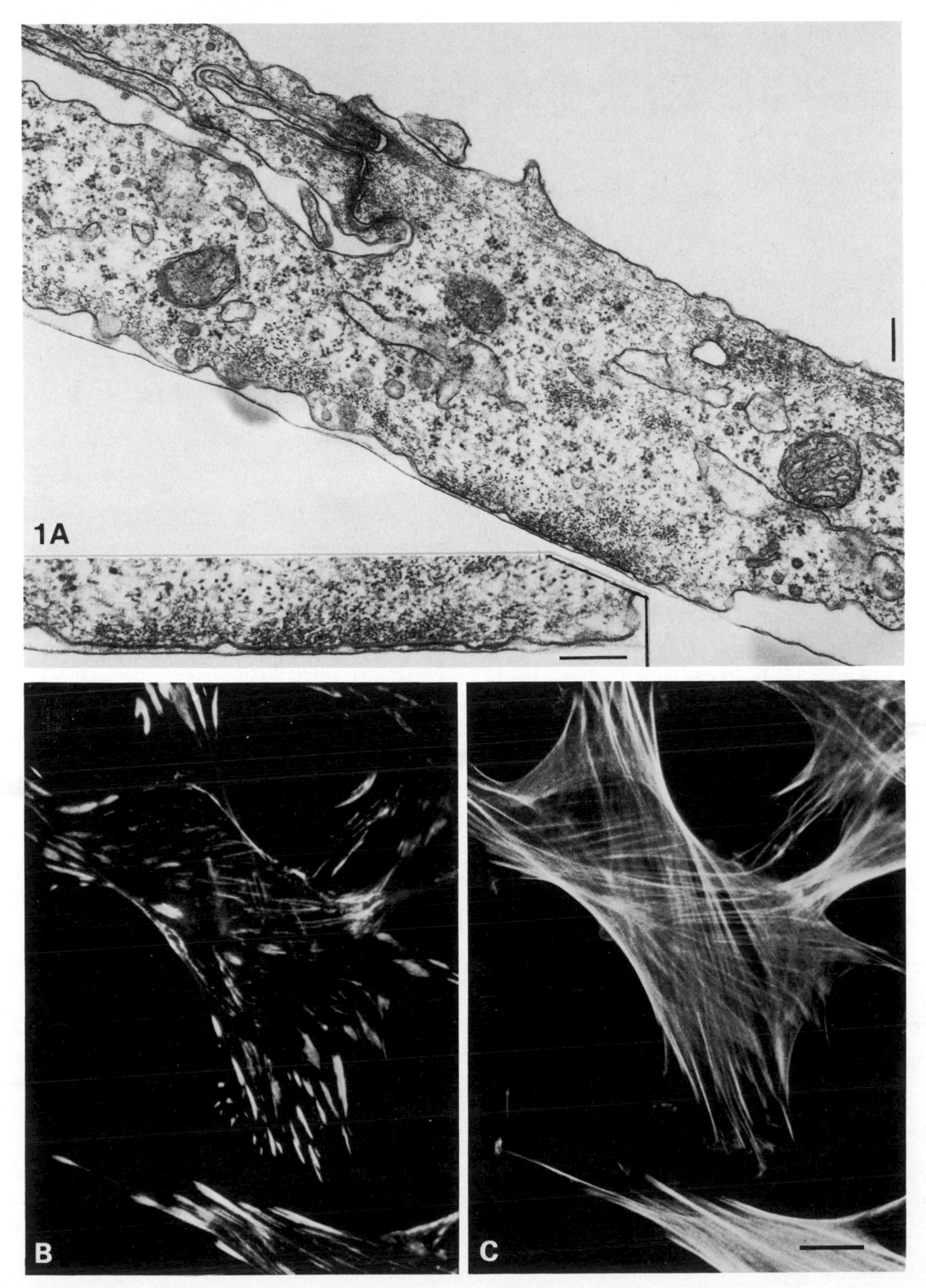
1A
B
C

the termini of actin-rich stress fibres. The vinculin distribution pattern shown in Fig. 1 is somewhat misleading, as it was obtained after mild extraction and fixation of the cells and thus it reveals only membrane-bound vinculin. Another major fraction of cellular vinculin is a diffusible cytoplasmic pool, which maintains a dynamic equilibrium with the membrane-bound fraction (Kreis *et al.* 1984; Geiger *et al.* 1984*b*), as will be discussed below. Our earlier studies concerning the role of vinculin in contact formation suggested that the establishment of new surface contacts with suitable substrata leads to the local accumulation of some putative transmembrane 'contact receptors', which in turn may bind vinculin to their clustered cytoplasmic moieties. Subsequently, these vinculin-rich plaques may nucleate actin bundle assembly (Geiger, 1982, 1983; Geiger *et al.* 1984*a*,*b*). Since this model was formulated several new adherens junction components have been found, which enables us to reassess various aspects of this model. We would like to reiterate that most of our studies support the view that adherens junctions contain three major molecular domains (cytoskeletal, plaque, membrane) and that the assembly of this structure is a vectorial process that is initiated by the contact itself (Geiger, 1982; Geiger *et al.* 1985*b*).

As pointed out above, focal contacts serve as both interesting and convenient models for studies on the structure and dynamics of adherens-type junctions. Yet there are many other structurally diverse types of adherens junction, which may be formed by cells in culture or in the living organism. Among these are contacts with extracellular matrix elements, e.g. dense plaques of smooth muscle (Geiger *et al.* 1981; Small, 1985; Volberg *et al.* 1986), tendenous–muscular interactions, attachments to basement membranes and, at least in some cases, neuromuscular or related junctions (Bloch & Geiger, 1980; Bloch & Hall, 1983). Other contacts are the intercellular junctions, which may form extensive belt-like structures (zonulae adherentes) as seen in polar epithelia, patches (fasciae adherentes) as seen in cardiac muscle, as well as non-desmosomal spot contacts as seen in cultured fibroblasts and other cell types (Farquhar & Palade, 1963; Staehelin, 1974; Tokuyasu *et al.* 1981; Geiger *et al.* 1983). Some examples of vinculin-rich junctions are shown in Fig. 2. In all these systems vinculin is apparently present (therefore we classified them as one family), yet further examination revealed notable molecular differences, which are apparently of some significance for the fine structural and functional properties of these diverse junctions.

MOLECULAR AND STRUCTURAL VARIABILITY AMONG ADHERENS-TYPE CONTACTS

Using vinculin as a major molecular landmark was the basis for the classification of all the above-mentioned cell contacts into one group of homologous structures. This, somewhat artificial, classification leads to some intrinsic controversies, which become apparent when one considers the different functional properties of cell–matrix, as compared to cell–cell, contacts. The former are usually involved in cell

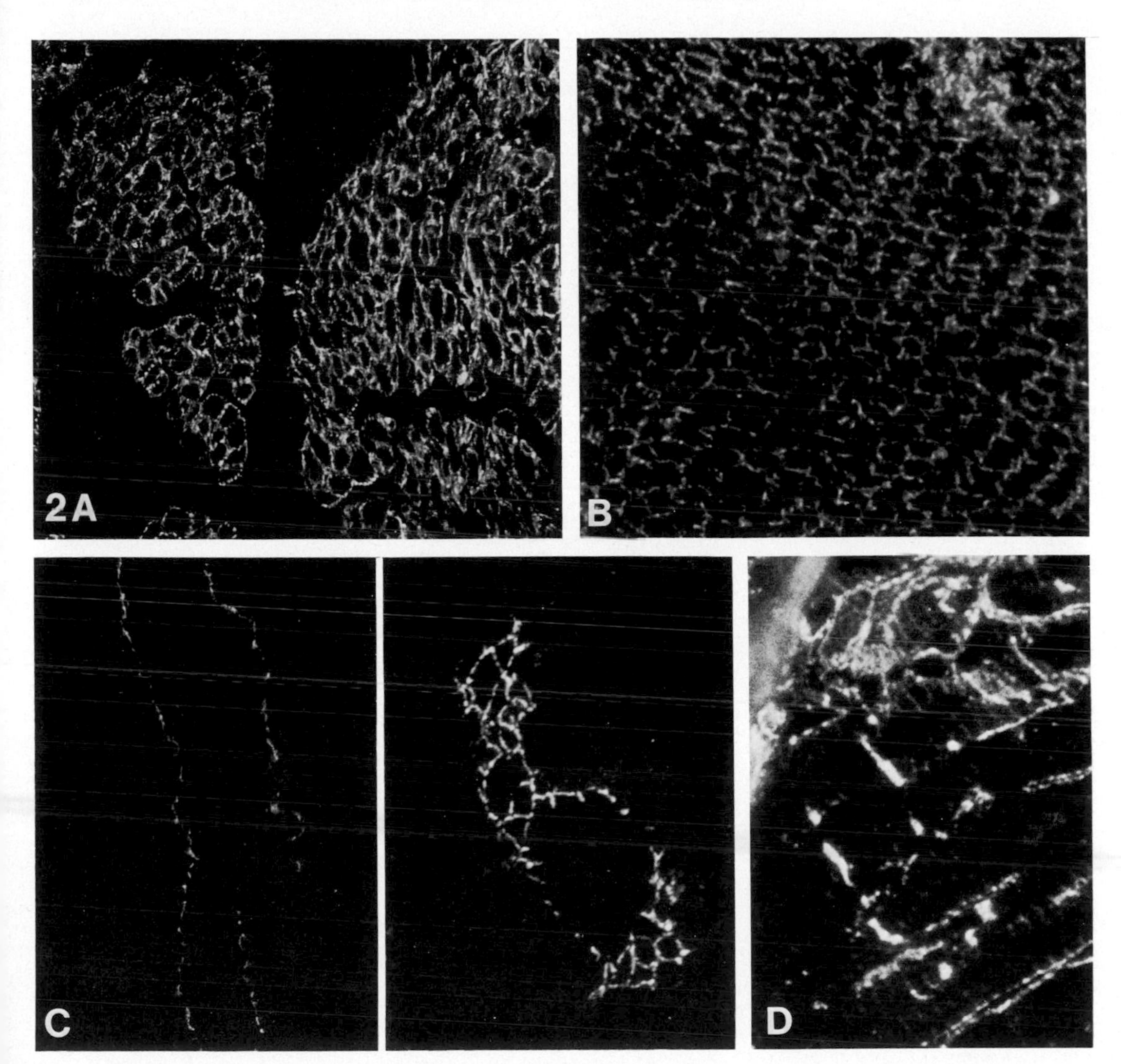

Fig. 2. Immunofluorescence localization of vinculin in chicken gizzard smooth muscle (A); chicken lens (B), chicken intestine (C) (two micrographs), chicken cardiac muscle (D). Notice the association of vinculin with the dense plaques of smooth muscle, with the intercellular junctions of the lens, with the apical junctional complex of the intestine (in both cross- and longitudinal sections) and with the fasciae adherentes in the heart.

spreading, translocation and normal growth (e.g. see Folkman & Moscona, 1978; Gospodarowicz *et al.* 1978; Ben Ze'ev *et al.* 1980), whereas cell–cell attachments limit cell spreading, block motility and usually arrest cell growth (Abercrombie, 1970; Heaysman & Pegrum, 1973; Vasiliev & Gelfand, 1981).

Characterization of the fine structure of different junctional subdomains has provided direct evidence that the two functionally distinct subfamilies of cell junctions also display differences in their molecular composition. Such indications

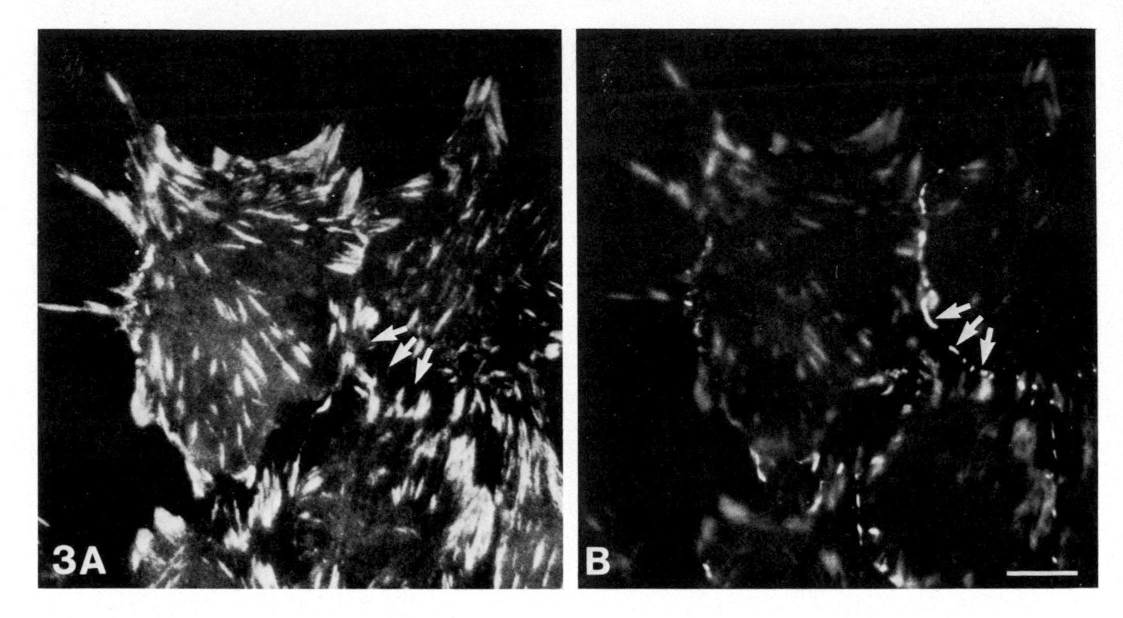

Fig. 3. Spatial inter-relationships between talin (A) and vinculin (B), revealed by double immunofluorescent labelling of cultured chicken lens cells. Note that focal contacts are extensively labelled with antibodies to both proteins, while intercellular adhesions (marked with matching arrows) contain only vinculin and are apparently devoid of talin. Bar, 10 μm.

were obtained through efforts to identify new components of the cell–substratum and cell–cell adherens junctions. One such component is the protein talin. This $215\times10^3 M_r$ protein was originally isolated by Burridge and co-workers from smooth muscle and identified as a new focal contact-associated molecule that displays distribution patterns similar to those of vinculin (Burridge & Connell, 1983*a*,*b* and see Burridge *et al.*, this volume). Talin was later identified as p-235 of platelets (O'Halloran *et al.* 1985) and localized in both cardiac muscle and in the dense plaques of smooth muscle (Volberg *et al.* 1986). However, double immunofluorescent labelling of various cultured cells and intact tissues revealed conspicuous differences between the distribution profiles of talin and vinculin. The latter was associated with all adherens contacts, while the former was exclusively located in cell–substratum (or cell–matrix) attachments (Geiger *et al.* 1985*a*). These differential distributions are best visualized in cultured epithelioid cells as demonstrated in Fig. 3. In these cells both vinculin and talin are present in the focal contacts, while the apical intercellular junctions contain only vinculin (for further details, see Geiger *et al.* 1985*a*).

The molecular heterogeneity of adherens junctions described above provides some insight into the possible molecular interactions between the various components that constitute these complex structures. Biochemical studies carried out with isolated proteins indicated that vinculin can bind to talin (Otto, 1983; Burridge & Mangeat, 1984). Less-direct evidence suggests that vinculin may also interact with α-actinin

(Craig, 1985) and, under appropriate conditions, may undergo self-assembly. The latter notion is based on the non-saturating kinetics of vinculin binding to focal contacts (Avnur *et al.* 1983).

Some years ago it was proposed that vinculin could bind to actin and induce its bundling (Jockusch & Isenberg, 1981, 1982) or capping (Wilkins & Lin; 1982; Lin *et al.* 1982). Further studies, however, suggested that these activities could not be attributed to vinculin itself but rather to a low molecular weight ($25\times10^3 M_r$) actin-capping protein that was present in the vinculin-rich fractions (Evans *et al.* 1984; Schroer & Wegner, 1985; Wilkins & Lin, 1986).

In recent studies carried out in this laboratory we have purified this molecule (denoted by us 25 K-ACP) and found by immunocytochemical labelling that there is no spatial relationship between this molecule and the vinculin-rich contacts in cells and tissues (Miron *et al.* unpublished results). It is noteworthy that in spite of the definitive affinity between vinculin and talin, the two only partially coincide, even within the same cell as described above (see also Geiger *et al.* 1985*a*; Volberg *et al.* 1986).

Studies on the nature of the extracellular matrix (or substratum)-binding components in focal contacts have created some confusion. Some reports indicated that fibronectin and its receptor are associated with focal contacts (Singer & Paradiso, 1981; Hynes *et al.* 1982; Damsky *et al.* 1985), whereas others indicated that fibronectin is excluded and that cells may actively remove fibronectin from underneath focal contacts in a centripetal direction leading to the formation of small fibronectin cables (Birchmeier *et al.* 1980; Avnur & Geiger, 1981; Chen & Singer, 1980, 1982). This discrepancy led to the suggestion that the continuous interaction of fibronectin with its receptor is not obligatory for substratum adhesion in focal contacts, although it may initiate or promote their formation. It seems that one has to distinguish between two distinct stages in fibronectin-mediated attachment: the establishment of stable substratum contacts (which may be formed with a fibronectin matrix) and the subsequent mobilization of the underlying matrix. It appears that the latter process is affected by culture conditions and that cells growing in serum-free or low-serum media tend to concentrate fibronectin under the focal contacts, while cells cultured in the presence of serum remove the protein from these sites (Grinnell, 1987). Beside the interesting implications that this finding has for the dynamic properties of focal contact components, it also suggests that the fibronectin–fibronectin receptor complexes may constitute part of the transmembrane linkage in focal contacts although they are apparently not an obligatory component of this system. The nature of other putative membrane molecules in that area is still unclear. It is noteworthy that recent studies suggest that constituents of the fibronectin receptor (e.g. integrin), may react with fibronectin (and possibly with laminin) at the cell exterior and with talin at the cytoplasmic faces of the focal contact (Horwitz *et al.* 1985, 1986 and see Buck & Horwitz, this volume).

Other studies of the molecular architecture of intercellular adherens-type junctions have revealed that some additional components are present in these sites in addition to vinculin and actin. In our attempts to identify the contact receptor(s) of these junctions a new molecule with an apparent molecular weight of 135×10^3 was identified and later denoted A-CAM (for adherens junction-specific cell-adhesion molecule). As will be described below, A-CAM is a membrane-associated glycoprotein the major part of which is expressed at the junctional cleft (Volk & Geiger, 1984, 1986*a*). It is present in the adherens junctions of many cultured cells as well as

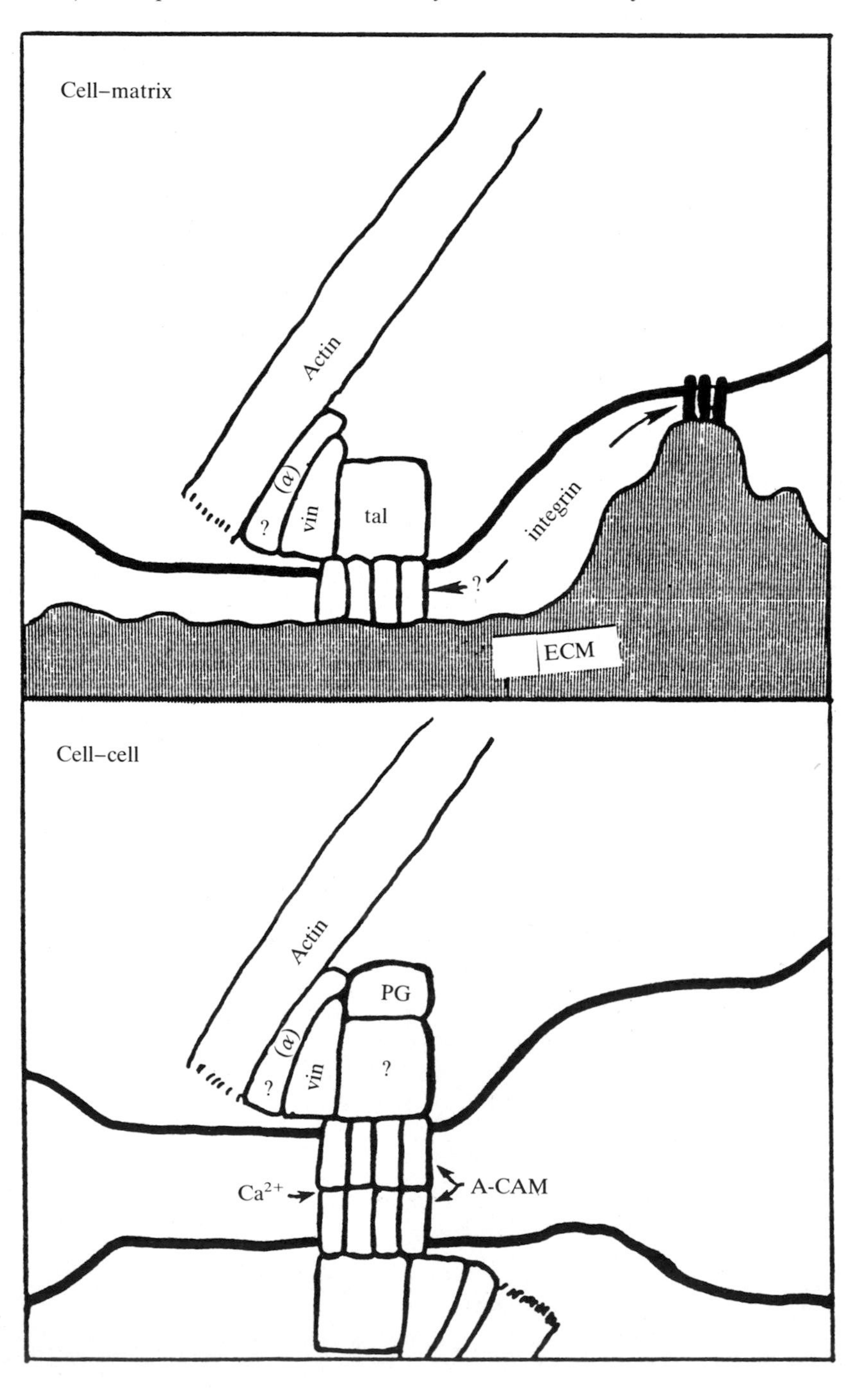

of several adult tissues including cardiac muscle, eye lens and others. A study of A-CAM expression has indicated that this molecule is a primary, Ca^{2+}-dependent CAM, which is most abundant in various epithelia of early chick embryos (Duband *et al.* unpublished results). Notably, many adherens junctions-containing epithelia in the adult animal are devoid of A-CAM and apparently contain another Ca^{2+}-dependent cell-adhesion molecule, namely L-CAM (or uvomorulin) (Boller *et al.* 1985; for review, see Edelman, 1985). In some tissues (endothelium, for example), neither A-CAM nor L-CAM is found and the nature of their specific junctional receptor in them is not clear.

Another component that is associated with intercellular adherens junctions is a plaque protein that was originally detected in desmosomes. This $83\times10^3 M_r$ protein is a globular molecule first identified as desmoplakin 3 and later, denoted plakoglobin (Cowin *et al.* 1986). Plakoglobin is detected in a large variety of intercellular adherens type junctions and is clearly absent from cell–matrix (or cell–substratum) attachments. Taken together, these results provide a possible outline for the major links of the transmembrane chain of interactions in focal contacts, which may include elements of the extracellular matrix, integrin, talin, vinculin, α-actinin and actin (see model in Fig. 4). This model is extremely preliminary and additional studies will be necessary to substantiate or disprove it.

In conclusion, adherens-type junctions seem to be a molecularly heterogeneous family of cell contacts. Besides common components (such as vinculin, α-actinin and actin) there are proteins that selectively associate with several types of adherens junctions and not with others. Among these are talin, which is present only in cell–matrix contacts, and A- or L-CAM as well as plakoglobin, which are associated with cell–cell contacts. It is, nevertheless, clear that the present knowledge of the repertoire of junctional components is incomplete, as implied by the unidentified components presented in the hypothetical molecular model shown in Fig. 4. Extensive efforts will be necessary to obtain a more complete picture of the molecular structure of the junctions and to determine the interactions between their various components.

Fig. 4. A hypothetical scheme depicting intermolecular interactions in cell–matrix and cell–cell adherens-type contacts. In constructing this scheme we have assumed some similarity in the overall molecular organization of the two types of contact as well as some specific differences. In view of the highly speculative nature of the model it seems necessary to add a brief explanation: (1) *integrin* may be present in focal contacts (though not obligatorily) and may therefore also be located outside. (2) *Talin* (tal) may be attached to both integrin and vinculin (vin). (3) *Vinculin* may bind to talin and to α-actinin (α) as well as to itself. (4) *α-Actinin* certainly binds to actin and cross-links it. If it does indeed bind to vinculin (for which there is still only preliminary evidence) it may serve to bind the cytoskeletal domain of the junction to the plaque. The major uncertainties in this model are the exact nature of the adhesion molecule (in those cases where integrin is absent) and of the vinculin–actin linker. The intercellular junction contains (1) *A-CAM* (or L-CAM in some cells), which is bound to a plaque molecule; (2) an unknown molecule (?), which plays an equivalent role to talin in the cell–matrix contacts. (3) This molecule may be related to *plakoglobin* or associated with it. (4) The rest of the junctional elements may be organized as described above for cell–matrix contacts.

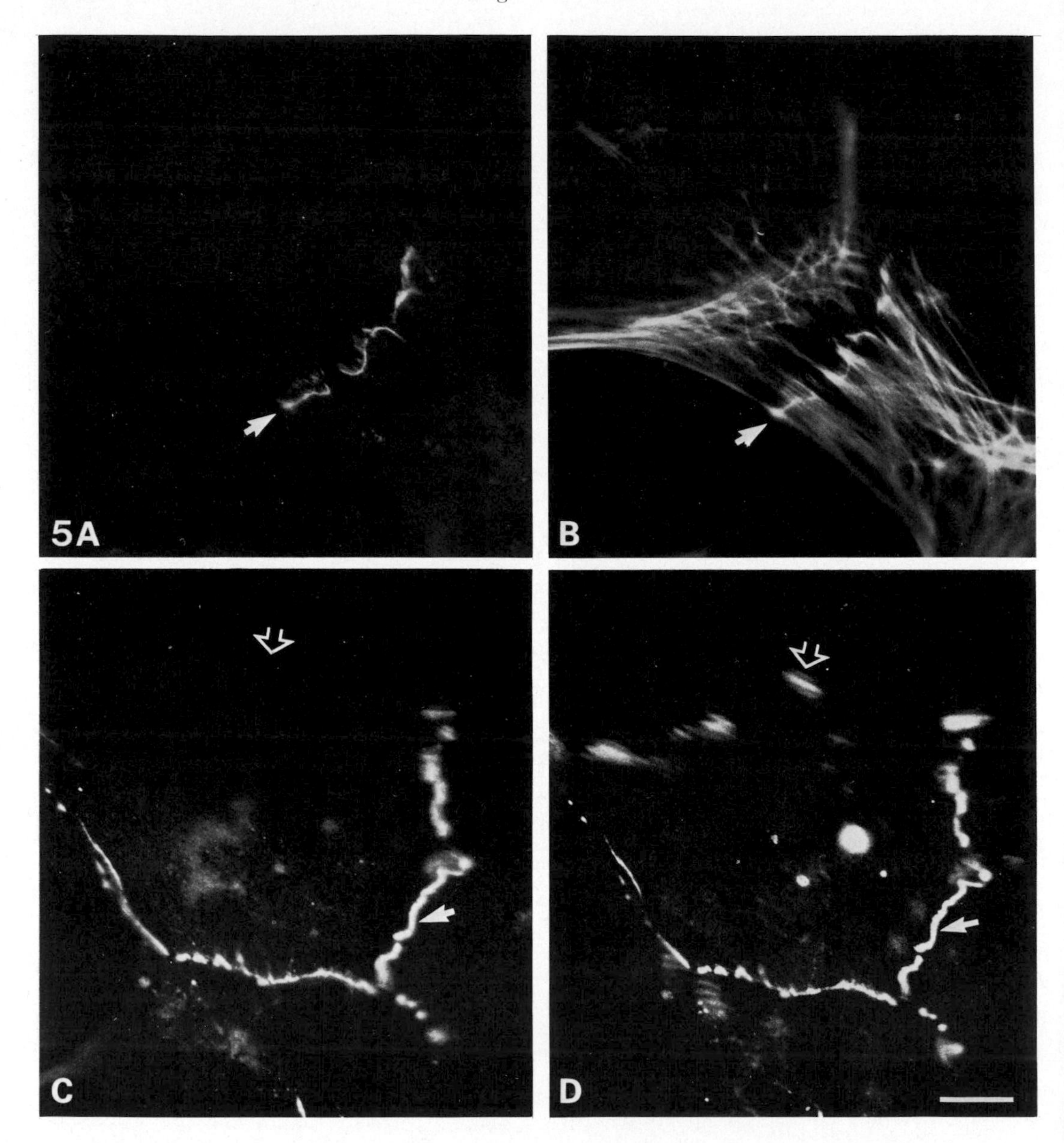

Fig. 5. Spatial relationships between A-CAM (A,C) and actin (B) or vinculin (D). Notice that A-CAM is specifically enriched in cell contacts where actin filaments apparently terminate (arrows in A and B), and is closely associated with vinculin (arrows in C and D). Comparison of A-CAM and vinculin patterns also indicate that the former is absent from cell–substrate focal contacts (open arrows in C and D). Bar, 10 μm.

THE ASSEMBLY AND DYNAMIC FEATURES OF ADHERENS JUNCTIONS

Examination of focal contacts of cultured cells by interference reflection microscopy as carried out by Abercrombie and co-workers (Abercrombie & Dunn, 1975; Heaysman & Pegrum, 1982), as well as by others (e.g. Izzard & Lochner, 1976,

1980; Chen, 1981*a*,*b*; Couchman *et al.* 1983), revealed several important features of these structures. Focal contacts are formed in a polar fashion primarily under the lamellipodia at the periphery of the cell. In locomotory cells new contacts are continuously formed under the 'leading edge'. Once formed, focal contacts appear to be relatively static structures; their dimensions may change but their location and position relative to the substratum are essentially fixed. These observations raised a number of questions: what initiates and controls the formation of focal contacts? What are the inter-relationships between the junctional and extrajunctional pools of the various proteins? How does the contact affect the assembly of the microfilament system and *vice versa*? How is the polar formation of focal contacts under the leading edge of motile cells coordinated? etc. Answers to these questions are essential for a full understanding of the mechanisms of cell locomotion and junction formation.

Several years ago we studied the early focal contact-like structures formed during cell spreading. One of the striking features of these contacts is their periodic patchy appearance at the cell periphery. Together with L. Segel from this Institute we outlined a mathematical model, which describes the transition from a nearly uniform state to a periodic patchy array of contacts (Segel *et al.* 1983). Postulating the existence of positive cooperativity in membrane substratum binding we have shown that small disturbances to the uniform state may develop into sets of contacts with defined periodicity. On a theoretical basis we have also suggested which variables may affect the observed periodicity of the early radial focal contacts. Another interesting feature of the early adhesions is related to temporal stages in their assembly, i.e. double immunofluorescence labelling of freshly plated cells for actin and vinculin indicated that the latter was associated with discrete radial substratum contacts before actin bundles were apparent in these areas (Geiger, 1981). We have postulated that this finding supports the view that the assembly of the membrane-bound, vinculin-rich plaques precedes the local bundling of actin and possibly induces it.

A more direct experimental examination of focal contact dynamics was made using the fluorescence photobleaching recovery (FPR) technique (for review of the methodology, see Axelrod *et al.* 1976). In our studies we have measured the lateral mobilities of a lipid probe and of surface proteins in focal contacts as compared to non-attached regions of the ventral cell membrane (Geiger *et al.* 1982). Measurements of the extent of fluorescence recovery and the rate of diffusion of the different components indicated that both lipids and proteins moved through focal contacts at a reduced speed. Moreover, a significant proportion of the labelled proteins was essentially immobilized in the contact areas. These findings suggested that focal contacts are unique membrane domains in which many of the proteins are anchored, probably due to their interactions with the substratum, the cytoskeleton or both. Yet they are apparently not 'diffusion barriers', and thus components that are not immobilized can diffuse through them.

Another set of studies was directed towards the characterization of the dynamics of vinculin, α-actinin and actin. These studies involved fluorescent labelling of the respective proteins, their microinjection into living cells and FPR analysis of their

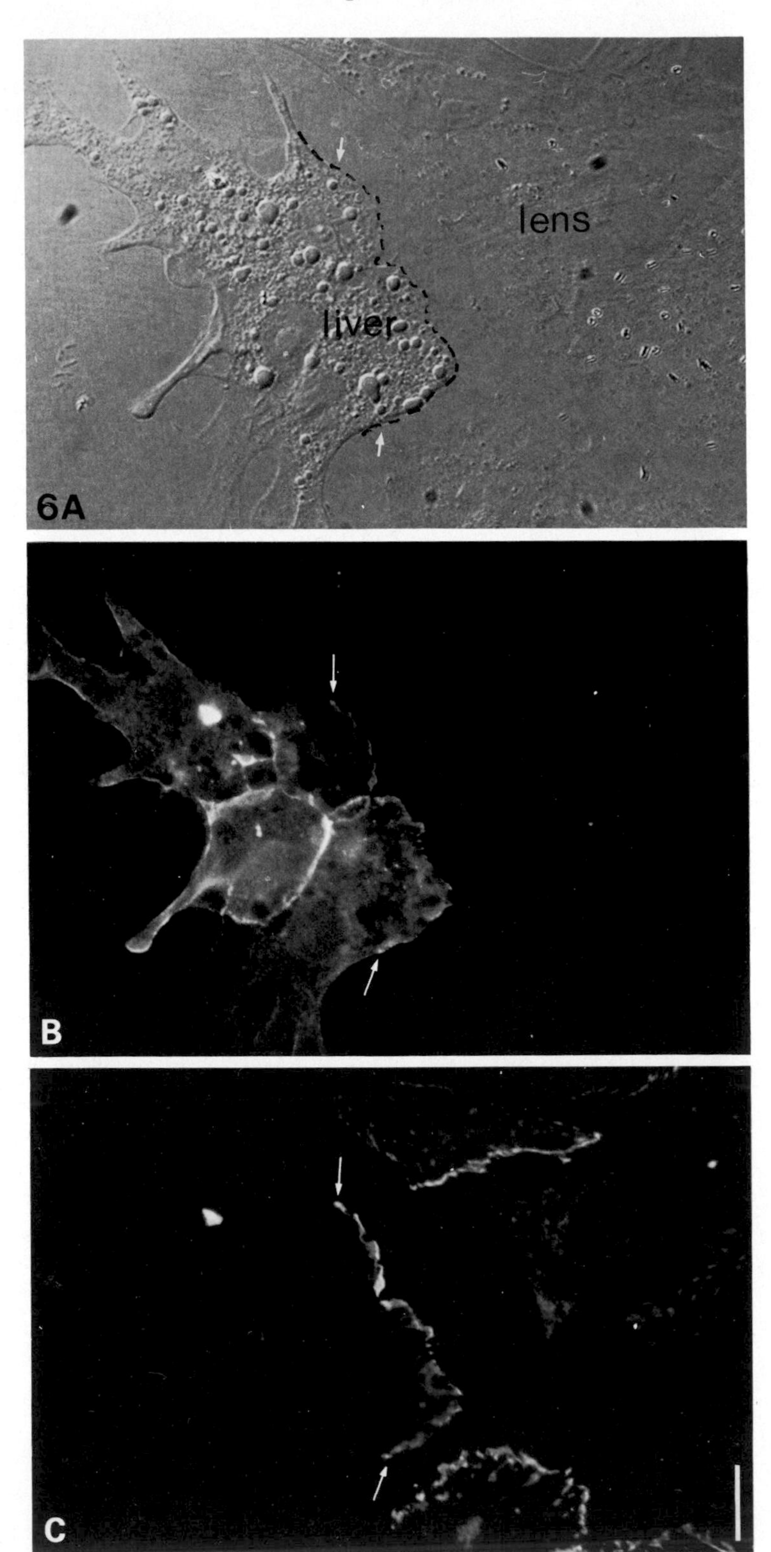
lens
liver
6A
B
C

behaviour in areas containing focal contacts (for details, see Kreis *et al.* 1982, 1984). The FPR measurements indicated that the three proteins were present both in a soluble (diffusible) cytoplasmic pool and in an anchored form. It was, however, evident that the two pools maintained a continuous exchange of components between them. The half-life of this exchange was in the range of 2–5 min. On the basis of the various FPR experiments we have proposed that focal contacts, and probably other adherens-type junctions are dynamic structures that maintain a continuous exchange with their extrajunctional pools. Controlled shifts in this equilibrium in one direction or the other may lead to an enlargement of the junction or to its diminution. Such control mechanism, the nature of which is unclear at present, could coordinate contact formation both spatially and temporally.

Some suggestions as to the possible involvement of microtubules in the coordination of focal contact formation emerged from recent studies carried out in collaboration with G. Rinnerthaller and V. Small (Small *et al.* 1985; Small & Rinnerthaler, 1985; Geiger *et al.* 1984*a*). These studies involved time-lapse cinematographic recording of motile cells followed by triple fluorescent labelling for actin, vinculin and tubulin. The results pointed to a most remarkable coincidence of apparently free-end microtubules with the nascent focal contacts. The sequence of events that occurs during focal contact formation in motile cultured cells involves local ruffling, extension of microtubule(s) into that area and the initiation of vinculin organization in the nascent ventral contact. The functional inter-relationships between these events are not clear to us at present; we do not know the mechanism directing these peripheral microtubules into the leading edge, or in what way this process affects ruffling and focal contact formation or *vice versa*. One possibility is that the focal contact-related microtubules stabilize this region and thus promote its assembly. It should be mentioned, that in contrast to our view on the contact-dependent assembly of membrane-bound vinculin, other investigators have proposed that actin and vinculin may become organized prior to the establishment of focal contacts and possibly define the site for their formation (e.g. see Izzard *et al.* 1985). However, regardless of some ambiguities, it seems now clear that the formation of focal contacts is at least partially controlled by a complex central coordinating system. The observed behaviour of microtubules may be a part of this system, the rest of which is yet to be discovered.

A-CAM: RECEPTOR OF INTERCELLULAR ADHERENS-TYPE JUNCTIONS

In a previous section we briefly mentioned A-CAM as a specific membrane-associated junctional receptor present in intercellular contacts of the adherens type. As pointed out above, such molecules are apparently most important both for

Fig. 6. The formation of heterotypic lens–liver intercellular junctions and the distributions of L-CAM (B) and A-CAM (C) in these cultures. Note that the liver cells (identified on the Nomarsky micrograph in A) are intensely labelled with L-CAM-specific antibodies, while the lens cells are selectively labelled with anti-A-CAM only. However, in the interphase between the lens and liver colonies, heterotypic junctions are formed (area between the arrows) containing both CAMs. Bar, 10 μm.

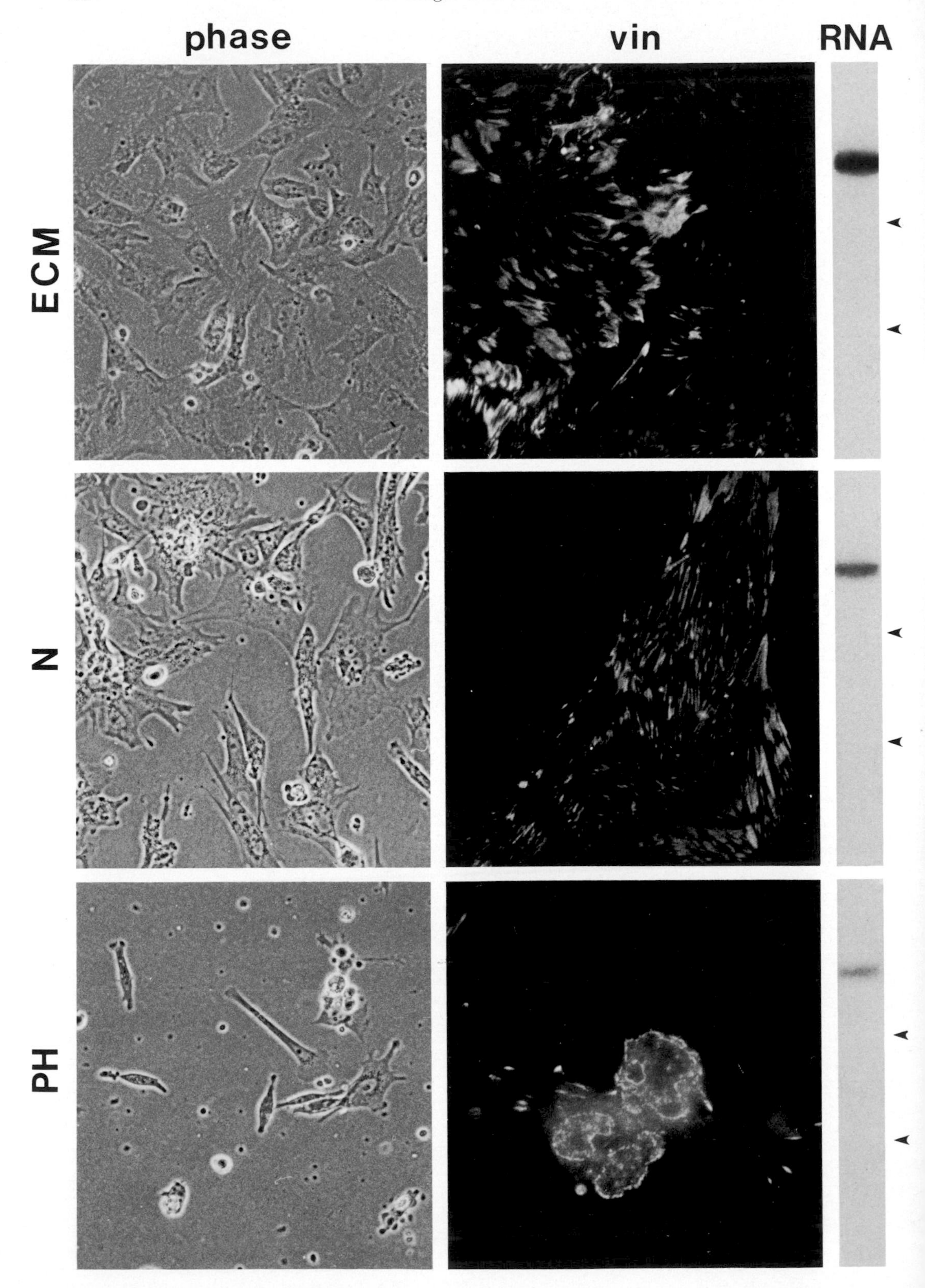
phase
vin
RNA
ECM
N
PH

cell–cell adhesion in general and for the induction of the transmembrane interactions typical of these junctions.

The experimental strategy that we adopted in our attempts to identify the junctional receptor was based on the immunization of mice with junctional membrane proteins (from cardiac muscle intercalated discs), the preparation of hybridomas and the selection of clones secreting junction-reactive antibodies. This approach resulted in the identification of a new $135\times10^3 M_r$ protein, which was abundant in cardiac muscle and lens (Volk & Geiger, 1984) as well as in many embryonic epithelia (Duband *et al.* unpublished results).

Immunocytochemical localization of this 135K ($K = 10^3 M_r$) protein (which was later named A-CAM) in cells and tissues pointed to its close spatial relationships to vinculin and actin (Fig. 5). Yet immunoelectron microscopic labelling of ultrathin frozen sections indicated that A-CAM is closely associated with the junctional membrane, unlike vinculin, which was present throughout the junctional plaque (Geiger *et al.* 1985*a*,*b*; Volk & Geiger, 1986*a*). Moreover, we were able to show that the major part of the A-CAM molecule (approx. 100K) was exposed to the junctional cleft. Immunofluorescent labelling of living cells with anti A-CAM showed only very limited labelling, which could be augmented considerably by a short (few seconds) pre-exposure to EGTA (Volk & Geiger, 1984). Further experiments showed that, following chelation of Ca^{2+}, A-CAM in living cells becomes trypsin-sensitive and that a ≈90K fragment of the molecule can be clipped off leaving the antigenic epitope on the cell surface (Volk & Geiger, 1986*a*). Prolonged incubations in DMEM resulted in the appearance of a ≈100K fragment in the medium bearing the same antigenic epitope, indicating that the extracellular moiety of A-CAM has an apparent size of 90–100K (unpublished results).

A most important property of A-CAM (and the justification for its inclusion in the CAM family) resides in its apparent involvement in intercellular interactions. The experimental approach taken in these studies was largely similar to that employed in the past for N-CAM, L-CAM and the various cadherins (Hyafil *et al.* 1980; Yoshida & Takeichi, 1982; Damsky *et al.* 1983; Gallin *et al.* 1983; Takeichi *et al.* 1985), namely the capacity of antibodies to disrupt cell contacts or prevent their formation. To our surprise, intact anti-A-CAM did not disrupt junctions nor did it prevent junction formation, yet the monovalent Fab fragment of anti-A-CAM was very effective in blocking junction formation (Volk & Geiger, 1986*b*). Interestingly, adherens junctions that were formed in the presence of divalent antibodies became

Fig. 7. The effect of substratum adhesiveness on the morphology (phase), vinculin distribution (vin) and specific vinculin mRNA (RNA) in cultured chicken fibroblasts. The cells were plated either on endothelial ECM, regular tissue culture dish (N) or poly(HEMA)-coated dish (PH), and cultured for 2 days. Note that the cells on the ECM are very well-spread, displaying numerous large vinculin-rich focal contacts. The cells on poly(HEMA) remain rounded or spindle-shaped with poor and distorted focal contacts. Northern blot analysis of equal amount of total RNA (10 μg) shows the relative levels of specific vinculin transcripts in cells plated on the three substrata (right-hand column). Comparison of the blots demonstrates the remarkable effects of substratum adhesiveness; cells growing on the ECM having the greatest amounts of vinculin mRNA and those growing on poly(HEMA), the least.

essentially Ca^{2+}-independent, pointing to the possibility that the newly formed junctions are bridged by the antibody itself.

As mentioned earlier, a study of a wide variety of cells and tissues indicated that A-CAM is apparently not the only CAM involved in adherens junction formation. Many mature epithelia contain another Ca^{2+}-dependent cell adhesion molecule, namely L-CAM or uvomorulin (Boller *et al.* 1985; Thiery *et al.* 1984; see also Edelman, 1983, 1985). The expression of either of the two CAMs by cells is apparently related to the state of development and its expression is strictly regulated during embryogenesis.

A common feature of both A-CAM- and L-CAM-mediated interactions is that the two molecules are believed to mediate homotypic interactions, that is interactions between cells of the same origin and stage of differentiation (such as in cardiac myocytes, intestinal epithelium etc.). Moreover, it has been proposed (although on the basis of limited and indirect information) that both A-CAM and L-CAM commonly form homophilic contacts in which each molecule binds to another molecule of the same kind on the other cell's membrane (Edelman, 1985). This view supports the idea that the two CAMs might some-how be involved in tissue sorting during development.

To study A-CAM/L-CAM relationships directly we cultured chicken hepatocytes (expressing only L-CAM) together with lens epithelial cells (expressing only A-CAM) and looked for heterotypic junction formation. These studies indicated that the two cell types, when cultured together, form heterologous junctions with submembranous vinculin and actin. These junctions, contain L-CAM on the surface of the liver cell partner and A-CAM on the lens cell partner (see Fig. 6). These observations were corroborated by electron microscopy and by several additional important observation from control experiments, such as the capacity of both anti-L-CAM and anti-A-CAM to block the formation of lens–liver mixed junctions. It should be pointed out that these heterotypic junctions provide us with some insight into the molecular relationship between the two molecules. In view of the apparent non-discriminatory binding specificities of these two molecules in heterotypic junctions, and the putative homophilic interactions in the homotypic junctions, it seems likely that A-CAM and L-CAM bear some structural homology. This idea will hopefully be directly examined once detailed information on the molecular properties of the two CAMs is available.

REGULATION OF VINCULIN SYNTHESIS IN CELLS: STUDIES AT THE PROTEIN AND mRNA LEVELS

Many of the observations, made over the last few years indicate that the organization of vinculin can be altered when cultured cells are exposed to various different environmental conditions (Geiger *et al.* 1985*a*). Some of these alterations could be attributed to variations in the adhesiveness of external surfaces, which are expected to alter the rate of contact formation and determine its morphology. Recently we have shown, in collaboration with A. Ben-zeev and F. Ungar (Ungar *et al.* 1986), that the expression of vinculin in cultured cells is affected by the state and extent of their cellular contacts. Thus, sparsely plated fibroblasts express significantly less vinculin than cells plated at near confluent densities. Moreover, plating of cells on poly(HEMA), which is a poorly adhesive substratum, further decrease the rate of vinculin synthesis. Comparison between the two extreme conditions (namely cells on poly(HEMA) and densely plated cells on a normal substratum) indicated that the differences in vinculin expression may be by a factor of up to 20.

We realized, however, that any further progress towards understanding the contact-dependent control of vinculin expression required a study at the genetic level. In fact, many of the studies of the molecular properties of vinculin, its various isoforms and different cellular interactions were hampered by limited information regarding its detailed structure. We have therefore set out to clone the vinculin gene. We started by screening a chicken embryo fibroblast cDNA expression library in phage λgt11 (kindly supplied by Richard Hynes from MIT) using vinculin-specific antibodies (Huynh *et al.* 1986). Four independent clones were identified, ranging in size from $3{\cdot}0$ to $5{\cdot}0\times10^3$ base-pairs. The authenticity of these putative vinculin clones was verified by several independent assays: the product expressed in the bacterial host was immunoreactive not only with the serum used for the primary screening but also with polyclonal affinity-purified antibodies as well as five independent monoclonal antibodies. Southern blot analysis (Southern, 1975) showed that all the isolated clones reacted with similar, though not identical, patterns of restriction fragments obtained after digestion of chicken spleen DNA with various enzymes. Further identification of these cDNA clones was obtained by hybrid selection (Ricciardi *et al.* 1976) of total cellular chicken fibroblast RNA and its *in vitro* translation. The results indicated that the selected mRNA was translated into a polypeptide of 130K, which comigrates with purified chicken vinculin. Northern blot analysis of total RNA (or polyA$^+$RNA) from various chicken sources revealed a single transcript of about 6·5 kb (considerably larger than apparently required to code for a 130K protein).

The availability of these vinculin-specific cDNA probes enabled us to quantify the vinculin-specific mRNA in cells growing under different environmental conditions. Studying the effects of substratum adhesiveness on vinculin expression, we used normal Falcon tissue culture dishes, substrata coated with extracellular matrix (ECM) from bovine corneal endothelial cells (obtained from I. Vlodavsky, of the Hebrew University in Jerusalem), and plates coated with poly(HEMA) as described by Folkman & Moscona (1978). Comparison of the vinculin-staining patterns revealed marked differences between the substrata. There was a far larger focal contact area in the ECM-attached cells as compared to the normal cultures. The cells attached to the poly(HEMA) were mostly rounded or spindle-shaped and displayed few and distorted vinculin containing focal contacts (Fig. 7). Comparison of the relative contents of vinculin transcripts indicated that cells growing on the ECM, normal dishes and poly(HEMA) contained specific mRNA in ratios of 3:1:0·5, respectively.

The results obtained on the regulation of vinculin expression at the protein and mRNA levels, despite their preliminary nature, indicate that there is some feedback mechanism that is affected by cell contact formation and is capable of regulating vinculin synthesis. The mechanism of such a regulatory system and the way in which cell contacts may control gene expression are extremely interesting, important and totally unknown. In view of the interplay between the membrane-bound and cytoplasmic 'soluble' vinculin (Geiger, 1982; Kreis *et al.* 1984, and see above), one may speculate that this soluble vinculin may somehow inhibit the expression of its own gene but that the establishment of cell contacts depletes vinculin from this 'inhibitory' soluble pool, leading to an increase in its expression. Though we have, no direct evidence to support this hypothesis, it should be mentioned that similar mechanism has been shown to operate in the regulation of tubulin expression. Here, soluble, unassembled tubulin was found to specifically regulate the level of tubulin mRNA (Ben-Ze'ev *et al.* 1979; Cleveland *et al.* 1981). We may further speculate that if indeed cytoplasmic vinculin controls its own gene expression it might also regulate the expression of other proteins related to anchorage dependence.

We acknowledge with much gratitude the superb help we obtained from H. Sabanai with electron microscopic studies, from D. Salomon with the preparation of vinculin-specific cDNA clones, and from E. Gross with the typing of this article. Different phases of the study described here were supported by research grants from the Muscular Dystrophy Association, The Weizmann-Rockefeller Foundation, and the Erna Rotstein Foundations. R.B. is a fellow of the Israel Cancer Research Fund. B.G. is an Erwin Neter Professor in Cell and Tumor Biology.

REFERENCES

ABERCROMBIE, M. (1970). Contact inhibition in tissue culture. *In Vitro* **6**, 128–142.

ABERCROMBIE, M. & DUNN, G. A. (1975). Adhesions of fibroblasts to substratum during contact inhibition observed by interference reflection microscopy. *Expl Cell Res.* **92**, 57–62.

ABERCROMBIE, M. J., HEAYSMAN, J. E. M. & PEGRUM, S. M. (1971). The locomotion of fibroblasts in culture. IV. Electron microscopy of the leading lamella. *Expl Cell Res.* **67**, 359–367.

AVNUR, A. & GEIGER, B. (1981). The removal of extracellular fibronectin from areas of cell–substrate contract. *Cell* **25**, 121–132.

AVNUR, Z., SMALL, J. V. & GEIGER, B. (1983). Actin-independent association of vinculin with the cytoplasmic aspect of the plasma membrane in cell contact areas. *J. Cell Biol.* **96**, 1622–1630.

AXELROD, D., KOPPEL, D. E., SCHLESSINGER, J., ELSON, E. L. & WEBB, W. W. (1976). Mobility measurement by analysis of fluorescence photobleaching recovery kinetics. *Biophys. J.* **16**, 1055–1069.

BEN-ZE'EV, A., FARMER, S. R. & PENMAN, S. (1979). Mechanisms of regulating tubulin synthesis in cultured mammalian cells. *Cell* **17**, 319–327.

BEN-ZE'EV, A., FARMER, S. R. & PENMAN, S. (1980). Protein synthesis requires cell-surface contact while nuclear events respond to cell-shape in anchorage dependent fibroblasts. *Cell* **21**, 365–372.

BIRCHMEIER, C., KREIS, T. E., EPPENBERGER, H. M., WINTERHALTER, K. H. & BIRCHMEIER, W. (1980). Corrugated attachment membrane in WI-38 fibroblasts: Altering fibronectin fibers and actin-containing focal contacts. *Proc. natn. Acad. Sci. U.S.A.* **77**(7), 4108–4112.

BLOCH, R. J. & GEIGER, B. (1980). The localization of acetylcholine receptor clusters in areas of cell–substrate contact in cultures of rat myotubes. *Cell* **21**, 25–35.

BLOCH, R. J. & HALL, Z. W. (1983). Cytoskeletal components of the vertebrate neuromuscular junction. *J. Cell Biol.* **97**, 217–223.

BOLLER, K., VESTWEBER, D. & KEMLER, R. (1985). Cell adhesion molecule uvomorulin is localized in the intermediate junctions of adult intestinal epithelial cells. *J. Cell Biol.* **100**, 327–332.

BUCK, C. A. & HORWITZ, A. F. (1987). Integrin, a transmembrane glycoprotein complex mediating cell–substratum adhesion. *J. Cell Sci. Suppl. 8*, 231–250.

BURRIDGE, K. & CONNELL, L. (1983*a*). A new protein of adhesion plaques and ruffling membranes. *J. Cell Biol.* **97**, 359–367.

BURRIDGE, K. & CONNELL, L. (1983*b*). Talin: a cytoskeletal component concentrated in adhesion plaques and other sites of actin membrane interaction. *Cell Motil.* **3**, 405–417.

BURRIDGE, K., MOLONY, L. & KELLY, T. (1987). Adhesion plaques: sites of transmembrane interaction between the extracellular matrix and the actin cytoskeleton. *J. Cell Sci. Suppl. 8*, 211–229.

BURRIDGE, K. & MANGEAT, P. (1984). An interaction between vinculin and talin. *Nature, Lond.* **308**, 744–745.

CHEN, W.-T. (1981*a*). Surface changes during retraction-induced spreading of fibroblasts. *J. Cell Sci.* **49**, 1–13.

CHEN, W.-T. (1981*b*). Mechanism of retraction of the trailing edge during fibroblast movement. *J. Cell Biol.* **90**, 187–200.

CHEN, W.-T. & SINGER, S. J. (1980). Fibronectin is not present in the focal adhesions formed between normal cultured fibroblasts and their substrate. *Proc. natn. Acad. Sci. U.S.A.* **72**, 1132–1136.

CHEN, W.-T. & SINGER, S. J. (1982). Immunoelectron microscopic studies of the sites of cell–substratum and cell–cell contacts in cultured fibroblasts. *J. Cell Biol.* **95**, 205–222.

CLEVELAND, D. W., LOPATA, M. A., SHERLINE, P., & KIRSCHNER, M. W. (1981). Unpolymerized tubulin modulates the level of tubulin mRNA. *Cell* **25**, 537–547.

COUCHMAN, J. R., BADLEY, R. A. & REES, D. A. (1983). Redistribution of microfilament associated proteins during the formation of focal contacts and adhesions in chick fibroblasts. *J. Muscle Res. Cell Motil.* **4**, 647–661.

COWIN, P., KAPPRELL, H.-P., FRANKE, W. W., TAMBUN, J. & HYNES, R. O. (1986). Plakoglobin: a protein common to different kinds of intercellular adhering junctions. *Cell* **46**, 1063–1073.

CRAIG, S. W. (1985). Alpha-actinin, an F-actin cross linking protein, interacts directly with vinculin and metavinculin. *J. Cell Biol.* **101**, 136a.

DAMSKY, C. H., KNUDSEN, K. A., BRADLY, D., BUCK, C. A. & HORWITZ, A. T. (1985). Distribution of the cell–substratum attachment (CSAT) antigen on myogenic and fibroblastic cells in culture. *J. Cell Biol.* **100**, 1528–1539.

DAMSKY, C. H., RICHA, J., SOLTER, D., KNUDSEN, K. & BUCK, C. A. (1983). Identification and purification of a cell surface glycoprotein mediating intercellular adhesion in embryonic and adult tissue. *Cell* **34**, 455–466.

EDELMAN, G. M. (1983). Cell adhesion molecules. *Science* **219**, 450–457.

EDELMAN, G. M. (1985). Specific cell adhesion in histogenesis and morphogenesis. In *The Cell in Contact* (ed. G. M. Edelman & J. P. Thiery), pp. 139–168. NY: John Wiley and Sons.

EVANS, R. R., ROBSON, R. M. & STROMER, M. H. (1984). Properties of smooth muscle vinculin. *J. biol. Chem.* **259**, 3916–3924.

FARQUHAR, M. G. & PALADE, G. E. (1963). Junctional complexes in various epithelia. *J. Cell Biol.* **17**, 375–409.

FOLKMAN, J. & MOSCONA, A. (1978). Role of cell shape in growth control. *Nature, Lond.* **273**, 345–349.

GALLIN, W. J., EDELMAN, G. M. & CUNNINGHAM, B. A. (1983). Characterization of L-CAM, a major cell adhesion molecule from embryonic liver cells. *Proc. natn. Acad. Sci. U.S.A.* **80**, 1038–1042.

GEIGER, B. (1979). A 130-K protein from chicken gizzard: Its localization at the termini of microfilament bundles in cultured chicken cells. *Cell* **18**, 193–205.

GEIGER, B. (1981). Transmembrane linkage and cell attachment: the role of vinculin. In *International Cell Biology 1980–1981* (ed. H. G. Schweiger). Heidelberg: Springer-Verlag.

GEIGER, B. (1982). Involvement of vinculin in contact-induced cytoskeletal interaction. *Cold Spring Harbor Symp. quant. Biol.* **46**, 671–682.

GEIGER, B. (1983). Membrane–cytoskeleton interaction. *Biochim. biophys. Acta* **737**, 305–341.

GEIGER, B., AVNUR, Z., KREIS, T. T. & SCHLESSINGER, J. (1984*b*). The dynamics of cytoskeletal organization in areas of cell contact. In *Cell and Muscle Motility*, vol. 5 (ed. J. W. Shay), pp. 195–234. New York: Plenum.

GEIGER, B., AVNUR, Z., RINNERTHALER, G., HINSSEN, H. & SMALL, V. J. (1984*a*). Microfilament organizing centers in areas of cell contact: Cytoskeletal interactions during cell attachment and locomotion. *J. Cell Biol.* **99**, 83s–91s.

GEIGER, B., AVNUR, Z. & SCHLESSINGER, J. (1982). Restricted mobility of membrane constituents in cell–substrate focal contacts of chicken fibroblasts. *J. Cell Biol.* **93**, 495–500.

GEIGER, B., AVNUR, Z., VOLBERG, T. & VOLK, T. (1985*b*). Molecular domains of adherens junction. In *The Cell in Contact: Adhesions and Junctions as Morphogenetic Determinants* (ed. G. M. Edelman & J. P. Thiery), pp. 461–469. New York: John Wiley and Sons.

GEIGER, B., DUTTON, A. H., TOKUYASU, K. T. & SINGER, S. J. (1981). Immunoelectron microscope studies of membrane–microfilament interactions: Distributions of α-actinin, tropomyosin and vinculin in intestinal epithelial brush border and chicken gizzard smooth muscle cells. *J. Cell Biol.* **91**, 614–628.

GEIGER, B., SCHMID, E. & FRANKE, W. W. (1983). Spatial distribution of proteins specific for desmosomes and adherens junction in epithelial cells demonstrated by double immunofluorescence microscopy. *Differentiation* **23**, 189–205.

GEIGER, B., VOLK, T. & VOLBERG, T. (1985*a*). Molecular heterogeneity of adherens junctions. *J. Cell Biol.* **101**, 1523–1531.

GOSPODAROWICZ, D., GREENBURG, G. & BIRDWELL, C. R. (1978). Determination of a cellular shape by the extracellular matrix and its correlation with the control of cellular growth. *Cancer Res.* **38**, 4155–4171.

GRINNELL, F. (1987). Focal adhesion sites and the removal of substratum-bound fibronectin. *J. Cell Biol.* **103**, 2697–2706.

HEATH, J. P. & DUNN, G. A. (1978). Cell-to-substratum contact of chick fibroblasts and their relation to the microfilament system: A correlated interference reflexion and high voltage electron microscopy study. *J. Cell Sci.* **29**, 197–212.

HEAYSMAN, J. M. & PEGRUM, S. M. (1973). Early contacts between fibroblasts. *Expl Cell Res.* **78**, 71–78.

HEAYSMAN, J. M. & PEGRUM, S. M. (1982). Early cell contacts in culture. In *Cell Behavior* (ed. R.Bellairs, A. Curtis & G. Dunn), pp. 49–76. Cambridge University Press.

HORWITZ, A., DUGGAN, K., BUCK, C., BECKERLE, M. C. & BURRIDGE, K. (1986). Interaction of plasma membrane fibronectin receptor with talin, a transmembrane linkage. *Nature, Lond.* **320**, 531–533.

HORWITZ, A., DUGGAN, K., GREGGS, R., DECKER, C. & BUCK, C. (1985). The cell–substrate attachment (CSAT) antigen has properties of a receptor for laminin and fibronectin. *J. Cell Biol.* **101**, 2134–2144.

HUYNH, T. V., YOUNG, R. A. & DAVIS, R. W. (1986). Constructing and screening of DNA Libraries in λgt10 and λgt11. In *DNA Cloning Techniques. A Practical Approach* (ed. D. Clover), pp. 49–78. Oxford: IRL Press.

HYAFIL, F., MORELLO, D., BABINET, C. & JACOB, F. (1980). A cell surface glyoprotein involved in the compaction of embryonal carcinoma cells and cleavage stage embryos. *Cell* **21**, 927–934.

HYNES, R. O., DESTREE, A. T. & WAGNER, D. D. (1982). Relationships between microfilaments, cell–substratum adhesion and fibronectin. *Cold Spring Harbor Symp. quant. Biol.* **46**, 659–670.

IZZARD, C. S. & LOCHNER, L. R. (1976). Cell to substrate contacts in living fibroblasts: An interference reflexion study with an evaluation of the technique. *J. Cell Sci.* **21**, 129–159.

IZZARD, C. S. & LOCHNER, L. R. (1980). Formation of cell-to-substrate contacts during fibroblasts motility: An interference reflexion study. *J. Cell Sci.* **42**, 81–116.

IZZARD, C. S., IZZARD, S. L. & DEPASQUALE, A. (1985). Molecular basis of cell–substrate adhesions. In *Motility of Vertebrate Cells in Culture and in the Organism* (ed. G. Haemmerli & P. Strauli), pp. 1–22. Basel: S. Karger.

JOCKUSCH, B. M. & ISENBERG, G. (1981). Interaction of α-actinin and vinculin with actin: Opposite effects on filament network formation. *Proc. natn. Acad. Sci. U.S.A.* **78**, 3005–3009.

JOCKUSCH, B. M. & ISENBERG, G. (1982). Vinculin and α-actinin: Interaction with actin and effect on microfilament network formation. *Cold Spring Harbor Symp. quant. Biol.* **46**, 613–623.

KREIS, T. E., AVNUR, Z., SCHLESSINGER, J. & GEIGER, B. (1984). In *Molecular Biology of the Cytoskeleton* (ed. G. Borisy, D. Cleveland & D. Murphy), pp. 45–57. Cold Spring Harbor, NY: Cold Spring Harbor Laboratory Press.

KREIS, T. E., GEIGER, B. & SCHLESSINGER, J. (1982). Mobility of microinjected rhodamine actin within living chicken gizzard cells determined by fluorescence photobleaching recovery. *Cell* **29**, 835–845.

LIN, S., WILKINS, J. A., CRIBBS, D. H., GRUMET, M. & LIN, D. C. (1982). Proteins and complexes that affect actin-filament assembly and interactions. *Cold Spring Harbor Symp. quant. Biol.* **46**, 625–632.

O'HALLORAN, T., BECKERLE, M. C. & BURRIDGE, K. (1985). Identification of talin as a major cytoplasmic protein implicated in platelet activation. *Nature, Lond.* **317**, 449–451.

OTTO, J. (1983). Detection of vinculin-binding proteins with an ^{125}I-vinculin overlay technique. *J. Cell Biol.* **97**, 1283–1287.

RICCIARDI, R. P., MILLER, J. S. & ROBERS, B. E. (1976). Purification and mapping of specific mRNA by hybridization selection and cell free translation. *Proc. natn. Acad. Sci. U.S.A.* **76**, 4927–4931.

SCHROER, E. & WEGNER, A. (1985). Purification and localization of a protein from chicken gizzard, which inhibits actin polymerization. *Eur. J. Biochem.* **153**, 515–520.

SEGEL, L. A., VOLK, T. & GEIGER, B. (1983). On spatial periodicity in the formation of cell adhesions to a substrate. *Cell Biophys.* **5**, 95–104.

SINGER, I. I. & PARADISO, P. R. (1981). A transmembrane relationship between fibronectin and vinculin (130 Kd protein) serum modulation in normal and transformed hamster fibroblasts. *Cell* **24**, 481–492.

SMALL, J. V. (1985). The geometry of actin–membrane attachments in the smooth muscle cell: The localization of vinculin and α-actinin. *EMBO J.* **4**, 45–49.

SMALL, J. V. & RINNERTHALER, G. (1985). Cytostructural dynamics of contact formation during fibroblasts locomotion *in vitro*. In *Motility of Vertebrate Cells in Culture and in the Organism* (ed. G. Haemmerli & P. Strauli), pp. 54–68. Basel: S. Karger.

SMALL, J. V., RINNERTHALER, G., AVNUR, Z. & GEIGER, B. (1985). Cytoarchitectural changes associated with fibroblast locomotion: involvement of ruffling and microtubules in the establishment of new substrate contacts at the leading edge. In *Proc. 1st Int. Congr. Contractile Proteins*, pp. 363–381. Sassari: Temple University.

SOUTHERN, E. M. (1975). Detection of specific sequences among DNA fragments separated by gel electrophoresis. *J. molec. Biol.* **98**, 503–517.

STAEHELIN, A. (1974). Structure and function of intercellular junctions. *Int. Rev. Cytol.* **39**, 191–283.

TAKEICHI, M., HATTA, K. & NAGAFUCHI, A. (1985). In *Molecular Determinants of Animal Form* (ed. G. M. Edelman), pp. 223–233. New York: Alan R. Liss.

THIERY, J. P., DELOUVEE, A., GALLIN, W., CUNNINGHAM, B. A. & EDELMAN, G. M. (1984). Ontogenetic expression of cell adhesion molecules: L-CAM is found in epithelia derived from the three primary germ layers. *Devl Biol.* **102**, 61–78.

TOKUYASU, K. T., DUTTON, A. H., GEIGER, B. & SINGER, S. J. (1981). Ultrastructure of chicken cardiac muscle as studied by double immunolabeling in electron microscopy. *Proc. natn. Acad. Sci. U.S.A.* **78**, 7619–7623.

UNGAR, F., GEIGER, B. & BEN-ZE'EV, A. (1986). Cell contact- and shape-dependent regulation of vinculin synthesis in cultured fibroblasts. *Nature, Lond.* **319**, 787–791.

VASILIEV, J. M. & GELFAND, I. M. (eds) (1981). In *Neoplastic and Normal Cells in Culture*. Cambridge University Press.

VOLBERG, T., SABANAY, H. & GEIGER, B. (1986). Spatial and temporal relationships between vinculin and talin in the developing chicken gizzard smooth muscle. *Differentiation* **32**, 34–43.

VOLK, T. & GEIGER, B. (1984). A 135 Kd membrane protein of intercellular adherens junction. *EMBO J.* **3**, 2249–2260.

VOLK, T. & GEIGER, B. (1986*a*). A-CAM: A 135-Kd receptor of intercellular adherens junction. (a) Immunoelectron microscopic localization and biochemical studies. *J. Cell Biol.* **103**, 1441–1450.

VOLK, T. & GEIGER, B. (1986*b*). A-CAM: A 135 Kd receptor of intercellular adherens junction. (b) Antibody mediated modulation of junction formation. *J. Cell Biol.* **103**, 1451–1464.

WILKINS, J. A. & LIN, S. (1982). High-affinity interaction of vinculin with actin filaments *in vitro*. *Cell* **28**, 83–90.

WILKINS, J. A. & LIN, S. (1986). A re-examination of the interaction of vinculin with actin. *J. Cell Biol.* **102**, 1085–1092.

YOSHIDA, C. & TAKEICHI, M. (1982). Teratocarcinoma cell adhesion: identification of a cell surface protein involved in calcium-dependent cell aggregation. *Cell* **28**, 217–224.

J. Cell Sci. Suppl. 8, 273–291 (1987)

ADHESIVE INTERACTIONS AND THE METABOLIC ACTIVITY OF HEPATOCYTES

R. COLIN HUGHES* AND STAMATIS C. STAMATOGLOU
National Institute for Medical Research, The Ridgeway, Mill Hill, London NW7 1AA, UK

SUMMARY

The nature and influence of adhesive interactions of rat hepatocytes with components of the extracellular matrix has been studied in culture. Hepatocytes interact with different kinetics to substrata composed of collagen type IV, laminin or fibronectin and adopt significantly different morphologies. The receptors mediating these various responses appear to be specific, according to the matrix, and in the case of fibronectin are complex, implicating several components of the hepatocyte surface. Collagen type IV maintains a differentiated phenotype more efficiently than fibronectin or laminin as measured by the production of adult hepatocyte markers such as albumin and repression of α-foetoprotein synthesis. Formation of matrix components is also influenced by the substratum: synthesis and secretion of fibronectin or collagen type IV is down-regulated when cells are cultured on the homologous substratum. Hepatocytes cultured *in vitro* secrete components of the coagulation cascade and also mediate fibrinolysis on addition of exogenous plasmin. The results are discussed in relation to the normal phenotype of the mature hepatocyte *in vivo*.

INTRODUCTION

The liver is a very suitable tissue in which to study the relationships between adhesive interactions and metabolic activity. A single cell type, the hepatocyte, constitutes in most mammalian species over 90% of organ mass. Hepatocytes are easily isolated and separated from accessory cells such as endothelial cells, fat cells and macrophages, and they secrete well-characterized plasma proteins. Like other epithelial cells, the hepatocyte *in situ* is structurally and functionally polarized (Fig. 1). Junctional specializations of the lateral domains maintain cell to cell contacts and separate a putative 'apical' surface (canalicular domain) from a 'basal' surface (sinusoidal domain). The protein and glycoprotein composition of these domains is well established (Wisher & Evans, 1975; Bartles *et al.* 1985; Enrich & Gahmberg, 1985). Unlike other epithelia there is no morphologically identifiable basement membrane close to the putative basal surface of the hepatocyte. However, the sinusoids contain typical matrix components that appear to contact the sparse endothelial cells as well as the hepatocytes, and these components are found elsewhere through the tissue, indicating that an extracellular matrix is a structurally important contributor to the tissue mass playing important roles in liver function.

* Author for correspondence.

THE LIVER EXTRACELLULAR MATRIX

Characterization and distribution of the liver matrix have been studied by biochemical and immunolocalization methods (Rojkind & Ponce-Noyola, 1982; Hahn *et al.* 1980; Clement *et al.* 1985; Martinez-Hernandez, 1984). The major collagen types are I, III, IV and V; the matrix glycoproteins fibronectin and laminin, and heparan sulphate proteoglycans are also present. Collagen type I is present in the liver capsule, portal stroma and in contact with the hepatocyte 'basal' surface in the perisinusoidal space at branching or inflexion points indicating a structural role supporting the hepatocyte layer at intra-lobular regions. Interestingly, the hepatocyte is the only cell of ectodermal or endodermal origin interacting with collagen type I in the adult organism. Normally these cells contact a basement membrane based on collagen type IV and are separated from interstitial connective tissue. Collagen type III appears to be present only in stroma in liver and is not in direct contact with the hepatocyte surface. Collagen type IV and laminin are present as expected in ductal, neural and vascular basement membranes, and also as small discrete deposits between hepatocytes and endothelial cells in sinusoids (Fig. 2). This discontinuous distribution, as visualized by electron microscopy (Martinez-Hernandez, 1984), argues against a simple supporting role like that operating in other epithelia in contact with a more typical basement membrane. Perhaps a basement membrane forms transiently during parenchymal development and initially performs a supporting role but is degraded once tissue modelling is accomplished, to facilitate the rapid exchange of plasma metabolites bathing the hepatocyte sinusoidal surface. This

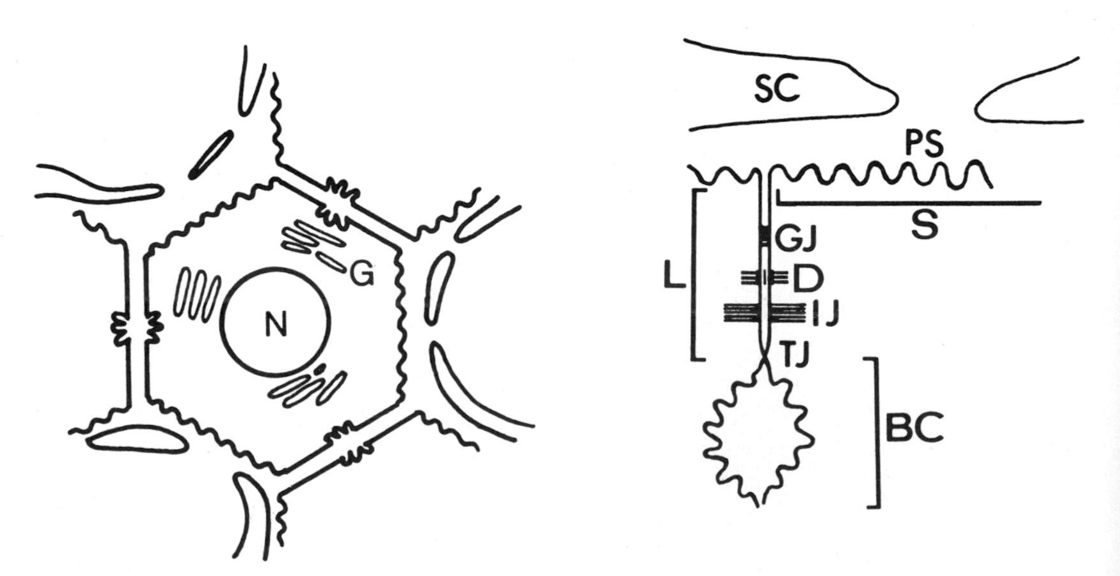

Fig. 1. Surface domains of the hepatocyte. A single hepatocyte is shown in simplified form. N, nucleus; G, Golgi apparatus. The cells contact at lateral (L) domains rich in tight junctions (TJ), intermediate junctions (IJ), desmosomes (D) and gap junctions (GJ). The lateral domains are separated by bile canalicular domains (BC). The sinusoidal domains (S) face sparse sinusoidal cells (SC) and the perisinusoidal space (PS).

possibility may explain both the discontinuous distribution of collagen type IV in the perisinusoidal space and the failure in some studies (Hahn *et al.* 1980; Martinez-Hernandez, 1984) to find laminin at this location. Fibronectin is most prominent in the peri-sinusoidal space where it is in direct contact with hepatocyte microvilli and separated from the endothelial cell surface. Fibronectin is present also in the liver capsule and portal stroma but not in the basement membranes containing collagen type IV and laminin. In our study (Fig. 2) fibronectin is also detected in bile ducts and at lateral surfaces between contacting hepatocytes. Several heparan sulphate proteoglycans have been isolated from liver, one of which has been localized in close proximity to the sinusoidal surface of hepatocytes (Hook *et al.* 1986; Stow *et al.* 1985). This distribution is quite different from that of a basement membrane-type heparan proteoglycan, localized in liver sections by antibodies directed against

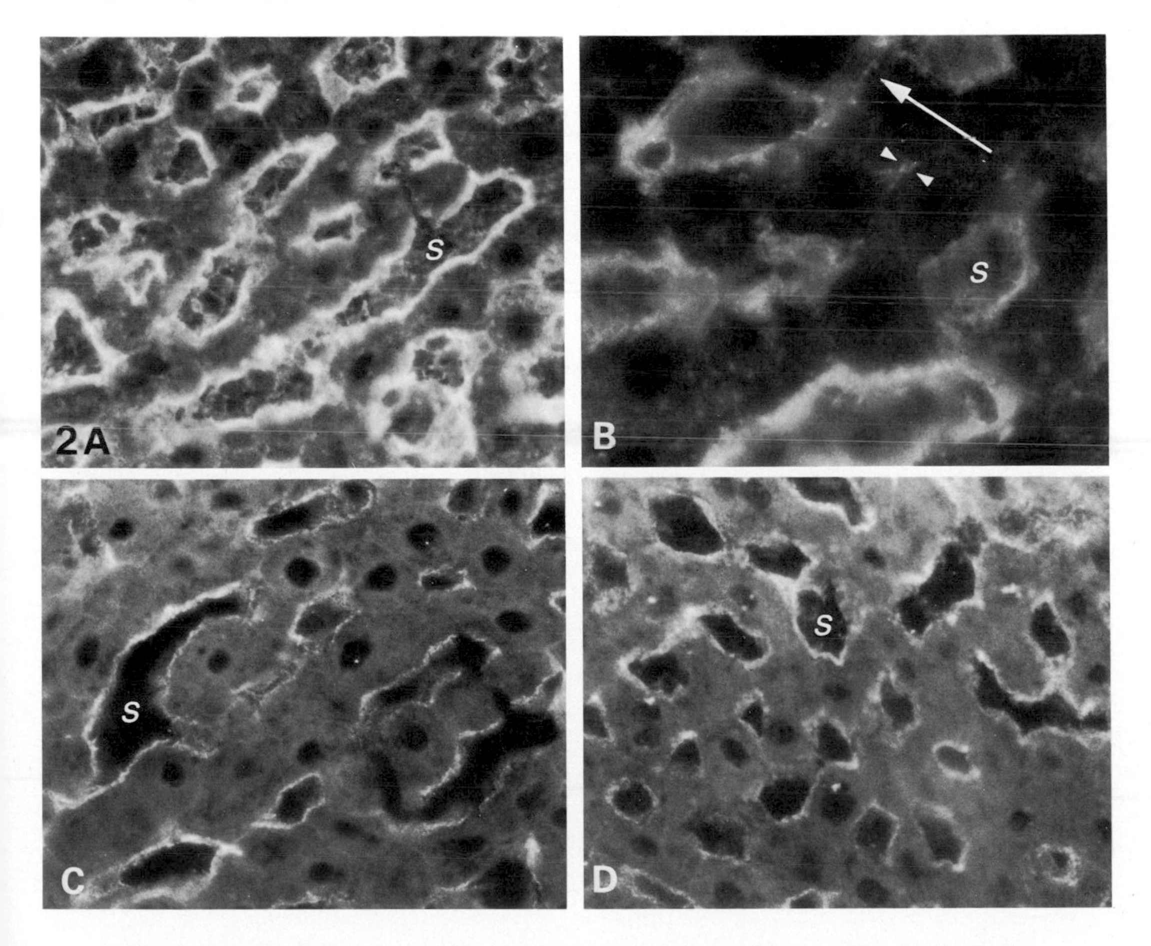

Fig. 2. Immunofluorescent antibody staining of adult rat liver sections. A,B. Anti-fibronectin. All three cell surface domains are stained, including bile ducts (arrowheads) and lateral surfaces (long arrow) shown at higher magnification (B). Some of the staining seen in sinusoidal spaces (*s*) may be due to residual plasma fibronectin, since the liver was not perfused before sectioning and staining. C. Anti-collagen type IV. Staining is confined to sinusoidal spaces; D, anti-laminin. A,C,D, ×500; B, ×800.

kidney glomerulus proteoglycans (see Discussion by M. G. Farquhar: Höök *et al.* 1986).

Taken together these results indicate a close interaction of the hepatocyte surface with several matrix components including collagens I and IV, fibronectin and laminin. There is no convincing evidence that any of these components play a purely structural role except possibly transiently during development of the tissue. Other roles involving regulation of hepatocyte metabolism are therefore intriguing possibilities.

ADHESIVE RESPONSE OF HEPATOCYTES TO EXTRACELLULAR MATRIX COMPONENTS

When liver is disaggregated and the hepatocytes plated out in serum-containing medium, the cells attach rapidly and spread due to the presence of serum-spreading factors. Similar behaviour is obtained in serum-free conditions using surfaces coated with adhesive proteins (Rubin *et al.* 1978, 1981; Johansson *et al.* 1981). In either case the cells may then be cultured in serum-free medium for several days, during which the cells form epithelial colonies with intercellular contacts consisting of tight junctions, desmosomes and gap junctions as seen by electron microscopy. The desmosomal junctions, as detected by immunofluorescence using polyclonal antibodies against bovine muzzle desmosomal proteins (a gift from E. Penn, Mill Hill) are shown in Fig. 3A. In spread cells on all substrata the ventral surface is in closest apposition to the substratum at the cell periphery as shown (Nermut *et al.* 1986) by interference reflection microscopy and electron microscopy. Actin is assembled in a peripheral ring, possibly at the level of the substratum and also associated with zonula adherens junctions (Fig. 3B). In addition to intercellular junctions, structures reminiscent of hemidesmosomes have also been observed in cell–substratum contacts (Fig. 4B) and other features morphologically similar to structures seen *in vivo* appear after culture for 2–3 days, including bile canicular-like domains between cells and in the central portion of the ventral surface (Fig. 4A). These latter spaces seem to fill up with vesicles.

Detailed examination of the requirements for hepatocyte attachment and spreading on a substratum is best carried out using protein-derivatized glass coverslips (Bissell *et al.* 1986). Using this method the concentration of matrix component can be exactly determined and the interacting cells can be easily viewed by light or electron microscopy. Cell attachment is measured 30 min after plating as a function of the density of protein coupled per unit area of glass surface. When the attachment-promoting characteristics of laminin, fibronectin and collagen type IV are compared, the amount of collagen type IV supporting half-maximal attachment ($1\,\mathrm{ng\,cm^{-2}}$) is much lower than the corresponding values (5 and $20\,\mathrm{ng\,cm^{-2}}$) for fibronectin and laminin. Attachment to each matrix levels off at high surface densities compatible with saturation of available binding sites on the cell surface. Following initial attachment, spreading takes place and the cells reach a stable morphology on each matrix after about 2 h (Fig. 5). Initially spreading involves peripherally symmetrical extensions of basal cytoplasmic lamellae followed by flattening of the whole cell that nevertheless retains a circular shape as judged by overhead views. No shape polarization, as seen with fibroblasts, is observed. Hence the extent of spreading can be quantified by measuring the width of the contact area of cells viewed at acute angles. For all three matrix proteins, the extent of spreading is dependent on the density of substratum protein and the matrix density of collagen type IV required to trigger half-maximal spreading (5 ng cm^{-2}) is 1/100th of that using either fibronectin or laminin. The general conclusions of this study are: (1) attachment of hepatocytes

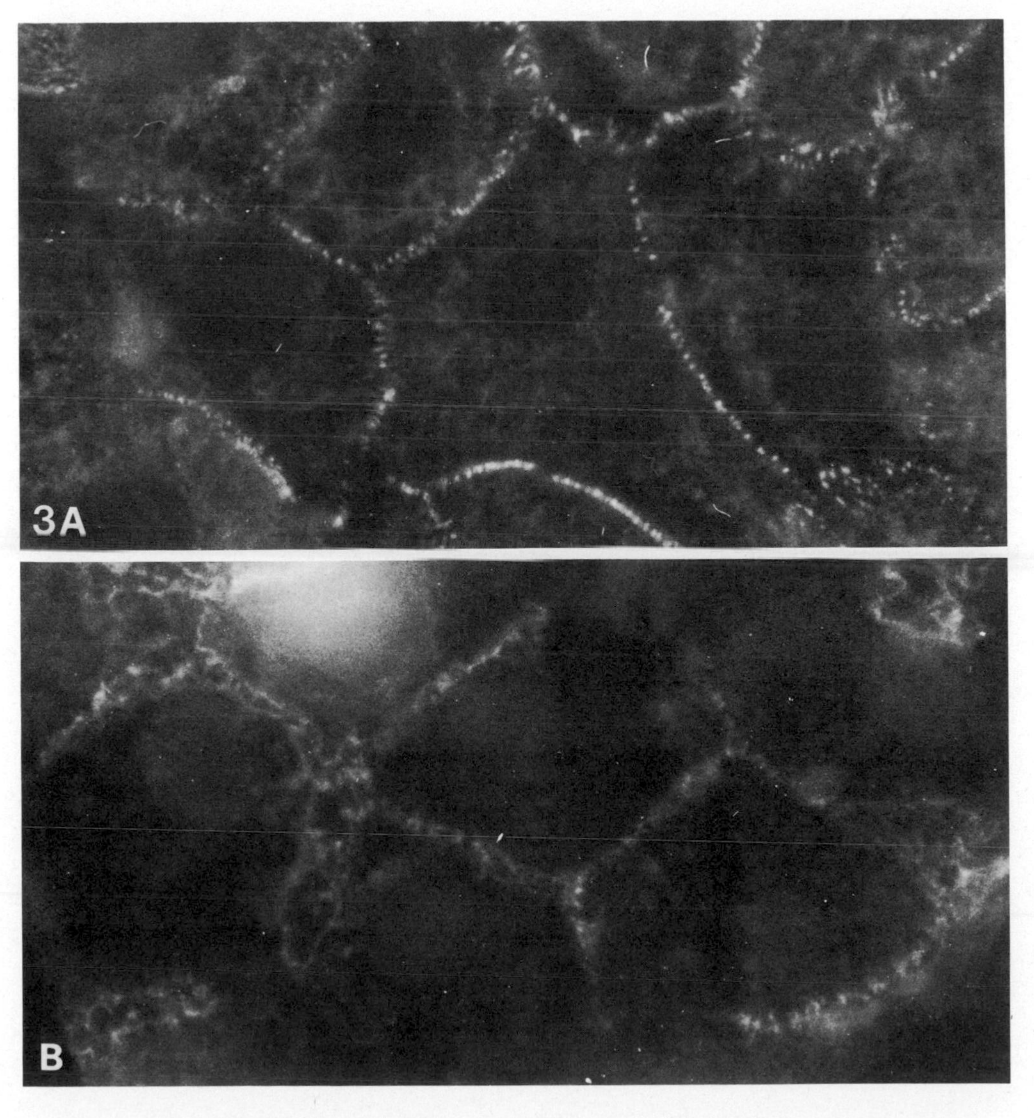

Fig. 3. Desmosomal junctions (A) and actin filaments (B) in adult rat hepatocytes cultured for 30 h on fibronectin substratum. Fixed and permeabilized cells were stained by indirect immunofluorescence with antibodies against desmosomal components (A) or with FITC-phalloidin (B). ×1500.

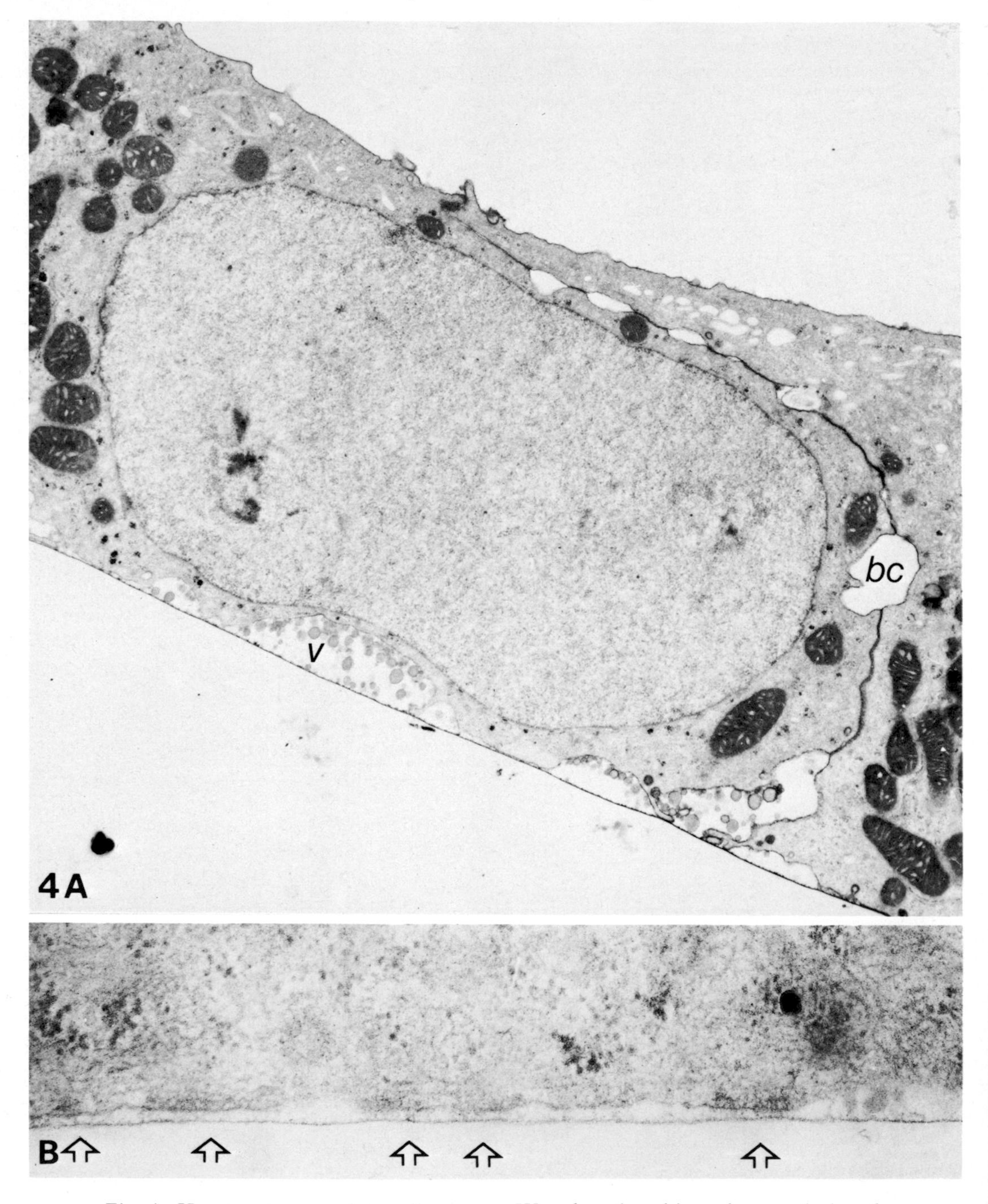

Fig. 4. Hepatocytes spread on collagen type IV and sectioned in a plane vertical to the substratum showing: A, bile canalicular-like structures (*bc*) between cells and spaces between cells and substratum filled with vesicles (*v*); B, specialized cell–substratum contacts (arrows). A, ×9400; B, ×60 000.

to collagen type IV, fibronectin or laminin substrata occurs with distinct kinetics and is saturable; (2) the fact that a 5- to 10-fold greater surface density of each matrix protein is required to trigger maximal spreading than attachment shows that the two

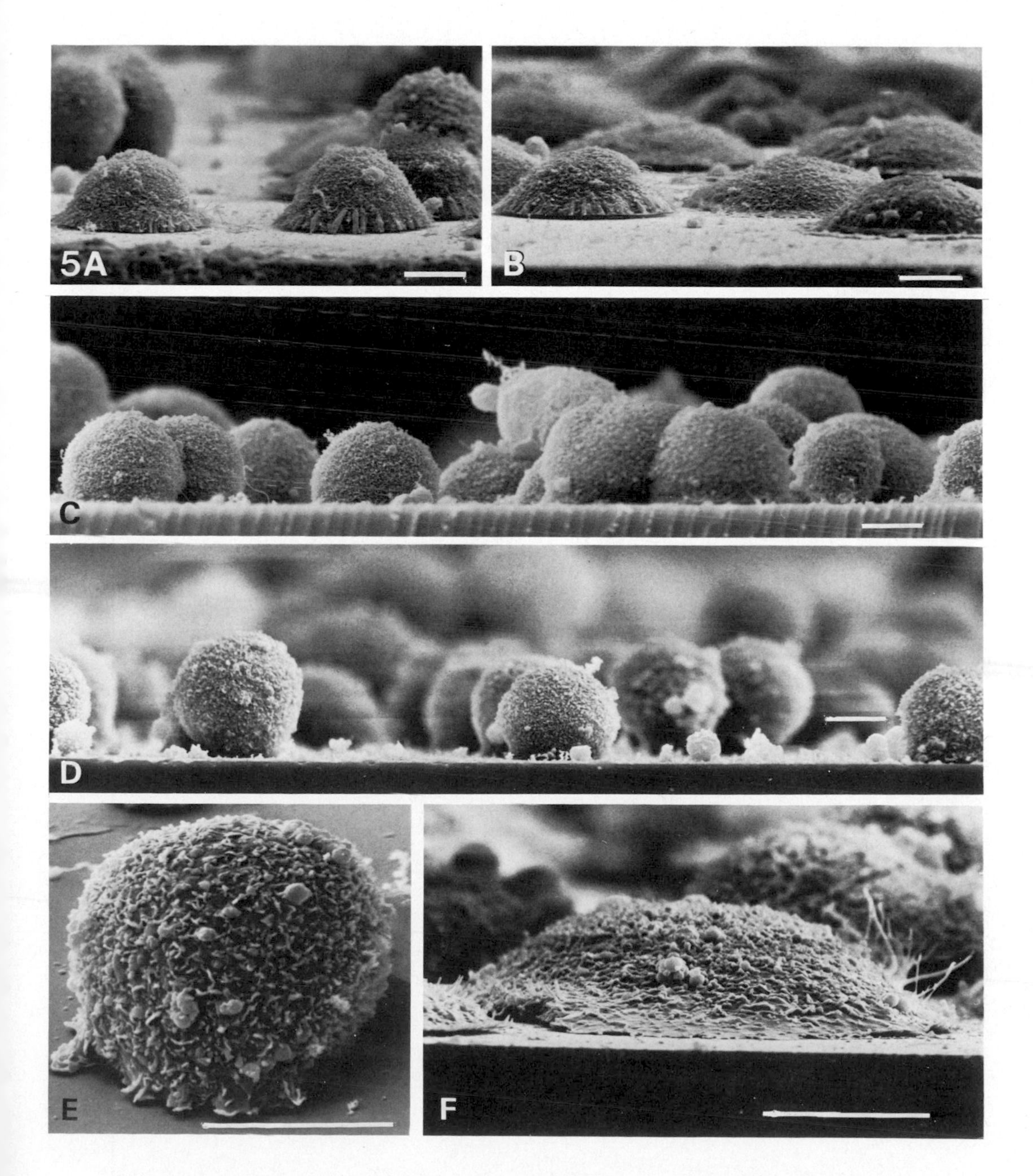

Fig. 5. Scanning electron microscopy of rat adult hepatocytes cultured for 3 h on glass derivatized with: A,B, type IV collagen at 4 and 22 ng cm^{-2}; C, laminin at 32 ng cm^{-2}; D, fibronectin at 23 ng cm^{-2}; E,F, type IV collagen at 0·5 and 110 ng cm^{-2}. Bar, 1 μm.

events are mechanistically different, in agreement with other studies (Johansson & Höök, 1984). Presumably, cell attachment represents simple receptor–ligand kinetics, whereas spreading is more complex, involving the recruitment of surface receptors to the contact area and perhaps linkage to the cytoskeleton; (3) hepatocytes display distinct surface receptors for collagen type IV, fibronectin and laminin.

RECEPTORS AND MATRIX PROTEINS

The idea of specific receptors for each matrix protein agrees with previous studies using antibodies directed against the hepatocyte surface that inhibited adhesion to collagen but not to fibronectin (Rubin *et al.* 1979), and with blocking experiments in which addition of soluble fibronectin inhibited initial cell attachment to fibronectin but not to laminin substrata, presumably through selective competition for fibronectin-binding sites on the cell surface (Johannson, 1985; Johansson *et al.* 1981). Our finding of a high-affinity interaction between hepatocytes and collagen type IV differs from other suggestions for a low-affinity interaction with a peptide determinant common to all collagens. The disparity may be due to the fact that Rubin *et al.* (1981) used collagen fragments or synthetic peptides based on collagen-like sequences, and hence specific high-affinity interactions with intact collagen type IV may have been missed.

Characterization of the surface components involved in these interactions of hepatocytes with various matrix proteins is consistent with the idea of separate receptors. Photoactivation cross-linking experiments using hepatocytes in contact with a laminin substratum indicate a receptor protein of approximately $68\times10^3 M_r$, that is also revealed by blotting with radio-iodinated laminin (Bissell *et al.* 1984). Laminin-binding receptors of similar size have been isolated from other cells (Lesot *et al.* 1983; Malinoff & Wicha, 1983; Rao *et al.* 1983), but the relatedness of these proteins remains to be determined. So far our attempts to isolate larger amounts of a liver laminin receptor by affinity chromatography have not been successful. Affinity chromatography of detergent extracts of isolated hepatocytes on collagen type IV has produced several collagen-binding proteins eluting at low (0·3 M) and high (1·5 M) salt concentrations (T. D. Butters & R. C. Hughes, unpublished). The 0·3 M salt eluate, after re-chromatography on collagen type IV using a salt gradient (0–0·3 M), is fractionated into major components with molecular weights of about 30×10^3 and 75×10^3. The $30\times10^3 M_r$ component shows little specificity for collagen type, since it binds to collagen type I and gelatin and may be related to the molecule(s) mediating the interactions studied by Rubin *et al.* (1981). The 1·5 M salt eluate contains the $75\times10^3 M_r$ component and higher molecular weight (100×10^3) components. The specificity of binding of these higher molecular weight components to various collagen is not yet known.

Examination of the surface components involved in hepatocyte interactions with a fibronectin substratum has revealed an unexpected complexity. In other cells the best-characterized cell surface receptor for fibronectin is a glycoprotein complex consisting of non-equivalent subunits migrating in reduced SDS–polyacrylamide gels, with approximate molecular size of 130–140($\times 10^3$) M_r. The complex has been called integrin in a chick system and analogous factors have been identified in mammalian cells (Tamkun *et al.* 1986). Integrin and related molecules appear to recognize a specific sequence in a type III repeat of the fibronectin subunits (reviewed by Hynes, 1985; and see Buck & Horwitz, this volume). The key peptide sequence is RGD (one-letter code) and using several cell lines it has been shown that peptides such as GRGDS effectively inhibit attachment to fibronectin-coated substrata. Furthermore, substrata composed of bovine serum albumin coupled to RGD-based peptides support the attachment and spreading of some fibroblastic cells (Ruoslahti & Pierschbacher, 1986). Recently, evidence for cellular interactions with fibronectin not involving the RGD sequence has been reported (McCarthy *et al.* 1986; McKeown-Longo & Mosher, 1985; Humphries *et al.* 1986), implicating other fibronectin-binding surface components. Melanoma cells interact with fragments of fibronectin that lack the type III repeat containing the RGD sequence (Humphries *et al.* 1986). Some cell lines that form productive interactions with fibronectin do not express integrin-like molecules but do contain another putative fibronectin receptor of $47\times 10^3 M_r$ (Urushihara & Yamada, 1986), possibly identical to a glycoprotein isolated from BHK fibroblasts by a photoactivation cross-linking procedure (Aplin *et al.* 1981). Cell lines expressing at least two putative receptors (130–140, 45–47($\times 10^3$) M_r) have also been described (Urushihara & Yamada, 1986; Lehto & Virtanen, 1985): whether these receptor systems act synergistically or separately or even have the same function is unknown. The smaller glycoprotein may be related to a 48–50($\times 10^3$) M_r glycoprotein induced, together with fibronectin, by dexamethasone in fibroblastic cells (Raghow *et al.* 1986; McKeown-Longo & Etzler, 1987) and possibly involved in initiation of cell surface assembly of a fibronectin matrix (McKeown-Longo & Etzler, 1987).

In experiments designed to identify fibronectin-binding components of rat hepatocytes we have applied cell extracts to affinity chromatography, on immobilized wheat-germ agglutinin and then we subjected the bound glycoprotein fraction to a fibronectin column. Elution with high salt concentrations has produced a glycoprotein of $110\times 10^3 M_r$ in reducing or non-reducing SDS–polyacrylamide gel electrophoresis. The $110\times 10^3 M_r$ glycoprotein in enzyme-linked assays can be shown to bind with high affinity (K_a 10^{-8} M) to fibronectin but not to laminin or collagen type IV. The binding to fibronectin is calcium-dependent, requiring 1–2 mM concentrations and is not inhibited by GRGDS or related peptides. The $110\times 10^3 M_r$ glycoprotein is at least partly exposed on the cell surface as shown by its labelling by lactoperoxidase-catalysed iodination and distributes into the detergent phase after extraction with Triton X-114, indicating a hydrophobic, membrane-intercalated character. Antibody Fab fragments raised against the $110\times 10^3 M_r$ glycoprotein cause an immediate retraction of hepatocytes spread out on a fibronectin substratum but not on laminin or collagen type IV substrata, nor do the antibodies inhibit initial attachment to fibronectin substrata. Immunoblotting of equal amounts of sinusoidal, canalicular and lateral membrane fractions of rat liver shows a dominant localization of the $110\times10^3 M_r$ glycoprotein in the canalicular-derived plasma membrane fraction. Immunofluorescent staining of liver sections also shows a predominantly canalicular location. As mentioned previously, the canalicular surface of the hepatocyte contacts fibronectin *in vivo*, so the presence of a canalicular membrane component with affinity for fibronectin is not unexpected. However, the bulk of the fibronectin located in liver sections is present in the peri-sinusoidal space. The $110\times10^3 M_r$ glycoprotein may be present in relatively small amounts at this domain but other fibronectin-binding glycoproteins may also be expressed there. Recently, Staffan Johansson of Uppsala University (personal communication) isolated from rat liver an RGD-sensitive fibronectin-binding glycoprotein with properties similar to integrin. It migrates as two bands on SDS–polyacrylamide gel electrophoresis under non-reducing conditions with $M_r\,155\times10^3$ and 115×10^3. After reduction the $155\times10^3 M_r$ band gives polypeptides of 145×10^3 and 20×10^3, while the 115×10^3 band migrates as 130×10^3. Antibodies to the glycoprotein prevent cell attachment to a fibronectin substratum. There is no immunological cross-reaction between this glycoprotein and our $110\times10^3 M_r$ glycoprotein (S. Johansson, personal communication). Hence, adult rat hepatocytes contain at least two fibronectin-binding components that appear to be distinct immunologically.

Several liver plasma membrane glycoproteins of about $110\times10^3 M_r$ have been described. Hanski *et al.* (1985) have implicated dipeptidyl peptidase (DPP IV) in hepatocyte adhesion to collagen mediated by fibronectin: our $110\times10^3 M_r$ glycoprotein is immunologically distinct from DPP IV (W. Reutter, personal communication). Another glycoprotein cell CAM 105 has been isolated by Öbrink and colleagues from rat liver (Odin *et al.* 1986). It is a constituent of canalicular domains and shares some properties with our $110\times10^3 M_r$ glycoprotein. In addition to a similar molecular weight in reducing gels the pI of both glycoproteins is about 4. However, unlike our $110\times10^3 M_r$ glycoprotein, cell CAM 105 runs anomalously in non-reducing gels giving a lower apparent molecular weight and indicating a high cystine content.

The functions of the various fibronectin-binding glycoproteins in hepatocytes is not clear. As described previously, there is no evidence that in adult liver the matrix supports hepatocyte organization in the way a conventional basement membrane interacts with other epithelia. Although, a role for fibronectin and a specific receptor at lateral surface domains in cell–cell contacts cannot be excluded, other roles may be considered. The hepatocyte is a major source of plasma fibronectin (Voss *et al.* 1979; Tamkun & Hynes, 1983) and intracellular transport to the sinusoidal domains might require a specific fibronectin-binding component. Intracellular trafficking in the hepatocyte is known to be highly specific, by which proteins are transported from biosynthetic sites in the endoplasmic reticulum exclusively to the sinusoidal, lateral or canalicular surfaces (Simons & Fuller, 1985). We find fibronectin at all domains suggesting that various intracellular transport routes are utilized for its export, perhaps requiring separate receptor systems. Experiments carried out by Carlos Enrich & Carl Gahmberg (unpublished) have revealed distinct structural differences between the fibronectin components of sinusoidal, lateral and canalicular domains. The sinusoidal component appears similar to plasma fibronectin: it is water-soluble and contains two subunits migrating in SDS–polyacrylamide gel electrophoresis as a clearly separated doublet. By contrast, the canalicular fibronectin migrates as a single band in SDS–polyacrylamide gel electrophoresis. Fibronectin identified by immunoblotting in lateral membranes differs in character from both sinusoidal and canalicular fibronectins (Carlos Enrich, personal communication). During SDS–polyacrylamide gel electrophoresis it runs mostly as very high molecular weight material, possibly cross-linked, and partly as a diffuse pattern of three bands (220, 190 and 180($\times 10^3$) M_r). Lateral membrane fibronectin uniquely has a hydrophobic character, as shown by its distribution into the detergent phase after extraction of membranes with Triton X-114. Perhaps the $110\times 10^3 M_r$ glycoprotein identified in our studies is involved *in vivo* predominantly in transport of a fibronectin species to canalicular domains and other fibronectin-binding components are responsible for transport to sinusoidal or lateral domains. This proposal is a radical departure from a role of fibronectin-binding components in cellular adhesive interactions with the extracellular matrix and may be more likely in cells such as hepatocytes with a stable and non-motile organization not apparently requiring continuing interactions with extracellular matrix elements. However, a transient adhesive role for matrix protein–receptor interactions during early tissue formation cannot be excluded nor can additional roles in dictating cytoskeletal organization and hence cell shape. The latter possibilities in particular may relate directly to regulatory roles of matrix components in hepatocyte metabolism.

MATRIX INFLUENCES ON PROTEIN SYNTHESIS AND SECRETION

Many attempts have been made to maintain normal adult hepatocytes in a metabolically active form (Reid & Jefferson, 1984). In general, however, cells cultured in serum-containing medium on plastic rapidly show abnormal morphological changes and a marked decrease in the transcription of liver-specific mRNA sequences, but not of mRNAs for proteins common to non-liver cells. Similar findings are reported for other epithelial cells in culture and are believed to be due to several variables, including deprivation of nutrients, since simple epithelial cells (but perhaps not hepatocytes: see preceding section) attach and spread to substrata through the basal surface and are forced to feed through apical surface domains lacking critical transport proteins (Simons & Fuller, 1985). Other requirements such as specific hormones or growth factors produced by minor populations of accessory cells may also not be satisfactorily supplied in simple tissue culture. A central role of cell contacts in maintenance of the normal phenotype of hepatocytes is also clear (Nakamura *et al.* 1983; Clayton *et al.* 1985; Fraslin *et al.* 1985). Hepatocytes cultured as tissue slices where cell contacts and tissue organization are not dissociated, retain tissue-specific transcription at near normal levels without additional exogenous hormones or growth factors indicating that cell-adhesive interactions and not nutritional components are most critical in maintaining a high rate of liver-specific transcription (Clayton *et al.* 1985). However, these experiments do not distinguish between a direct effect of cell contacts on gene expression or an indirect effect; for example, the induction of hormonal or growth-promoting activities upon cell contact.

Some of the success in using liver slices may be achieved by culturing isolated hepatocytes on suitable substrata. Simple substrata composed of type I collagen or more complex matrices obtained from cell cultures by detergent extraction significantly alter the morphology of epithelial cells attached to them and better promote growth and maintain tissue-specific protein synthesis. For example, Enat *et al.* (1984) have shown that normal rat hepatocytes survive significantly better when seeded onto a substratum covered with an extracellular matrix derived from normal or regenerating liver. The best results were obtained using a low seeding density and a defined serum-free medium containing insulin, glucagon, EGF, growth hormone and prolactin. Typically, the cells initially decreased their differentiated functions, which they then recovered, reaching a peak after 3–4 weeks in culture, and then maintaining steady levels thereafter. In our recent study (Sudhakaran *et al.* 1986) we used artificial matrices of glass derivatized with fibronectin, laminin or collagen type IV. The results show that albumin synthesis and secretion by hepatocytes isolated from adult rats was best maintained on a collagen type IV surface whereas laminin was much less compatible. Interestingly, synthesis and secretion of α-foetoprotein, not normally expressed in adult hepatocytes, was highest on a laminin substratum and lowest on collagen type IV. These differences were very significant: on collagen type IV, albumin synthesis continued at 60 % of *in vivo* levels after 4 days in culture whereas on a laminin substratum the value was less than 10 % of normal activity. Further analysis is required to substantiate these findings with regard to other hepatocyte-specific functions such as hormonal induction of specific enzymes, expression of cytochrome P-450 and ability to activate chemical carcinogens. We have measured the induction of tyrosine aminotransferase by glucocorticoids and find that cells incubated for 1–4 days on laminin, fibronectin or collagen type IV all show a 10- to 12-fold increase in enzyme activity over basal levels.

The regulation of synthesis of components of the extracellular matrix by cultured hepatocytes is of special interest. The liver has a remarkable ability to regenerate in an orderly way, with restoration of normal tissue organization. In fibrotic disease there is, by contrast, an irreversible alteration in normal liver structure and function, characterized most strikingly by a disordered assembly of an extracellular matrix enriched in collagen, that may contribute directly to the tissue pathology (Rojkind & Ponce-Noyola, 1982). Clearly, therefore, it is important to understand the regulation of matrix synthesis in normal liver. Direct evidence for the production of fibronectin, laminin and collagen type IV by hepatocytes in culture has been obtained by pulse-labelling with [^{35}S]methionine and immunoprecipitation of proteins from the cell layers and secretions by specific antibodies (Sudhakaran *et al.* 1986). Two experimental protocols were used: hepatocytes were seeded onto plastic in serum-containing medium to induce cell attachment and spreading and after 3 h were maintained in serum-free medium for up to 5 days. Alternatively, the cells were seeded in serum-free medium on surfaces derivatized with laminin, fibronectin or collagen type IV, or mixtures of these components at concentrations mediating maximal cell attachment and spreading. In all cases a relatively low basal level of synthesis and secretion of matrix proteins was measured during the first day in culture and this increased 10- to 20-fold over the following 4 days in culture. In the case of fibronectin the analysis suggested an increase in the proportion of the cellular form of fibronectin relative to the plasma form with time in culture, both in the cell layers and in the secretions, a change that may reflect a switch from production of a fibronectin species characteristic of adult differentiated cells to one appropriate to a less-differentiated state (Sekiguchi *et al.* 1986; Borsi *et al.* 1987), such as may exist under stress when hepatocytes are placed in culture conditions.

Although increased synthesis and secretion of collagen type IV, fibronectin and laminin were observed using hepatocytes cultured on all substrata examined, the nature of the substratum modulated the effect in a striking manner. The magnitude of the increased synthesis and secretion of a particular matrix component was least when cells were cultured on the homologous protein substratum, suggesting a negative feed-back mechanism on matrix synthesis. The effect was readily demonstrated using mixed substrata. Cells were plated onto a series of substrata consisting of a fixed amount of laminin and various amounts of fibronectin, cultured for 3 days, and the rates of synthesis and secretion of fibronectin were then determined. The extent of fibronectin synthesis decreased proportionately with the amount of substratum-associated exogenous fibronectin. In these experiments the down-regulation was observed for matrix components secreted into the culture medium and also incorporated into the cell layer in matrix form. These data show that hepatocytes can synthesize matrix components and suggest that the extracellular matrix *in vivo* can modulate its own production. This phenomenon may have physiological significance, since in conditions when liver is stimulated to regenerate, the relative proportion of liver cells to matrix and the make-up of the matrix remain constant, implying a regulation of overall matrix assembly, part of which may be due to feedback controls.

Immunofluorescent antibody staining of hepatocytes cultured in serum-free conditions as described above has shown a cell surface location for laminin and collagen type IV but no filamentous staining is observed with these antibodies or with antibodies specific for collagen types I and III. By contrast, immunofluorescence staining with fibronectin antibodies has revealed (Fig. 6B,C) an extensive filamentous network extending directly from the cell surface between cells, on the substratum and covering the dorsal surface of adherent cells. The latter could often be seen under phase optics (Fig. 6A). The matrix develops rapidly and becomes very extensive 20 h after seeding on serum-coated plastic or glass coverslips derivitized with fibronectin, laminin or collagen type IV. Double antibody staining (Fig. 6C,D) confirms that the fibrils contain fibronectin and fibrinogen but not any collagen, and the filamentous network persists after treatment of the cultures with collagenases. In the next section we show further that the fibrils consist of fibrin–fibronectin polymerized assemblies, an *in vitro* system of blood coagulation.

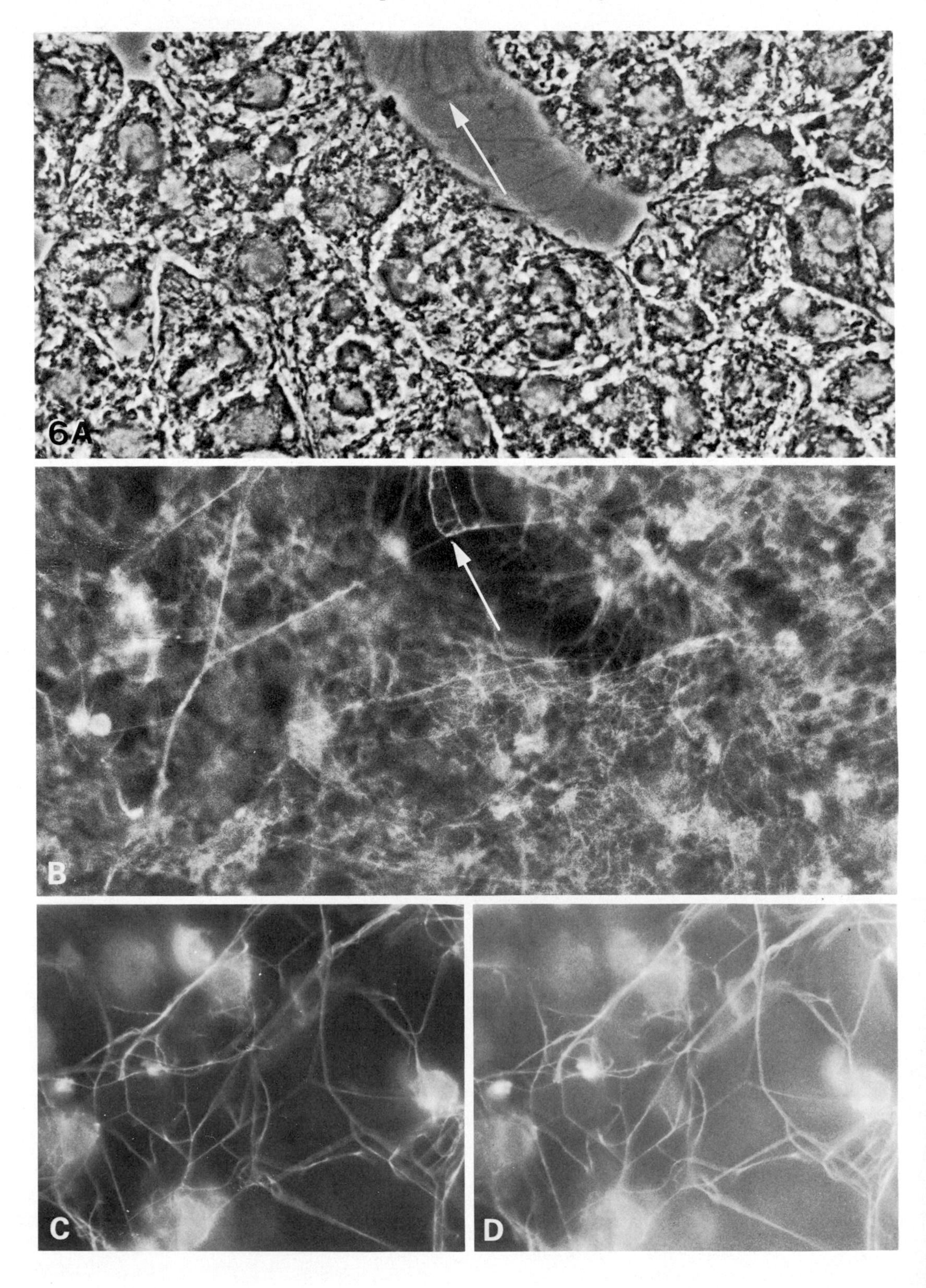
6A
B
C
D

THE COAGULATION AND FIBRINOLYTIC CASCADES *IN VITRO*

Fig. 7 shows some major enzymes and other proteins involved in the coagulation and fibrinolytic cascades. It is known that the liver is the source of most of these factors with the notable exception of plasminogen (Colman & Rubin, 1982). Serum does contain plasminogen and the extensive filamentous assemblies do not form in hepatocytes kept on various substrata in serum-containing medium. Any matrix that forms probably dissolves rapidly by plasmin-catalysed disassembly, since hepatocytes secrete plasminogen activator (Williams *et al.* 1978). We have found that addition of plasmin to hepatocyte cultures rapidly dissolves the matrix formed and when added at the beginning of culture prevents matrix formation. In addition, serine protease inhibitors present in serum may block activation of prothrombin and initiation of the coagulation cascade. The fibrils formed by hepatocytes in serum-free conditions on various substrata can be isolated mechanically in small amounts by picking up on a glass needle. In SDS–polyacrylamide gel electrophoresis the predominant band detected is fibrin β-chain ($58\times10^3 M_r$) that is also labelled metabolically and is blotted by specific antibodies. Fibrin γ-chains and dimers and fibronectin subunits were also detected by metabolic labelling and by immunoblotting. By contrast, fibrin α-chains were not detected, probably because these were extensively cross-linked by transglutaminase during assembly of the fibrin matrix and did not enter the resolving gel. Further evidence for the fibrin β-chain has been obtained by comparative peptide mapping with authentic fibrinogen standard.

At present we do not know the event initiating coagulation in hepatocyte cultures. Activation of prothrombin *in vivo* involves factor Xa, produced from factor X by the intrinsic or extrinsic pathway, either of which could be involved in our system. Whichever pathway is involved, the hepatocytes *in vitro* evidently elaborate a full complement of proteins necessary for its functioning. An independent pathway of prothrombin activation by thromboplastin can be excluded, since assays for thromboplastin in hepatocyte cultures have proved negative. *In vivo* the formation of fibrin occurs following adhesion of platelets to sub-endothelial layers of damaged vessel walls, probably by a morphological change in the platelet membrane and generation of a surface optimal for activation of prothrombin. In the hepatocyte culture system this activation is independent of platelets and may be initiated by cell interaction with a suitable substratum. In general, however, the culture system approximates the coagulation phenomenon observed *in vivo* rather closely. For example, we have found that matrix formation is powerfully inhibited by hirudin, an anti-coagulant protein specific for thrombin, and heparin, an enhancer of anti-thrombin III (Rosenberg, 1985) or heparin cofactor II (Linhardt *et al.* 1986)-

Fig. 6. A fibrin-based matrix in cultures of adult rat hepatocytes. Cells maintained for 30 h in serum-free medium on collagen type IV were viewed by phase optics (A) and by fluorescence microscopy after staining with anti-fibronectin (B,C) or anti-fibrinogen (D). The same point of the matrix is indicated by arrows in A and B. In C and D the cells were labelled simultaneously with both antibodies. A,B, ×640; C,D, ×500.

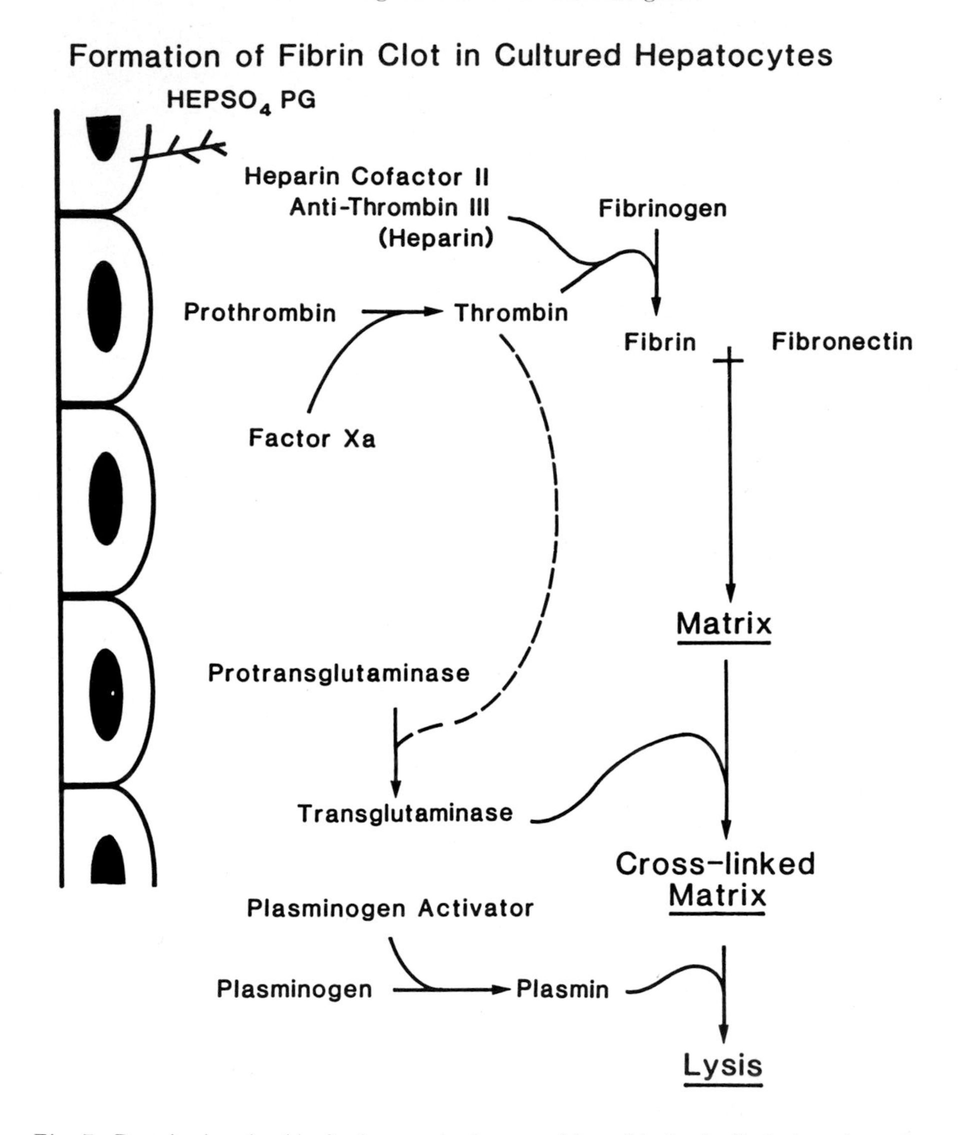

Fig. 7. Proteins involved in final events in the assembly and lysis of a fibrin-based matrix. Adult rat hepatocytes cultured on a substratum *in vitro* are shown. Conversion of prothrombin to thrombin presumably occurs by the action of activated factor X. HEPSO$_4$ PG, heparan sulphate proteoglycan.

mediated inhibition of thrombin. Heparin fragments (supplied by Ulf Lindahl, Uppsala, Sweden) containing nine or more disaccharides with high affinity for anti-thrombin III inhibit matrix formation at ng concentrations whereas shorter fragments or fragments with low affinity for anti-thrombin III (Bjork & Lindahl, 1982; Lane *et al.* 1984) had significant effects only at μg concentrations. Dermatan sulphate also was inhibitory, confirming the presence of heparin cofactor II in the hepatocyte cultures, since this sulphated polysaccharide has no effect on anti-thrombin III (Ofosu *et al.* 1984; Teien *et al.* 1976; McGuire & Tollefsen, 1987).

Presumably, the endogenous heparan sulphate proteoglycan in liver parenchyma does not possess anti-coagulant properties, in contrast to proteoglycans found in other tissues, for example rat skin (Jacobsson *et al.* 1986).

In conclusion, hepatocytes in culture are fully competent in coagulation pathways and with the addition of exogenous plasminogen in fibrinolysis also. This simple culture model may be useful for the study of the regulation of these pathways and the efficacy of anti-coagulant drugs. Using biopsy material the system may also have application to the identification of metabolic disorders of blood coagulation, such as disseminated intravascular coagulation (Colman *et al.* 1979).

REFERENCES

APLIN, J. D., HUGHES, R. C., JAFFE, C. L. & SHARON, N. (1981). Reversible cross-linking of cell components of adherent fibroblasts to fibronectin and lectin-coated substrata. *Expl Cell Res.* **134**, 488–494.

BARTLES, J. R., BRAITERMAN, L. T. & HUBBARD, A. L. (1985). Biochemical characterization of domain-specific glycoproteins of the rat hepatocyte plasma membrane. *J. biol. Chem.* **260**, 12792–12802.

BISSELL, D. M., NERMUT, M. V. & HUGHES, R. C. (1984). Laminin receptors on rat hepatocytes. *Eur. J. Cell Biol.* **33**, *Suppl. 6*, 3.

BISSELL, D. M., STAMATOGLOU, S. C., NERMUT, M. V. & HUGHES, R. C. (1986). Interaction of rat hepatocytes with type IV collagen, fibronectin and laminin matrices. Distinct matrix controlled modes of attachment and spreading. *Eur. J. Cell Biol.* **40**, 72–78.

BJORK, I. & LINDAHL, U. (1982). Mechanism of the anticoagulant action of heparin. *Molec. cell. Biochem.* **48**, 161–182.

BORSI, L., CARNEMOLLA, B., CASTELLANI, P., ROSELLINI, C., VECCHIO, D., ALTEMANNI, G., CHANG, S. E., TAYLOR-PAPADIMITRIOU, J., PANDE, H. & ZARDI, L. (1987). Monoclonal antibodies in the analysis of fibronectin isoforms generated by alternative splicing of mRNA precursors in normal and transformed human cells. *J. Cell Biol.* **104**, 595–600.

BUCK, C. A. & HORWITZ, A. F. (1987). Integrin, a transmembrane glycoprotein complex mediating cell–substratum adhesion. *J. Cell Sci. Suppl. 8*, 231–250.

CLAYTON, D. F., HARRELSON, A. L. & DARNELL, J. E. (1985). Dependence of liver specific transcription on tissue organization. *Molec. cell. Biol.* **5**, 2623–2632.

CLEMENT, B. M., RISSEL, S., PEYROL, Y., MAZURIER, Y., GRIMAUD, J. A. & GUILLOUZO, A. (1985). A procedure for light and electron microscopic intracellular immunolocalization of collagen and fibronectin in rat liver. *J. Histochem. Cytochem.* **33**, 407–414.

COLMAN, R. W., ROBBOY, S. J. & MINNA, J. D. (1979). Disseminated intravascular coagulation: a reappraisal. *A. Rev. Med.* **30**, 359–374.

COLMAN, R. W. & RUBIN, R. N. (1982). Blood coagulation. In *The Liver: Biology and Pathobiology* (ed. I. M. Arias, D. Schachter, H. Popper & D. A. Shatritz), pp. 761–768. New York: Raven Press.

ENAT, R., JEFFERSON, D. M., RUIZ-OPAZO, N., GATMAITIN, Z., LEINWAND, L. A. & REID, L. M. (1984). Hepatocyte proliferation *in vitro*: its dependence on the use of serum-free hormonally defined medium and substrata of extracellular matrix. *Proc. natn. Acad. Sci. U.S.A.* **81**, 1411–1415.

ENRICH, C. & GAHMBERG, C. G. (1985). Characterization of plasma-membrane glycoproteins from functional domains of the rat hepatocyte. *Biochem. J.* **227**, 565–572.

FRASLIN, J. M., KNEIP, B., VAULONT, S., GLAISE, O., MUNNICH, A. & GUGUEN-GUILLOUZO, C. (1985). Dependence of hepatocyte-specific gene expression on cell–cell interactions in primary culture. *EMBO J.* **4**, 2487–2491.

HAHN, E., WICK, G., PENCEV, D. & TIMPL, R. (1980). Distribution of basement membrane proteins in normal and fibrotic human liver. *Gut* **21**, 63–72.

Hanski, C., Huhle, T. & Reutter, W. (1985). Involvement of plasma membrane dipeptidyl peptidase IV in fibronectin-mediated adhesion of cells on collagen. *Hoppe-Seyler's biol. Chem.* **366**, 1169–1176.

Höök, M., Woods, A., Johannsson, S., Kjellen, L. & Couchman, J. R. (1986). Functions of proteoglycans at the cell surface. In *Functions of the Proteoglycans. CIBA Symp.* 124, pp. 143–151. Chichester: John Wiley.

Humphries, M. J., Akiyama, S. K., Komoriya, A., Olden, K. & Yamada, K. M. (1986). Identification of an alternatively spliced site in human plasma fibronectin that mediates cell type-specific adhesion. *J. Cell Biol.* **103**, 2637–2647.

Hynes, R. O. (1985). Molecular biology of fibronectin. *A. Rev. Cell Biol.* **1**, 67–80.

Jacobson, K.-G., Lindahl, U. & Horner, A. A. (1986). Location of anti-thrombin binding regions in rat skin heparin proteoglycans. *Biochem. J.* **240**, 625–632.

Johansson, S. (1985). Demonstration of high affinity fibronectin receptors on rat hepatocytes in suspension. *J. biol. Chem.* **260**, 1557–1561.

Johansson, S. & Höök, M. (1984). Substrate adhesion of rat hepatocytes: on the mechanism of attachment to fibronectin. *J. Cell Biol.* **98**, 810–817.

Johansson, S., Kjellen, L., Höök, M. & Timpl, R. (1981). Substrate adhesion of rat hepatocytes: a comparison of laminin and fibronectin as attachment proteins. *J. Cell Biol.* **90**, 260–264.

Lane, D. A., Denton, J., Flynn, A. M., Thunberg, L. & Lindahl, U. (1984). Anticoagulant activities of heparin oligosaccharides and their neutralization by platelet factor 4. *Biochem. J.* **218**, 725–732.

Lehto, V. P. & Virtanen, I. (1985). Formation of stress fibres and focal adhesion sites in monensin-exposed cultured human fibroblasts in response to exogenously added cellular fibronectin. *Expl Cell Res.* **158**, 563–569.

Linhardt, R. J., Rice, K. G., Merchant, Z. M., Kim, Y. S. & Lohse, D. L. (1986). Structure and activity of a unique heparin-derived hexasaccharide. *J. biol. Chem.* **261**, 14 448–14 454.

Lesot, H. U., Kohl, K. & Von der Mark, K. (1983). Isolation of a laminin-binding protein from muscle cell membranes. *EMBO J.* **2**, 861–865.

Malinoff, H. L. & Wicha, M. S. (1983). Isolation of a cell-surface receptor protein for laminin from murine fibrosarcoma cells. *J. Cell Biol.* **96**, 1475–1479.

Martinez-Hernandez, A. (1984). The hepatic extracellular matrix. 1. Electron immunohistochemical studies in normal rat liver. *Lab. Invest.* **51**, 57–74.

McCarthy, J. B., Hagen, S. T. & Furcht, L. T. (1986). Human fibronectin contains distinct adhesion and motility-promoting domains for metastatic melanoma cells. *J. Cell Biol.* **102**, 179–188.

McGuire, E. A. & Tollefsen, D. M. (1987). Activation of heparin cofactor II by fibroblasts and vascular smooth muscle cells. *J. biol. Chem.* **262**, 169–175.

McKeown-Longo, P. J. & Etzler, C. A. (1987). Induction of fibronectin-matrix assembly in human fibrosarcoma cells by dexamethasone. *J. Cell Biol.* **104**, 601–610.

McKeown-Longo, P. J. & Mosher, D. F. (1985). Interaction of the 70,000 mol.wt. amino-terminal fragment of fibronectin with the matrix-assembly receptor of fibroblasts. *J. Cell Biol.* **100**, 364–374.

Nakamura, T., Yoshimoto, K., Nakayama, Y., Tomita, Y. & Ichibara, A. (1983). Reciprocal modulation of growth and differentiated functions of mature rat hepatocytes in primary culture by cell–cell contact and cell membranes. *Proc. natn. Acad. Sci. U.S.A.* **80**, 7229–7233.

Nermut, M. V., Williams, L. D., Stamatoglou, S. C. & Bissell, D. M. (1986). Ultrastructure of ventral membranes of rat hepatocytes spread on type IV collagen. *Eur. J. Cell Biol.* **42**, 35–44.

Odin, P., Tingstrom, A. & Öbrink, B. (1986). Chemical characterization of cell CAM 105, a cell adhesion molecule isolated from rat liver membranes. *Biochem. J.* **236**, 559–568.

Ofosu, F. A., Modi, G. J., Smith, L. M., Cerskus, A. L., Hirsh, J. & Blajchman, M. A. (1984). Heparan sulphate and dermatan sulphate inhibit the generation of thrombin activity in plasma by complementary pathways. *Blood* **64**, 742–747.

Raghow, R., Gossage, D. & Kang, A. H. (1986). Pretranslational regulation of type I collagen, fibronectin and a 50-Kilodalton noncollagenous extracellular protein by dexamethasone in rat fibroblasts. *J. biol. Chem.* **261**, 4677–4684.

RAO, N. C., BARSHY, S. H., TERRANOVA, V. P. & LIOTTA, L. A. (1983). Isolation of a tumour cell laminin receptor. *Biochem. biophys. Res. Commun.* **111**, 804–808.

REID, L. M. & JEFFERSON, D. M. (1984). Cell culture studies using extracts of extracellular matrix to study growth and differentiation in mammalian cells. In *Mammalian Cell Culture*, pp. 239–280. New York: Plenum.

ROJKIND, M. & PONCE-NOYOLA, P. (1982). The extracellular matrix of the liver. *Collagen Rel. Res.* **2**, 151–175.

ROSENBERG, R. D. (1985). Role of heparin and heparin-like molecules in thrombosis and artherosclerosis. *Fedn Proc. Fedn Am. Socs exp. Biol.* **44**, 404–409.

RUBIN, K., HÖÖK, M., ÖBRINK, B. & TIMPL, R. (1981). Substrate adhesion of rat hepatocytes: mechanism of attachment to collagen substrates. *Cell* **24**, 463–470.

RUBIN, K., JOHANSSON, S., PETTERSSON, I., OCKLIND, C., ÖBRINK, B. & HÖÖK, M. (1979). Attachment of rat hepatocytes to collagen and fibronectin. A study using antibodies directed against cell surface components. *Biochem. biophys. Res. Commun.* **91**, 86–94.

RUBIN, K., OLDBERG, A., HÖÖK, M. & ÖBRINK, B. (1978). Adhesion of rat hepatocytes to collagen. *Expl Cell Res.* **117**, 165–177.

RUOSLAHTI, E. & PIERSCHBACHER, M. D. (1986). Arg. Gly. Asp: A versatile cell recognition signal. *Cell* **44**, 517–518.

SEKIGUCHI, K., KOS, A. M., HIROHASHI, S. & HAKOMORI, S. I. (1986). Human tissue fibronectin: expression of different isotypes in the adult and fetal tissues. *Biochem. biophys. Res. Commun.* **141**, 1012–1017.

SIMONS, K. & FULLER, S. D. (1985). Cell surface polarity in epithelia. *A. Rev. Cell Biol.* **1**, 243–288.

STOW, J. L., KJELLEN, L., UNGER, E., HÖÖK, M. & FARQUAHAR, M. G. (1985). Heparan sulphate proteoglycans are concentrated on the sinusoidal plasmalemmal domains and in intracellular organelles of hepatocytes. *J. Cell Biol.* **100**, 975–980.

SUDHAKARAN, P. R., STAMATOGLOU, S. C. & HUGHES, R. C. (1986). Modulation of protein synthesis and secretion by substratum in primary cultures of rat hepatocytes. *Expl Cell Res.* **167**, 505–516.

TAMKUN, J. W., DESIMONE, D. W., FONDA, D., PATEL, R. S., BUCK, C., HORWITZ, A. F. & HYNES, R. O. (1986). Structure of integrin, a glycoprotein involved in the transmembrane linkage between fibronectin and actin. *Cell* **46**, 271–282.

TAMKUN, J. W. & HYNES, R. O. (1983). Plasma fibronectin is synthesized and secreted by heptocytes. *J. biol. Chem.* **258**, 4641–4647.

TEIEN, A. N., ABILDGAARD, U. & HÖÖK, M. (1976). The anticoagulant effect of heparan sulphate and dermatan sulphate. *Thromb. Res.* **8**, 859–867.

URUSHIHARA, H. & YAMADA, K. M. (1986). Evidence for involvement of more than one class of glycoprotein in cell interactions with fibronectin. *J. cell. Physiol.* **126**, 323–332.

VOSS, B., ALLAM, S., RAUTERBERG, J., ULRICH, K., GIESELMANN, V. & VAN FIGURA, K. (1979). Primary cultures of rat hepatocytes synthesize fibronectin. *Biochem. biophys. Res. Commun.* **90**, 1348–1354.

WILLIAMS, G. M., BERMUDEZ, E., SAN, R. H. C., GOLDBLATT, P. J. & LASPIA, M. F. (1978). Rat hepatocyte primary cultures. IV. Maintenance in defined medium and the role of production of plasminogen activator and other proteases. *In Vitro* **14**, 824–837.

WISHER, M. H. & EVANS, W. H. (1975). Functional polarity of rat hepatocyte surface membrane: isolation and characterization of plasma membrane subfractions from the blood–sinusoidal bile canalicular and contiguous surfaces of the hepatocyte. *Biochem. J.* **146**, 375–388.

J. Cell Sci. Suppl. 8, 293–312 (1987)

THE ROLE OF CHANGES IN CELL SHAPE AND CONTACTS IN THE REGULATION OF CYTOSKELETON EXPRESSION DURING DIFFERENTIATION

AVRI BEN-ZE'EV

Department of Genetics, The Weizmann Institute of Science, Rehovot, 76100, Israel

SUMMARY

As a model for investigating gene regulation in relation to cell and tissue morphogenesis, we studied the expression of the adherens junction proteins, vinculin, α-actinin and actin, and that of desmosomal junctions containing the desmoplakin–cytokeratin complex, in response to changes in cell contacts and configuration. In monolayer or suspension cultures of kidney epithelial cells we found high levels of synthesis of cytokeratin and desmoplakin where extensive cell–cell contacts were established. In contrast, cells in sparse monolayers had high levels of the vimentin-type intermediate filaments, but very low levels of cytokeratins and desmoplakin I. Whereas in kidney epithelial cells all cytokeratins were coordinately regulated in response to changes in culture conditions, in mammary epithelial cells a new $45\times10^3 M_r$ cytokeratin was induced in dense monolayer and suspension cultures. By treating cells with TPA, intercellular junctions were rapidly disrupted and expression of cytokeratin and desmoplakin was dramatically reduced; however, vimentin expression was not affected. In mammary epithelial cells only synthesis of the $45\times10^3 M_r$ cytokeratin was reduced in TPA-treated cells. Thus the synthesis of the cytokeratin–desmoplakin complex was coordinately regulated in response to changes in cell–cell contact and cell shape in a way that is compatible with the organization of these cells *in vivo*.

The relationship between the organization and expression of adherens junction proteins and their role in the acquisition of the differentiated phenotype was studied in fibroblasts and in differentiating ovarian granulosa cells. The synthesis of vinculin in cultured fibroblasts increased dramatically when the cell culture density was high, concomitant with the establishment of extensive cell–substratum and cell–cell contacts of the adherens type. When fibroblasts were plated on substrata of varying adhesiveness, to modulate cell shape from a flat and well-spread to a poorly adherent spherical shape, there was a relationship between vinculin organization and expression: vinculin synthesis decreased dramatically in round cells.

The differentiation of freshly isolated ovarian granulosa cells (as measured by production of high levels of progesterone) in response to gonadotropic hormones was followed by dramatic changes in cell shape and organization and expression of adherens junction proteins. Cell shape changed from a flat fibroblastic type to a spherical one, with a reduction in vinculin-containing plaques and the disappearance of actin-containing stress fibres. Synthesis of vinculin, α-actinin and actin was significantly reduced but that of tubulin and vimentin was unchanged. Interestingly, when granulosa cells were plated on an extracellular matrix derived from endothelial cells, they underwent differentiation, even in the absence of gonadotropins, producing high levels of progesterone with similar changes in adherens junction protein synthesis and organization. The involvement of changes in organization and expression of adherens junctions in granulosa cell differentiation was further suggested by the observation that treatment with cytochalasin B alone was sufficient to induce simultaneous changes in adherens junction protein expression and progesterone production. Thus the modulation of expression and organization of these junctional proteins may be a central part of the programme of granulosa cell differentiation.

The experimental systems described in this overview demonstrate a link between changes in cell contacts, cell configuration and the expression of differentiated tissue functions. They also provide us with a model with which to study the regulation of the organization and expression of junctional components in response to changes in cellular and tissue morphogenesis.

INTRODUCTION

Changes in cell shape and cell contacts have long been recognized as processes that play a central role in the regulation)of tissue morphogenesis during embryonic development (for recent reviews, see Hay, 1984; Ingber & Jamieson, 1985). The very complex shapes of the mature multicellular higher eukaryotic organisms are genetically determined, as revealed by their extensive conservation during evolution. A major unsolved question is how tissue morphogenesis and organism form arise from the information encoded in the genome. The concept that the architectural features of eukaryotic cells, which determine cell shape and contacts, are also important for cell growth (Folkman & Moscona, 1978), gene expression (Ben-Ze'ev *et al.* 1980) and differentiation is becoming a central paradigm of cell biology (reviewed by Bissell *et al.* 1982; Ben-Ze'ev, 1985*a*, 1986*b*; Watt, 1986; see also Bissell & Barcellos-Hoff; Watt, 1987).

From studies both *in vivo* and *in vitro* there is ample evidence suggesting that cell shape is determined by the interaction of the cell with the extracellular matrix and/or with neighbouring cells (for review, see Edelman & Thiery, 1985). The areas of cellular interaction with the environment are characterized by the specific organization in the cytoplasmic domain of cytoskeletal elements in defined structures (Geiger *et al.* 1985*a*). The molecular characterization of these structural assemblies, which are, most probably, involved in transmitting and determining growth and differentiation patterns, is a rapidly developing research area (for a review, see Edelman & Thiery, 1985).

In this overview I describe our studies on two well-defined membrane–cytoskeleton structural assemblies: the actin–α-actinin–vinculin complex, which is involved in the formation of cell–substratum and cell–cell contacts of the adherens type (Chen & Singer, 1982; Geiger *et al.* 1985*b*); and the cytokeratin–desmoplakin complex, which determines the desmosomal intercellular junctional complex (Cowin *et al.* 1985). Our results show that the regulation of expression of these cytoskeletal elements is related to changes in the patterns of cell shape and cell contacts, and that such changes may be central to the acquisition of the differentiated phenotype.

REGULATION OF VIMENTIN SYNTHESIS BY CHANGES IN CELL SHAPE

In earlier studies we have shown that changes in cell shape and in the organization of the major cytoskeletal elements (microtubules and microfilaments) influence expression of the corresponding cytoskeletal proteins (Benecke *et al.* 1978; Ben-Ze'ev *et al.* 1979; Farmer *et al.* 1983). More recently we started to consider these questions with regard to the intermediate filament (IF) cytoskeletal system, because it constitutes a family of highly polymorphic filaments whose expression is cell type-specific and related to pathways of embryonic differentiation (Osborn & Weber, 1986). While in muscle and mesenchymal cells IF are assembled from single proteins (desmin and vimentin, respectively), in epithelial cells IF are assembled from multiple polypeptides known as cytokeratins (Moll *et al.* 1982).

When comparing the levels of vimentin synthesis in mesenchymal cells in monolayer with that in suspension culture, we found that the switch in cell shape from a flat and adherent cell type to a spherical and non-adherent one, is accompanied by a dramatic decrease in vimentin synthesis (Ben-Ze'ev, 1983). Upon reattachment and spreading of cells from suspension culture, a rapid increase in the synthesis of vimentin occurs (Ben-Ze'ev, 1983; Ben-Ze'ev *et al.* 1986). Since the reversible decrease in vimentin synthesis was obtained both in normal and in a variety of transformed cells, we suggest that expression of vimentin is linked to the extent of cell spreading on the substratum and to the concomitant change in vimentin organization. This suggestion is further supported by results obtained with cells in which the organization of the vimentin network was severely altered either by SV40 infection (Ben-Ze'ev, 1984*a*) or by treatment with cycloheximide (Ben-Ze'ev & Raz, 1985). In such cells both vimentin synthesis and mRNA content decreased dramatically without a similar change in other cytoskeletal proteins.

DIFFERENTIAL REGULATION OF EXPRESSION OF VIMENTIN AND CYTOKERATIN BY CHANGES IN CELL SHAPE AND CELL–CELL CONTACTS IN CULTURED EPITHELIAL CELLS

The majority of epithelial cells *in vivo* express only one type of IF, that of cytokeratins. However, co-expression of cytokeratin- and vimentin-type IF was recently reported in mesothelial cells and in granulosa cells *in vivo* (Connel & Rheinwald, 1983; Czernobilsky *et al.* 1985). Since similar co-expression was found in a population of motile embryonic cells, such as parietal endodermal cells (Lane *et al.* 1983), it was suggested that release of the constraints imposed by three-dimensional tissue organization may cause induction of vimentin expression in epithelial cells. In line with this suggestion is the fact that many epithelial cell lines and primary cultures of epithelial cells co-express cytokeratins and vimentin (Franke *et al.* 1979).

We have used bovine (MDBK) and canine (MDCK) kidney epithelial cell lines to assess whether changes in cell shape and extent of cell–cell contact affect expression of cytokeratin and vimentin-type IF in these cells (Ben-Ze'ev, 1984*b*). Cells were grown either as a monolayer (Fig. 1A,B), or in suspension on non-adhesive substrata (Fig. 1C,D) in sparse and dense cultures, to vary cell–cell contact and the extent of cell spreading on the substratum. The level of vimentin and cytokeratin synthesis was determined in [^{35}S]methionine-labelled cells by two-dimensional (2D) gel electrophoresis. We found that sparse monolayer cultures (Fig. 1E) synthesize high levels of vimentin and low levels of cytokeratins, while dense monolayer (Fig. 1F) and dense suspension cultures (Fig. 1H) synthesize high levels of cytokeratins and low levels of vimentin. Sparse cultures of suspended cells expressed low levels of either cytokeratins or vimentin (Fig. 1G). These results demonstrate that cytokeratin synthesis and vimentin synthesis in the same cell are differentially regulated.

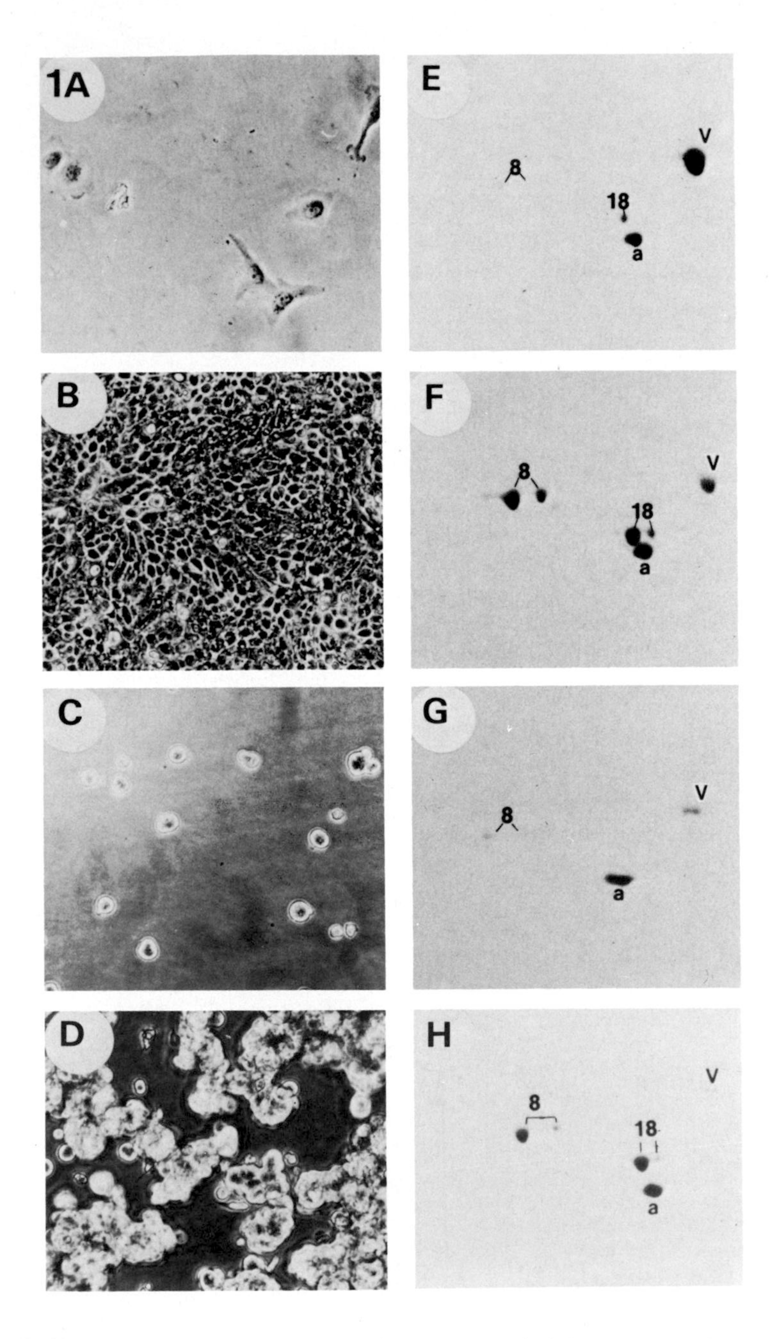

Fig. 1. Differential regulation of cytokeratins and vimentin in response to changes in cell shape and contacts. Sparse (A,E) and dense (B,F) monolayer cultures, and sparse (C,G) and dense (D,H) suspension cultures of MDBK cells were labelled with [^{35}S]methionine and the IF fraction was analysed by two-dimensional gel electrophoresis (2D) (E–H). a, Actin; V, vimentin; 8, 18, cytokeratins. (From Ben-Ze'ev (1986*b*), reproduced by permission from *Trends Biochem. Sci.*, copyright Elsevier Publications Cambridge.)

Thus, vimentin synthesis was highest in cells that were well spread on the substrate (Fig. 1A) and was low in very dense monolayer cultures (Fig. 1B) or in suspension (Fig. 1C,D), where the projected cell area is minimal (spherical cell shape). The expression of cytokeratins, on the other hand, appeared to be maximal under conditions of extensive cell–cell contact (Fig. 1B,D). Similar results obtained with mesothelial cells, which co-express these IF both *in vivo* and *in vitro*, were interpreted according to the level of cell growth under the various culture conditions (Connel & Rheinwald, 1983). However, in our system, we could not induce changes in the level of IF protein synthesis through changing growth rates by either depriving cells of serum growth factors, or by directly inhibiting DNA synthesis. The variations in IF synthesis as shown in Fig. 1 were reflected also at the level of mRNA translatability *in vitro* (Fig. 2A–D) and content (Fig. 2E–J), as determined by hybridization of RNA blots with cDNA probes to vimentin and cytokeratins. It appears therefore that these two IF systems, in addition to being organized in non-overlapping cellular compartments (Franke *et al.* 1979), are also regulated differentially by changes in cell shape and the extent of cell–cell contact.

Both in kidney epithelial cell lines and in mesothelial cells there is coordinated regulation of all cytokeratins in response to changes in culture conditions. Interestingly, in several bovine mammary epithelial cell lines, we found an induction of a new cytokeratin of $45\times10^3 M_r$ in dense monolayer (Fig. 3B) and dense suspension (Fig. 3C) cultures. These cells have a very flat 'pancake'-type morphology in sparse monolayer culture, while in dense monolayer culture they become elongated displaying a fibroblastic shape (Ben-Ze'ev, 1985*b*). In both sparse and dense monolayer cultures these cells maintained a high level of projected cell area and therefore a high level of vimentin synthesis (Fig. 3A,B). Vimentin synthesis decreased, as expected, in spherical suspended cells (Fig. 3C). Although synthesis of the two cytokeratins, numbers 8 and 18, was not significantly affected by changes in culture conditions, when extensive cell–cell contact was established, in either dense monolayer or suspension cultures, the synthesis of this new acidic $45\times10^3 M_r$ cytokeratin was induced (Fig. 3B,C). By *in vitro* translation (Fig. 4A–C) and RNA blot hybridization (Fig. 4D,E) increases in the translatability of an RNA coding for this cytokeratin and in the content of the acidic group of cytokeratin mRNAs were also observed.

Since desmosome-type junctional complexes, which consist of cytokeratins looping in and out of the desmosomal plaque, are characteristic of epithelial cells, we have also followed the synthesis of a common desmosomal plaque protein (desmoplakin I) under various culture conditions (Ben-Ze'ev, 1986*a*). We found that the synthesis of desmoplakin I is enhanced in dense monolayer and suspension cultures of both kidney epithelial cells and mammary epithelial cells (Fig. 5), in parallel with that of the cytokeratins. This suggests a coordinated regulation in the expression of the cytokeratin–desmoplakin complex under conditions that favour the formation of desmosomal junctions in these cells. At the same time, synthesis of the mesenchymal vimentin IF protein in these cells decreased significantly. It is possible therefore that by mimicking *in vitro* patterns of organization that occur *in vivo*, one can switch the programme of gene expression to one that is more compatible with the characteristic structure and function of these cells *in vivo*.

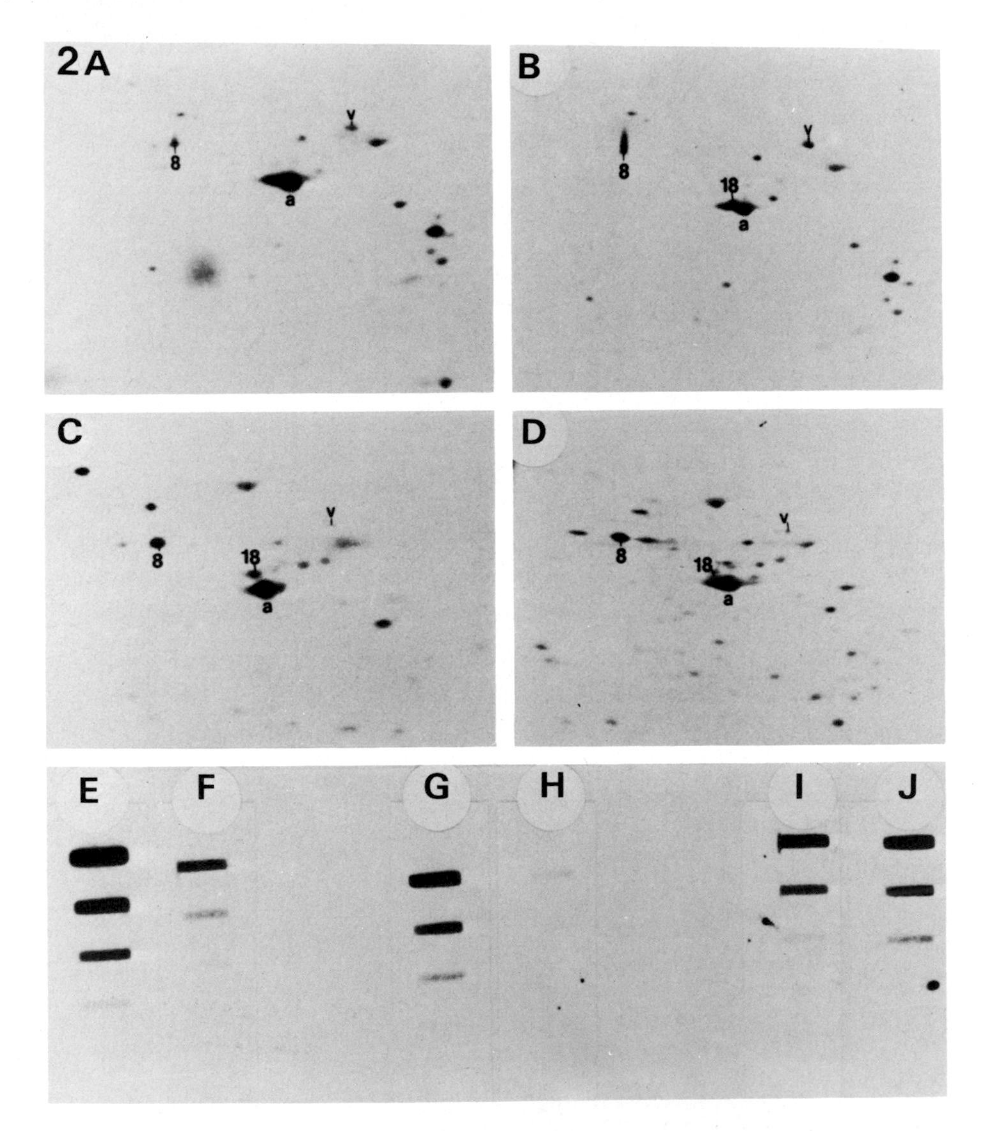

Fig. 2. Assay of activity and content of cytokeratin and vimentin mRNA in sparse and dense cultures by *in vitro* translation assay and RNA blot hybridization. Poly(A)-containing RNA was translated in a reticulocyte cell-free system and the proteins were analysed by 2D gel electrophoresis. A. RNA from sparse monolayer cultures 24 h after seeding; B, RNA from dense monolayer cultures 24 h after seeding, or 5 days after seeding (C); D, RNA from dense suspension culture 5 days after seeding. Slot blot hybridization of poly$(A)^+$ RNA from sparse monolayer (E,H,I) or dense monolayer cultures 3 days after seeding (F,G,J) with nick-translated vimentin cDNA (E,F), cytokeratins cDNA (G,H), and tubulin cDNA (I,J). Symbols as defined in Fig. 1. (From Ben-Ze'ev (1984*b*), reproduced from *J. Cell Biol.* (1984) **99**, 1424–1433, by copyright permission of the Rockefeller University Press.)

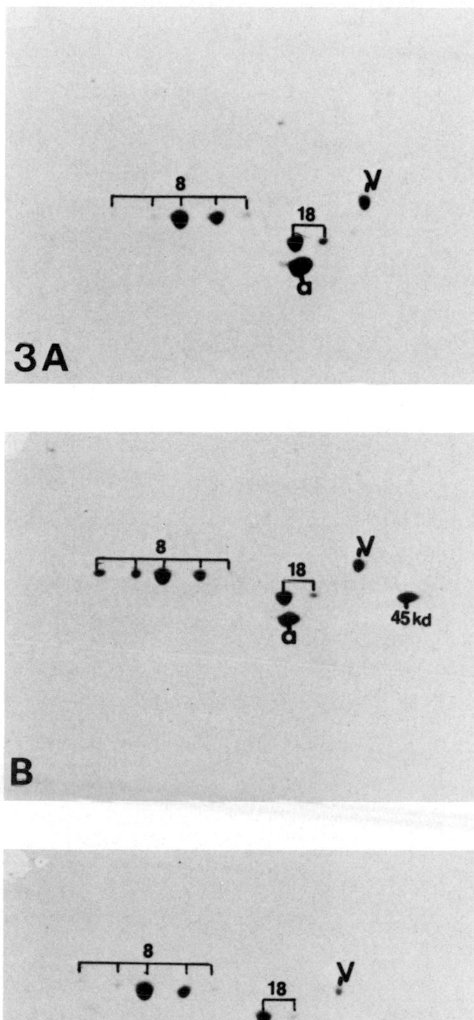

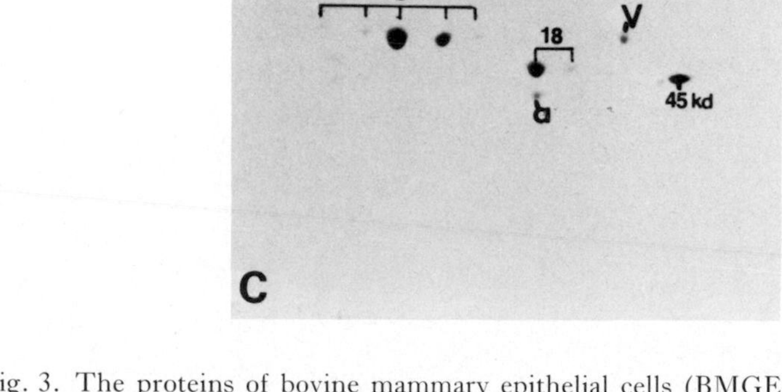

Fig. 3. The proteins of bovine mammary epithelial cells (BMGE-H) in sparse monolayer, dense monolayer and suspension cultures. A. Sparse monolayer; B, dense monolayer; and C, dense suspension cultures of BMGE-H cells were labelled with $[^{35}S]$methionine 3 days after seeding, and the Triton X-100-insoluble fraction was analysed by 2D gel electrophoresis. Equal cts min^{-1} of total cell protein were analysed on each gel. a, Actin; V, vimentin; 8 and 18 are cytokeratins. 45 kd, $45\times10^3 M_r$. (From Ben-Ze'ev (1985*b*), reproduced by permission from *Expl Cell Res.*, copyright Academic Press.)

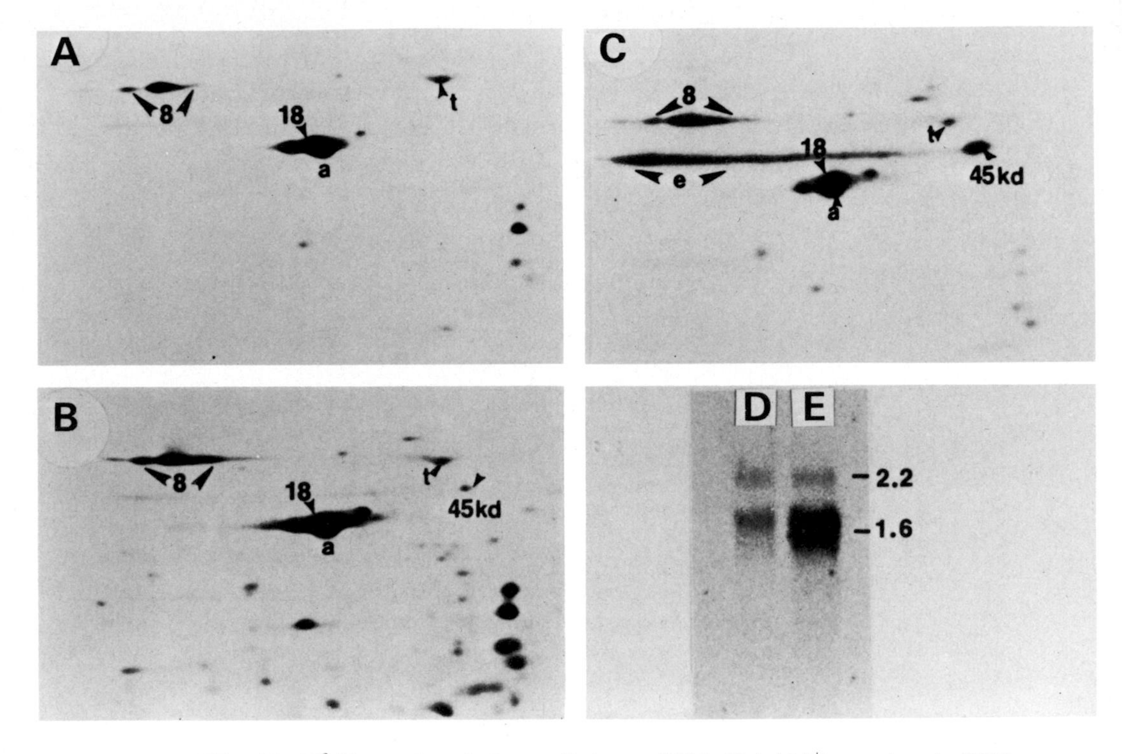

Fig. 4. The $45\times10^3\,M_r$ cytokeratin has a distinct mRNA. Poly(A)$^+$ cytoplasmic RNA was prepared from: A, sparse monolayer, B, dense monolayer, C, dense suspension cultures of BMGE-H cells. The RNA was used for *in vitro* translation and the proteins obtained were analysed on 2D gels. e, Endogenous background incorporation of the reticulocyte lysate; t, β-tubulin. D. RNA from sparse; and E, from dense cultures analysed on Northern blots and hybridized with a mixture of nick-translated ^{32}P-labelled cDNA against basic (2·2 kb) and acidic (1·6 kb) cytokeratins. 45 kd, $45\times10^3\,M_r$. kb, 10^3 bases. (Modified from Ben-Ze'ev (1985*b*), reproduced by permission from *Expl Cell Res.*, copyright Academic Press.)

In contrast to microtubules and microfilaments, which can be specifically disrupted by certain drugs, drug-induced disorganization of IFs is not readily achieved. However, it was recently reported that the tumour promoter TPA causes a rapid alteration in epithelial colony morphology (Fig. 6A,E) and in the organization of the IF network (Fey & Penman, 1984). Junctional complexes between these cells are disrupted, as demonstrated by the reorganization of desmoplakin I (Fig. 6D,H). In such cells we found a coordinated decrease in synthesis of all cytokeratins (Fig. 6B,C,F,G), and a slight increase in vimentin synthesis. This is compatible with the formation, in TPA-treated cells, of long cellular processes that are rich in vimentin (Laszlo & Bissell, 1983). Most interesting was the response of mammary epithelial cells to TPA treatment. In these cells only synthesis of the $45\times10^3\,M_r$ acidic cytokeratin decreased significantly (Fig. 7), in addition to that of desmoplakin I. This is in agreement with studies in dense cell cultures where synthesis of these same proteins was enhanced (Figs 3, 5). Very dense kidney epithelial cells when treated with TPA lose their tight junctions, but remain connected by desmosomes

(Ojakian, 1981; Ben-Ze'ev, 1986*a*). In such cells TPA did not affect synthesis of the cytokeratin–desmoplakin complex (Ben-Ze'ev, 1986*a*).

Taken together these data suggest that elements of the desmosomal junction can be regulated coordinately *in vitro* in response to changes in cell shape and contacts, and independently of the vimentin network that is co-expressed in the same cells. In addition, by imposing patterns of cellular organization in culture that are similar to the organization of these cells *in vivo*, one can modulate cytoskeleton expression in a way that reflects these structural changes.

CELL–SUBSTRATE AND CELL–CELL CONTACTS IN THE REGULATION OF SYNTHESIS OF ADHERENS JUNCTION PROTEINS

Cell shape and contacts with other cells and with the extracellular matrix are determined to a large extent by the actin-containing stress fibres and their associated proteins (for a review, see Byers *et al.* 1983). The relationships between components of the extracellular matrix, cell membrane receptors and connecting internal

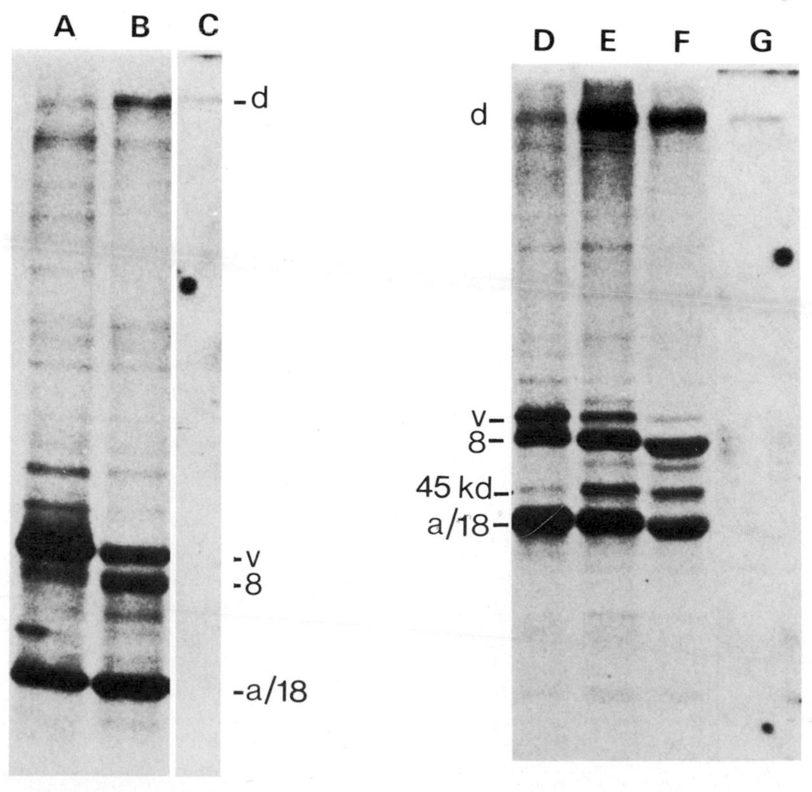

Fig. 5. Induction of desmoplakin I in dense epithelial cell cultures. The IF fraction of sparse monolayer cultures of MDBK (A) and BMGE (D) cells, dense monolayers of MDBK (B) and BMGE (E), and dense suspension cultures of BMGE cells (F) was analysed in [^{35}S]methionine-labelled cells. Immunoblot with antibody against desmoplakins I and II on dense monolayer cultures of MDBK (C) and BMGE (G) cells. d, Desmoplakin I; a, actin; v, vimentin; 8, 18, cytokeratins. (Modified from Ben-Ze'ev (1986*a*), reproduced by permission from *Expl Cell Res.*, copyright Academic Press.)

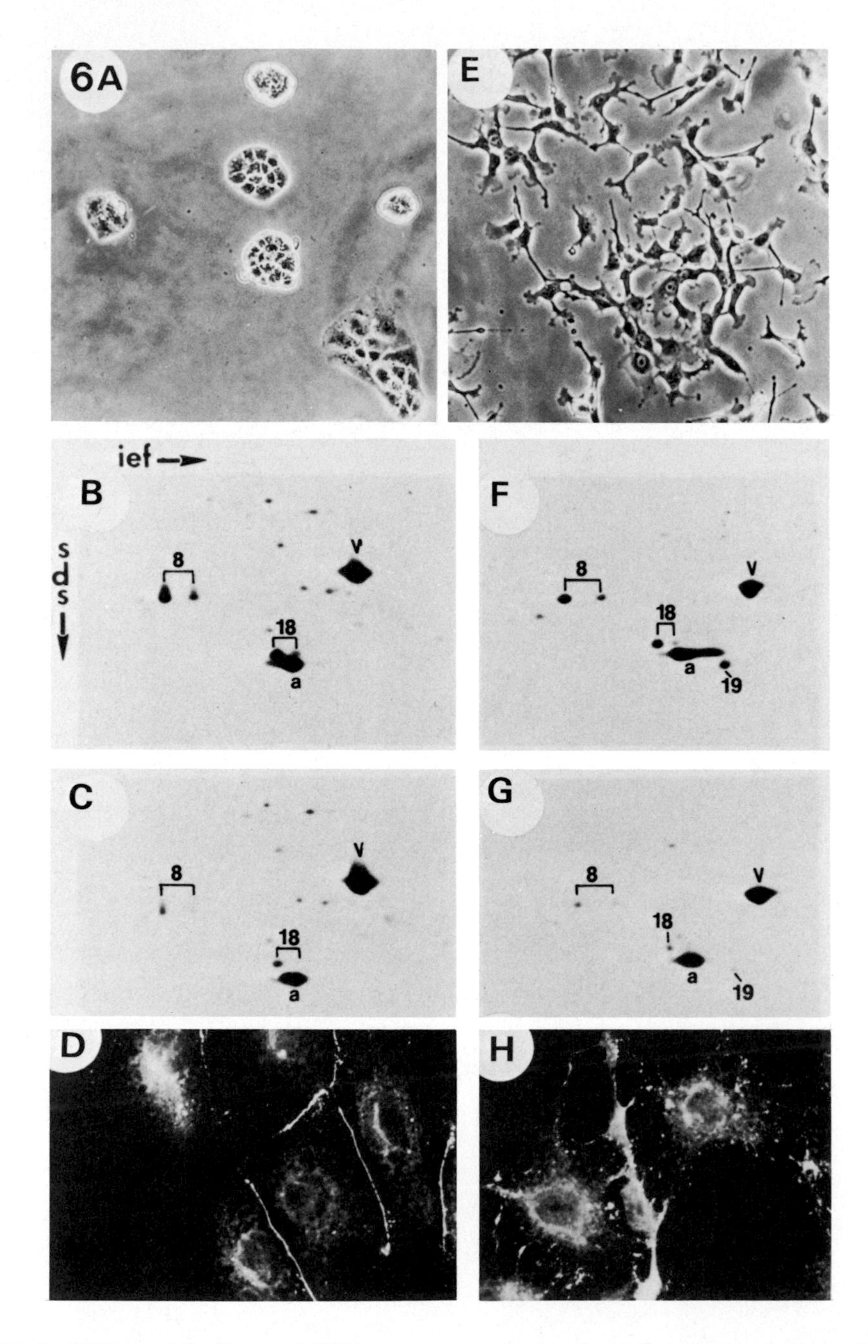

Fig. 6. Differential effects of TPA on the synthesis of cytokeratins and vimentin. MDCK (A,E,F,G) and MDBK (B,C,D,H) cells were treated with $50\,ng\,ml^{-1}$ of TPA (E,G,H) for 24 h, or were left untreated (A,B,F), pulse-labelled with [^{35}S]methionine (B–G). The IF-enriched fraction was analysed on 2D gels, or the cells were immunostained with anti-desmoplakin I, II antibody (D,H). (Modified from Ben-Ze'ev (1986*b*), reproduced by permission from *Trends Biochem. Sci.*, copyright Elsevier Publications Cambridge.)

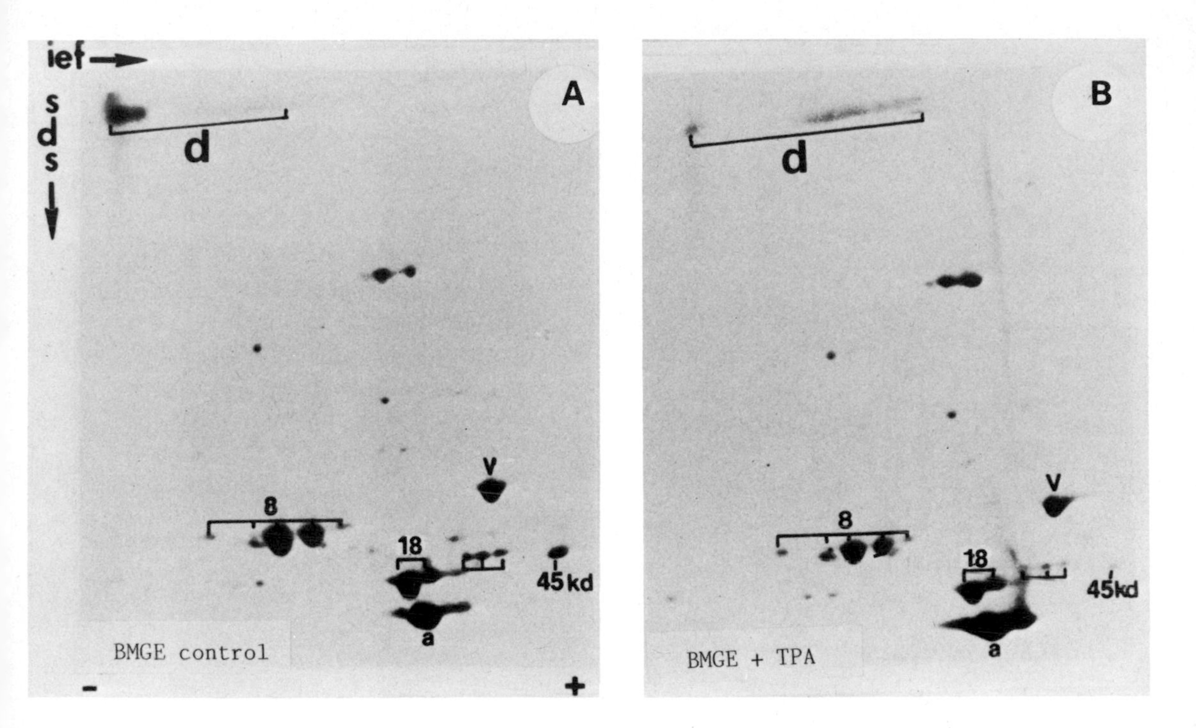

Fig. 7. Differential effects of TPA on the $45 \times 10^3 M_r$ cytokeratin in bovine mammary epithelial cells. BMGE cells were treated with TPA for 2 days (B) or left untreated (A). The [^{35}S]methionine-labelled proteins were analysed on 2D gels. (Modified from Ben-Ze'ev (1986*a*), reproduced by permission from *Expl Cell Res.*, copyright Academic Press.)

cytoskeletal elements, which consist of the actin-binding proteins vinculin, talin and α-actinin, is very complex (Mangeat & Burridge, 1984; Geiger *et al.* 1985*a*). Since vinculin is codistributed with both focal contacts and cell–cell junctional contacts of the adherens type (Geiger *et al.* 1985*b*), we were interested in following the regulation of its synthesis under conditions of varied cell–substratum and cell–cell contacts (Ungar *et al.* 1986).

When fibroblasts were cultured at increasing cell densities (Fig. 8A–C), we found a dramatic (about 7-fold) increase in the labelling of vinculin (Fig. 8D–F). The induction of vinculin synthesis in dense fibroblast cultures most probably reflects the increase in the formation of cell–cell contacts of the adherens type (Fig. 8G,H), that contain vinculin (Fig. 8I,J). The relationship between changes in cell shape and vinculin synthesis was followed in sparse cell cultures (under conditions of limited cell–cell contact) on substrata coated with increasing concentrations of the non-adhesive polymer poly(HEMA) (Folkman & Moscona, 1978; Ben-Ze'ev *et al.* 1980). On these substrata cell shape varied between a well-spread, fully flat (Fig. 9A), and a poorly adherent spherical type (Fig. 9D). Vinculin synthesis decreased markedly in the poorly adherent cells (Fig. 9H) when compared with that of the flat cells

(Fig. 9E). The synthesis of actin also decreased in spherical cells (Fig. 9H), in agreement with our previous findings showing a post-transcriptional down-regulation of actin synthesis in suspension-cultured fibroblasts (Farmer *et al.* 1983).

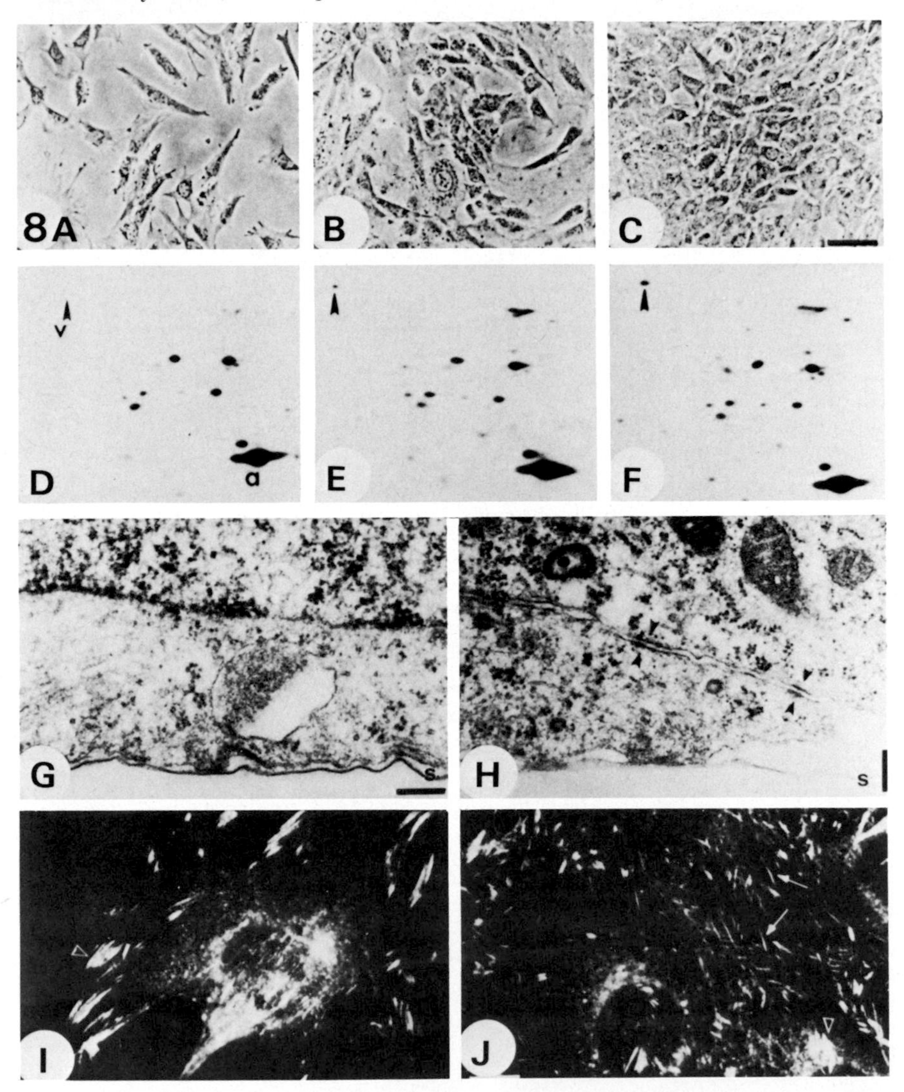

Fig. 8. Vinculin synthesis and cell-contact formation in 3T3 cells plated at different densities. A–C. Phase-contrast photomicrographs of 3T3 cells plated for 2 days at 2×10^4 (A), 10^5 (B) and 5×10^5 (C) cells per 35 mm dish. D–F. Analysis of proteins from corresponding samples labelled with [^{35}S]methionine. a, Actin; v and arrowheads point to vinculin. G,H, Electron micrographs of 3T3 cells plated at either 2×10^4 cells (G) or 5×10^5 cells per dish (H) for 2 days. s, Substratum; arrowheads point to intercellular adherens-type junctions with submembrane electron density. (I,J) Indirect immunofluorescence staining of sparse (I) and dense (J) 3T3 cultures with monoclonal antibody against chicken gizzard vinculin and rhodaminated goat anti-mouse IgG. Arrowheads point to large vinculin-containing adhesion plaques; arrows mark thin vinculin-containing structures corresponding to cell–cell contacts. (From Ungar *et al.* (1986), reprinted by permission from *Nature*, copyright Macmillan Magazines Ltd.)

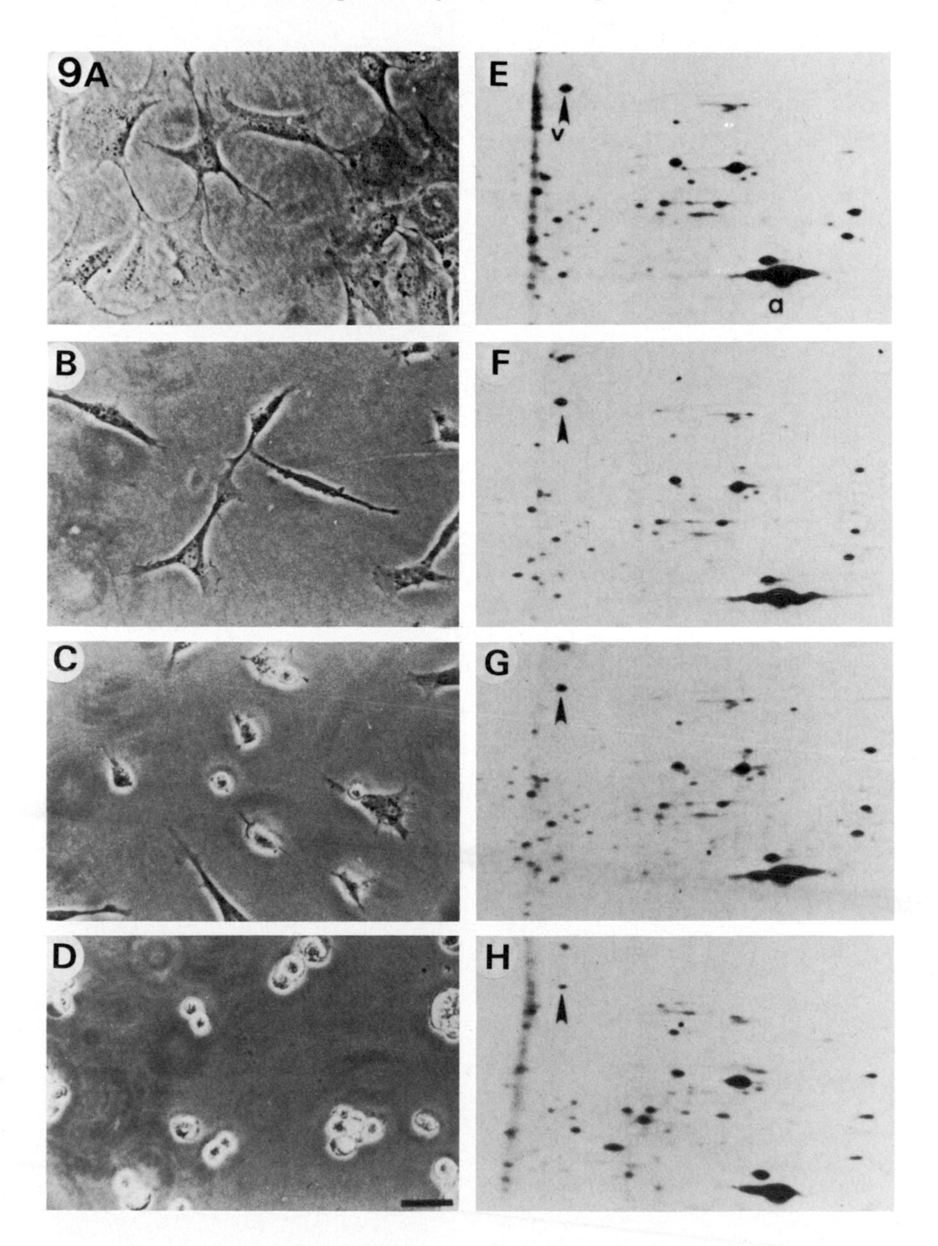

Fig. 9. Analysis of cell morphology and vinculin synthesis in 3T3 cells plated on substrates of varying adhesiveness. A–D. Phase-contrast photomicrographs of 3T3 cells grown on poly(HEMA)-coated plastic plates. Tissue-culture plates (5 cm diameter) were treated with 2·5 ml of either ethanol (A) or poly(HEMA)–ethanol solutions of 96 $\mu g\,ml^{-1}$ (B); 120 $\mu g\,ml^{-1}$ (C); or 1200 $\mu g\,ml^{-1}$ (D). Cells at 10^5 per plate were seeded on the treated substrata and incubated for 2 days, then labelled with [^{35}S]methionine. 2D gel electrophoresis of the [^{35}S]methionine-labelled proteins from the respective samples (E–H). Arrowheads point to vinculin; a, actin. (From Ungar *et al.* (1986), reprinted by permission from *Nature*, copyright Macmillan Magazines Ltd.)

When suspension-arrested fibroblasts were allowed to reattach and spread on a substratum very high levels of actin expression were induced by increases in the level of actin mRNA and protein synthesis in the cytoplasm (Benecke *et al.* 1978; Farmer *et al.* 1978, 1983). This increase in actin expression is most probably related to the transition of cells from a quiescent to a proliferative state, since it was also detected in quiescent fibroblasts that were stimulated to grow with serum growth factors (Riddle *et al.* 1979; Elder *et al.* 1984; Greenberg & Ziff, 1984). Most interestingly, such stimulation with growth factors is followed within 2–5 min by a rapid reorganization of vinculin (Herman & Pledger, 1985) and its release from adhesion plaques to a Triton X-100-soluble fraction (Ben-Ze'ev, Dyke & Farmer, unpublished observations). Thus changes in cell shape and contacts, and the organization and expression of proteins of adherens junctions could be central elements in the regulation of growth.

THE ORGANIZATION AND EXPRESSION OF ADHERENS JUNCTIONS IN THE REGULATION OF DIFFERENTIATION

There is ample evidence from a variety of experimental systems that there is a direct relationship between changes in cell shape and the expression of the differentiated phenotype (Allan & Harrison, 1980; Aggeler *et al.* 1984; Benya & Shaffer, 1982; Glowacki *et al.* 1983; Gospodarowicz *et al.* 1978; Emerman & Pitelka, 1977; Lee *et al.* 1984; Spiegelman & Ginty, 1983; for a recent review, see Watt, 1986). In order to study the possible role of changes in the organization and expression of molecularly defined cell–substratum and cell–cell contacts in regulating the differentiation programme *in vivo*, we have chosen to study primary cultures of ovarian granulosa cells. The functional unit of the ovary, the follicle, consists of inner layers of granulosa cells, which are separated from blood vessels and other cells by a basement membrane. In response to gonadotropins secreted from the pituitary, granulosa cells secrete progesterone and produce the fertilized ovum (for a review, see Hsueh *et al.* 1984). By removing the ovaries and puncturing the follicles with a needle, granulosa cells are readily released from the tissue, thus providing a very clean population of freshly isolated cells.

The addition of gonadotropins to freshly plated granulosa cells resulted in dramatic changes in cell shape and aggregation (Fig. 10A,B). While granulosa cells cultured in serum-free and growth-factor-free medium were elongated and formed elaborate stress fibres (Fig. 10C), terminating in large vinculin-containing focal contacts (Fig. 10B), the epitheloid gonadotropin-treated granulosa cells had very few vinculin-containing plaques (Fig. 10F), and the actin of these cells was not found in stress fibres, but rather in a subcortical ring near the cell membrane (Fig. 10G). Terminal differentiation of granulosa cells in response to gonadotropins included the production of very high levels of progesterone and, accordingly, the appearance of well-developed mitochondria and endoplasmic reticulum (Ben-Ze'ev *et al.* 1987). The changes in cell shape and in the organization of the actin–vinculin complex of

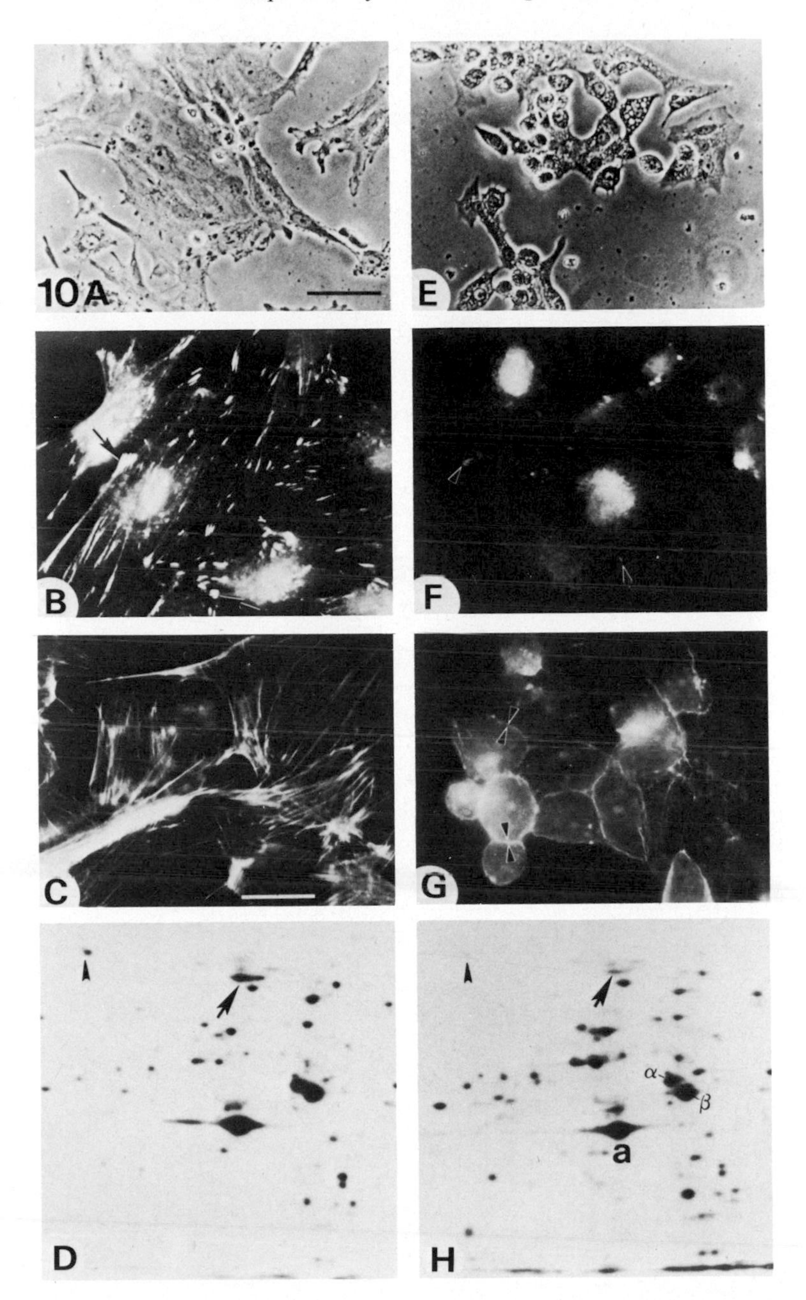

Fig. 10. Coordinate regulation of organization and expression of adherens junction proteins in differentiating granulosa cells. Granulosa cells plated for 48 h on plastic in the absence (A–D) or in the presence (E–H) of gonadotropins. A,E, Phase photomicrographs; B,F, immunofluorescent staining for vinculin; C,G, fluorescent staining of actin with rhodamine–phalloidin; D,H, cells labelled with [^{35}S]methionine and proteins analysed by 2D gel electrophoresis. Small arrowhead points to vinculin; large arrow to α-actinin; α, α-tubulin; β, β-tubulin; a, actin.

gonadotropin-treated cells were followed by a specific down-regulation in the synthesis of vinculin, α-actinin and actin (Fig. 10H) when compared with untreated cells (Fig. 10D). The decrease in the synthesis of proteins involved in the formation of focal contacts and in cell–cell contacts of the adherens type was reflected at the

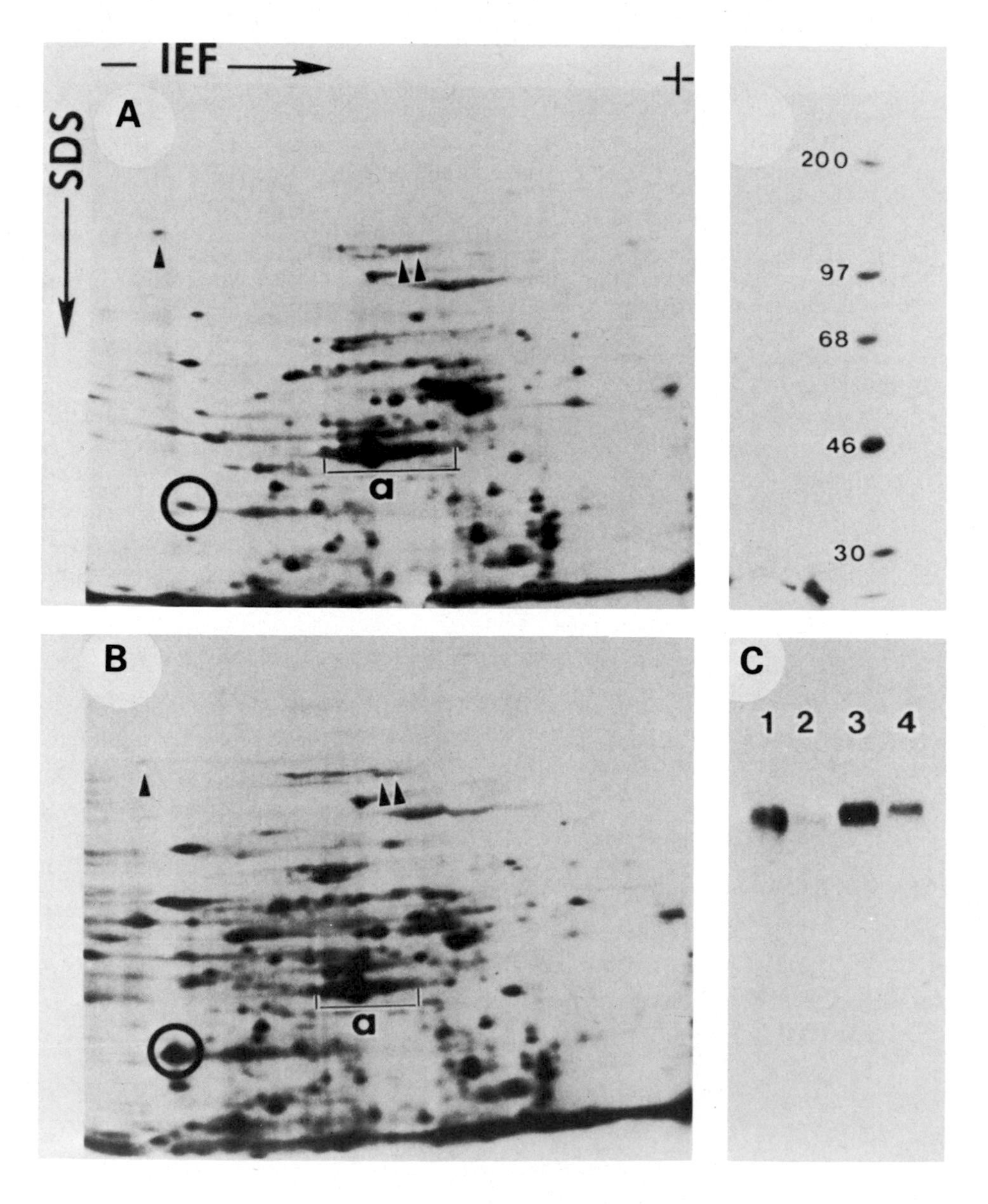

Fig. 11. Down-regulation of mRNA translatability and content of adherens junction proteins in gonadotropin-treated cells. Granulosa cells were seeded in the absence (A, C_1, C_3) and in the presence (B, C_2, C_4) of gonadotropins for 48 h. Poly(A)$^+$ RNA was translated *in vitro* and the proteins were analysed on 2D gels (A,B). Poly(A)$^+$ (C_3, C_4) and poly(A)$^-$ RNA (C_1, C_2) were also analysed on Northern blots with [^{32}P]cDNA to actin. Single arrowheads point to vinculin; double arrowheads point to α-actinin.

level of the corresponding mRNA translatability *in vitro* (Fig. 11A,B), and in the case of actin, also at the level of mRNA content (Fig. 11C).

The importance of changes in cell shape and contacts in the programme of granulosa cell differentiation was further studied by plating cells on a complex extracellular matrix (ECM) secreted on the culture dish by endothelial cells. On such a matrix, even in the absence of gonadotropins, granulosa cells underwent similar changes in their shape and in the organization and expression of the actin–α-actinin–vinculin complex and secreted high levels of progesterone (Ben-Ze'ev & Amsterdam, 1986). Furthermore, when the cells were seeded on fibronectin-coated substrata, they attained a well-spread morphology, which could not be changed by the addition of gonadotropins. Granulosa cells on fibronectin secreted very low levels of progesterone and displayed a high degree of organization and expression of actin and vinculin (Ben-Ze'ev & Amsterdam, 1987). The involvement of changes in the actin cytoskeleton in the programme of granulosa cell differentiation was also suggested by studies in which we treated cells with cytochalasin B and again induced progesterone production and simultaneous changes in synthesis and organization of actin–vinculin–α-actinin (Ben-Ze'ev & Amsterdam, 1987). Therefore, the modulation of organization and expression of adherens junction proteins may be an essential feature of the programmed differentiation of granulosa cells *in vivo*.

CONCLUDING REMARKS

In the experiments summarized in this overview we have used expression of molecularly defined cytoskeletal assemblies as a model system to study how changes in cell contacts and configuration affect gene expression in relation to cell and tissue morphogenesis. The underlying hypothesis of these studies is that the function of a differentiated tissue is determined to a large extent by the inter-relationships between gene products that determine cell–cell and cell–substrate contacts. Dissection at the molecular level of these interactions and how they affect differentiation-related gene expression will bring us closer to understanding how form and pattern arise from genetic information.

REFERENCES

Aggeler, J., Frisch, S. M. & Werb, Z. (1984). Changes in cell shape correlate with collagenase gene expression in rabbit synovial fibroblasts. *J. Cell Biol.* **98**, 1662–1671.

Allan, M. & Harrison, P. (1980). Co-expression of differentiation markers in hybrids between Friend cells and lymphoid cells and the influence of the cell shape. *Cell* **19**, 437–447.

Benecke, B. J., Ben-Ze'ev, A. & Penman, S. (1978). The control of mRNA production, translation and turnover in suspended and reattached anchorage-dependent fibroblasts. *Cell* **14**, 931–939.

Benya, P. D. & Shaffer, J. D. (1982). Dedifferentiated chondrocytes reexpress the differentiated collagen phenotype when cultured in agarose gels. *Cell* **30**, 215–224.

Ben-Ze'ev, A. (1983). Cell configuration related control of vimentin biosynthesis and phosphorylation in cultured mammalian cells. *J. Cell Biol.* **97**, 858–863.

Ben-Ze'ev, A. (1984*a*). Inhibition of vimentin synthesis and disruption of intermediate filaments in SV40 infected monkey kidney cells. *Molec. cell. Biol.* **4**, 1880–1889.

BEN-ZE'EV, A. (1984*b*). Differential control of cytokeratins and vimentin synthesis by cell–cell contact and cell spreading in cultured epithelial cells. *J. Cell Biol.* **99**, 1424–1433.

BEN-ZE'EV, A. (1985*a*). Cell shape, the complex cellular networks and gene expression: cytoskeletal protein genes as a model system. In *Cell and Muscle Motility*, vol. 6 (ed. J. W. Shay), pp. 23–54. New York: Plenum Press.

BEN-ZE'EV, A. (1985*b*). Cell density and cell shape related regulation of vimentin and cytokeratin synthesis: inhibition of vimentin and induction of a new cytokeratin in dense epithelial cell cultures. *Expl Cell Res.* **157**, 520–532.

BEN-ZE'EV, A. (1986*a*). Tumor promoter-induced disruption of junctional complexes in cultured epithelial cells is followed by the inhibition of cytokeratin and desmoplakin synthesis. *Expl Cell Res.* **164**, 335–352.

BEN-ZE'EV, A. (1986*b*). The relationship between cytoplasmic organization, gene expression and morphogenesis. *Trends Biochem. Sci.* **22**, 478–481.

BEN-ZE'EV, A. & AMSTERDAM, A. (1986). Regulation of cytoskeletal proteins involved in cell contact formation during differentiation of granulosa cells on ECM. *Proc. natn. Acad. Sci. U.S.A.* **82**, 2894–2898.

BEN-ZE'EV, A. & AMSTERDAM, A. (1987). In vitro regulation of granulosa cell differentiation: involvement of cytoskeletal protein expression. *J. biol. Chem.* **262**, 5366–5376.

BEN-ZE'EV, A., FARMER, S. R. & PENMAN, S. (1979). Mechanisms of regulating tubulin synthesis in cultured mammalian cells. *Cell* **17**, 315–319.

BEN-ZE'EV, A., FARMER, S. R. & PENMAN, S. (1980). Protein synthesis requires cell-surface contact while nuclear events respond to cell shape in anchorage-dependent fibroblasts. *Cell* **21**, 365–372.

BEN-ZE'EV, A., KOHEN, F. & AMSTERDAM, A. (1987). Gonadotropin-induced differentiation of granulosa cells is associated with the co-ordinated regulation of cytoskeletal proteins involved in cell-contact formation. *Differentiation* (in press).

BEN-ZE'EV, A. & RAZ, A. (1985). The relationship between the organization and synthesis of vimentin and the metastatic capability of B16 melanoma cells. *Cancer Res.* **45**, 2632–2641.

BEN-ZE'EV, A., ZOLLER, M. & RAZ, A. (1986). Differential expression of intermediate filament proteins in metastatic and non metastatic variants of the BSp73 tumor. *Cancer Res.* **46**, 785–790.

BISSELL, M. & BARCELLOS-HOFF, M. H. (1987). The influence of extracellular matrix on gene expression: is structure the message? *J. Cell Sci. Suppl. 8*, 327–343.

BISSELL, M., HALL, H. G. & PARRY, G. (1982). How does the extracellular matrix direct gene expression? *J. theor. Biol.* **99**, 31–68.

BYERS, H. R., WHITE, G. E. & FUJIWARA, K. (1983). Organization and function of stress fibers in cells in vitro and in situ. In *Cell and Muscle Motility*, vol. 5 (ed. J. W. Shay), pp. 83–137. New York: Plenum Press.

CHEN, W. T. & SINGER, S. J. (1982). Immunoelectron microscopic studies of the sites of cell–substratum and cell–cell contacts in cultured fibroblasts. *J. Cell Biol.* **95**, 205–222.

CONNEL, N. D. & RHEINWALD, J. G. (1983). Regulation of cytoskeletal composition in mesothelial cells: reversible loss of keratin and increase in vimentin during rapid growth in culture. *Cell* **34**, 245–253.

COWIN, P., FRANKE, W. W., GRUND, C., KAPPREL, H. P. & KARTENBECK, J. (1985). The desmosome–intermediate filament complex. In *The Cell in Contact* (ed. G. M. Edelman & J. P. Thiery), pp. 427–460. New York: J. Wiley & Sons.

CZERNOBILSKY, B., MOLL, R., LEVY, R. & FRANKE, W. W. (1985). Co-expression of cytokeratin and vimentin filaments in mesothelial, granulosa and rete ovarii of the human ovary. *Eur. J. Cell Biol.* **37**, 175–190.

EDELMAN, G. M. & THIERY, J. P., eds (1985). Adhesions and junctions as morphogenetic determinants. *The Cell in Contact.* New York: John Wiley & Sons.

ELDER, P. K., SCHMIDT, I. L. J., TETSUYA, O. & GETZ, M. J. (1984). Specific stimulation of actin gene transcription by epidermal growth factor and cycloheximide. *Proc. natn. Acad. Sci. U.S.A.* **81**, 7476–7480.

EMERMAN, J. T. & PITELKA, D. R. (1977). Maintenance and induction of morphological differentiation in dissociated mammary epithelium on floating collagen membranes. *In Vitro* **13**, 316–328.

FARMER, S., BEN-ZE'EV, A., BENECKE, B. J. & PENMAN, S. (1978). Altered translatability of messenger RNA from suspended anchorage-dependent fibroblasts: reversal upon cell attachment to a surface. *Cell* **15**, 627–637.

FARMER, S., WAN, K., BEN-ZE'EV, A. & PENMAN, S. (1983). The regulation of actin mRNA levels and translation responds to changes in cell configuration. *Molec. Cell Biol.* **3**, 182–189.

FEY, E. G. & PENMAN, S. (1984). Tumor promoters induce a specific morphological signature in the nuclear matrix–intermediate filament scaffold of Madin-Darby canine kidney (MDCK) cell colonies. *Proc. natn. Acad. Sci. U.S.A.* **81**, 4409–4413.

FOLKMAN, J. & MOSCONA, A. (1978). Role of cell shape in growth control. *Nature, Lond.* **273**, 345–349.

FRANKE, W. W., SCHMID, E., WINTER, S., OSBORN, M. & WEBER, K. (1979). Widespread occurrence of intermediate-sized filaments of the vimentin-type in cultured cells from diverse vertebrates. *Expl Cell Res.* **123**, 25–46.

GEIGER, B., AVNUR, Z., VOLBERG, T. & VOLK, T. (1985*a*). Molecular domains of adherenes junctions. In *The Cell in Contact* (ed. G. M. Edelman & J. P. Thiery), pp. 461–489. New York: J. Wiley & Sons.

GEIGER, B., VOLK, T. & VOLBERG, T. (1985*b*). Molecular heterogeneity of adherens junctions. *J. Cell Biol.* **101**, 1523–1531.

GLOWACKI, J., TREPMAN, E. & FOLKMAN, J. (1983). Cell shape and phenotypic expression in chondrocytes. *Proc. Soc. exp. Biol. Med.* **172**, 93–98.

GOSPODAROWICZ, D., GREENBURG, G. & BIRDWELL, C. (1978). Determination of cellular shape by the extracellular matrix and its correlation with the control of cellular growth. *Cancer Res.* **38**, 4155–4171.

GREENBERG, M. E. & ZIFF, E. B. (1984). Stimulation of 3T3 cells induce transcription of the c-fos proto-oncogene. *Nature, Lond.* **311**, 433–438.

HAY, E. D. (1984). Cell–matrix interaction in the embryo: cell shape, cell surface, cell skeletons and their role in differentiation. In *The Role of Extracellular Matrix in Development* (ed. R. F. Trelstad), pp. 1–31. New York: Alan R. Liss.

HERMAN, B. & PLEDGER, W. J. (1985). Platelet-derived growth factor-induced alterations in vinculin and actin distribution in Balb/c-3T3 cells. *J. Cell Biol.* **100**, 1031–1040.

HSUEH, A. J. W., ADASHI, E. Y., JONES, P. B. C. & WELSH, T. H. (1984). Hormonal regulation of the differentiation of cultured ovarian granulosa cells. *Endocr. Rev.* **5**, 76–126.

INGBER, D. E. & JAMIESON, J. D. (1985). Cells as tensegrity structures: architectural regulation of histodifferentiation by physical forces transduced over basement membrane. In *Gene Expression During Normal and Malignant Differentiation* (ed. L. C. Andersson, G. C. Gahmberg & P. Ekblom), pp. 13–32. Orlando: Academic Press.

LANE, E. B., HOGAN, B. L. M., KURKINEN, M. & GARRELS, J. I. (1983). Co-expression of vimentin and cytokeratins in parietal endoderm cells of early mouse embryo. *Nature, Lond.* **303**, 701–704.

LASZLO, A. & BISSELL, M. J. (1983). TPA induces simultaneous alterations in the synthesis and organization of vimentin. *Expl Cell Res.* **148**, 221–234.

LEE, E. Y. H., PARRY, G. & BISSELL, M. J. (1984). Modulation of secreted proteins of mouse mammary epithelial cells by the collagenous substrata. *J. Cell Biol.* **98**, 146–155.

MANGEAT, P. & BURRIDGE, K. (1984). Actin–membrane interaction in fibroblasts: what proteins are involved in this association? *J. Cell Biol.* **99**, 95s–103s.

MOLL, R., FRANKE, W. W., SCHILLER, D., GEIGER, B. & KREPLER, R. (1982). The catalog of human cytokeratins: patterns of expression in normal epithelia, tumors and cultured cells. *Cell* **31**, 11–24.

OJAKIAN, G. K. (1981). Tumor promoter-induced changes in the permeability of epithelial cell tight junctions. *Cell* **23**, 95–103.

OSBORN, M. & WEBER, K. (1986). Intermediate filament proteins: a multigene family distinguishing major cell lineages. *Trends Biochem. Sci.* **11**, 469–472.

RIDDLE, V. G. H., DUBROW, R. & PARDEE, A. B. (1979). Changes in the synthesis of actin and other cell proteins after stimulation of serum-arrested cells. *Proc. natn. Acad. Sci. U.S.A.* **76**, 1298–1302.

SPIEGELMAN, B. M. & GINTHY, C. A. (1983). Fibronectin modulation of cell shape and lipogenic gene expression in 3T3-adipocytes. *Cell* **35**, 657–666.

UNGAR, F., GEIGER, B. & BEN-ZE'EV, A. (1986). Cell contact- and shape-related regulation of vinculin synthesis in fibroblasts. *Nature, Lond.* **319**, 787–791.
WATT, F. M. (1986). The extracellular matrix and cell shape. *Trends Biochem. Sci.* **11**, 482–485.
WATT, F. M. (1987). Influence of cell shape and adhesiveness on stratification and terminal differentiation of human keratinocytes in culture. *J. Cell Sci. Suppl. 8*, 313–326.

J. Cell Sci. Suppl. 8, 313–326 (1987)

INFLUENCE OF CELL SHAPE AND ADHESIVENESS ON STRATIFICATION AND TERMINAL DIFFERENTIATION OF HUMAN KERATINOCYTES IN CULTURE

FIONA M. WATT

Keratinocyte Laboratory, Imperial Cancer Research Fund, P.O. Box 123, Lincoln's Inn Fields, London, WC2A 3PX, UK

SUMMARY

Human epidermal keratinocytes can be grown in culture under conditions in which they assemble a tissue with the same basic organization as normal epidermis. The cells stratify, mitosis is restricted to the basal layer and terminal differentiation occurs as the cells move through the suprabasal layers. Keratinocytes do not have to leave the basal layer in order to undergo terminal differentiation, but the two processes are normally linked, because during terminal differentiation the adhesive affinity of keratinocytes for the culture substratum and for other keratinocytes is reduced. Down-regulation of synthesis of basement membrane components and their receptors may provide the molecular basis for the reduction in cell–substratum adhesiveness. However, the molecules that mediate changes in cohesiveness have not yet been identified. Restriction of substratum contact, so that cells are prevented from spreading, appears to be one signal that induces keratinocytes to stop dividing and undergo terminal differentiation.

INTRODUCTION

The epidermis consists of multiple layers of epithelial cells, called keratinocytes. Mitosis is largely restricted to the basal layer and keratinocytes that leave this layer undergo terminal differentiation as they move upwards towards the tissue surface. Three different suprabasal zones of cells, corresponding to different stages of terminal differentiation, can be distinguished on the basis of their position and histological appearance (Fig. 1). The rate of production of new cells, by division in the basal layer, is normally balanced by the rate of shedding of terminally differentiated cells from the outermost cornified layers. This, in turn, depends on selective migration from the basal layer of cells that are committed to terminal differentiation.

Human epidermal keratinocytes can be grown in culture under conditions in which they assemble a tissue with the same basic organization as normal epidermis (Green, 1980). The cells stratify (i.e. form multiple cell layers), mitosis takes place in the basal layer, and keratinocytes terminally differentiate in the suprabasal layers. These cultures provide a useful experimental model for investigating many aspects of epithelial cell behaviour; in particular, how the properties of individual cells at different stages of terminal differentiation determine the properties of the tissue they

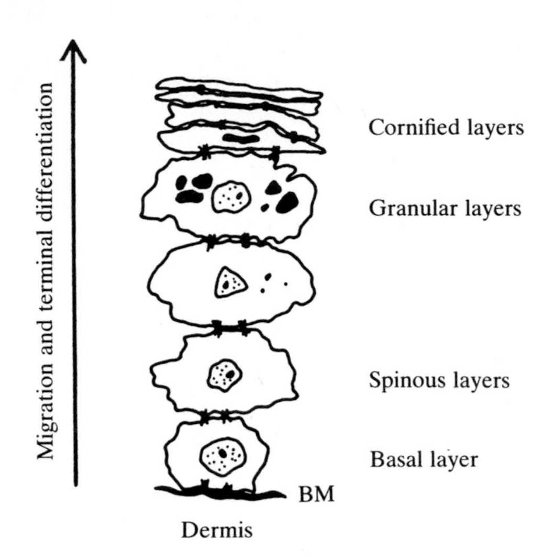

Fig. 1. Cross-section through human epidermis, showing the different layers of keratinocytes that can be distinguished by morphology. Note the correlation between terminal differentiation and migration upwards from the basal layer. (Re-drawn from Sengel (1976).)

comprise. In this article I shall describe recent evidence that changes in cell adhesiveness ensure the selective migration of terminally differentiating keratinocytes out of the basal layer and that restricted interaction with the culture substratum may act as a signal for terminal differentiation.

METHODS FOR GROWING HUMAN KERATINOCYTES IN CULTURE

Fig. 2 illustrates a technique for growing human keratinocytes that was developed by James Rheinwald and Howard Green (Rheinwald & Green, 1975) and is now in widespread use. The keratinocytes are seeded onto a feeder layer of mouse 3T3 cells, which conditions the culture medium and substratum to encourage attachment and proliferation. The feeder layer can be selectively removed at any stage during culture by aspiration with EDTA (Sun & Green, 1976). Supplements in the culture medium stimulate growth and prolong the lifespan of the cultures (Rheinwald & Green, 1977; Green, 1978; Watt & Green, 1981; Wu *et al.* 1982), so that keratinocytes from newborn foreskin epidermis can be routinely passaged more than 15 times prior to senescence (Watt, unpublished).

A number of other techniques for culturing keratinocytes have been developed. For some applications it is desirable to grow the cells in serum-free medium without a feeder layer, and defined media are available for this purpose (e.g. see Boyce & Ham, 1983). Attempts to recreate the normal epidermal environment improve the histological appearance of the cultures: cells can be grown on collagen gels (Karasek & Charlton, 1971), into which dermal fibroblasts may be incorporated (Bell *et al.* 1981); they can be fed from below; supported at the air–medium interface; and

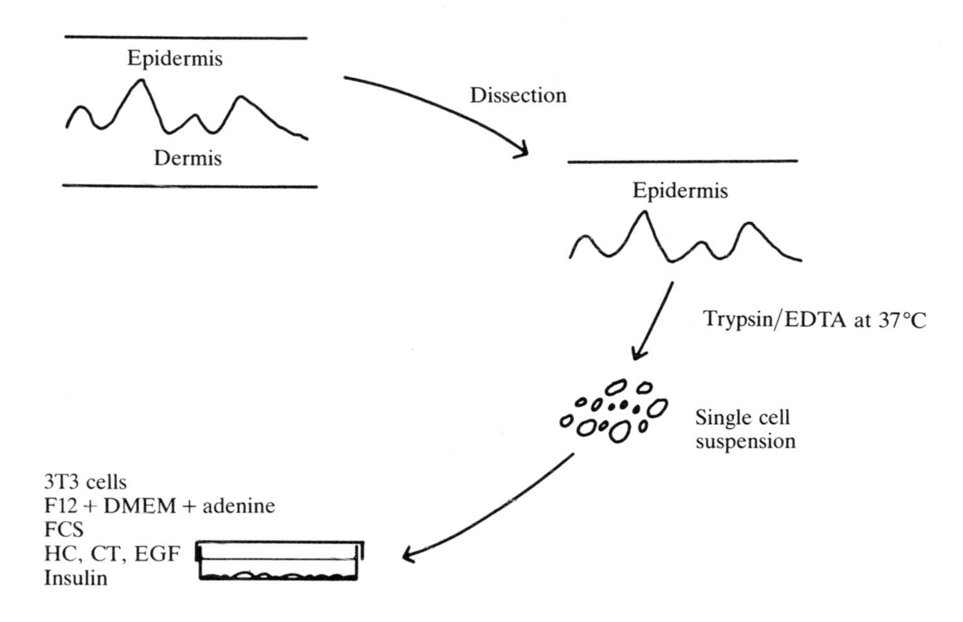

Fig. 2. Isolation and culture of human keratinocytes from epidermis, based on the method of Rheinwald & Green (1975). The composition of the culture medium is: 1 part Ham's F12 medium (F12) plus 3 parts Dulbecco's modified Eagle's medium (DMEM), supplemented with $1{\cdot}8\times10^{-4}$ M-adenine, 10% foetal calf serum (FCS), $0{\cdot}5\,\mu g\,ml^{-1}$ hydrocortisone (HC), 10^{-10} M-cholera toxin (CT), $10\,ng\,ml^{-1}$ epidermal growth factor (EGF) and $5\,\mu g\,ml^{-1}$ insulin.

cultured in the presence of dermis or basement membrane constituents (Prunléras *et al.* 1983; Fusenig *et al.* 1983).

INVOLUCRIN AS A MARKER OF TERMINAL DIFFERENTIATION

A characteristic feature of keratinocytes that have reached a late stage in terminal differentiation is the presence, closely apposed to the inner surface of the plasma membrane, of an insoluble protein envelope about 12 nm thick (Farbman, 1966; Hashimoto, 1969). This cornified envelope serves an important barrier function in protecting cells in the lower epidermal layers from desiccation and mechanical damage. The envelope is assembled by transglutaminase-catalysed cross-linking of several precursor proteins, the most abundant of which is involucrin (Rice & Green, 1979; Simon & Green, 1984).

Prior to cross-linking, involucrin is present in the cytoplasm as a soluble protein with an apparent molecular weight (on Laemmli polyacrylamide gels) of 140×10^3 (Simon & Green, 1984). In intact epidermis the onset of involucrin synthesis is usually in the upper spinous layers (Rice & Green, 1979). However, in culture involucrin is present in all suprabasal layers (Fig. 3; and Banks-Schlegel & Green, 1981; Watt *et al.* 1987). Involucrin therefore provides a useful marker for cultured keratinocytes that have begun to differentiate terminally and have left the basal layer.

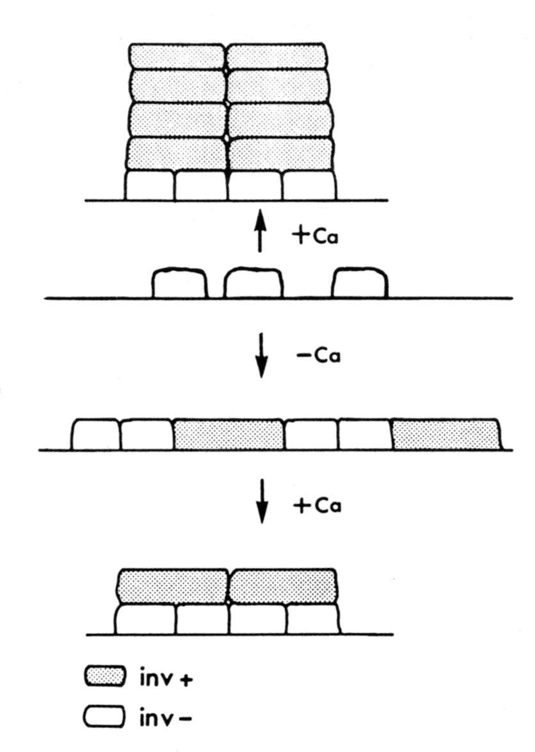

Fig. 3. Relative position of involucrin-positive (inv+) and -negative (inv−) keratinocytes grown in medium containing approximately 2 mM (+Ca) or 0·1 mM (−Ca) calcium ions.

MOVEMENT OUT OF THE BASAL LAYER IS NOT A PREREQUISITE FOR TERMINAL DIFFERENTIATION

In the epidermis the stage of terminal differentiation that a keratinocyte has reached is closely correlated with its position: cells in the outermost layers are at a later stage of terminal differentiation than cells that have just left the basal layer. There are two possible explanations for this: either position acts as a signal for terminal differentiation or else properties acquired during terminal differentiation determine position. To distinguish between these possibilities, keratinocytes have been grown under conditions that prevent stratification: when the calcium ion concentration of the medium is reduced from its normal level of approximately 2 mM to 0·1 mM, keratinocytes are able to divide, but desmosome assembly is inhibited and the cells grow as a monolayer (Hennings *et al.* 1980; Watt & Green, 1982).

When human basal keratinocytes (i.e. cells lacking involucrin) are seeded in low-calcium medium and grown to confluence, about 30–50% start to synthesize involucrin (Fig. 3), the same proportion as in control stratified cultures (Watt & Green, 1982). Initiation of involucrin synthesis under these conditions is not restricted to cells that were already committed to terminal differentiation before isolation, because new involucrin-positive cells continue to appear throughout the life of the culture. Furthermore, involucrin is not the only marker of terminal differentiation to be expressed in monolayer culture: human keratinocytes normally acquire the ability to bind peanut lectin when they have left the basal layer, but peanut lectin-binding cells are also present in low-calcium cultures (Watt, 1983).

These observations suggest that although terminal differentiation is normally linked to upward migration, movement out of the basal layer is not a prerequisite for terminal differentiation. Thus, the suprabasal position does not act as a signal for initiation of terminal differentiation. These conclusions are in good agreement with the observations that occasional involucrin-positive cells are present in the basal layer of stratified cultures (Banks-Schlegel & Green, 1981) and that in intact epidermis a small proportion of basal keratinocytes expresses the $67\times10^3 M_r$ keratin that is normally characteristic of suprabasal cells (Régnier *et al.* 1986).

Since departure from the basal layer is not a prerequisite for terminal differentiation the two processes must be linked in some other way. When stratification is induced, by raising the level of calcium ions in the medium of keratinocyte monolayers, the cells that move out of the basal layer are those that contain involucrin (Fig. 3; and Watt & Green, 1982; Magee *et al.* 1987). Selective migration of involucrin-positive cells occurs even in the presence of inhibitors of DNA and protein synthesis, and of glycosylation (Watt, 1984). These observations suggest that involucrin-positive cells in low-calcium monolayers already have the properties that will ensure their suprabasal location when stratification is induced, and that the primary effect of raising the calcium ion concentration in the medium is to induce assembly of desmosomes that provide the 'scaffolding' for cells to move out of the basal layer (Watt *et al.* 1984).

CHANGES IN CELL–SUBSTRATUM ADHESION DURING TERMINAL DIFFERENTIATION

One clue that changes in cell adhesiveness might play a role in the selective migration of terminally differentiating keratinocytes out of the basal layer came from immunofluorescence studies of postconfluent keratinocyte monolayers. Cell division continues after confluence and, since there is no space left on the dish to accommodate all the cells, keratinocytes start to accumulate either free in suspension or rounded up and loosely attached to the surface of the monolayer. Involucrin is present in all the rounded cells above the plane of the monolayer and in most cells that have become detached and are in the medium. This suggests that terminal differentiation is accompanied by a decrease in substratum adhesiveness (Watt & Green, 1982).

Further evidence that involucrin-positive cells have a lower adhesive affinity for the culture substratum than involucrin-negative cells comes from the experiment illustrated in Fig. 4. When a mixture of involucrin-positive and -negative cells is plated out in medium containing 2 mM-calcium at very high density (3×10^6 to 5×10^6 cells per 35 mm diameter Petri dish) it reassembles a stratified sheet within 16 h. If there is no difference in affinity for the culture substratum one would expect to find both involucrin-positive and -negative cells in the basal layer; if there is a difference,

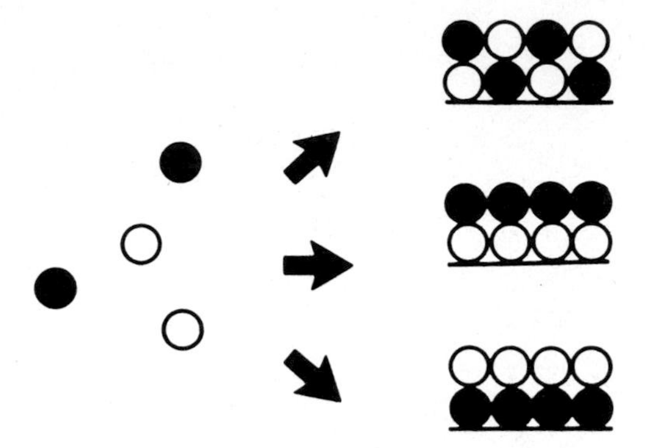

Fig. 4. Possible outcomes of seeding a mixture of involucrin-positive (○) and involucrin-negative (●) cells at high density on tissue culture plastic in medium containing 2 mM-calcium ions.

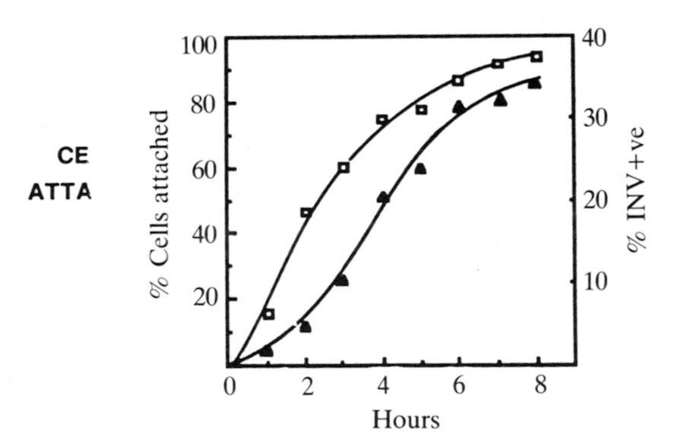

Fig. 5. Samples of 10^6 keratinocytes were seeded into 35 mm diameter Petri dishes and allowed to attach for up to 8 h. At intervals non-adherent cells were removed from triplicate dishes by washing twice in phosphate-buffered saline (PBS). The proportion of cells that had attached (□) was calculated by counting the number of cells in the medium and PBS rinses. The proportion of adherent involucrin-positive (Inv+) cells (△) was determined from photographs of adherent cells stained with antiserum to involucrin and a second fluoresceinated antibody (see Fig. 6; and Watt & Green, 1981).

then the basal layer might contain exclusively involucrin-positive or -negative cells (Fig. 4). In fact, the sheets contain only involucrin-negative cells in the basal layer, suggesting that they have a greater adhesive affinity for the culture substratum than involucrin-positive cells (Watt, 1984).

The kinetics of keratinocyte adhesion and spreading have also been measured. A mixture of involucrin-positive and -negative cells was plated onto tissue culture plastic and non-adherent cells were washed off at intervals (Figs 5, 6). Maximum attachment of the total population occurred 8 h after plating (Fig. 5). However, involucrin-negative cells attached and spread more rapidly than involucrin-positive cells. The proportion of involucrin-positive cells in the starting population was 38 %, yet the percentage of adherent cells expressing involucrin was less than 5 % after 2 h; this rose to 34 % at 8 h. Most involucrin-negative cells had spread by 6 h (Fig. 6), but there was little spreading of involucrin-positive cells even at 8 h. Involucrin-positive cells appeared to adhere preferentially to the surface of spread basal cells rather than directly to the culture plastic (Fig. 6).

In summary, terminally differentiating keratinocytes that are expressing involucrin have a lower adhesive affinity for the culture substratum than involucrin-negative keratinocytes. Basal keratinocytes are not only more adhesive to tissue culture plastic, but also to substrata of type I or type IV collagen (Stanley *et al.* 1980), fibronectin and basement membranes (Toda & Grinnell, 1987). Selective adhesion to collagen or plastic can be used to isolate basal cells from mixed populations of keratinocytes (Skerrow & Skerrow, 1983; Watt, unpublished).

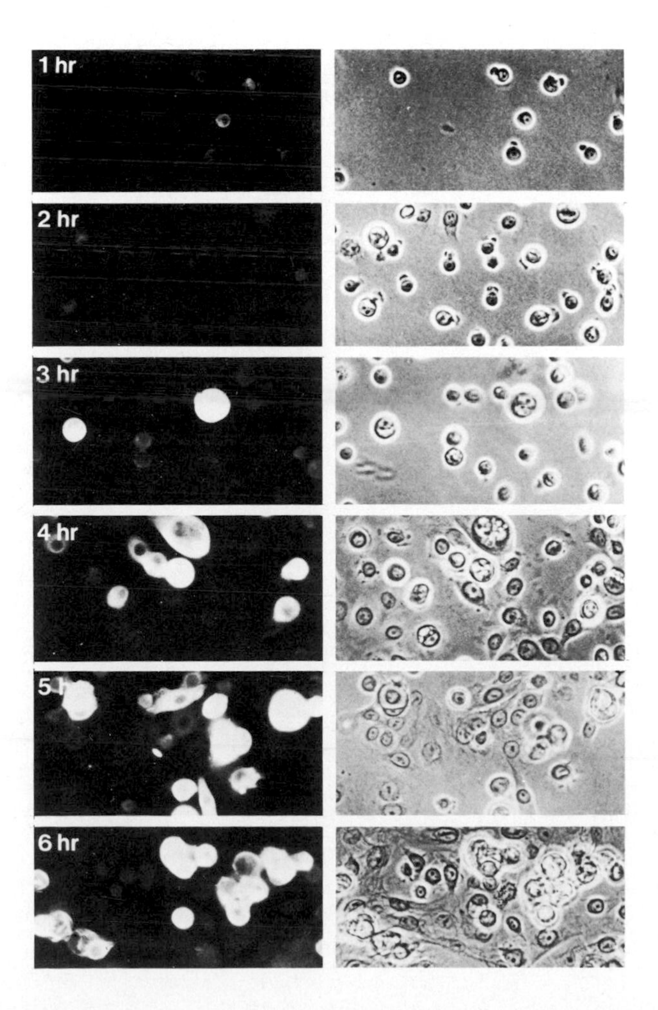

Fig. 6. Keratinocytes allowed to attach to tissue culture plastic for 1–6 h, as described for Fig. 5. Stained by immunofluorescence with antiserum to involucrin. ×180.

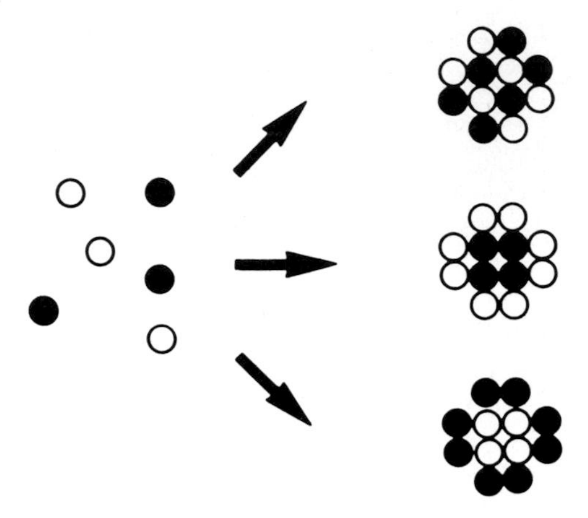

Fig. 7. Possible outcomes of aggregation of a mixture of involucrin-positive (○) and involucrin-negative (●) cells in suspension.

CHANGES IN CELL–CELL ADHESION DURING TERMINAL DIFFERENTIATION

In order to discover whether there are differences in cell–cell adhesiveness (cohesiveness) between basal and terminally differentiating keratinocytes, mixtures of involucrin-positive and -negative cells were allowed to aggregate, either free in suspension or encased in a capsule of agarose to which the cells do not adhere (Watt, 1984). Fig. 7 illustrates three possible positions of involucrin-positive and -negative cells within aggregates, showing the cells either interspersed throughout the aggregate or sorted to the centre or periphery. In fact, the cells sorted out, with involucrin-negative cells coming to the centre and involucrin-positive cells to the periphery of the aggregates (Fig. 8A) (Watt, 1984). Interpreting this result according to Steinberg's (1964) differential adhesion hypothesis, sorting out of the two subpopulations of cells indicates that they differ in cohesiveness, the involucrin-negative cells being more strongly cohesive, because they sort to the centre.

Sorting out of keratinocytes in aggregates has also been reported after injection of cells into host animals (Doran *et al.* 1980; Lavker & Sun, 1983). However, the polarity of the cysts formed *in vivo* is the opposite of that observed *in vitro*. The *in vivo* polarity can be mimicked *in vitro* by encasing keratinocytes in collagen instead of agarose (Fig. 8B): involucrin-negative cells adhere to the collagen and involucrin-positive cells become concentrated in the centre of the aggregate. Thus the presence of an adhesive substratum (host tissue in the case of the *in vivo* experiments) determines the relative positions of the cells.

MOLECULAR BASIS OF CHANGES IN KERATINOCYTE ADHESIVENESS

In vivo the basal layer of keratinocytes adheres to a basement membrane, the major components of which include laminin, fibronectin, type IV collagen and heparan sulphate proteoglycan (Briggaman, 1982). Keratinocytes in culture also synthesize basement membrane components (Kariniemi *et al.* 1982; Brown & Parkinson, 1984,

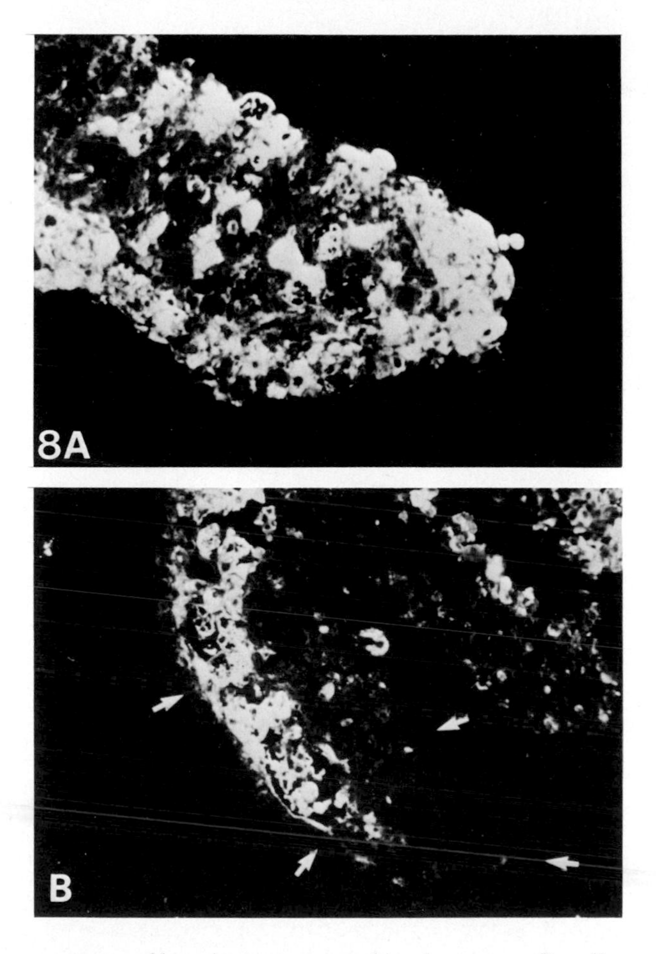

Fig. 8. Large aggregates of keratinocytes encased in: A, agarose; B, collagen. Stained by immunofluorescence with antiserum to involucrin. Note that in A involucrin-positive cells are concentrated at the periphery, while in B involucrin-negative cells are at the periphery, attached to collagen. Arrows in B indicate the boundary between cells and collagen. ×120.

1985; Kubo *et al.* 1984; O'Keefe *et al.* 1984; Bohnert *et al.* 1986) and synthesis is reduced during terminal differentiation (Brown & Parkinson, 1985). Keratinocytes in culture can adhere to purified substrata of fibronectin (Takashima & Grinnell, 1984; Clark *et al.* 1985; O'Keefe *et al.* 1985; and see Grinnell, this volume), laminin and collagen types I, III and IV (Stanley *et al.* 1980; Toda & Grinnell, 1987; Hicks & Watt, unpublished); and also to basement membrane secreted by parietal endoderm cells (Toda & Grinnell, 1987). The ability of cultured cells to adhere to these substrata is reduced during terminal differentiation (Stanley *et al.* 1980; Toda & Grinnell, 1987), suggesting that expression of functional receptors for basement membrane components is down-regulated.

Two other approaches are also proving useful in investigating the molecular basis of keratinocyte–substratum adhesion. One is to raise monoclonal antibodies against keratinocyte membranes and screen for antibodies that inhibit cell–substratum adhesion; the antigens recognized by the antibodies can then be identified (Katayama *et al.* 1986; Negi *et al.* 1986). The second is to identify the antigens recognized by antibodies circulating in the blood of patients with severe blistering disorders whose skin splits at the epidermal–dermal junction. For example, patients with bullous pemphigoid or epidermolysis bullosa acquisita have antibodies against antigens synthesized by normal keratinocytes (Woodley *et al.* 1982, 1985). In the former the antigen appears to be associated with hemidesmosomes (Westgate *et al.* 1985) and in the latter it is a $290 \times 10^3 M_r$ basement membrane component (Woodley *et al.* 1985).

Desmosomal junctions are thought to play an important role in mediating intercellular adhesion in epithelia, and keratinocytes in culture express and assemble all the major desmosomal proteins and glycoproteins (Watt *et al.* 1984). The main difference between desmosomal morphology *in vivo* and *in vitro* is that desmosomes formed *in vitro* tend to be smaller and lack a dense mid-line (Hennings & Holbrook, 1983; Magee *et al.* 1987). In intact epidermis the number of desmosomes per cell increases above the basal layer (Skerrow, 1978), making a role in the reduction of cohesiveness during terminal differentiation seem unlikely (nevertheless, there are no data on the numbers of desmosomes in the different layers of keratinocyte cultures). There is evidence of heterogeneity between desmosomal glycoproteins of the basal and suprabasal layers in intact epidermis and in culture (Parrish *et al.* 1986), and this would provide an alternative mechanism for changes in cellular cohesiveness. Other classes of intercellular junction expressed by keratinocytes in culture are tight junctions (Kitajima *et al.* 1983) and gap junctions (Pitts *et al.* 1987), but whether they have any role in mediating the changes in cohesiveness during terminal differentiation is unknown.

Several non-junctional membrane glycoproteins that mediate cell–cell adhesion in a range of cell types have now been described (Edelman, 1987). E-cadherin (Yoshida & Takeichi, 1982) (also known as L-CAM, uvomorulin, cell-CAM 120/80) is expressed by keratinocytes, both in intact epidermis (Damsky *et al.* 1983) and in culture (Watt, unpublished). However, E-cadherin is expressed by all living layers of keratinocytes, so again there is no evidence that it plays a role in the reduction of cohesiveness during terminal differentiation. An alternative possibility is that changes in keratinocyte surface carbohydrate during terminal differentiation, which take place *in vivo* (Reano *et al.* 1982; Nemanic *et al.* 1983; Watt, 1983; Bell & Skerrow, 1984) and in stratified cultures (Watt, 1983), could provide the molecular basis for the changes in cohesiveness.

In summary, there is some evidence that during terminal differentiation there is down-regulation of synthesis of basement membrane components and their receptors, and that this could provide the molecular basis of the observed reduction in cell–substratum adhesiveness. Although junctional and non-junctional molecules must be involved in cell–cell adhesion, the molecular basis for the reduction of cell cohesiveness during terminal differentiation is not clear.

CELL SHAPE AND TERMINAL DIFFERENTIATION

Restricted contact with the substratum leads to inhibition of proliferation and stimulation of differentiated gene expression in many non-transformed cell types (Watt, 1986; Ben-Ze'ev, this volume). When keratinocytes are cultured in suspension in methylcellulose, synthesis of protein (Rice & Green, 1978) and DNA (Rheinwald, 1979) is rapidly inhibited. In fibroblasts such inhibition can be reversed by replating onto an adhesive substratum (Benecke *et al.* 1978), but in keratinocytes the inhibition of DNA synthesis is irreversible and all colony-forming ability is lost after 24 h in suspension (Rheinwald, 1979). After 3 days in suspension the majority of keratinocytes form cornified envelopes (Rice & Green, 1978). By these criteria, namely loss of proliferative capacity and assembly of a cornified envelope, it appears that suspension culture induces premature terminal differentiation of keratinocytes.

Since adhesive affinity for the culture substratum is reduced during terminal differentiation, the possibility that artificially restricting substratum contact could act as a signal for keratinocyte terminal differentiation is clearly intriguing. To investigate this, we have made use of a technique developed by O'Neill *et al.* (1986) (see Ireland, this volume) in which cells are plated on circular palladium islands of defined size: island areas ranging from 400 to 5000 μm^2 permit cells to maintain shapes ranging from almost spherical to fully spread. We have plated involucrin-negative keratinocytes on these islands and measured the proportion of cells synthesizing DNA or expressing involucrin 3 days later (Watt, Jordan & O'Neill, unpublished). With increased spreading the proportion of cells that incorporate [^{3}H]thymidine into DNA increases and the proportion that contain involucrin decreases. This provides further evidence that cell shape can influence the proliferation and terminal differentiation of keratinocytes.

Keratinocytes enlarge during terminal differentiation (Watt & Green, 1981) and cells greater than a certain size are unable to divide (Barrandon & Green, 1985). Under conditions in which the area of substratum available is limited, both *in vivo* on basement membrane and *in vitro* on plastic, larger cells will have a smaller proportion of their surfaces involved in cell–substratum adhesion than smaller cells. One can therefore speculate that, if cell enlargement is an early stage in the commitment of keratinocytes to terminal differentiation, the simultaneous reduction in the proportion of cell surface involved in cell–substratum adhesion may lead to the down-regulation of basement membrane receptors and possibly, therefore, to migration out of the basal layer.

CONCLUSIONS

In this article I have reviewed evidence that changes in keratinocyte adhesiveness during terminal differentiation ensure cell migration out of the basal layer. In culture, expression of involucrin provides a useful marker of all cells that have left the basal layer, but in epidermis expression may be delayed until the upper spinous layers (Banks-Schlegel & Green, 1981). There is therefore no reason to propose that the onset of involucrin synthesis itself plays a role in changes in adhesiveness.

The molecular basis of the reduction in cell–substratum adhesion may be down-regulation of expression of basement membrane components and their receptors, but the molecular basis of the reduction in cohesiveness is largely a matter for speculation. At present the identification of these molecules is clearly of interest, not just for an understanding of how terminal differentiation is normally coupled to upward migration, but also because it may provide some insight into the abnormal organization of keratinocytes in tumours.

There is growing evidence that restricted substratum contact can act as a signal to keratinocytes to stop dividing and initiate terminal differentiation. The question of which comes first, reduced affinity for the substratum or reduced substratum contact, is clearly of interest for the future.

I am grateful to Jim Smith for providing the artwork for Figures 1, 2 and 3 and to Yvonne Thurley for typing the manuscript. I also thank the members of my laboratory, past and present, who share my enthusiasm for studying keratinocytes.

REFERENCES

BANKS-SCHLEGEL, S. & GREEN, H. (1981). Involucrin synthesis and tissue assembly by keratinocytes in natural and cultured human epithelia. *J. Cell Biol.* **90**, 732–737.

BARRANDON, Y. & GREEN, H. (1985). Cell size as a determinant of the clone-forming ability of human keratinocytes. *Proc. natn. Acad. Sci. U.S.A.* **82**, 5390–5394.

BELL, C. M. & SKERROW, C. J. (1984). Factors affecting the binding of lectins to normal human skin. *Br. J. Derm.* **111**, 517–526.

BELL, E., EHRLICH, H. P., BUTTLE, D. J. & NAKATSUJI, T. (1981). Living tissue formed *in vitro* and accepted as skin-equivalent tissue of full thickness. *Science* **211**, 1052–1054.

BENECKE, B. J., BEN-ZE'EV, A. & PENMAN, S. (1978). The control of mRNA production, translation and turnover in suspended and reattached anchorage-dependent fibroblasts. *Cell* **14**, 931–939.

BEN ZE'EV, A. (1987). The role of changes in cell shape and contacts in the regulation of cytoskeleton expression during differentiation. *J. Cell Sci. Suppl. 8*, 293–312.

BOHNERT, A., HORNUNG, J., MACKENZIE, I. C. & FUSENIG, N. E. (1986). Epithelial–mesenchymal interactions control basement membrane production and differentiation in cultured and transplanted mouse keratinocytes. *Cell Tiss. Res.* **244**, 413–429.

BOYCE, S. T. & HAM, R. G. (1983). Calcium-regulated differentiation of normal human epidermal keratinocytes in chemically defined clonal culture and serum-free serial culture. *J. invest. Derm.* **81**, 33s–40s.

BRIGGAMAN, R. A. (1982). Biochemical composition of the epidermal–dermal junction and other basement membrane. *J. invest. Derm.* **78**, 1–6.

BROWN, K. W. & PARKINSON, E. K. (1984). Extracellular matrix components produced by SV40-transformed human epidermal keratinocytes. *Int. J. Cancer* **33**, 257–263.

BROWN, K. W. & PARKINSON, E. K. (1985). Alteration of the extracellular matrix of cultured human keratinocytes by transformation and during differentiation. *Int. J. Cancer* **35**, 799–807.

CLARK, R. A. F., FOLKVORD, J. M. & WERTZ, R. L. (1985). Fibronectin, as well as other extracellular matrix proteins, mediate human keratinocyte adherence. *J. invest. Derm.* **84**, 378–383.

DAMSKY, C. H., RICHA, J., SOLTER, D., KNUSDEN, K. & BUCK, C. A. (1983). Identification and purification of a cell surface glycoprotein mediating intercellular adhesion in embryonic and adult tissue. *Cell* **34**, 455–466.

DORAN, T. I., VIDRICH, A. & SUN, T.-T. (1980). Intrinsic and extrinsic regulation of the differentiation of skin, corneal and esophageal epithelial cells. *Cell* **22**, 17–25.

EDELMAN, G. M. (1987). Epigenetic rules for expression of cell adhesion molecules during morphogenesis. In *Junctional Complexes of Epithelial Cells* (ed. G. Bock & S. Clarke), *Ciba Foundation Symp. 125*, pp. 192–216. Chichester, New York: John Wiley and Sons.

FARBMAN, A. I. (1966). Plasma membrane changes during keratinization. *Anat. Res.* **156**, 269–282.

FUSENIG, N. E., BREITKREUTZ, D., DZARLIEVA, R. T., BOUKAMP, P., BOHNERT, A. & TILGEN, W. (1983). Growth and differentiation characteristics of transformed keratinocytes from mouse and human skin in vitro and in vivo. *J. invest. Derm.* **81**, 168s–175s.

GREEN, H. (1978). Cyclic AMP in relation to proliferation of the epidermal cell: a new view. *Cell* **15**, 801–811.

GREEN, H. (1980). The keratinocyte as differentiated cell type. *Harvey Lectures* **74**, 101–139.

GRINNELL, F., TODA, K.-I. & TAKASHIMA, A. (1987). Activation of keratinocyte fibronectin receptor function during cutaneous wound healing. *J. Cell Sci. Suppl. 8*, 199–209.

HASHIMOTO, K. (1969). Cellular envelopes of keratinized cells of the human epidermis. *Arch. klin. exp. Derm.* **235**, 374–385.

HENNINGS, H. & HOLBROOK, K. A. (1983). Calcium regulation of cell–cell contact and differentiation of epidermal cells in culture. An ultrastructural study. *Expl Cell Res.* **143**, 127–142.

HENNINGS, H., MICHAEL, D., CHENG, C., STEINERT, P., HOLBROOK, K. & YUSPA, S. H. (1980). Calcium regulation of growth and differentiation of mouse epidermal cells in culture. *Cell* **19**, 245–254.

IRELAND, G. W., DOPPING-HEPENSTAL, P., JORDAN, P. & O'NEILL, C. (1987). Effect of patterned surfaces of adhesive islands on the shape, cytoskeleton, adhesion and behaviour of Swiss mouse 3T3 fibroblasts. *J. Cell Sci. Suppl. 8*, 19–33.

KARASEK, M. A. & CHARLTON, M. E. (1971). Growth of postembryonic skin epithelial cells on collagen gels. *J. invest. Derm.* **56**, 205–210.

KARINIEMI, A.-L., LEHTO, V.-P., VARTIO, T. & VIRTANEN, I. (1982). Cytoskeleton and pericellular matrix organization of pure adult human keratinocytes cultured from suction-blister roof epidermis. *J. Cell Sci.* **58**, 49–61.

KATAYAMA, H., KINO, J., ITAMI, S., TSUTSUI, M., KOIZUMI, H., HALPRIN, K. M. & ADACHI, K. (1986). Monoclonal antibodies against epidermal cell surface and dermal–epidermal junction: antigens which may be cell spreading factors. *Br. J. Derm.* **115**, 13–22.

KITAJIMA, Y., EGUCHI, K., OHNO, T., MORI, S. & YAOITA, H. (1983). Tight junctions of human keratinocytes in primary culture: a freeze fracture study. *J. Ultrastruct. Res.* **82**, 309–313.

KUBO, M., NORRIS, D. A., HOWELL, S. E., RYAN, S. R. & CLARK, R. A. F. (1984). Human keratinocytes synthesize, secrete, and deposit fibronectin in the pericellular matrix. *J. invest. Derm.* **82**, 580–586.

LAVKER, R. M. & SUN, T.-T. (1983). Rapid modulation of keratinocyte differentiation by the external environment. *J. invest. Derm.* **80**, 228–237.

MAGEE, A. I., LYTTON, N. A. & WATT, F. M. (1987). Calcium-induced changes in cytoskeleton and motility of cultured human keratinocytes. *Expl Cell. Res.* **172**, 43–53.

NEGI, M., LANE, A. T., MCCOON, P. E., FAIRLEY, J. A. & GOLDSMITH, L. A. (1986). Monoclonal antibody to a 35 kD epidermal protein induces cell detachment. *J. invest. Derm.* **86**, 634–637.

NEMANIC, M. K., WHITEHEAD, J. S. & ELIAS, P. M. (1983). Alterations in membrane sugars during epidermal differentiation: visualization with lectins and role of glycosidases. *J. Histochem. Cytochem.* **31**, 887–897.

O'KEEFE, E. J., PAYNE, R. E. JR, RUSSELL, N. & WOODLEY, D. T. (1985). Spreading and enhanced motility of human keratinocytes on fibronectin. *J. invest. Derm.* **85**, 125–130.

O'KEEFE, E. J., WOODLEY, D., CASTILLO, G., RUSSELL, N. & PAYNE, R. E. JR (1984). Production of soluble and cell-associated fibronectin by cultured keratinocytes. *J. invest. Derm.* **82**, 150–155.

O'NEILL, C., JORDAN, P. & IRELAND, G. (1986). Evidence for two distinct mechanisms of anchorage stimulation in freshly explanted and 3T3 Swiss mouse fibroblasts. *Cell* **41**, 489–496.

PARRISH, E. P., GARROD, D. R., MATTEY, D. L., HAND, L., STEART, P. V. & WELLER, R. O. (1986). Mouse antisera specific for desmosomal adhesion molecules of suprabasal skin cells, meninges and meningioma. *Proc. natn. Acad. Sci. U.S.A.* **83**, 2657–2661.

PITTS, J., KAM, E., MELVILLE, L. & WATT, F. M. (1987). Patterns of junctional communication in animal tissues. In *Junctional Complexes of Epithelial Cells* (ed. G. Bock & S. Clark), *Ciba Foundation Symp.* 125, pp. 140–153. Chichester, New York: John Wiley and Sons.

PRUNIÉRAS, M., RÉGNIER, M. & WOODLEY, D. (1983). Methods of cultivation of keratinocytes with an air–liquid interface. *J. invest. Derm.* **81**, 28s–33s.

REANO, A., FAURÉ, M., JACQUES, Y., REICHERT, U., SCHAEFER, H. & THIVOLET, J. (1982). Lectins as markers of human epidermal cell differentiation. *Differentiation* **22**, 205–210.

RÉGNIER, M., VAIGOT, P., DARMON, M. & PRUNIÉRAS, M. (1986). Onset of epidermal differentiation in rapidly proliferating basal keratinocytes. *J. invest. Derm.* **87**, 472–476.

RHEINWALD, J. G. (1979). The role of terminal differentiation in the finite culture lifetime of the human epidermal keratinocyte. *Int. Rev. Cytol. Suppl.* **10**, 25–33.

RHEINWALD, J. G. & GREEN, H. (1975). Serial cultivation of strains of human epidermal keratinocytes: the formation of keratinizing colonies from single cells. *Cell* **6**, 331–344.

RHEINWALD, J. G. & GREEN, H. (1977). Epidermal growth factor and the multiplication of cultured human epidermal keratinocytes. *Nature, Lond.* **265**, 421–424.

RICE, R. H. & GREEN, H. (1978). Relation of protein synthesis and transglutaminase activity to formation of the cross-linked envelope during terminal differentiation of the cultured human epidermal keratinocyte. *J. Cell Biol.* **76**, 705–711.

RICE, R. H. & GREEN, H. (1979). Presence in human epidermal cells of a soluble protein precursor of the cross-linked envelope: activation of the cross-linking by calcium ions. *Cell* **18**, 681–694.

SENGEL, P. (1976). *Morphogenesis of Skin.* Cambridge University Press.

SIMON, M. & GREEN, H. (1984). Participation of membrane-associated proteins in the formation of the cross-linked envelope of the keratinocyte. *Cell* **36**, 827–834.

SKERROW, C. J. (1978). Intercellular adhesion and its role in epidermal differentiation. *Invest. Cell Path.* **1**, 23–37.

SKERROW, D. & SKERROW, C. J. (1983). Tonofilament differentiation in human epidermis, isolation and polypeptide chain composition of keratinocyte subpopulations. *Expl Cell Res.* **143**, 27–35.

STANLEY, J. R., FOIDART, J.-M., MURRAY, J. C., MARTIN, G. R. & KATZ, S. I. (1980). The epidermal cell which selectively adheres to a collagen substrate is the basal cell. *J. invest. Derm.* **74**, 54–58.

STEINBERG, M. S. (1964). The problem of adhesive selectivity in cellular interactions. In *Cellular Membranes in Development* (ed. M. Locke), pp. 321–366. New York, London: Academic Press.

SUN, T.-T. & GREEN, H. (1976). Differentiation of the epidermal keratinocyte in cell culture: Formation of the cornified envelope. *Cell* **9**, 511–521.

TAKASHIMA, A. & GRINNELL, F. (1984). Human keratinocyte adhesion and phagocytosis promoted by fibronectin. *J. invest. Derm.* **83**, 352–358.

TODA, K. & GRINNELL, F. (1987). Activation of human keratinocyte fibronectin receptor function in relation to other ligand–receptor interactions. *J. invest. Derm.* **88**, 412–417.

WATT, F. M. (1983). Involucrin and other markers of keratinocyte terminal differentiation. *J. invest. Derm.* **81**, 100s–103s.

WATT, F. M. (1984). Selective migration of terminally differentiating cells from the basal layer of cultured human epidermis. *J. Cell Biol.* **98**, 16–21.

WATT, F. M. (1986). The extracellular matrix and cell shape. *Trends Biochem. Sci.* **11**, 482–485.

WATT, F. M., BOUKAMP, P., HORNUNG, J. & FUSENIG, N. E. (1987). Effect of growth environment on spatial expression of involucrin by human epidermal keratinocytes. *Archs Derm. Res.* **279**, 335–340.

WATT, F. M. & GREEN, H. (1981). Involucrin synthesis is correlated with cell size in human epidermal cultures. *J. Cell Biol.* **90**, 738–742.

WATT, F. M. & GREEN, H. (1982). Stratification and terminal differentiation of cultured epidermal cells. *Nature, Lond.* **295**, 434–436.

WATT, F. M., MATTEY, D. L. & GARROD, D. R. (1984). Calcium-induced reorganisation of desmosomal components in cultured human keratinocytes. *J. Cell Biol.* **99**, 2211–2215.

WESTGATE, G. E., WEAVER, A. C. & COUCHMAN, J. R. (1985). Bullous pemphigoid antigen localization suggests an intracellular association with hemidesmosomes. *J. invest. Derm.* **84**, 218–224.

WOODLEY, D. T., BRIGGAMAN, R. A., GAMMON, W. R. & O'KEEFE, E. J. (1985). Epidermolysis bullosa acquisita antigen is synthesized by human keratinocytes cultured in serum-free medium. *Biochem. biophys. Res. Commun.* **130**, 1267–1272.

WOODLEY, D., SAURAT, J. H., PRUNIÉRAS, M. & RÉGNIER, M. (1982). Pemphigoid, pemiphigus and Pr antigens in adult human keratinocytes grown on nonviable substrates. *J. invest. Derm.* **79**, 23–29.

WU, Y.-J., PARKER, L. M., BINDER, N. E., BECKETT, M. A., SINARD, J. H., GRIFFITHS, C. T. & RHEINWALD, J. G. (1982). The mesothelial keratins: a new family of cytoskeletal proteins identified in cultured mesothelial cells and nonkeratinizing epithelia. *Cell* **31**, 693–703.

YOSHIDA, C. & TAKEICHI, M. (1982). Teratocarcinoma cell adhesion: identification of a cell-surface protein involved in calcium-dependent cell aggregation. *Cell* **28**, 217–224.

J. Cell Sci. Suppl. 8, 327–343 (1987)

THE INFLUENCE OF EXTRACELLULAR MATRIX ON GENE EXPRESSION: IS STRUCTURE THE MESSAGE?

MINA J. BISSELL AND MARY HELEN BARCELLOS-HOFF

Laboratory of Cell Biology, Division Biology and Medicine, Lawrence Berkeley Laboratory, UC Berkeley, CA 94720, USA

SUMMARY

The study of the regulation of gene expression in cultured cells, particularly in epithelial cells, has been both hampered and facilitated by the loss of function that accompanies culture on traditional plastic substrata. Initially, investigations of differentiated function were thwarted by the inadequacy of tissue culture methods developed to support growth of mesenchymal cells. However, with the recognition that the unit of function in higher organisms is larger than the cell itself, and that gene expression is dependent upon cell interactions with hormones, substrata and other cells, came the understanding that the epithelial cell phenotype is profoundly influenced by the extracellular environment. In the last decade research on epithelial cells has centred on culture conditions that recreate the appropriate environment for function with very promising and important results. The investigations into the modulation of phenotype in culture produced not only a better model, but also contributed to a better understanding of the regulation of normal function. Using cultured mammary gland epithelial cells as a primary model of these interactions, our studies of gene expression are based on three premises.

(1) That the extracellular matrix (ECM) on which the cells sit is an extension of the cells and an active participant in the regulation of cellular function; i.e. the ECM is an 'informational' entity in the sense that it receives, imparts and integrates structural and functional signals.

(2) That ECM-induced functional differentiation in the mammary gland is mediated through changes in cell shape, i.e. that the structure is in large part 'the message' required to maintain differentiated gene expression.

(3) That the unit of function includes the cell plus its extracellular matrix; in a larger context, the unit is the organ itself.

These tenets and the data presented below are consistent with a model of 'Dynamic Reciprocity', where the ECM is postulated to exert an influence on gene expression *via* transmembrane proteins and cytoskeletal components. In turn, cytoskeletal association with polyribosomes affects mRNA stability and rates of protein synthesis, while its interaction with the nuclear matrix could affect mRNA processing and, possibly, rates of transcription.

THE INFLUENCE OF EXTRACELLULAR MATRIX ON GENE EXPRESSION

One of the major aims of tissue culturists during the early part of this century was to study the regulation of gene expression (Paul, 1970; Davidson, 1964). However, the challenge of growing pieces of tissues and, later, single cells proved to be all-consuming, and the study of function was generally relegated to a secondary position. In addition, tissue-specific traits were so rapidly altered in culture, and often in such unexpected ways, that it was frequently unclear what one studied. Therefore, the relationship between studies of gene expression in cultured cells and regulation of differentiated function *in vivo* remained obscure for decades.

Nevertheless, the loss of function in culture itself pointed to the crucial role of the cellular environment in regulation of tissue-specific genes (for review, see M. J. Bissell, 1981). Since almost all functional changes in primary cultures, and even in some cell lines, are due to phenotypic alteration, differentiated cell behaviour is inextricably connected with the extracellular environment, i.e. media, hormones and the substrata on which the cells are cultured. Indeed the events that accompany the loss of function in culture can be used to advantage in studying regulation of normal function (D. M. Bissell, 1976). Thus, for studies of regulation of gene expression, the most useful system is one in which function can be modulated by culture conditions so that one can discern the regulatory factors and mechanisms (Bissell, 1981). Studies of cultured epithelial cells presented a special challenge in this regard since function, and even growth, on traditional (two-dimensional) plastic culture dishes was limited and difficult to regulate.

It has been known for some time that extracellular matrix (ECM) plays a vital role in tissue organization and in migration of embryonic cells during development (Wessells, 1977; Adamson, 1982). In the last decade, there has been an increasing appreciation that ECM also plays an important role in regulation of tissue-specific gene expression (for review, see Bissell *et al.* 1982), and the mammary gland has provided a versatile model for studying this relationship. Profound morphological changes occur during the natural progression of the gland *in vivo* as well as when secretory mammary epithelial cells are isolated and placed in culture. Since morphology is an important key to epithelial differentiation *in vivo*, cytostructure in culture provides an indication of degree of differentiation. The success of culture conditions can also be measured by comparing the patterns of synthesis and secretion of milk proteins against milk composition *in vivo*. Finally, responsiveness to lactogenic hormones offers a further indication of tissue-specific physiological function in culture.

PROMOTION OF MORPHOLOGICAL DIFFERENTIATION

Following the example of Elsdale & Bard (1972) and Emerman & Pitelka (1977), we (Emerman *et al.* 1981; Bissell *et al.* 1982; Lee *et al.* 1984, 1985, 1987; Parry *et al.* 1985; Li *et al.* 1987) and others (Shannon & Pitelka, 1981; Haeuptle *et al.* 1983; Rocha *et al.* 1985; Wicha, 1984) have shown that several aspects of functional epithelium can be maintained when primary mouse mammary epithelial (PMME) cells are cultured on 'released' (or 'floating') collagen type I gels or on reconstituted basement membranes (EHS; Engelbreth-Holmes-Swarm tumour matrix; Kleinman *et al.* 1986) instead of plastic or flat gels. Viewed by scanning EM, cells on plastic (Fig. 1A) are flat and have few microvilli, while cells on floating collagen gel or EHS (Fig. 1B) are rounded and their surfaces are covered with microvilli. Viewed by transmission electron miscroscopy (TEM), PMME cells on plastic or flat collagen gels have a high nuclear/cytoplasmic ratio, lack internal polarization and secretory apparatus and have short, stubby microvilli on their apical surfaces (Emerman & Pitelka, 1977). By contrast, after the gel is released cells become columnar and polar,

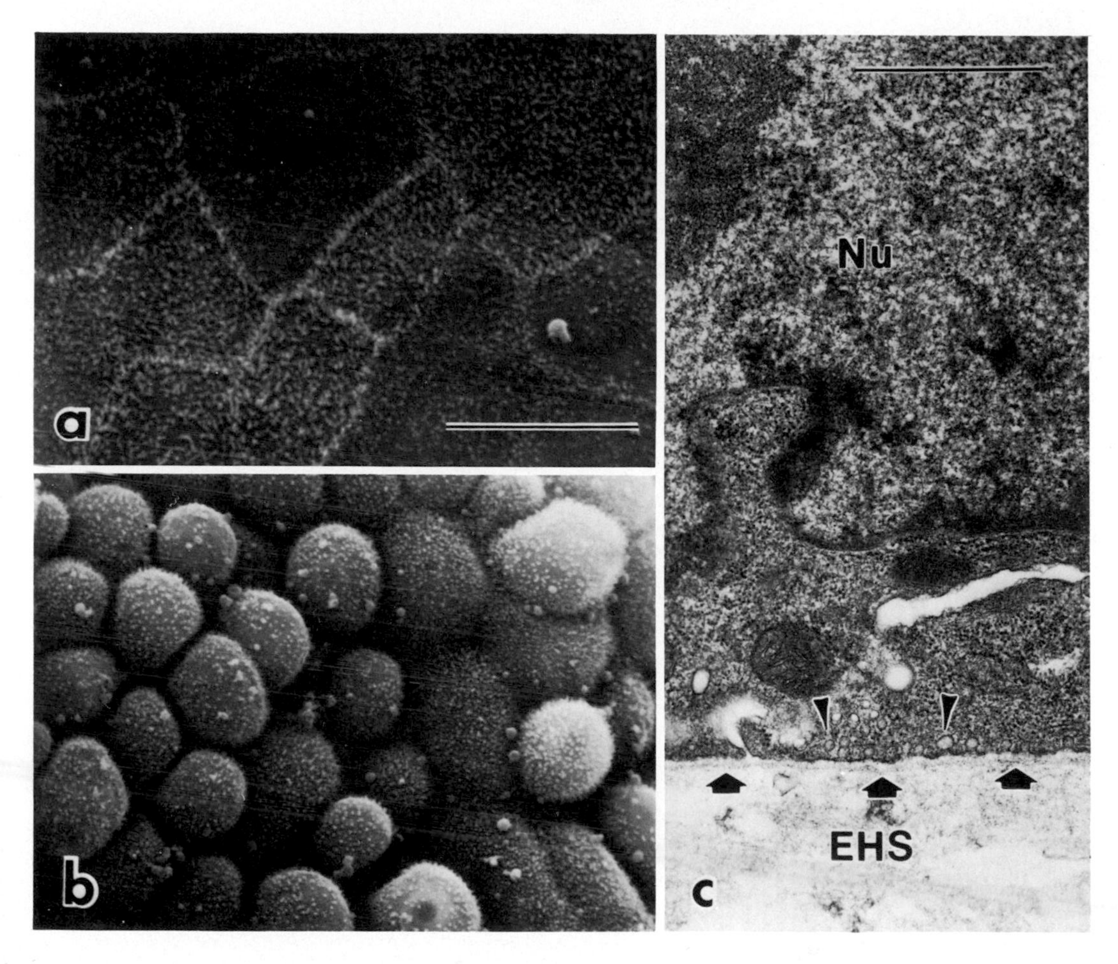

Fig. 1. EM of PMME on different substrata: 7-day cultures of PMME in the presence of lactogenic hormones were fixed and processed for SEM or TEM as described (Li *et al.* 1987). A. On plastic, cells are flat and have short microvilli. B. On EHS, cells are rounded and covered with microvilli. C. When observed by transmission EM, the basal surfaces of the cells making up the alveolar structures on EHS are seen to be completely covered by a thin, continuous basal lamina (arrows); numerous small vesicles are found at, or near, the adjacent plasma membrane (arrowheads). Bars: A,B, 10 μm; C, 1 μm. (Bissell & Aggeler, 1987, reproduced with permission.)

and contain an extensive network of distended rough endoplasmic reticulum, Golgi apparati, secretory vesicles and fat droplets. A visible and continuous basal lamina separates the epithelium from the gel, cells have tight junctions and they display extensive microvilli on their apical surface that are reminiscent of lactating mammary epithelium (Emerman & Pitelka, 1977). Cells on EHS are also morphologically differentiated and are surrounded by a thin, but continuous, basal lamina, which separates them from the less-dense matrix in which they are embedded (Fig. 1C).

The ECM has a profound effect not only on an individual cell's cytostructure, but also on the organization of cells in tissue-like forms. As was shown for thyroid cells

(Chambord *et al.* 1981; see Mauchamp *et al.*, this volume), mammary cell lines and MDCK cells (Hall *et al.* 1982) form lumina when sandwiched between two layers of collagen gels. Three-dimensional organization of PMME also change with the type of substrata (Fig. 2). Cells on plastic, while capable of forming large and small domes (Fig. 2A) depending on age and culture density, demonstrate low levels of functional and morphological differentiation (Fig. 3A). Cells on flat gels, while slightly more polar, remain poorly differentiated (not shown), but when the gel is released the cells contract the gel to form a three-dimensional structure that enhances morphological differentiation (Fig. 2B) such as the cell–cell contacts that are necessary for a physiological transporting epithelium (Bisbee *et al.* 1979). The most striking approximation of *in vivo* organization and morphology occurs when PMME are plated onto a thin layer of EHS. The cells form domes and duct-like structures as seen by phase-contrast microscopy (Fig. 2C), and are clearly composed of polar epithelial cells organized around a central lumen (Fig. 1C, 3B).

EXPRESSION OF FUNCTIONAL DIFFERENTIATION

The dramatic morphological changes observed when mammary cells are seeded onto collagen gels and floated are accompanied by multiple and complex functional changes. Using the two-dimensional pattern of mouse skim-milk proteins as a reference, we analysed the secreted proteins of PMME cells maintained on plastic, on attached collagen type I gels, or on released gels (Lee *et al.* 1984). The pattern of secreted proteins is more complex than that of milk under all three conditions. Furthermore, there are both substratum- and shape-specific changes. The secreted proteins fall into at least four categories: (1) milk proteins, such as transferrin, that, although substratum-sensitive, are present under all conditions. (2) Milk proteins, such as caseins, that are extremely hormone-, substratum- and shape-dependent. (3) Proteins that are not detected in skim milk but are present in culture medium. Some of these are related to milk fat globule proteins, which are routinely removed from milk and thus are not present in the skim-milk profile; others are unknown proteins that are not present in either milk or in medium from freshly isolated cells and are thus either suppressed *in vivo* or induced in culture. (4) Milk proteins, such as whey acidic protein (WAP) and α-lactalbumin, that are essentially absent even in medium from released gel cultures (Lee *et al.* 1984). Thus, while the substratum profoundly influences the secretion of the hormonally sensitive caseins, regulation of milk proteins is not coordinated and requires lactogenic hormones, proper ECM and other undetermined factors for full expression.

To determine whether proteins were synthesized but retained intracellularly, we immunoprecipitated cellular proteins with a broad spectrum polyclonal antibody to skim-milk proteins. These experiments showed that secretion was a reasonably good measure of protein synthetic rate (Fig. 4; Lee *et al.* 1985). The exception was the β-casein pool in cells on plastic (and flat gels) where an intracellular pool existed in the absence of secretion (Fig. 4). Pulse–chase experiments clearly indicated that the

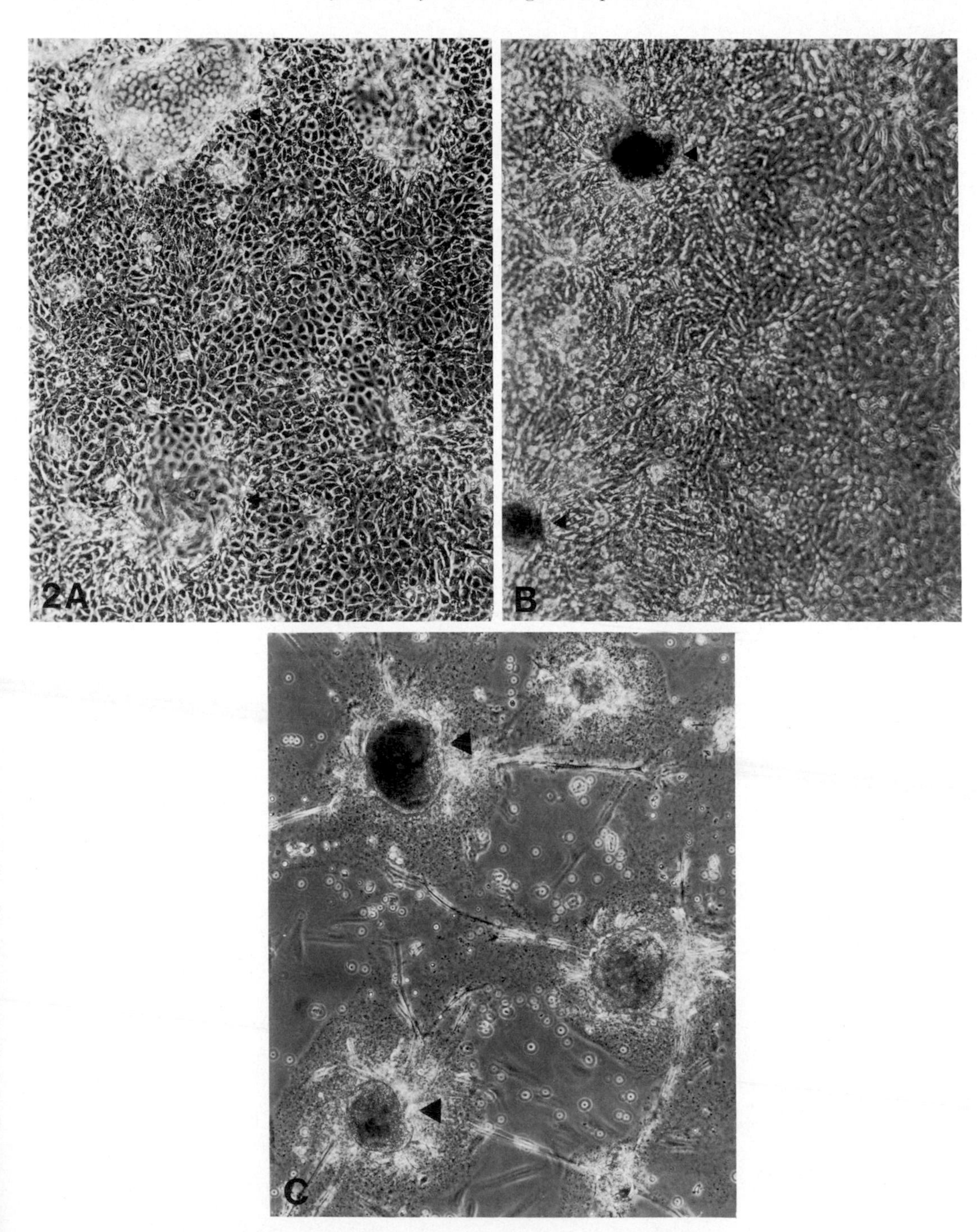

Fig. 2. Morphology of PMME on various substrata. Phase-contrast of 6-day cultures of PMME on: A, plastic; B, floating collagen gel (part of plane is out of focus because of gel thickness); C, EHS. Although domes (small arrowheads) are present on plastic and collagen gel, PMME on EHS also form striking alveolar-like structures (large arrowheads).

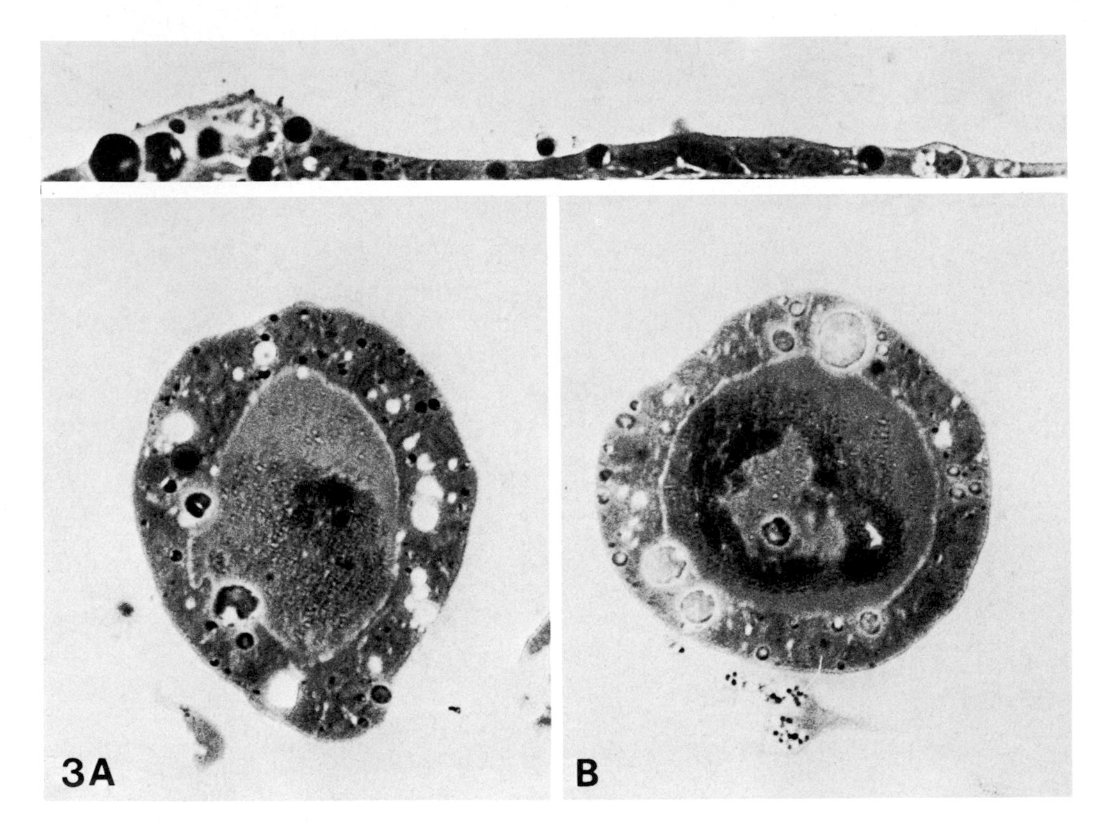

Fig. 3. Morphology of PMME on plastic and EHS substrata. PMME from 8-day cultures incubated in the presence of lactogenic hormones were fixed, embedded in Epon, and thick sections were cut. A. Flattened cells on plastic. B. Alveolar lumina formed by cells cultured on EHS matrix. (Bissel & Aggeler, 1987, reproduced with permission.)

intracellular pool of β-casein in cells on plastic was rapidly degraded (Lee *et al.* 1985), suggesting that the changes in cell shape and possibly establishment of cell–cell junctions that accompany culture on floating gels may be essential to β-casein secretion.

During pregnancy the mammary epithelium has paracellular pathways that enable the vascular network and gland lumen to be in communication. Shortly after parturition, however, the epithelium forms tight junctions that seal the lumen from extracellular spaces in order to facilitate transport of isotonic fluid and enhance vectorial segregation of milk proteins (Neville, 1987). The tight junctions observed between cells on released gels suggest that a polar, functional epithelium is being created. Studies on the electrophysiological and ion-transport characteristics of PMME cells (Bisbee *et al.* 1979) and polar secretion of milk proteins (Neville, 1987) support this conclusion. Cells on EHS also demonstrate tight junctions and are further organized into polarized lumina (Fig. 3). We have determined that this morphology is accompanied by vectorial secretion of milk proteins by comparing the protein composition of the external medium with that obtained from the EDTA-treated lumina (Fig. 5; Barcellos-Hoff *et al.* 1987). A comparison of the immunoprecipitated protein patterns from the medium with that from the 'lumina' of cells grown on EHS indicates that a great proportion of milk proteins is secreted into the lumen by cells on EHS (Fig. 5). The presence of milk proteins in the medium of EHS cultures may be a function of the extent of the areas of monolayer growth.

In experiments reported recently (Li *et al.* 1987), a high percentage (>90 %) of PMME cells grown on EHS-coated plates expressed high levels of β-casein as detected with immunofluorescence, while 30–40 % of cells on released gels and only 2–10 % of cells on plastic produced β-casein. Since only 40 % of cells from late-pregnant gland were producing β-casein before culture in this experiment, the EHS matrix appears to both 'induce' and maintain an increased level of casein gene expression. Effects of substratum and shape on milk protein expression are not restricted to translational and post-translational events, but also involve transcription and post-transcriptional regulation, as evidenced by β-casein and transferrin mRNA accumulation that reflects protein secretion patterns (Lee *et al.* 1985; Chen *et al.*

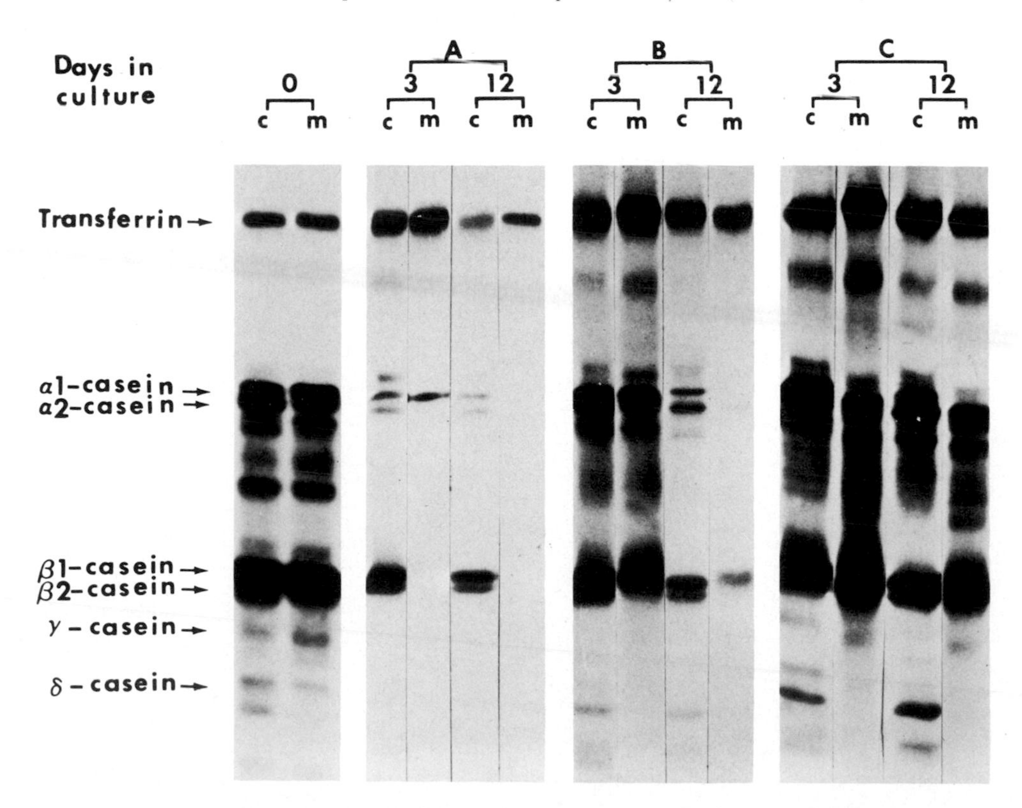

Fig. 4. Time course of production and secretion of milk proteins on plastic and on attached and released gels. Mammary epithelial cells from 14- to 16-day pregnant mice were labelled immediately after isolation (0) or cultured on different substrata and labelled on day 3 or 12 as indicated. Samples were immunoprecipitated with mouse milk polyclonal antibody and subjected to SDS–polyacrylamide gel electrophoresis. c, Cellular proteins; m, media proteins. Lanes: A, plastic; B, attached gel; C, released gel (Lee *et al.* 1985).

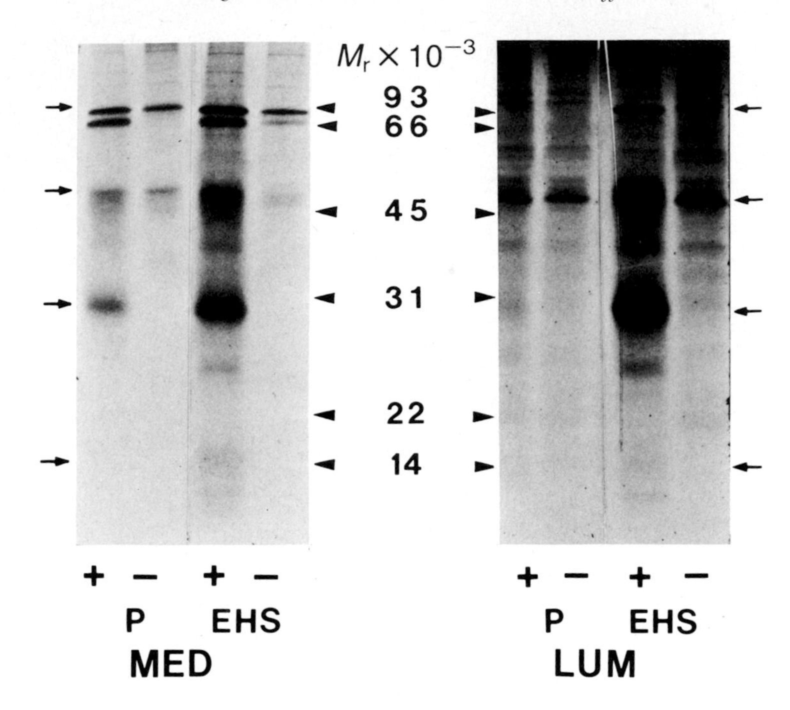

Fig. 5. Milk protein production and secretion of PMME cells on plastic and EHS. PMME cells were labelled on day 6 of culture on plastic (P) and EHS in the presence (+) or absence (−) of lactogenic hormones. Equal counts from samples were immunoprecipitated with mouse milk polyclonal antibody and equal volumes subjected to SDS–polyacrylamide gel electrophoresis. Arrowheads indicate molecular weight markers ($\times 10^{-3}$); small arrows indicate location of abundant milk proteins. MED, media; LUM, lumen contents extracted with 2·5 mM-EDTA (Barcellos-Hoff & Bissell, unpublished).

1986; Li *et al.* 1987). Since cDNA probes to many milk proteins are available, it is possible to study the regulation of milk protein mRNA as a function of substratum and shape. The immunofluorescence data cited above were accompanied by an 18-fold increase in β-casein mRNA over that of cells on plastic. A film of EHS coated on top of a flat gel increased β-casein mRNA further (22-fold plastic), while releasing the EHS-coated gel from the culture dish produced a remarkable increase of 70-fold more message than that detected from cells on plastic. That the ECM can also modulate β-casein gene expression in consecutive passages of COMMA-1D, a cell strain derived from pregnant mouse gland, further demonstrates the reversibility and inducibility of ECM effects (Medina *et al.* 1987).

The reconstituted EHS-derived basement membrane is composed of laminin, type IV collagen, heparan sulphate proteoglycan (HSPG) and entactin (Kleinman *et al.* 1986). Individual components of basement membranes are not nearly as effective as EHS, suggesting that a complex matrix is needed for producing increased expression of mammary-specific function. This appears to be true also for hepatocytes (D. M. Bissell *et al.* 1987). Of the individual components of basement membranes tested, collagen type IV and fibronectin appear to have no effect on morphology or casein gene expression in PMME cells under the conditions tested, while laminin and

HSPG increase β-casein mRNA from 3- to 10-fold, respectively (Li *et al.* 1987). However, there is little or no concomitant increase in secreted β-casein from cells grown on HSPG even though other proteins are secreted at levels comparable to cells on other substrata. Cells on HSPG appear extremely flat and irregular when viewed by scanning EM (Li *et al.* 1987). It is thus possible that intracellular degradation is occurring as in cells on plastic, although other possibilities such as HSPG-induced toxicity leading to induced caseinolytic activity have not been ruled out.

AUGMENTATION OF HORMONAL RESPONSIVENESS

Maintenance and differentiation of mammary gland depend upon the presence of one or more of the lactogenic hormones, insulin, hydrocortisone and prolactin (Topper *et al.* 1986). Studies in mouse, rat and rabbit mammary gland cultures (Rosen *et al.* 1986; Lee *et al.* 1985; Houdebine *et al.* 1983; Haueptle *et al.* 1983) show that prolactin is essential for casein protein and mRNA expression. Our studies indicate that cells on all substrata retain the capability of responding to prolactin, but that the magnitude of response increases in cells on flat collagen gels in comparison to cells on plastic, and is even greater on released collagen gels (Lee *et al.* 1985) or EHS (unpublished data). Thus, the ECM enhances the ability of cells to respond to hormones. Conversely, the absence of prolactin unilaterally suppresses β-casein expression even in the somewhat morphologically differentiated cells on EHS (Bissell & Aggeler, 1987).

Not all milk proteins are sensitive to prolactin, however. On plastic, transferrin is synthesized and secreted in the absence of prolactin (Lee *et al.* 1987). Since there is a tremendous increase in transferrin protein level in the pregnant mouse (Lee *et al.* 1987) factors other than prolactin must therefore regulate its level. In culture, ECM rather than prolactin appear to be the over-riding influence on transferrin mRNA levels (Fig. 6; Bissell & Hall, 1987; Chen & Bissell, 1987). Since the composition of the mRNAs for ECM components is altered when the animal becomes pregnant (Park & Bissell, 1986; also see below), it is possible that the nature and the composition of the ECM determines transferrin levels *in vivo* as well as in culture.

RECIPROCAL EFFECTS ON ECM DEPOSITION

The basement membrane of mammary gland changes as a function of hormonal state during the reproductive cycle and its composition may represent an important determinant of function (Warburton *et al.* 1982*b*). Many studies have described production of basement membrane components by mammary cells in culture (Martinez-Hernandez *et al.* 1976; Warburton *et al.* 1981, 1982*a*, 1984). Studies with mammary and other cell types have shown that exogenous ECM can modulate the level and the composition of the cell-synthesized ECM (Emerman & Pitelka, 1977; Parry *et al.* 1982, 1985; Kato & Gospodarowicz, 1985). Our preliminary data indicate that the composition of mRNA for ECM components changes as a function of the reproductive cycle *in vivo* and the substrata in culture (Park & Bissell, 1986).

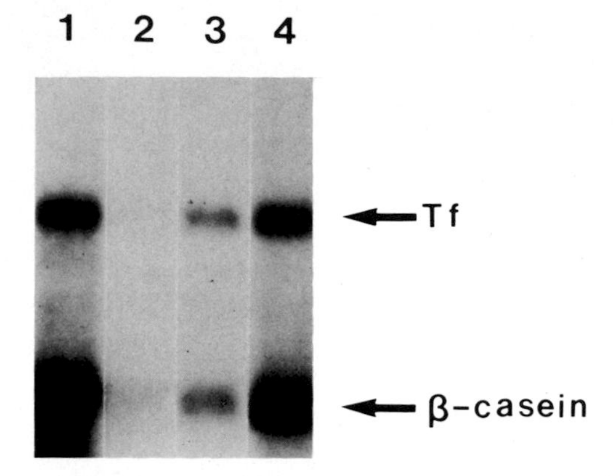

Fig. 6. Northern blot of β-casein and transferrin (Tf) mRNA. Lanes: 1, lactating gland; 2, PMME cells grown on plastic (6-day culture); 3, PMME cells on EHS (6-day culture); 4, PMME cells on floating collagen gel (6-day culture). Upper arrow indicates transferrin mRNA and lower arrow indicates β-casein (Chen & Bissell, 1987). RNA was extracted and run on nitrocellulose as described (Maniatis *et al.* 1982).

Significant modulations occur as a function of the reproductive cycle and culture substrata for types I, III and IV collagens, laminin and fibronectin (Park & Bissell, 1986). While these data are preliminary, the effects of substrata (i.e. plastic *versus* EHS) and cell shape (i.e. flat *versus* released collagen gel, plastic *versus* EHS) on mammary gland function may be modulated by stimulating the production of mammary basement membrane components deposited by cells on released gels and on EHS. This interaction would fulfil one aspect of the 'dynamic reciprocity' model outlined below (Bissell *et al.* 1982).

IS STRUCTURE THE MESSAGE?

How does the interaction of the cell and the ECM instigate and/or promote differentiated function in cultured epithelial cells? In the studies cited above we have shown that substrata affect both morphology and function in the mammary gland and that the attainment of functional epithelium in culture is accompanied by cell shape changes and the deposition of basement membrane components.

Over five years ago we presented a model that described the minimum required unit for tissue-specific functions as the cell plus its ECM (Fig. 7; Bissell *et al.* 1982). Our hypothesis was that the influence of the ECM is communicated through the organization of the cytoskeleton (itself with connections to the nuclear matrix), possibly mediated by cell shape changes, which results in regulation of gene expression at all levels: transcription, mRNA processing, translation, post-translational modifications, secretion and extracellular organization. The concept that shape *per se* regulates function is difficult to translate into mechanism; what is needed is a translation of 'shape' into an alphabet of molecules and discrete steps. We are only now beginning to understand and unravel this language. On the basis of the

"DYNAMIC RECIPROCITY"

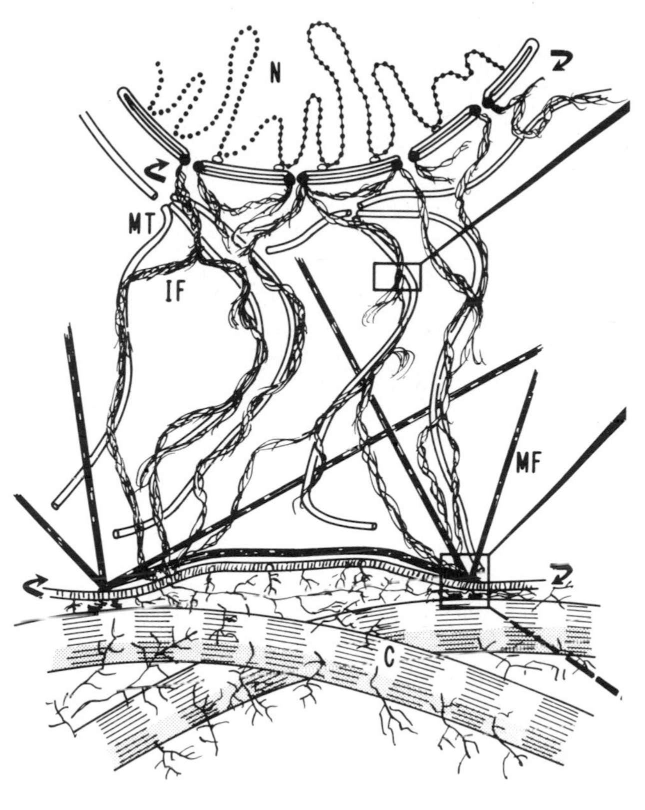

Fig. 7. Model of Dynamic Reciprocity: this is the postulated minimum required unit for tissue-specific function (cell plus its ECM) (Bissell *et al.* 1982; reproduced with permission). N, nucleus; MT, microtubule; IF, intermediate filament; MF, microfilament; C, collagen.

evidence we have presented in this chapter, it is clear that functional integrity (production of milk proteins, and appropriate response to physiological hormones) in culture requires morphological differentiation, which in turn is dependent upon ECM. These results and that of recent published work (Reid *et al.* 1986; Clayton *et al.* 1985*a*) could be used to argue that the correct structure of the tissue is crucial for functional integrity.

Evidence now indicates that there is a connection between transcribed genes and the nuclear matrix (Cook *et al.* 1982; Fey *et al.* 1986), between transcription of tissue-specific genes and mature tissue structure (Clayton *et al.* 1985*a*), and between mRNA and the cytoskeletal structures (for a brief review, see Nielsen *et al.* 1983). In many cell types, 70–80 % of the poly$(A)^+$ mRNA is found in the cytoskeletal fraction (Lenk *et al.* 1977; van Venrooij *et al.* 1981; Jeffrey, 1982). The association of mRNA with the cytoskeleton is also indirectly suggested by the finding that mRNA in oocytes and embryos and in single cells is not uniformly distributed (Ernst *et al.*

1980; Fulton *et al.* 1980; Capco & Jäckle, 1982; Jeffrey, 1982; Lawrence & Singer, 1986). Our preliminary results indicate that more than 90% of β-casein and transferrin mRNA are associated with the Triton-extracted cytoskeleton of mouse mammary epithelial cells (L. H. Chen & M. J. Bissell, unpublished). Furthermore, it has been known for a number of years that colchicine and other microtubule-disrupting drugs inhibit milk protein synthensis and secretion as well as mRNA levels for β-casein (Ollivier-Bousquet, 1979; Nickerson *et al.* 1980; Houdebine & Djiane, 1980).

Our hypothesis is that changes of mRNA levels as a function of substrata (and hence cell shape) are due to increases in mRNA half-life occurring both in the nucleus as the result of cytoskeleton–nuclear matrix interactions, and in the cytoplasm as the result of polysome–cytoskeleton interactions (Nielsen *et al.* 1983; see also Bissell & Hall, 1987). Post-transcriptional regulation of tissue-specific genes has recently been demonstrated in several systems (Carneiro & Schibler, 1984; Jefferson *et al.* 1984; Clayton *et al.* 1985*b*; Reid *et al.* 1986; Fujita *et al.* 1987). The hypothesis that ECM could act post-transcriptionally by stabilizing the already-transcribed tissue-specific mRNA does not preclude the possibility that it may also act at the transcriptional level. Indeed, nuclear structure itself may be important for specific patterns of transcription, perhaps through enhancing the interaction between specific genes and transcription-promoting regions (Clayton *et al.* 1985*a*). This is only to emphasize that one aspect of basement membrane function is its ability to alter cell shape *via* interaction with transmembrane receptors, resulting in changes in mRNA levels by altering either its association with the cytoskeleton or its processing in the nucleus.

This is evidence that cytoskeletal mRNAs themselves change as a function of shape (Farmer *et al.* 1983; Ben Ze'ev, 1984; see Ben Ze'ev, this volume). There is additional evidence, some of which has been reviewed (Nielsen *et al.* 1983), that the cytoskeleton is involved in protein synthesis. Equally intriguing, however, are findings to support the notion that cytoskeletal proteins may be involved in nuclear regulation of mRNA processing (Müller *et al.* 1983). Recent findings have shown that the nuclear lamins, which comprise the nuclear envelope, are members of the intermediate-filament protein gene family (McKeon *et al.* 1986; Aebi *et al.* 1986), suggesting that cytoskeletal structures may indeed have a close relationship to both the nuclear envelope and nuclear pores. Other reports have substantiated the association of hnRNA with the nuclear matrix (Fey *et al.* 1986). Thus, although we still have a long way to go before we can delineate which cytoskeletal structure is associated with which mRNA, how cytoskeletal components participate in mRNA processing, and in what manner the ECM affects these processes, the model of dynamic reciprocity has gained credence from various experimental studies in the last five years. A scheme representing the type of interactions necessary to promote function in culture is outlined in Fig. 8 (Aggeler *et al.* 1987).

We have previously proposed that the minimum unit of function is the cell plus its ECM (Bissell *et al.* 1982). This is particularly true in culture where the outcome of these investigations has been the realization that expression of differentiated function

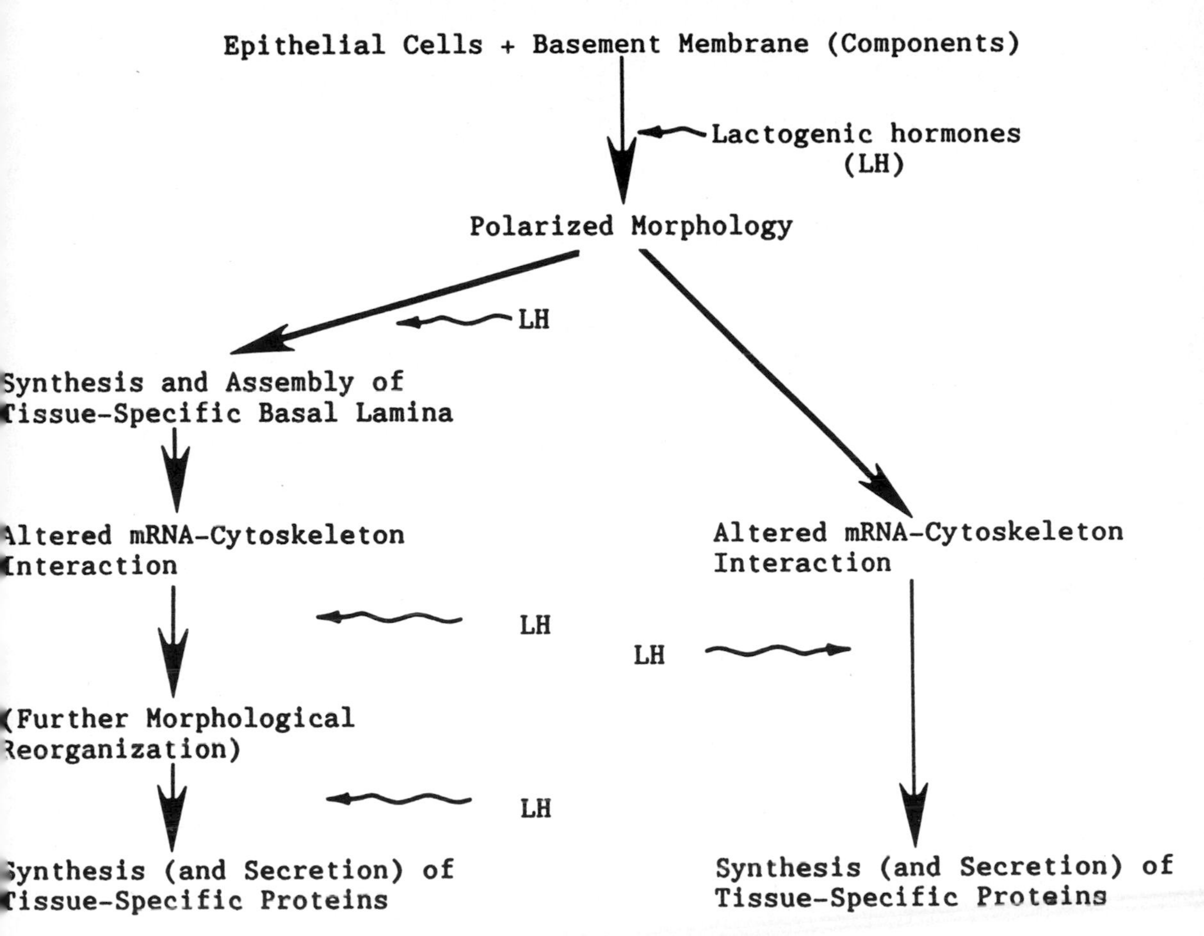

Fig. 8. Scheme indicating cascade of events leading to function in culture (Bissell & Aggeler, 1987, reproduced with permission).

is the result of epigenetic regulation by hormones and ECM. Mature tissue structure, however, entails additional levels of organization: subpopulations within tissues; cell–cell and epithelium–mesenchyme interaction; microregions consisting of different ECMs or vascularity; flux in hormones, nutrients, autocrine factors and oxygenation. A reciprocal and dynamic interaction exists not only between the ECM and the cell but also between stroma and epithelium, as is well documented for the mammary gland (Kratochwil, 1969; Sakakura *et al*. 1976, 1982; Chiquet-Ehrismann *et al*. 1986). In the last analysis, a unit of function is the three-dimensional tissue itself. While this complexity is at present difficult to study in cultured cell models, nonetheless its importance should be borne in mind when cells in culture fail to attain the completeness of function and the exquisite regulation observed *in vivo*. The final goal of the tissue-culturists should indeed be the tissue itself.

These investigations were supported by the Health Effects Research Division, Office of Health and Environmental Research, US DOE, contract DE-AC03-76SF00098, and a gift for research from Monsanto Company to M.J.B. We thank J. Aggeler for unpublished photographs and Karen Springsteen and Lucinda Olney for expert secretarial assistance.

REFERENCES

ADAMSON, E. D. (1982). The effect of collagen on cell division, cellular differentiation and embryonic development. In *Collagen in Health and Disease* (ed. J. B. Weiss & M. I. V. Jayson), pp. 218–243. Edinburgh: Churchill Livingstone.

AEBI, U., COHN, J., BUHLE, L. & GERACE, L. (1986). The nuclear lamina is a meshwork of intermediate-type filaments. *Nature, Lond.* **323**, 560–562.

AGGELER, J., PARK, C. S. & BISSELL, M. J. (1987). Regulation of milk protein and basement membrane gene expression: influence of the extracellular matrix. *J. Dairy Sci.* (in press).

BARCELLOS-HOFF, M. H., NEVILLE, P. N., AGGELER, J. & BISSELL, M. J. (1987). Polarized secretion by mammary epithelial cell cultures on EHS-matrix. *J. Cell Biol.* **105**, 220a.

BEN ZE'EV, A. (1984). Differential control of cytokeratins and vimentin synthesis by cell–cell contact and cell spreading in cultured epithelial cells. *J. Cell Biol.* **99**, 1424–1433.

BEN ZE'EV, A. (1987). The role of changes in cell shape and contacts in the regulation of cytoskeleton expression during differentiation. *J. Cell Sci. Suppl. 8*, 293–312.

BISBEE, C. A., MACHEN, T. E. & BERN, H. A. (1979). Mouse mammary epithelial cells on floating collagen gels: transepithelial ion transport and effects of prolactin. *Proc. natn. Acad. Sci. U.S.A.* **76**, 537–640.

BISSELL, D. M. (1976). Study of hepatocyte function in cell culture. In *Progress in Liver Diseases*, vol. 5 (ed. H. Popper & F. Schaffner), pp. 69–82. New York: Grune & Stratton.

BISSELL, D. M., ARENSON, D. M., MAHER, J. J. & ROLL, F. J. (1987). Support of cultured hepatocytes by a laminin-rich gel. *J. clin. Invest.* **79**, 801–812.

BISSELL, M. J. (1981). The differentiated state of normal and malignant cells or how to define a "normal" cell in culture. *Int. Rev. Cytol.* **70**, 27–100.

BISSELL, M. J. & AGGELER, J. (1987). Dynamic reciprocity: How do extracellular matrix and hormones direct gene expression? In *Mechanisms of Signal Transduction by Hormones and Growth Factors* (ed. M. Cabot). New York: Alan R. Liss (in press).

BISSELL, M. J. & HALL, H. G. (1987). Form and function in the mammary gland: The role of extracellular matrix. In *The Mammary Gland: Development, Regulation and Function* (ed. M. C. Neville & C. Daniel). New York: Plenum Press (in press).

BISSELL, M. J., HALL, H. G. & PARRY, G. (1982). How does the extracellular matrix direct gene expression. *J. theor. Biol.* **99**, 31–68.

CAPCO, D. G. & JÄCKLE, H. (1982). Localized protein synthesis during oogenesis of *Xenopus laevis*. Analysis by *in situ* hybridization. *Devl Biol.* **94**, 41–50.

CARNEIRO, M. & SCHIBLER, U. (1984). Accumulation of rare and moderately abundant mRNAs in mouse L-cells is mainly post-transcriptionally regulated. *J. molec. Biol.* **178**, 869–880.

CHAMBORD, M., GABRION, J. & MAUCHAMP, J. (1981). Influence of collagen gel on the orientation of epithelial cell polarity: Follicle formation from isolated thyroid cells and from preformed monolayers. *J. Cell Biol.* **91**, 157–166.

CHEN, L.-H. & BISSELL, M. J. (1987). Transferrin mRNA level in the mouse mammary gland is regulated by pregnancy and extracellular matrix. *J. biol. Chem.* (in press).

CHEN, L.-H., LI, M. & BISSELL, M. J. (1986). Transferrin mRNA is highly modulated in the gland and is responsive to substrata in culture. *J. Cell Biol.* **103**, 178a.

CHIQUET-EHRISMANN, R., MACKIE, E. J., PEARSON, C. A. & SAKAKURA, T. (1986). Tenascin: an extracellular matrix protein involved in tissue interactions during fetal development and oncogenesis. *Cell* **47**, 131–139.

CLAYTON, D. F., HARRELSON, A. L. & DARNELL, J. E. (1985*a*). Dependence of liver-specific transcription on tissue organization. *Molec. Cell Biol.* **5**, 2623–2632.

CLAYTON, D. F., WEISS, M. & DARNELL, J. E. (1985*b*). Liver-specific mRNA metabolism in hepatoma cells: Variations in transcription rates and mRNA levels. *Molec. Cell Biol.* **5**, 2633–2641.

COOK, P. R., WANG, J., HAYDAY, A., LANIA, L., FRIED, M., CHISWELL, D. J. & WYKE, J. A. (1982). Active viral genes in transformed cells lie close to the nuclear cage. *EMBO J.* **1**, 447–452.

DAVIDSON, E. H. (1964). Differentiation in monolayer tissue culture cells. *Adv. Genet.* **12**, 143–280.

ELSDALE, T. & BARD, J. (1972). Collagen substrata for studies on cell behavior. *J. Cell Biol.* **54**, 626–637.

EMERMAN, J. T., BARTLEY, J. C. & BISSELL, M. J. (1981). Glucose metabolite patterns as markers of functional differentiation in freshly isolated and cultured mouse mammary epithelial cells. *Expl Cell Res.* **134**, 241–250.

EMERMAN, J. T. & PITELKA, D. R. (1977). Maintenance and identification of morphological differentiation in dissociated mammary epithelium on floating colagen membranes. *In Vitro* **13**, 316–328.

ERNST, S. G., HOUGH-EVANS, B. R., BRITTEN, R. J. & DAVIDSON, E. H. (1980). Limited complexity of the RNA in micromeres of sixteen-cell sea urchin embryo. *Devl Biol.* **79**, 119–127.

FARMER, S. R., WAN, K. M., BEN-ZE'EV, A. & PENMAN, S. (1983). Regulation of actin mRNA levels and translation responds to changes in cell configuration. *Molec. Cell Biol.* **3**, 182–189.

FEY, E. G., KROCHMALNIC, G. & PENMAN, S. (1986). The nonchromatin substructures of the nucleus the ribonucleoprotein (RNP)-containing and RNP-depleted matrices analyzed by sequential fractionation and resinless section electron microscopy. *J. Cell Biol.* **102**, 1654–1665.

FUJITA, M., SPRAY, D. C., CHOI, H., SAEZ, J. C., WATANABE, T., ROSENBERG, L. C., HERTZBERG, E. L. & REID, L. M. (1987). Glycosaminoglycans and proteoglycans induce gap junction expression and restore transcription of tissue-specific mRNAs in primary liver culture. *Hepatology* **7**, 1S–9S.

FULTON, A. B., WAN, K. M. & PENMAN, S. (1980). The spatial distribution of polyribosomes in 3T3 cells and the associated assembly of proteins into the skeletal framework. *Cell* **20**, 849–857.

HAEUPTLE, M.-T., SUARD, Y. L. M., BOGENMANN, E., REGGIO, H., RACINE, L. & KRAEHENBUHL, J.-P. (1983). Effect of cell shape change on the function and differentiation of rabbit mammary cells in culture. *J. Cell Biol.* **96**, 1425–1434.

HALL, H. G., FARSON, D. A. & BISSELL, M. J. (1982). Lumen formation by epithelial cell lines in response to collagen overlay: A morphogenetic model in culture. *Proc. natn. Acad. Sci. U.S.A.* **79**, 4672–4676.

HOUDEBINE, L.-M. & DJIANE, J. (1980). Effects of lysosomotropic agents and of microfilament and microtubule disrupting drugs on the activation of casein-gene expression by prolactin in the mammary gland. *Molec. cell. Endocrinol.* **17**, 1–15.

HOUDEBINE, L.-M., DJIANE, J., TEYSSOT, B., SERVELY, J.-L., KELLY, P. A., DE LOUIS, C., OLLIVIER-BOUSQUET, M., DEVINOY, E. (1983). Prolactin and casein gene expression in the mammary cell. In *Regulation of Gene Expression by Hormones* (ed. K. W. McKerns), pp. 71–101. New York: Plenum.

JEFFERSON, D. M., CLAYTON, D. F., DARNELL, J. E. & REID, L. M. (1984). Post-transcriptional modulation of gene expression in cultured rat hepatocytes. *Molec. Cell Biol.* **4**, 1929–1934.

JEFFERY, W. R. (1982). Messenger RNA in the cytoskeletal framework: Analysis by in situ hybridization. *J. Cell Biol.* **95**, 1–7.

KATO, Y. & GOSPODAROWICZ, D. (1985). Effect of exogenous extracellular matrices on proteoglycan synthesis by cultured rabbit costal chrondrocytes. *J. Cell Biol.* **100**, 486–495.

KLEINMAN, H. K., MCGARVEY, M. L., HASSELL, J. R., STAR, V. L., CANNON, F. B., LAURIE, G. W. & MARTIN, G. R. (1986). Basement membrane complexes with biological activity. *Biochemistry* **25**, 312–318.

KRATOCHWIL, K. (1969). Organ specificity in mesenchymal induction demonstrated in the embryonic development of the mammary gland of the mouse. *Devl Biol.* **20**, 46–71.

LAWRENCE, J. B. & SINGER, R. H. (1986). Intracellular localization of messenger RNAs for cytoskeletal proteins. *Cell* **45**, 407–415.

LEE, E. Y.-H., BARCELLOS-HOFF, M. H., CHEN, L.-H., PARRY, G. & BISSELL, M. J. (1987). Transferrin is a major mouse milk protein and is synthesized by mammary epithelial cells. *In Vitro Cell Devl Biol.* **23**, 221–226.

LEE, E. Y.-H., LEE, W.-H., KAETZEL, C. S., PARRY, G. & BISSELL, M. J. (1985). Interaction of mouse mammary epithelial cells with collagenous substrata: Regulation of casein gene expression and secretion. *Proc. natn. Acad. Sci. U.S.A.* **82**, 1419–1423.

LEE, E. Y.-H., PARRY, G. & BISSELL, M. J. (1984). Modulation of secreted proteins of mouse mammary epithelial cells by the extracellular matrix. *J. Cell Biol.* **98**, 146–155.

LENK, R., RANSOM, L., KAUFMANN, Y. & PENMAN, S. (1977). A cytoskeletal structure with associated polyribosomes obtained from HeLa cells. *Cell* **10**, 67–74.

LI, M.-L., AGGELER, J., FARSON, D. A., HATIER, C., HASSELL, J. & BISSELL, M. J. (1987). Influence of a reconstituted basement membrane and its components on casein gene expression and secretion in mouse mammary epithelial cells. *Proc. natn. Acad. Sci. U.S.A.* **84**, 136–140.

MANIATAS, T., FRITSCH, E. F. & SANBROOK, J. (1982). *Molecular Cloning: A Laboratory Manual*. New York: Cold Spring Harbor Laboratory Press.

MARTINEZ-HERNANDEZ, A., FINK, L. M. & PIERCE, G. B. (1976). Removal of basement membrane in the involuting breast. *Lab. Invest.* **34**, 455–462.

MAUCHAMP, J., CHAMBARD, M., VERRIER, B., GABRION, J., CHABAUD, O., GERARD, C., PENEL, C., PIALAT, B. & ANFOSSO, F. (1987). Epithelial cell polarization in culture: orientation of cell polarity and expression of specific functions, studied with cultured thyroid cells. *J. Cell Sci. Suppl. 8*, 345–358.

MCKEON, F. D., KIRSCHNER, M. W. & CAPUT, D. (1986). Homologies in both primary and secondary structure between nuclear envelope and intermediate filament proteins. *Nature, Lond.* **319**, 463–468.

MEDINA, D., LI, M. L., OBORN, C. J. & BISSELL, M. J. (1987). Casein gene expression in mouse mammary epithelial cell lines: Dependence upon extracellular matrix and cell type. *Expl Cell Res.* (in press).

MÜLLER, W. E. G., BERND, A. & SCHRODER, H. C. (1983). Modulation of poly(A)$^+$ mRNA-metabolizing and transporting systems under special consideration of microtubule protein and actin. *Molec. cell. Biochem.* **53/54**, 197–220.

NEVILLE, M. C. (1987). Mammary cultures on floating gels: A model system for mammary function. *News Physiol. Sci.* (in press).

NICKERSON, S. C., SMITH, J. J. & KEENAN, T. W. (1980). Role of microtubules in milk secretion – action of colchicine on microtubules and exocytosis of secretory vesicles in rat mammary epithelial cells. *Cell Tiss. Res.* **207**, 361–376.

NIELSEN, P., GOELZ, S. & TRACHSEL, H. (1983). The role of the cytoskeleton in eukaryotic protein synthesis. *Cell Biol. Int. Rep.* **7**, 245–254.

OLLIVIER-BOUSQUET, M. (1979). Effets de la cytochalasine B et de la colchicine sur l'action rapide de la prolactine dans la glands mammaire de lapine en lactation. *Eur. J. Cell Biol.* **19**, 168–174.

PARK, C. & BISSELL, M. J. (1986). Messenger RNA for basement membrane components in the mouse mammary gland and in cells in culture. *J. Cell Biol.* **103**, 101 (abstract).

PARRY, G., LEE, E. Y.-H. & BISSELL, M. J. (1982). Modulation of the differentiated phenotype of cultured mouse mammary epithelial cells by collagen substrata. In *The Extracellular Matrix* (ed. S. P. Hawkes & J. Wang), pp. 303–308. New York: Academic Press.

PARRY, G., LEE, E. Y.-H., FARSON, D., KOVAL, M. & BISSELL, M. J. (1985). Collagenous substrata regulate the nature and distribution of glycosaminoglycans produced by differentiated cultures of mouse mammary epithelial cells. *Expl Cell Res.* **156**, 487–499.

PAUL, J. (1970). *Cell and Tissue Culture*. Edinburgh: Livingstone.

REID, L. M., NARITA, M., FUJITA, M., MURRAY, Z., LIVERPOOL, C. & ROSENBERG, L. (1986). Matrix and hormonal regulation of differentiation in liver cultures. In *Isolated and Cultured Hepatocytes* (ed. A. Guillouzo & C. Guguen-Guillouza), pp. 225–258. INSERM/John Libbey Eurotext Ltd.

ROCHA, V., RINGO, D. L. & READ, D. B. (1985). Casein production during differentiation of mammary epithelial cells in collagen gel culture. *Expl Cell Res.* **159**, 201–210.

ROSEN, J. M., RODGERS, J. R., COUCH, C. H., BISBEE, C. A., DAVID-INOUYE, Y., CAMPBELL, S. M. & YU-LEE, L.-Y. (1986). Multihormonal regulation of milk protein gene expression. In *Metabolic Regulation: Application of Recombinant DNA Techniques*, vol. 478 (ed. R. Hanson & A. Goodridge), pp. 63–76. New York: Ann. N.Y. Acad. Sci.

SAKAKURA, T., NISHIZUKA, Y. & DAWE, C. J. (1976). Mesenchyme-dependent morphogenesis and epithelium-specific cytodifferentiation in mouse mammary gland. *Science* **194**, 1439–1441.

SAKAKURA, T., SAKAFAMI, Y. & NISHIZUKA, Y. (1982). Dual origin of mesenchymal tissues participating in mouse mammary gland embryogenesis. *Devl Biol.* **91**, 202–207.

SHANNON, J. M. & PITELKA, D. R. (1981). The influence of cell shape on the induction of functional differentiation in mouse mammary cells in vitro. *In Vitro* **17**, 1016–1028.

TOPPER, Y. J., SANKARAN, L., CHOMCZNSKI, P., PROSSER, C. & QASBA, P. (1986). Three stages of responsiveness to hormones in the mammary cell. *Ann. N.Y. Acad. Sci.* **464**, 1–10.

VAN VENROOIJ, W. J., SILLEKENS, P. T. G., EKELEN, C. A. G. & REINDERS, R. J. (1981). On the association of mRNA with the cytoskeleton in uninfected and adenovirus-infected human KB cells. *Expl Cell Res.* **135**, 79–91.

WARBURTON, M. J., FERNS, S. A. & RUDLAND, P. S. (1982*a*). Enhanced synthesis of basement membrane proteins during the differentiation of rat mammary tumour epithelial cells in myoepithelial-like cells in vitro. *Expl Cell Res.* **137**, 373–380.

WARBURTON, M. J., MITCHELL, D., ORMEROD, E. J. & RUDLAND, P. S. (1982*b*). Distribution of myoepithelial cells and basement membrane proteins in the resting, pregnant, lactating and involuting rat mammary gland. *J. Histochem. Cytochem.* **30**, 667–676.

WARBURTON, M. J., MONOGHAN, P., FERNS, S. A., RUDLAND, P. S., PERUSINGHE, N. & CHUNG, A. E. (1984). Distribution of entactin in the basement membrane of the rat mammary gland. *Expl Cell Res.* **152**, 240–254.

WARBURTON, M. J., ORMEROD, E. J., MONAGHAN, P., FERNS, S. & RUDLAND, P. S. (1981). Characterization of a myoepithelial cell line derived from a neonatal rat mammary gland. *J. Cell Biol.* **91**, 827–856.

WESSELLS, N. K. (1977). *Tissue Interactions and Development*. California: Benjamin/Cummings.

WICHA, M. S. (1984). Interaction of rat mammary epithelium with extracellular matrix components. In *New Approaches to the Study of Benign Prostatic Hyperplasia*, pp. 129–142. New York: Alan R. Liss.

J. Cell Sci. Suppl. 8, 345–358 (1987)
Printed in Great Britain

EPITHELIAL CELL POLARIZATION IN CULTURE: ORIENTATION OF CELL POLARITY AND EXPRESSION OF SPECIFIC FUNCTIONS, STUDIED WITH CULTURED THYROID CELLS

JEAN MAUCHAMP*, MARIANNE CHAMBARD,
BERNARD VERRIER, JACQUELINE GABRION, ODILE CHABAUD,
CORINNE GERARD, CLAUDE PENEL, BERNARD PIALAT
AND FRANCINE ANFOSSO

INSERM Unité 270, Faculté de Médecine Nord, Boulevard Pierre Dramard, F 13326, Marseille cedex 15, France

SUMMARY

Isolated porcine thyroid cells reorganize in culture into various types of multicellular structure, which differ in the orientation of cell polarity and in the surface of the cell layer accessible to molecules present in the culture medium. The types of structure are: (1) *follicles*: the basal pole is oriented toward the medium; (2) *inside-out follicles* or monolayers: the apical pole is facing the culture medium; (3) *monolayers on a permeable substratum*: both sides of the cell layer are accessible to the medium. Follicles can be transformed into inside-out follicles or monolayers and *vice versa* by manipulation of the external cell environment and without dissociating the cells. Cells concentrate iodide and respond to acute stimulation by thyroid-stimulating hormone (TSH) when the basal pole is accessible, and organification occurs only when cells form a closed follicular lumen.

In porous-bottomed culture chambers monolayers are formed with the basal surface accessible to the medium and the apical compartment separated from the medium. Under these conditions 85–95 % of the thyroglobulin produced is secreted apically and 5–15 % basally. Thyrotropin stimulates (×3) apical accumulation without modifying secretion in the basal compartment.

Sodium transport across the cell layer has been characterized. An amiloride-sensitive influx occurs at the apical pole whereas the Na^+/K^+-ATPase, localized in the basolateral membrane, mediates ouabain-sensitive efflux at the basal pole. The thyroid epithelium in culture appears therefore as a Na^+-absorbing epithelium. The role of this transport in the stabilization of cell polarity is discussed.

INTRODUCTION

For several years the aim of our work has been to investigate the relations existing between cell organization within a tissue and expression of tissue-specific functions. For these studies thyroid cells in culture have been used. In this article I shall first set our work in its conceptual context and then report and discuss our results and related data from other systems.

DESCRIPTION OF THE BIOLOGICAL SYSTEMS

Biological systems can be described by two types of parameter: (1) numbers allow measurement of enzymic *activities*, synthesis and degradation rates, intermolecular

* Author for correspondence.

interactions, etc.; (2) pictures are necessary to describe the *organization* of molecules and organelles within cells and of cells within tissues. Organization of space and the generation of compartments are prominent features of living systems and the study of transfer of material from one compartment to another requires the use of both types of parameter. Numbers describe the properties of various compartments and the flux of molecules between them; pictures describe their shapes, sizes and relative positions.

The formation of specific boundaries between compartments requires molecular sorting and addressing, permitting the maintenance of cellular and supracellular organization despite continuous turnover of various elements (proteins, lipids). These boundaries are formed by membranes at the cell level and by cell layers at the multicellular level. Their properties, i.e. molecular composition and enzymic activity for membranes, and cellular composition for cell layers, are responsible for generating the transboundary asymmetry. This might be, by itself, a stabilization factor for the boundary, which appears therefore as an *autostabilized structure*.

THE MONOSTRATIFIED EPITHELIUM

One of the simplest examples of multicellular organization is the monostratified epithelium formed by a single layer of polarized epithelial cells. This type of organization is very common and is found, for example, in linings of internal cavities (intestinal tract, lung, etc.), the urinary tract (kidney, urinary bladder), all exocrine glands and the thyroid gland. In this type of tissue the consequences of cell organization can be summarized in one word: *polarization*. This polarization can be defined at two successive levels: at the level of the cell layer and at the level of individual cells.

The cell layer is polarized and separates two compartments. One compartment is the serosal or basolateral compartment containing the milieu interieur, source of nutrients and stimulators and limited by the basement membrane in contact with the basal pole of the cells; the other is the mucosal or apical compartment, the composition of which is specific for each tissue. The function of the tissue is often the transport of molecules, ions or water from one compartment to the other or secretion of macromolecules into the apical compartment. Parameters that depend on the existence of the continuous cell layer include transepithelial electrical properties (potential difference, resistance) and transepithelial transport of ions and macromolecules. The tight junctions formed between cells close the intercellular space, resulting in a diffusion barrier to ions and macromolecules present in each compartment.

Individual cells are polarized. The tight-junctional belt that closes the intercellular space separates two plasma membrane domains with different compositions and functions. The apical domain is orientated towards the mucosal compartment; it is often covered with more or less dense microvilli. The basal and lateral domains are not separated by a clear boundary, but the basal domain is in contact with the basement membrane and the lateral one is adjacent to neighbouring cells, bearing gap junctions and intercellular desmosomes. Each membrane domain, apical and basolateral, contains specific proteins and has specific functions, transport properties or enzymic activities; the asymmetry of membrane domains is responsible for the asymmetry of the cell layer and for the specific composition of the apical compartment. The cytoplasmic mass of the cell is also polarized, with the centriole and Golgi complex usually located in the apical portion of the cytoplasm and the cytoskeleton associated with microvilli and tight junctions also revealing polarization.

THE THYROID EPITHELIUM

We have studied the organization of epithelial thyroid cells in culture in relation to the expression of specific functions. I will review these results together with data obtained by others on similar systems such as kidney cell lines (MDCK or LLCPK1) or mammary cells.

The thyroid gland is an endocrine gland that shows the histological organization of an exocrine gland except that it lacks secretory ducts. Epithelial thyroid cells are organized into closed spherical structures, the follicles, formed by a single layer of cells surrounding a cavity filled with a concentrated solution of thyroglobulin. This protein synthesized by thyroid cells is secreted into the lumen where it is iodinated by a membrane peroxidase and used as a substrate for the synthesis of thyroid hormones, thyroxine and triiodothyronine. Thyroglobulin stored in the colloid vesicle is endocytosed by epithelial cells at their apical pole and hydrolysed in phagolysosomes. The thyroid hormones liberated upon hydrolysis are secreted into the circulation at the basal pole of the thyrocyte. Thyroid function requires bidirectional transfer of material in the thyroid cell and polarization appears to be a major feature of thyroid cell differentiation.

POLARITY OF ISOLATED EPITHELIAL CELLS

Polarized epithelial cells can be dissociated from tissue or from cell cultures by conventional trypsin–EDTA (or EGTA) treatment and maintained for a few hours in suspension. In all systems so far studied, redistribution of membrane proteins over the whole cell surface is observed under these conditions (Pisam & Ripoche, 1976; Ziomek *et al.* 1980; Feracci *et al.* 1981) and results from the disappearance of the tight junctions that limit the membrane domains. Morphological polarity, as defined by the existence of organized brush border or localized microvilli, can persist after isolation (Ziomek *et al.* 1980; Nord *et al.* 1986), perhaps due to the stability of the internal cytoskeleton. However, loss of functional polarization is also observed since viruses that bud asymmetrically in polarized MDCK cells emerge over the whole surface of isolated cells (Rodriguez-Boulan *et al.* 1983).

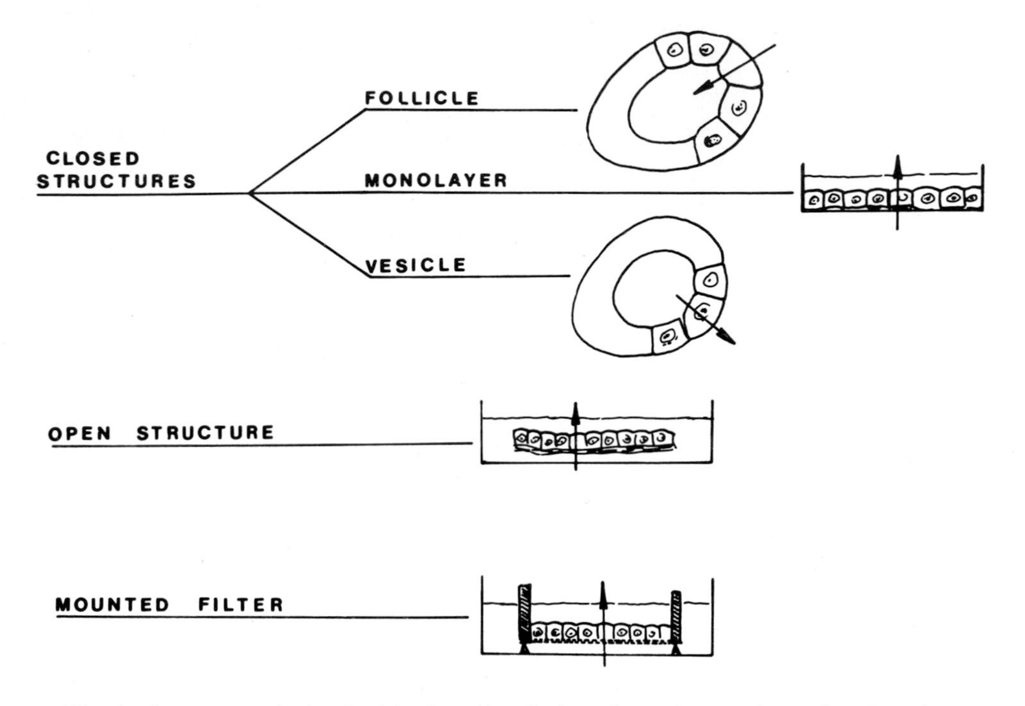

Fig. 1. Structures obtained with thyroid cells in culture (arrow shows basolateral to apical orientation). (From Mauchamp *et al.* (1983).)

REORGANIZATION OF EPITHELIAL CELLS IN CULTURE

The reorganization of epithelial cells in culture implies the formation of intercellular tight junctions, their extension to the whole cell population and polarization of the cells. The identification of factors that play a part in the orientation of cell polarity is an important goal in the study of this reorganization. We have used three sets of culture conditions that create basically different environments for the isolated cell at the onset of culturing and induce various types of organization of isolated porcine thyroid cells (Fig. 1). These are: culture on adhesive substrata; in suspension; or within collagen gels.

Culture on adhesive substrata

Formation of monolayers. The attachment of an isolated epithelial cell to an adhesive substratum induces polarization of the cell. As assessed by polarized virus budding from infected MDCK cells, the equivalent of a basal pole is formed in contact with the substratum and the apical cell surface is free, orientated towards the culture medium (Rodriguez-Boulan *et al.* 1983).

Thyroid cells, like other epithelial cells (primary cultures or cell lines), form monolayers on adhesive substrata. Cells adhere to the substratum, spread and form intercellular tight junctions at points of cell–cell contact. As a result of adhesion-induced polarization the basal surface of the cell layer is in contact with the substratum and the apical surface is orientated towards the culture medium (Mauchamp *et al.* 1979*c*; Louvard, 1980; Rabito, 1986). Various substrata can be used: classical ones, such as polystyrene or glass, are impermeable to water and solutes, but more recently water-permeable substrata such as collagen gels or filters (Millipore, Nuclepore) have been introduced.

When cells form a monolayer on an impermeable substratum the apical compartment contains the culture medium and the basolateral compartment is located between the substratum and the cell layer. The existence of tight junctions restricts the accessibility of the basolateral domain of the cell membrane to molecules present in the culture medium. The monolayer detaches locally from the culture substratum forming fluid-filled hemicysts, or domes, which reveal an apical-to-basolateral water transport and local weakness of cell–substratum adhesion (Sugahara *et al.* 1984).

In contrast, when the monolayer is formed on the surface of a permeable substratum (floating collagen gel or filters) the basolateral surface of the cell layer can be reached by molecules present in the medium by diffusion through the substratum. Domes are not observed under these conditions. Accessibility of both surfaces of the cell layer has important consequences for the expression of specific thyroid functions in culture.

Formation of attached follicles. Porcine (or ovine) thyroid cells seeded in tissue culture polystyrene dishes at high cell density in thyrotropin (TSH)-supplemented medium (more than 1 munit ml^{-1}) or in serum-free NCTC 109 on polylysine-coated dishes form follicle-like structures that attach to the plastic substratum (Lissitzky *et al.* 1971; Fayet *et al.* 1982). Cells forming these structures have a spontaneous tendency to migrate and spread on the substratum, leading to the disaggregation of the follicles and to the formation of monolayers within 3–5 days.

Culture in suspension

The adhesive substratum is the orienting factor that determines the polarity of adherent monolayers. Adhesion can be prevented by culturing cells in dishes with a hydrophobic surface (bacteriological polystyrene or hydrophobic Petriperm-Heraeus) or an agarose-coated surface (thin layer of 1% agarose) as an unstirred suspension. Cells do not attach, but form aggregates and organize within these aggregates. We observe that the orientation of cell polarity, at least for thyroid cells, is dependent on the presence of stimulators in the culture medium: follicles of normal or 'inside-out' polarity may be formed.

In standard media supplemented with calf serum (>1%) porcine thyroid cells organize into inside-out follicles or cysts (Mauchamp *et al.* 1979*a*,*b*,*c*; Herzog & Miller, 1981). Cells form closed spheres, consisting of a single layer of epithelial cells impermeable to high molecular weight tracers. The structural polarity of all cells is reversed as compared to genuine follicles. The apical pole is orientated towards the culture medium as found for monolayer cells, whereas the basolateral surface limits the interior of the sphere. The tight junction limiting the apical pole is close to the outer surface of the cell layer. Such an inverted orientation of cell polarity has been reported for other epithelial cells cultured under these conditions: LLCPK1 cells (Wohlwend *et al.* 1985) and MDCK cells (Valentich *et al.* 1979).

When isolated porcine or ovine thyroid cells are seeded at high density (2×10^6 cells ml^{-1}) in agarose-coated dishes in medium containing TSH (>50 μunits ml^{-1}) or another stimulator of the cyclic AMP system (10^{-6} M-prostaglandin E2, 5 mM-8-chloro-cyclic AMP, 5 mM-dibutyryl cyclic AMP) the polarity of the cell layer formed within cell aggregates reproduces the orientation found in follicles *in vivo* (Mauchamp *et al.* 1979*a*,*b*,*c*; Inoué *et al.* 1980). The apical pole is orientated towards the lumen limited by the cell-layer and the basolateral surface is in contact with the culture medium. Such follicles are stable for several days but have a tendency to form large aggregates. Such an effect of stimulating agents on the orientation of cell polarity has not been described for other epithelial cell types.

Culture within collagen matrices

A collagen gel can be used as a permeable substratum for cell culture but the polymerization protocol (Elsdale & Bard, 1972) also permits the embedding of cells within the gel. Porcine thyroid cells embedded inside a collagen matrix at a sufficiently high cell density organize into follicle-like structures within the matrix (Chambard *et al.* 1981). These follicles are stable and can be maintained for weeks. The basal poles of the cells are in contact with the collagen fibres and the orientation of cell polarity is due to this cell–collagen interaction. Culture in collagen gels has also been widely used for culturing mammary gland cells (Yang & Nandi, 1983) and submandibular epithelial cells (Yang *et al.* 1982).

EXPRESSION OF SPECIFIC FUNCTIONS IN CULTURE

We have studied two important properties of thyroid cells in relation to their organization: cyclic AMP response to thyrotropin, and iodide trapping and organification. An acute cyclic AMP response to TSH stimulation and iodide concentration was observed only when the basolateral surface of the cell layer was directly accessible to molecules present in the culture medium. This occurred when cells were either organized into follicles, attached or in suspension (Lissitzky *et al.* 1971; Mauchamp *et al.* 1979*a*), or when cells formed monolayers on a floating permeable substratum (Chambard *et al.* 1983). Iodide organification on thyroglobulin molecules was observed only when cells were organized into follicles, permitting the accumulation of thyroglobulin in the closed lumen.

THE STABILITY OF POLARIZED STRUCTURES

In vivo, polarized epithelial structures are stable. The orientation of cell polarity does not change despite turnover of molecular components of the cells and renewal of the cells themselves. Moreover, the transepithelial asymmetry must be maintained and leakage of material, macromolecules or ions, across the cell layer must be controlled. Cell contact with the extracellular matrix, mainly the basement lamina, and transepithelial ionic asymmetry (potential difference, pH difference, etc.) might play a role in stabilizing the orientation of cell polarity.

In contrast, inversion of thyroid cell polarity can occur *in vitro*, permitting the transformation of follicles into inside-out follicles and of follicles into monolayer, and *vice versa*, without disaggregating the cells.

Transformation of follicles into inside-out follicles

Earlier we discussed the organization of isolated cells into various types of structure. Intact follicles can also be obtained by dissociating thyroid glands through mild treatment with collagenase and gentle mechanical dissociation (Gartner *et al.* 1985; Miyagawa *et al.* 1982; Nitsch & Wollman, 1980*a*). Thyroid follicles with preserved polarity were maintained in suspension culture in non-adhesive dishes, in the presence of 0·5 % serum. When isolated follicles were cultured in the presence of high concentrations of serum (5–10 %), a spontaneous inversion of cell polarity was observed within 24–48 h. The tight junction appears to migrate along the lateral borders and an apical pole, characterized by microvilli and a cilium, forms on the external surface of the structure (Kitajima *et al.* 1985; Nitsch & Wollman, 1980*b*). It is possible that in low concentrations of serum remnants of the basement membrane are responsible for stabilizing the original orientation.

Transformation of inside-out follicles into follicles

Once organized, inside-out follicles cannot be transformed into follicles by simple modifications of the composition of the culture medium. However, when embedded in a collagen gel an inversion of polarity is observed within 24–48 h (Chambard *et al.* 1981). Interaction of the collagen fibres with the apical surface of the cell layer induces two types of morphological change (Barriere *et al.* 1986). In some areas the microvilli-rich, cilium-bearing apical surface undergoes progressive transformation into a smooth-surfaced basal membrane. In other areas, invaginations of the cell layer appear, with subsequent formation of new tight junctions between cells at the lips of the invagination. These two processes cooperate in the formation of follicles.

Such an inversion of the orientation of cell polarity in collagen gels has also been reported for cysts formed in suspension culture by the porcine kidney cell line LLCPK1 (Wohlwend *et al.* 1985). In cyst-forming cells, the basal cell membranes are not adherent to a substratum located in the cavity of inside-out structures. Hence, the interaction of the external apical surface with the adhesive collagen gel can trigger the reorientation of cells without being hindered by substratum adhesion. The orientating potency of adhesive surfaces appears stronger than the stabilization that prevails in inside-out structures.

Transformation of monolayers into follicles

The existence of an adhesive surface fixes the orientation of thyroid cell monolayers. Once the cells have polarized, a second adhesive surface of collagen gel can be polymerized in close contact with the preformed apical surface. This leads to reorganization into follicles. Some cells do not move, while others migrate as a sheet on the superior adhesive surface, closing cavities in which thyroglobulin accumulates (Chambard *et al.* 1981). Similar behaviour was observed with MDCK cells and a normal murine mammary gland cell line (Hall *et al.* 1982): a second adhesive surface offered to the cells disturbs the preformed monolayer; migration and further growth is possible, giving closed structures in the adhesive sandwich.

Transformation of follicles into monolayers

Follicles formed in suspension from isolated cells or directly isolated by collagenase treatment of thyroid glands readily adhere to tissue culture plastic or collagen gels. Adhesion induces cell migration and the disruption of the follicular structure within hours. This migration is delayed by the presence of TSH, which stabilizes the follicular structure, but it is accelerated by EGF, which antagonizes the TSH effect (Waters *et al.* 1987).

Re-expression of specific functions following changes in cell polarity

As pointed out earlier, iodide metabolism and sensitivity to TSH stimulation are strongly dependent on cellular organization. We have followed the expression of these functions when cells forming inside-out follicles reorganize into follicles after embedding in collagen gels (Chambard *et al.* 1984). As expected, when polarity reversal occurred, iodide trapping and acute sensitivity to TSH reappeared. Maximal levels were obtained 3 days after embedding, when all cells were organized into follicles. Accumulation of thyroglobulin in the newly formed lumina occurred within 2–3 days and organification of iodide on thyroglobulin molecules was observed simultaneously.

Re-expression occurred in the absence of TSH, as a result of collagen-induced follicle formation. TSH greatly increased basal levels of iodide trapping and organification when added to the culture medium 4 days after embedding, i.e. after follicle formation. In contrast, TSH had no effect on these parameters when added to the culture medium of inside-out follicles in suspension.

CLOSED AND OPEN STRUCTURES

In vivo, monolayer formation in epithelial tissues results in polarization of the cell layer and in the separation of two compartments. The epithelial structures described above are of two distinct types (Mauchamp *et al.* 1983): open and closed (Fig. 1).

In follicles, inside-out follicles, or monolayers on impermeable substrates, the cell layer separates a compartment from the culture medium and direct access is possible to only one side of the cell layer: these are *closed structures*. In follicles, the basal surface is in contact with the culture medium, accessible to nutrient and stimulators, while the apical compartment is closed and thyroglobulin can accumulate inside the lumen. Thus, follicles are functional structures. In contrast, in inside-out follicles or monolayers on plastic, the apical surface is in contact with the medium; expression of specific thyroid function is minimal; thyroglobulin is secreted in the culture medium; iodide trapping and organification are not expressed; and cells do not respond acutely to TSH.

When cells are cultured as a monolayer on floating, permeable substrates, such as collagen gels or filters, no compartments are separated, even though the cell layer is polarized. Both surfaces are accessible to molecules present in the medium. These are *open structures*. They express only part of their function, since thyroglobulin cannot accumulate in a closed lumen and ionic asymmetry cannot be generated.

EPITHELIAL CELL CULTURE IN POROUS-BOTTOMED CULTURE CHAMBERS

Each type of structure formed in culture has its advantages and its drawbacks. We have tried to gather all the advantages in a new culture system designed for culturing epithelial cells: the porous-bottomed culture chamber.

A culture dish is fabricated by attaching a flat porous membrane to a glass, polycarbonate or polystyrene ring (Steele *et al.* 1986). The membrane forms the bottom of the dish and the ring forms the sides. Small feet are attached below the ring. Various types of filter can be used (Millipore HATF or Nuclepore 3 or 0·45 μm). The porous-bottomed dish is placed in a Petri dish or multi-well plate containing medium.

Cells are seeded inside the ring and adhere to the filter bottom. Depending on the cell type and on the nature of the filter, adhesion can be improved by coating the bottom with collagen. If the seeding density is high enough, cells rapidly form a confluent polarized layer, which separates a luminal compartment inside the ring from a basal compartment outside the ring. Access is possible to both sides of the cell layer as with open structures (see above), but compartments are separated as in closed structures (Fig. 1).

This type of design, initially introduced by Handler *et al.* (1979), has been widely used by physiologists to study transport processes (Handler, 1986) and by cell biologists to study the asymmetry of epithelial cell layers (Simons & Fuller, 1985). Such culture chambers are now commercially available from two companies: Millicell from Millipore and Transwell from Costar.

We have studied some properties of thyroid cells cultured in such porous-bottomed dishes (filter coated with collagen).

Polarization of the 'iodide pump' and TSH receptor–adenyl cyclase complex

Thyroid cells form a monolayer within 2–3 days in porous-bottomed culture chambers and their ability to concentrate iodide and to respond to TSH stimulation was tested after 4–8 days in culture (Chambard *et al.* 1983). Iodide added to the basal compartment was actively concentrated, with a concentration ratio of about 10. In contrast, iodide present in the apical compartment was not concentrated by the cells. TSH caused a marked increase in the level of cellular cyclic AMP only when added to the basal medium. This response was accompanied by the formation of pseudopods on the apical cell surface. TSH added to the apical compartment had no marked effect. This shows rather clearly that the iodide-concentrating mechanism (iodide 'pump') and the TSH receptor–adenyl cyclase complex are localized on the basolateral domain of the plasma membrane.

Polarized secretion of thyroglobulin

In vivo, the colloid content is an almost pure concentrated solution of thyroglobulin, but some thyroglobulin is also found in the circulation. The use of porous-bottomed culture chambers permits the study of polarized thyroglobulin secretion (Chambard *et al.* 1987). Cells were seeded in serum-free medium at high density and after 4 days, when the monolayer was confluent, serum (10 %) was added to the basal compartment. Serum protein concentration in the apical compartment was followed by a protein assay and polyacrylamide gel electrophoresis (PAGE). It remained very low (less than $36\,\mu g\,ml^{-1}$ (i.e. 0·6 % of basal concentration)), providing a good test for the tightness of the cell monolayer. Labelled thyroglobulin added to the apical compartment crossed the cell layer at a very low rate. Only 0·5 % of added thyroglobulin was found in the basal compartment after 48 h, whereas concentration equilibrium was reached within 24 h in the absence of cells.

The secretion of newly synthesized ^{35}S-labelled thyroglobulin in both compartments was followed after adding [^{35}S]methionine to the basal medium. High molecular weight thyroglobulin, identified by immunoprecipitation and by PAGE followed by autoradiography, accumulated linearly in the apical compartment but only a minor amount (5–15 %) was found in the basal compartment. When TSH ($100\,\mu\,units\,ml^{-1}$) was added to the basal medium a two- to threefold increase of apical thyroglobulin accumulation was observed. This increase was correlated with a threefold higher level of thyroglobulin-specific mRNA. In contrast, the amount of thyroglobulin found in the basal compartment was not increased after treatment by TSH.

The relatively high quantity of thyroglobulin found in the basal compartment precluded the possibility that it originates from apically secreted protein. It is therefore suggested that the majority of newly synthesized thyroglobulin molecules were apically secreted while 5–10 % of them was directly secreted through the basolateral membrane. This route of secretion appeared unmodified after chronic treatment by TSH.

Net water transport from apical to basal compartment

While studying the secretion of thyroglobulin we observed a net transfer of fluid from the apical to the basal compartment (Chambard *et al.* 1987). A flux of $2{\cdot}5\,\mu l\,h^{-1}$ per chamber ($5{\cdot}5\,cm^2$) was calculated for resting monolayers and $8{\cdot}5\,\mu l\,h^{-1}$ per chamber when cells were stimulated by TSH ($100\,\mu\,units\,ml^{-1}$). Stimulation appears to be cyclic AMP-mediated since 8-chloro-cyclic AMP or cholera toxin were also stimulatory. This water transfer was active enough under stimulation to pump within 4 days almost all the fluid present in the apical compartment, which had to be refilled.

The reduction of apical volume results in a concentration of thyroglobulin in the apical compartment. The mechanism of this water transport *in vitro* has to be related with ion transport in the thyroid cell and its relation to the situation *in vivo*, where the follicular lumen is closed, has to be found.

ORIENTATION AND STABILIZATION OF EPITHELIAL CELL POLARITY: ORIENTING FACTORS

As seen from the above results, two completely different factors appear to be involved in the orientation of cell polarity. When cells are cultured on an adhesive substratum or in an adhesive matrix, adhesion is the determinant of cell polarization, the basal pole being formed in contact with the substratum. When cells are cultured in suspension, aggregates transform either into follicles or into inside-out follicles, depending on the presence of cell stimulators. Moreover, follicles have a spontaneous tendency to invert to inside-out structures when the stimulator is withdrawn or when the serum level is raised. Adhesion to a substratum is not involved in these situations, therefore other factors must be involved.

Several years ago, Jaffe (1981) pointed out the importance of ionic currents in establishing developmental patterns and put forward a model of the reversal of thyroid cell polarity. This model proposed a serum (or stimulator)-induced modification of apical, basal and transepithelial ionic currents resulting in a change in intracellular Na^+, Ca^{2+} and pH gradients. Little was known about ion transport in thyroid cells and almost nothing about transepithelial electrical properties. Using porcine thyroid cells in culture we have started to study these parameters.

When puncturing cells organized into follicles or into inside-out follicles we observed that a transepithelial potential difference can be measured, the apical compartment being negative (Mauchamp *et al.* 1979*b*; Takasu *et al.* 1984). With reference to the culture medium the follicular lumen is negative and the cavity of inside-out follicles (basal compartment) is positive. Morphological and electrical polarization have the same orientation. The Na^+/K^+-ATPase has been localized on the basolateral domain of the cell plasma membrane by immunohistochemistry, both in the gland and in cultured cells (Gerard *et al.* 1985*a*). The study of Na^+ uptake by cells cultured in monolayers on plastic showed that an amiloride-sensitive sodium uptake occurred at the apical pole of thyroid cells. This uptake was stimulated by cholera toxin and prostaglandin E, which increased cyclic AMP levels in monolayers (Gerard *et al.* 1985*b*).

More recently, using porcine thyroid cell monolayers formed on collagen-coated filters and mounted in Ussing chambers, we have characterized transepithelial sodium transport responsible for the observed transepithelial potential difference. Amiloride blocked sodium transport from the apical side, whereas ouabain was inhibitory from the basal compartment. This current was stimulated by basal TSH, which increased transepithelial potential difference (Penel *et al.* 1987). The existence of a basal Na^+ channel and of a TSH-induced thyroid cell depolarization involving this channel has recently been reported (Hambleton *et al.* 1986; Manley *et al.* 1986) using cultured porcine thyroid cells.

The importance of these ion transport processes, occurring at the basal and apical poles of thyroid cells, in the maintenance of cell polarity and in the generation of transepithelial asymmetry must be studied further. The influence of environmental stimuli on the orientation of H^+ and HCO_3^- secretion by cells of the rat kidney collecting tubule has been demonstrated (Schwartz *et al.* 1985). The polarity of transepithelial H^+ transport can be reversed and the HCO_3^--secreting cell can be induced to change its functional polarity to that of the H^+-secreting cell by loading the animal with acid.

This paper is dedicated to the memory of Professor Serge Lissitzky; the research on porcine thyroid cell polarity was initiated in his laboratory some years ago. This work was supported by INSERM (U270), by CNRS (UAC 99) and by Fondation de la Recherche Medicale. We acknowledge the expert technical assistance of Danielle DePetris, Sylvie Alloing and Jean-Claude Bugeia, and the expert assistance of Chantal Aubert in preparing the manuscript.

REFERENCES

BARRIERE, H., CHAMBARD, M., MAUCHAMP, J. & GABRION, J. (1986). Polarity reversal of inside-out follicles cultured within collagen gel: an ultrastructural study. *Biol. Cell* **57**, 29–52.

CHAMBARD, M., GABRION, J. & MAUCHAMP, J. (1981). Influence of collagen gel on the orientation of epithelial cell polarity: follicle formation from isolated thyroid cells and from preformed monolayers. *J. Cell Biol.* **91**, 157–166.

CHAMBARD, M., MAUCHAMP, J. & CHABAUD, O. (1987). Synthesis and apical and basolateral secretion of thyroglobulin by thyroid cell monolayers on permeable substrates: modulation by thyrotropin. *J. cell. Physiol.* (in press).

CHAMBARD, M., VERRIER, B., GABRION, J. & MAUCHAMP, J. (1983). Polarization of thyroid cells in culture: evidence for the basolateral localization of the iodide "pump" and of the thyroid-stimulating hormone receptor-adenyl cyclase complex. *J. Cell Biol.* **96**, 1172–1177.

CHAMBARD, M., VERRIER, B., GABRION, J. & MAUCHAMP, J. (1984). Polarity reversal of inside-out follicles cultured within collagen gel: reexpression of specific functions. *Biol. Cell* **51**, 315–326.

ELSDALE, T. & BARD, J. (1972). Collagen substrate for studies on cell behaviour. *J. Cell Biol.* **54**, 626–637.

FAYET, G., HOVSEPIAN, S., DICKSON, J. G. & LISSITSKY, S. (1982). Reorganization of porcine thyroid cells into functional follicles in a chemically defined, serum and thyrotropin free medium. *J. Cell Biol.* **93**, 479–488.

FERACCI, H., BERNADAC, A., FAYET, G. & MAROUX, S. (1981). Aminopeptidase N is a marker for the apical pole of porcine thyroid epithelial cells in vivo and in culture. *Cell Tiss. Res.* **221**, 137–146.

GARTNER, R., GREIL, W., STRUBNER, D., PERMANETTER, W., HORN, K. & PICKARDT, C. R. (1985). Preparation of porcine thyroid follicles with preserved polarity: functional and morphological properties in comparison to inside-out follicles. *Molec. cell. Endocrinol.* **40**, 9–16.

GERARD, C., GABRION, J., VERRIER, B., REGGIO, H. & MAUCHAMP, J. (1985*a*). Localization of the Na^+/K^+ ATPase and of an amiloride sensitive Na^+ uptake on thyroid epithelial cells. *Eur. J. Cell Biol.* **38**, 134–141.

GERARD, C., VERRIER, B. & MAUCHAMP, J. (1985*b*). Effect of prostaglandin E2 and cholera toxin on apical sodium uptake in thyroid epithelial cells: role of cAMP. *FEBS Lett.* **180**, 9–12.

HALL, H. G., FARSON, D. A. & BISSELL, M. J. (1982). Lumen formation by epithelial cell lines in response to collagen overlay: a morphogenetic model in culture. *Proc. natn. Acad. Sci. U.S.A.* **79**, 4672–4676.

HAMBLETON, T. A., BOURKE, J. R., HUSEHAM, G. J. & MANLEY, S. W. (1986). Sodium dependence of the thyrotropin-induced depolarization in cultured porcine thyroid cells. *J. Endocrinol.* **108**, 225–230.

HANDLER, J. S. (1986). Studies of kidney cells in culture. *Kidney Int.* **30**, 208–215.

HANDLER, J. S., STEELE, R. E., SAHIB, M. K., NADE, J. B., PRESTON, A. S., LAWSON, N. L. & JOHNSON, J. P. (1979). Toad urinary bladder epithelial cells in culture: maintenance of epithelial structure, sodium transport and response to hormones. *Proc. natn. Acad. Sci. U.S.A.* **76**, 4151–4155.

HERZOG, V. & MILLER, F. (1981). Structural and functional polarity of inside-out follicles prepared from pig thyroid gland. *Eur. J. Cell Biol.* **24**, 74–84.

INOUÉ, K., HORINCHI, R. & KONDO, Y. (1980). Effect of thyrotropin on cell orientation and follicle reconstruction in rotated suspension culture of hog thyroid cells. *Endocrinology* **107**, 1162–1168.

JAFFE, L. F. (1981). The role of ionic currents in establishing developmental pattern. *Phil. Trans. R. Soc. Lond.* B **295**, 553–566.

KITAJIMA, K., YAMASHITA, K. & FUJITA, H. (1985). Fine structural aspects of the shift of zonula occludens and cytoorganelles during the inversion of cell polarity in cultured porcine thyroid follicles. *Cell Tiss. Res.* **242**, 221–224.

LISSITZKY, S., FAYET, G., GIRAUD, A., VERRIER, B. & TORRESANI, J. (1971). Thyrotropin-induced aggregation and reorganization into follicles of isolated porcine thyroid cells 1. Mechanism of action of thyrotropin and metabolic properties. *Eur. J. Biochem.* **24**, 88–99.

LOUVARD, D. (1980). Apical membrane aminopeptidase appears at site of cell–cell contact in cultured kidney epithelial cells. *Proc. natn. Acad. Sci. U.S.A.* **77**, 4132–4236.

MANLEY, S. W., HUXHAM, G. J. & BOURKE, J. R. (1986). Role of sodium influx in thyrotropin action: effects of the sodium channel agonist veratridine and thyrotrophin on radioiodide turnover and membrane potential in cultured porcine thyroid cells. *J. Endocrinol.* **110**, 459–466.

MAUCHAMP, J., CHAMBARD, M., GABRION, J. & VERRIER, B. (1983). Polarized multicellular structures designed for the in vitro study of thyroid cell function and polarization. *Meth. Enzym.* **98**, 477–486.

MAUCHAMP, J., CHARRIER, B., TAKASU, N., MARGOTAT, A., CHAMBARD, M. & DUMAS, D. (1979*a*). Modulation by thyrotropin, prostaglandin E and catecholamines of sensitivity to acute stimulation in cultured thyroid cells. In *Hormone and Cell Regulation*, vol. 3 (ed. J. Dumont & J. Nunez), pp. 51–68. Amsterdam: Elsevier North Holland.

MAUCHAMP, J., GABRION, J. & BERNARD, P. (1979*b*). Morphological and electrical polarity of the thyroid epithelium reconstructed in culture. *Les Colloques de l'INSERM* **85**, 43–52.

MAUCHAMP, J., MARGOTAT, A., CHAMBARD, M., CHARRIER, B., REMY, L. & MICHEL-BECHET, M. (1979*c*). Polarity of three-dimensional structures derived from isolated hog thyroid cells in primary culture. *Cell Tiss. Res.* **204**, 417–430.

MIYAGAWA, J., FUJITA, H. & MATSUDA, H. (1982). Fine structural aspects of inverted follicles in cultured porcine thyroids. *Archs Histol., Japan* **45**, 385–392.

NITSCH, L. & WOLLMAN, S. H. (1980*a*). Suspensions culture of separated follicles consisting of differentiated thyroid epithelial cells. *Proc. natn. Acad. Sci. U.S.A.* **77**, 472–476.

NITSCH, L. & WOLLMAN, S. H. (1980*b*). Ultrastructure of intermediate stages in polarity reversal of thyroid epithelium in follicles in suspension culture. *J. Cell Biol.* **86**, 875–880.

NORD, E. P., GOLDFARB, D., MIKHAIL, N., MORADESHAGI, P., AFREZI, A., VAYSTUB, S., CRAGOE, E. J. & FINE, L. G. (1986). Characteristics of the Na^+/H^+ antiporter in the intact renal proximal tubular cell. *Am. J. Physiol.* **286**, F539–F550.

PENEL, C., GERARD, C. & VERRIER, B. (1987). Thyroid transepithelial sodium transport. *Annls Endocr.* **48**, 114a.

PISAM, M. & RIPOCHE, P. (1976). Redistribution of surface macromolecules in dissociated epithelial cells. *J. Cell Biol.* **71**, 907–920.

RABITO, C. A. (1986). Occluding junctions in a renal cell line (LLC-PK1) with characteristics of proximal tubular cells. *Am. J. Physiol.* **250**, F734–F743.

RODRIGUEZ-BOULAN, E., PASKIET, K. T. & SABATINI, D. D. (1983). Assembly of enveloped virsuses in Madin-Darby canine kidney cells: polarized budding from single attached cells and from clusters of cells in suspension. *J. Cell Biol.* **96**, 866–874.

SCHWARTZ, G. P., BARASCH, J. & AL AWQUATI, Q. (1985). Plasticity of functional epithelial polarity. *Nature, Lond.* **318**, 368–371.

Simons, K. & Fuller, S. D. (1985). Cell surface polarity in epithelia. *A. Rev. Cell Biol.* **1**, 243–288.

Steele, R. E., Preston, A. S., Johnson, J. P. & Handler, J. S. (1986). Porous-bottom dishes for culture of polarized cells. *Am. J. Physiol.* **251**, C136–C139.

Sugahara, K., Caldwell, J. H. & Mason, R. J. (1984). Electrical currents flow out of domes formed by cultured epithelial cells. *J. Cell Biol.* **99**, 1541–1546.

Takasu, N., Handa, Y., Shimizu, Y. & Yamada, T. (1984). Electrophysiological and morphological cell polarity and iodine metabolism in cultured porcine and human (normal and Graves') thyroid cells. *J. Endocr.* **101**, 189–196.

Valentich, J. D., Tchao, R. & Leighton, J. (1979). Hemicyst formation stimulated by cyclic AMP in dog kidney cell line MDCK. *J. cell. Physiol.* **100**, 291–304.

Waters, M. J., Tweedale, R. C., Whip, T. A., Shaw, G., Marney, S. W. & Bourke, J. R. (1987). Dedifferentiation of cultured thyroid cells by epidermal growth factor: some insights into the mechanism. *Molec. cell. Endocr.* **49**, 109–117.

Wohlwend, A., Montesano, R., Vassali, J. D. & Orci, L. (1985). LLC-PK1 cysts: a model for the study of epithelial polarity *J. cell. Physiol.* **125**, 533–539.

Yang, J., Flynn, D., Larson, L. & Hamamoto, S. (1982). Growth in primary culture of mouse submandibular epithelial cells embedded in collagen gels. *In Vitro* **18**, 435–442.

Yang, J. & Nandi, S. (1983). Growth of cultured cells using collagen as substrate. *Int. Rev. Cytol.* **81**, 249–286.

Ziomek, C. A., Schulman, S. & Edidin, M. (1980). Redistribution of membrane proteins in isolated mouse intestinal epithelial cells. *J. Cell Biol.* **86**, 849–857.

J. Cell Sci. Suppl. 8, 359–367 (1987)
Printed in Great Britain © *The Company of Biologists Limited 1987*

STUDIES ON THE MIGRATION OF MOUSE GERM CELLS

PETER J. DONOVAN, DAVID STOTT*, ISABELLE GODIN, JANET HEASMAN AND CHRISTOPHER C. WYLIE
Department of Anatomy, St George's Hospital Medical School, Cranmer Terrace, Tooting, London SW17 0RE, UK

SUMMARY

Primordial germ cells in the mouse embryo migrate from their site of origin to the gonad where they differentiate, giving rise eventually to the gametes of the mature adult animal. The migratory phase is transient and therefore permits analysis of factors regulating the motile activity of cells in tissues. Germ cells can be isolated during migration and cultured on feeder cells of an established cell line (STO). In this system the molecular interactions mediating germ cell adhesion can be probed using antibodies to both germ cell surface determinants and to extracellular matrix components.

INTRODUCTION

A number of embryonic cell types move from the site at which they first become established through the tissues of the embryo to a new site where they cease migration and enter the next phase of differentiation (see Browder, 1986, for reviews). In theory these migratory populations of cells are excellent systems for studying the control of motile activity. However, in practice we have very little detailed information on these controls, since the early migratory populations are very small, mostly impossible to see in the opaque embryo, and difficult to isolate in pure form. Because of these drawbacks our knowledge is confined to a very limited number of cell types. In this article we describe work on the culture of migrating mouse primordial germ cells (PGCs), which permit more detailed analysis of the controlling factors of cell migration in embryos.

The migratory phase of mouse primordial germ cells (PGCs) has been well established using alkaline phosphatase activity as a cell marker (Chiquoine, 1954; Mintz & Russell, 1957; Ozdzenski, 1967; Tam & Snow, 1981). Mouse PGCs are first identified at 8·5 days post coitus (d.p.c.) at the caudal end of the primitive streak near the root of the allantois. As the embryo turns they become incorporated into the developing hind gut from which they migrate into its mesentery. By 10·5 d.p.c. PGCs are found migrating through the dorsal mesentery and by the next day of gestation when they have reached the top of the mesentery they migrate laterally into

* Present address: National Institute of Medical Research, The Ridgeway, Mill Hill, London NW7 1AA, UK.

thickened ridges of tissue (the genital ridges). Here in the gonad anlagen they proliferate for a short while (as they do throughout the migratory phase) before entering the long process of differentiation into the gametes of the mature adult animal (see McLaren, 1981, for review).

The behaviour of early germ-line cells raises a number of important questions. (1) What factors switch these early cells into a migratory mode? (2) What factors control their adhesion and guidance to their target? (3) What factors switch off their migratory behaviour? Our initial aim was to identify mouse PGCs in such a way that we could culture them, observe their behaviour *in vitro* and identify molecules involved in their interaction with the substratum.

The mouse has several attractive features for this sort of study. Culture of mouse cells is well established and there are a large variety of established cell lines available. Moreover, there are glycosylation mutants of some cell lines that are defective in defined carbohydrate structures (Stanley, 1984, 1987; Hooper, 1985), on which adhesive mechanisms can be probed. It is also possible to select glycosylation mutants of a cell line of interest (see Hooper, 1985, for brief review). Cell lines of defined genetic background may also be used to analyse the effect of specific genes on cell adhesion or behaviour.

Amongst the large numbers of gene mutations in the mouse there are two well-described mutations, Steel and Dominant White spotting, which in the homozygous condition both cause complete sterility. In animals homozygous for either mutation, germ cells fail to proliferate or to migrate to the gonad (McCoshen & McCallion, 1975; Mintz & Russell, 1957). In Dominant White spotting the mutation is thought to affect directly the PGCs themselves, whilst in Steel the mutation is thought to affect the environment through which PGCs migrate (see Silvers, 1979, for review). These mutants therefore provide an opportunity to analyse both defective PGCs and a defective environment.

MARKERS OF THE GERM LINE

Alkaline phosphatase activity has been a useful PGC marker for elucidating the migratory route of the cells. However, the histochemical reaction required for its detection can only be carried out successfully on fixed tissues. In studying PGCs in culture, therefore, alkaline phosphatase can only be used as a retrospective marker. Although relatively pure populations of mouse PGCs can be isolated from developing gonads from 12·5 d.p.c. onwards (Heath, 1978; DeFelici & McLaren, 1982), no method has yet been devised for isolating pure populations of migrating PGCs from 10·5 d.p.c. mesenteries where they represent 1–2 % of the total cell population as determined by cell sorter analysis (Donovan, unpublished observations). Clearly, studying cells derived from the mesentery in the hope that some were PGCs would be a laborious task.

We have looked, instead, for immunological markers for PGCs that can be used to identify living cells. A number of monoclonal antibodies raised against early embryos and teratocarcinoma stem cells (embryonal carcinoma cells) are found to cross-react

GalNAcα1→3GalNAcβ1→3Galα1→4Galβ1→4Glc-Cer M1.22.25

(Forssman)

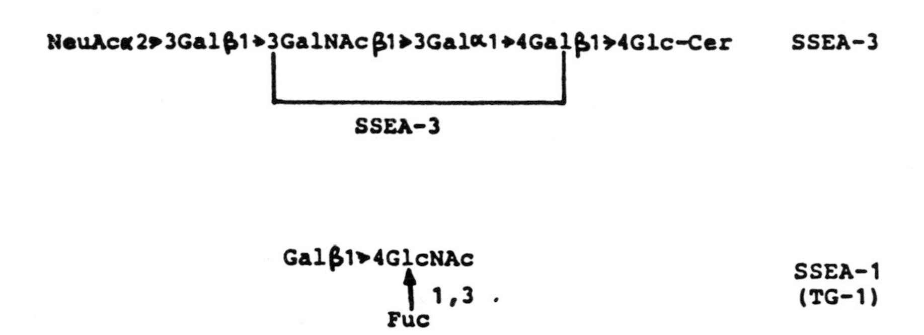

Fig. 1. Epitopes recognized by monoclonal antibodies reactive with mouse primordial germ cells. After Feizi (1985).

with germ-line cells (Eddy & Hahnel, 1983; Donovan *et al.* 1986; Wylie *et al.* 1986). The epitopes recognized by some of these antibodies are shown in Fig. 1.

The temporal expression of all the antibodies tested is essentially the same. Expression begins around the time of onset of migration, continues until the PGCs colonize the gonad, and then gradually disappears (Wylie *et al.* 1986). Clearly a major change in surface phenotyope takes place during the migratory phase. Furthermore, several antibodies specifically stain PGCs whilst they are migrating through the hind-gut mesentery, although they may stain other cell types at other stages in development. This makes them reliable markers for PGCs in experiments where they are extracted from isolated dorsal mesenteries.

THE CULTURE OF MIGRATING PGCs

There is considerable histochemical evidence that a number of matrix components surround migrating PGCs (Wylie *et al.* 1986) and that several specific antigens are present on PGC surfaces during migration (see above). However, the importance of these can only be tested under defined conditions in culture. In the last two years we have developed a method for culturing migrating PGCs by removing them from the hind-gut mesentery of 10·5-day mouse embryos. This is done by disaggregating excised mesenteries in calcium- and magnesium-free phosphate-buffered saline (PBS-A), and seeding the disaggregated cells (which consist of PGCs and other mesentery cells) onto a cellular feeder layer. PGCs are then identified by double labelling with TG-1 antibody (see Fig. 1) and alkaline phosphatase. Several feeder layers have been used, which support PGC adhesion and spreading to different extents (Donovan *et al.* 1986); of these, STO fibroblasts, derived originally from embryonic mice (Ware & Axelrad, 1972), are the best.

PGC BEHAVIOUR IN CULTURE

When PGCs from the migratory route are cultured on STO cells they show every appearance of motile cells (Donovan *et al.* 1986). They are elongated with leading lamellipodia and filopodia, and often a distinct uroid with retraction fibres. Filming and interference reflection studies show that they actively move at speeds of around $50\,\mu m\,h^{-1}$. PGCs can migrate beneath STO cells, often causing them to retract away from advancing PGCs. The interference reflection pattern of cell–substratum contacts is visible where PGCs are migrating on the glass substrate rather than the feeder cells, and shows no focal adhesions. Instead, the interference image resembles that of fast-moving cells such as leucocytes (Stott & Wylie, 1986).

The phenotype of migratory-stage PGCs in culture strongly supports the notion that PGCs *in vivo* actively migrate to the gonad, pushing other cells out of their way as they do so. If this is the case, then it becomes important to establish the mechanism whereby such locomotory behaviour is switched off once PGCs reach the gonad. This could be due either to intrinsic loss of motility by the PGCs, or to a non-permissive environment (e.g. a change in composition of the extracellular matrix). We therefore isolated PGCs from 13·5-day embryo gonads, and seeded them under identical conditions on STO feeder layers. We found that a very small proportion adhered to STO cells, and even fewer spread and showed motile behaviour. Furthermore, loss of cell motility occurred gradually from 11·5 to 13·5 days of gestation (Donovan *et al.* 1986). These studies suggest that an inherent change in adhesive and motile behaviour takes place in PGCs once they reach the gonad and that migration to the gonad is an active process. The change in motility correlates well with earlier electron-microscopical evidence that PGCs are polarized in the mesentery but rounded in the gonad (Clark & Eddy, 1975).

MOLECULES INVOLVED IN PGC ADHESION

The ability to culture migratory-stage PGCs provides two ways of analysing the factors involved in their adhesion: blocking experiments with specific antibodies, and culture on defined substrates. Some preliminary data on both these approaches are presented here, and will be published in more detail elsewhere.

In blocking experiments, gamma-irradiated STO cells are seeded at sub-confluent concentrations into 96-well plates. Once the feeder cells have spread (24–48 h later) cells from disaggregated mesentery, which include PGCs, are seeded onto them to give a calculated number of 100–200 PGCs per well. The number of PGCs that have attached after 1 h is measured for each treatment. The time-course of initial adhesion shows that most PGCs have attached after 1 h (Fig. 2).

Molecules that are present on the surface of migrating PGCs, and are lost after migration, are attractive candidates for a role in PGC adhesion or locomotion. We have therefore tested the TG-1 antibody in blocking experiments. As shown in Fig. 3, TG-1 IgM inhibited the initial adhesion of PGCs to STO cells by up to 50 %. Fab fragments of TG-1 also inhibited adhesion, whereas a monoclonal antibody against fibronectin, which stains the matrix around STO cells, did not. Since TG-1

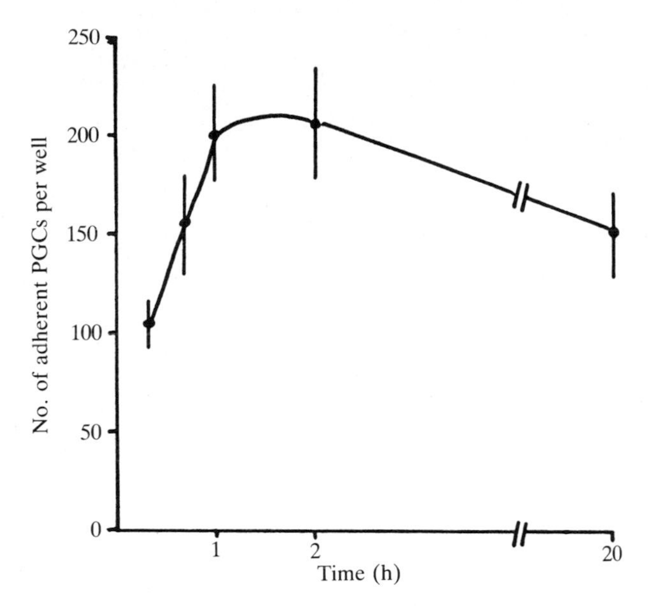

Fig. 2. Time-course of PGC adhesion to STO cell monolayers. PGC suspensions were added to confluent STO monolayers and the number of adherent PGCs was determined at intervals by staining for alkaline phosphatase. Points represent the mean (±S.D.) of 10 cultures.

inhibition was never more than 50 %, other molecules may also play a role in PGC adhesion to STO cells.

The finding that the TG-1 antigen is involved in PGC adhesion prompted us to try to identify the epitope, and to look for factors that cause it to appear when the cells begin to migrate and disappear at the end of migration.

The epitope for one of the other PGC binding antibodies, SSEA-1, is known to be a specific sugar, 3-fucosyl lactosamine (Feizi, 1985). We have shown that the same sugar inhibits staining of frozen sections with TG-1, whereas its close relative 2-fucosyl lactosamine does not. Therefore, TG-1 recognizes the same epitope (or an overlapping one) as does SSEA-1. The latter antibody has been shown to inhibit compaction in early mouse embryos (Bird & Kimber, 1984) and adhesion of F9 embryonal carcinoma cells to plastic, as well as laminin- and fibronectin-coated substrata (Nomoto *et al.* 1986). We are currently trying to identify the carrier molecule of TG-1 antigen on PGCs. On embryonal carcinoma cells the SSEA-1 antigen is carried by polydisperse, endo-β-galactosidase-sensitive lactosaminoglycans (Childs *et al.* 1983), in particular a molecule known as embryoglycan (Ozawa *et al.* 1985).

The TG-1/SSEA-1 antigen appears at 9·5 days of development (Donovan *et al.* 1986; Wylie *et al.* 1986). In early embryos the SSEA-1 antigen is thought to appear by fucosylation of a pre-existing glycoprotein, the I antigen (Gooi *et al.* 1981; Knowles *et al.* 1982). It is not known whether the I antigen is present on PGCs before SSEA-1 appears.

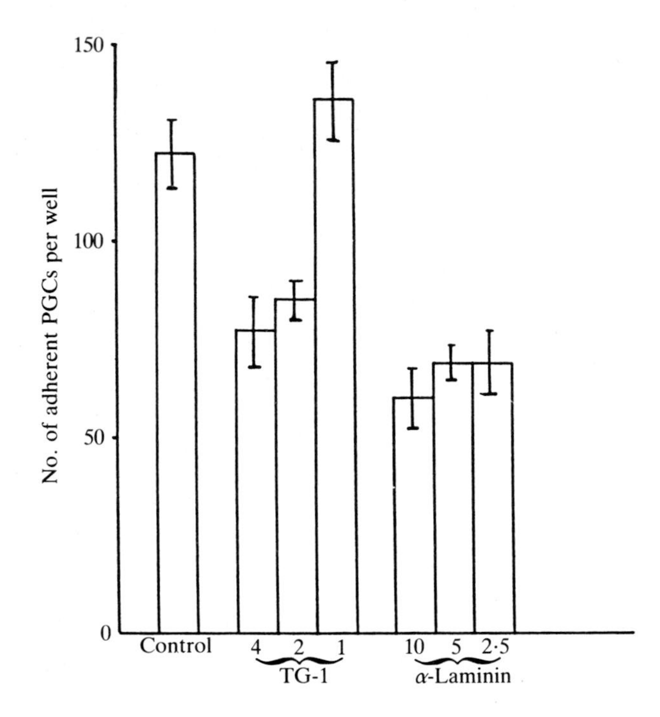

Fig. 3. PGC suspensions were plated onto confluent STO cell monolayers in DME+15 % FCS (control) or in DME+15 % FCS containing purified TG-1 IgM (1, 2 and 4 μg ml^{-1}) or purified anti-laminin monoclonal antibody (2·5, 5 and 10 μg ml^{-1}); 40 min after plating the cultures were washed, fixed and stained for alkaline phosphatase; the number of adherent PGCs per well was then determined. Bars represent the mean (±S.D.) of 10 wells.

The antigen disappears completely from gonads of both sexes by 14·5 days of development. In recent experiments we found that neuraminidase treatment (1 unit ml^{-1} in PGC for 1 h) of sections of 15·5-day embryos caused antibody reactivity to be restored. Chondroitinase ABC, hyaluronidase, periodic acid, 100 % ethanol and 100 % acetone had no effect. This suggests that the TG-1 antigen becomes sialylated after migration. Similar mechanisms of receptor modulation have been reported to accompany maturation of T lymphocytes in the immune system (Sharon, 1983; Pink, 1983, for reviews) and differentiation of embryonal carcinoma cells (Cossu *et al.* 1985). We do not yet know, however, whether removal of sialic acid from 15·5-day PGCs will restore their adhesive behaviour, or whether other post-migratory phenotypic changes take place.

The PGC surface molecules involved in adhesion must interact with surrounding cells and extracellular matrix. We have started a study of these interactions, particularly with respect to defined extracellular matrix molecules. In the embryo, PGCs migrate over an incomplete basal lamina underlying the coelomic epithelial cells (Clark & Eddy, 1975), which is composed of, amongst other things, type IV collagen, laminin and fibronectin (Fujimoto *et al.* 1985; Wylie *et al.* 1986). Fibronectin and laminin also surround the mesenchymal cells between which PGCs

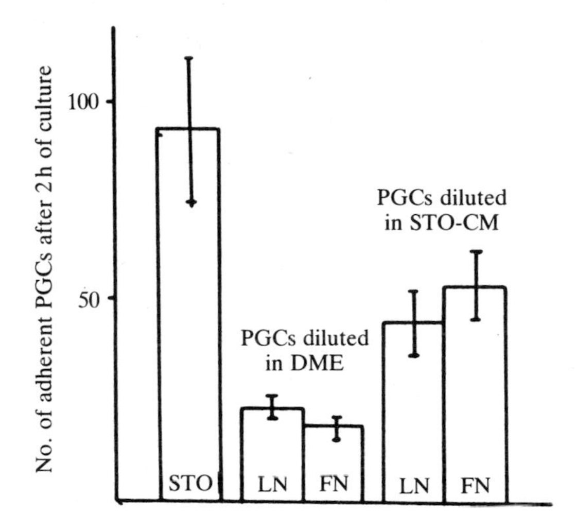

Fig. 4. PGC adhesion to laminin- or fibronectin-coated substrates. PGC-containing suspensions in DME+15 % FCS or in the same medium conditioned by STO cells were plated onto substrates coated with laminin or fibronectin ($10\,\mu g\,ml^{-1}$). After 2 h the numbers of adherent PGCs were determined (as described previously) and compared to the numbers adherent to STO cell monolayers. Bars represent the mean (±S.D.) of 12 cultures. LN, laminin; FN, fibronectin; STO-CM, STO cell conditioned medium; DME, Dulbecco's modified Eagle's medium.

migrate (Wylie *et al.* 1986). We have found that PGCs adhere to purified fibronectin and laminin, but in considerably smaller numbers than adhere to STO cells (Fig. 4; and Godin *et al.* unpublished observations). Furthermore, a monoclonal anti-laminin antibody raised in this laboratory, which precipitates both chains of laminin, partially blocks the initial adhesion of PGCs to STO cells (Fig. 3; and Stott *et al.* unpublished observations). This combination of blocking experiments and culture of PGCs on defined substrates is likely to increase our understanding of the factors involved in PGC migration.

In conclusion, embryonic migratory cells present an attractive system for study, even though they constitute a very small population of cells, and are difficult to isolate in pure form. The advent of antibody markers has permitted not only identification of PGCs, but also live labelling and therefore cell tracing. Furthermore, the fact that PGCs will adhere to defined extracellular molecules has finally made it possible to study the mechanism of their guidance, using, for example, the methods pioneered for neutrophils (Zigmond, 1978). Finally, these methods should permit the study of mutants in which PGCs do not migrate correctly.

Our grateful thanks go to the Cancer Research Campaign, who have funded this work, to Linda Cairns and Margaret Docherty for expert technical assistance, and to Melanie Coulton for typing part of this manuscript.

REFERENCES

BIRD, J. M. & KIMBER, S. J. (1984). Oligosaccharides containing fucose linked a(1-3) and a(1-4) to *N*-acetylglucosamine cause decompaction of mouse morulae. *Devl Biol.* **104**, 449–460.

BROWDER, L. (1986). *Developmental Biology: A Comprehensive Synthesis*, vol. 2, *The Cellular Basis of Morphogenesis*. New York: Plenum Press.

CHILDS, R. A., PENNINGTON, J., UEMURA, K., SCUDDER, P., GOODFELLOW, P. N., EVANS, M. J. & FEIZI, T. (1983). High molecular-weight glycoproteins are the major carriers of the carbohydrate differentiation antigens I, i and SSEA-1 of mouse teratocarcinoma cells. *Biochem. J.* **215**, 491–503.

CHIQUOINE, A. D. (1954). The identification, origin and migration of the primordial germ cells in the mouse embryo. *Anat. Rec.* **118**, 135–146.

CLARK, J. M. & EDDY, E. M. (1975). Fine structural observations on the origin and associations of primordial cells of the mouse. *Devl Biol.* **47**, 136–155.

COSSU, G., CORTESI, E. & WARREN, L. (1985). Increased sialylation of complex glycopeptides during differentiation of mouse embryonal carcinoma cells. *Differentiation* **29**, 63–67.

DEFELICI, M. & MCLAREN, A. (1982). Isolation of mouse primordial germ cells. *Expl Cell. Res.* **142**, 476–482.

DONOVAN, P. J., STOTT, D., CAIRNS, L. A., HEASMAN, J. & WYLIE, C. C. (1986). Migratory and postmigratory mouse primordial germ cells behave differently in culture. *Cell* **44**, 831–838.

EDDY, E. M. & HAHNEL, A. C. (1983). Establishment of the germ cell line in mammals. In *Current Problems in Germ Cell Differentiation* (ed. A. McLaren & C. C. Wylie), pp. 41–69. Cambridge University Press.

FEIZI, T. (1985). Demonstration by monoclonal antibodies that carbohydrate structures of glycoproteins and glycolipids are onco-developmental antigens. *Nature, Lond.* **314**, 53–57.

FUJIMOTO, T., YOSHINAGA, K. & KONO, I. (1985). Distribution of fibronectin on the migratory pathway of primordial germ cells in mice. *Anat. Rec.* **211**, 271–278.

GOOI, H. C., FEIZI, T., KAPADIA, A., KNOWLES, B. B., SOLTER, D. & EVANS, M. J. (1981). Stage-specific embryonic antigen involves a1-3 fucosylated type 2 blood group chains. *Nature, Lond.* **292**, 156–158.

HEATH, J. K. (1978). Mammalian primordial germ cells. In *Development in Mammals*, vol. 3 (ed. M. H. Johnson), pp. 267–298. New York: North Holland.

HOOPER, K. L. (1985). *Mammalian Cell Genetics*. New York: John Wiley and Sons.

KNOWLES, B. B., RAPPAPORT, J. & SOLTER, D. (1982). Murine embryonic antigen (SSEA-1) is expressed on human cells and structurally related human blood group antigen I is expressed on mouse embryos. *Devl Biol.* **93**, 54–58.

MCCOSHEN, J. A. & MCCALLION, D. J. (1975). A study of primordial germ cells during their migratory phase in steel mutant mice. *Experientia* **31**, 589–590.

MCLAREN, A. (1981). *Germ Cells and Soma: a New Look at an Old Problem*. New Haven: Yale University Press.

MINTZ, B. & RUSSELL, E. S. (1957). Gene-induced embryological modifications or primordial germ cells in the mouse. *J. exp. Zool.* **134**, 207–237.

NOMOTO, S., MURAMATSU, H., OZAWA, M., SUGANUMA, T., TASHIRO, M. & MURAMATSU, T. (1986). An anti-carbohydrate monoclonal antibody inhibits cell–substratum adhesion of F9 embryonal carcinoma cells. *Expl Cell Res.* **164**, 49–62.

OZAWA, M., MURAMATSU, T. & SOLTER, D. (1985). SSEA-1, a stage-specific embryonic antigen of the mouse, is carried by the glycoprotein-bound large carbohydrate in embryonal carcinoma cells. *Cell Differ.* **16**, 169–173.

OZDZENSKI, W. (1967). Observations on the origin of primordial germ cells in the mouse. *Zool. Polon.* **17**, 367–379.

PINK, J. R. L. (1983). Changes in T-lymphocyte glycoprotein structures associated with differentiation. *Contemp. Top. molec. Immun.* **9**, 89–113.

SHARON, N. (1983). Lectin receptors as lymphocyte surface markers. *Adv. Immunol.* **34**, 213–298.

SILVERS, W. K. (1979). *The Coat Colors of Mice*. New York: Springer-Verlag.

STANLEY, P. (1984). Glycosylation mutants of animal cells. *A. Rev. Genet.* **18**, 525–552.

STANLEY, P. (1987). Glycosylation mutants and the functions of mammalian carbohydrates. *Trends Genet.* **3**, 77–81.

STOTT, D. & WYLIE, C. C. (1986). Invasive behaviour of mouse primordial germ cells *in vitro*. *J. Cell Sci.* **86**, 133–144.

TAM, P. P. L. & SNOW, M. H. L. (1981). Proliferation and migration of primordial germ cells during compensatory growth in mouse embryos. *J. Embryol. exp. Morph.* **64**, 133–147.

Ware, L. M. & Axelrad, A. A. (1972). Inherited resistance to N- and B-tropic murine leukemia viruses *in vitro*: Evidence that congenic mouse strains SIM and SIM.R differ at the Fv-1 locus. *Virology* **50**, 339–348.

Wylie, C. C., Stott, D. & Donovan, P. J. (1986). Primordial germ cell migration. In *Developmental Biology: A Comprehensive Synthesis*, vol. 2, *The Cellular Basis of Morphogenesis* (ed. L. Browder), pp. 433–448. New York: Plenum Press.

Zigmond, S. H. (1978). Chemotaxis by polymorphonuclear leukocytes. *J. Cell Biol.* **77**, 269–287.

J. Cell Sci. Suppl. 8, 369–393 (1987)
Printed in Great Britain © The Company of Biologists Limited 1987

CELL BEHAVIOUR DURING ACTIVE CELL REARRANGEMENT: EVIDENCE AND SPECULATIONS

RAY KELLER*
Department of Zoology, University of California at Berkeley, Berkeley, CA 94720, USA

AND JEFF HARDIN
Group in Biophysics and Medical Physics, University of California at Berkeley, Berkeley, CA 94720, USA

SUMMARY

The cell behaviour and motility underlying cell rearrangement during gastrulation in amphibian and sea-urchin embryos are discussed. In particular, the cell behaviour of deep (non-epithelial) and epithelial cell populations that undergo cell rearrangement is compared and contrasted. Deep cell rearrangement in *Xenopus laevis* involves both convergence of cells towards the future dorsal midline and simultaneous axial extension of the mesodermal cell mass. Time-lapse cinemicrography and scanning electron microscopy suggest that asynchronous, repetitive motions of individual deep cells, involving local extensions and retractions of their margins, may provide the motive force for rearrangement. Such protrusive activity may be guided by local differences in cell–cell contacts in the marginal zone. Epithelial cell rearrangement in the sea-urchin embryo both elongates the archenteron and simultaneously closes the blastopore. Cell rearrangement is accompanied by stage-specific changes in protrusive activity and cell shape of the basal surfaces of cells in the wall of the gut rudiment, in contrast to the apical surfaces, which show little activity. These basal protrusions may be involved in the rearrangement process.

INTRODUCTION

The geometric necessity of cell rearrangement

The fate maps of early amphibian embryos (Vogt, 1929; Keller, 1975, 1976) show that embryonic tissues undergo massive changes in shape over relatively short periods of time. Waddington (1940, p. 109) pointed out that the dorsal sector of the early amphibian embryo elongates greatly through gastrulation and neurulation; he offered two explanations: either that the component cells change shape to reflect the elongation and narrowing of the tissue mass, or that the cells rearrange and, in the end, retain their original shape. If Waddington's thinking on this subject seems trivial, one has only to remember that the notion of cell rearrangement languished as a morphogenetic mechanism for 30 years, until it was revived by Fristrom's observation that *Drosophila* imaginal (limb) discs elongate during their evagination by cell rearrangement (see Fristrom, 1976). Geometric considerations suggest that any situation in which a disc is converted into a cylinder (Fristrom, 1976), in which

* Author for correspondence.

narrowing and elongation (convergence and extension) occur (Keller, 1978; Keller *et al.* 1985*a*,*b*), or in which a circumference such as the mouth of a blastopore (Hardin, 1986) or the margin of a cell sheet (Keller & Trinkaus, 1987) decreases markedly, is a prime candidate for cell rearrangement (see Keller, 1986).

Cell rearrangement occurs during many morphogenetic processes

There are many examples of epithelial cell rearrangement during morphogenesis. During evagination of *Drosophila* imaginal limb discs, the folded disc transforms into an elongated, segmented cylinder; this transformation is accompanied by a decrease in the number of cells in the circumference and an increase in the number of cells in the length of specific segments of the limb (Fristrom, 1976). During regeneration of transverse fragments of *Hydra*, the fragment regains the proper proportions by reorganizing itself to form a longer, narrower tissue, apparently by cell rearrangement (Bode & Bode, 1984). During secondary invagination of the archenteron of the sea-urchin gastrula, the archenteron becomes longer and narrower by rearrangement of epithelial cells, so that the archenteron consists of fewer cells in cross-section and a greater number along the length of the archenteron (Ettensohn, 1985; Hardin & Cheng, 1986). Nardi & MaGee-Adams (1986) have found that the scale patterns in the moth wing arise by cell rearrangement: the cells of the scale primordia are initially irregularly distributed and then become aligned in regularly spaced rows, probably through the action of long filiform basal processes that extend across several cell diameters. Similarly, Locke (1985) has found that contraction of basal 'feet' probably causes the shape transformations and cell rearrangement associated with insect pupal segment morphogenesis.

The notoplate region in the central part of the neural anlage of the urodele lengthens and narrows greatly during neurulation, a process that is accompanied by and perhaps driven by rearrangement of the epithelial cells of the notoplate (Jacobson & Gordon, 1976; Jacobson, 1982). During gastrulation and neurulation in *Xenopus*, the narrowing and lengthening (convergence and extension) of the dorsal sector of the embryo is accompanied by rearrangement of the epithelial cells, as shown by direct time-lapse cinemicrographic analysis (Keller, 1978). During teleost gastrulation, the dramatic epibolic movements of the enveloping layer involve marginal and submarginal cell rearrangement as the enveloping layer decreases in circumference as it approaches the vegetal pole of the egg (Kageyama, 1982; Keller & Trinkaus, 1982, 1987). Healing of wounds in the corneal epithelium of the cat is also accompanied by cell rearrangement (Honda *et al.* 1982).

Non-epithelial cells also rearrange during morphogenesis. During epiboly, the deep cells of *Xenopus* undergo radial intercalation to form fewer layers of greater area (Keller, 1980). Likewise, the deep cells of the circumblastoporal region of *Xenopus* gastrulae undergo circumferential intercalation to form a longer, narrower array (Keller, 1984; Keller *et al.* 1985*a*,*b*). Cell rearrangement continues at the neurula stage with the narrowing and lengthening of the notochord by cell intercalation (Keller *et al.* 1985*a*,*b*), a process that also occurs in the ascidian (Cloney, 1964; Miyamoto & Crowther, 1985). The elongation of the pronephric duct of the axolotl,

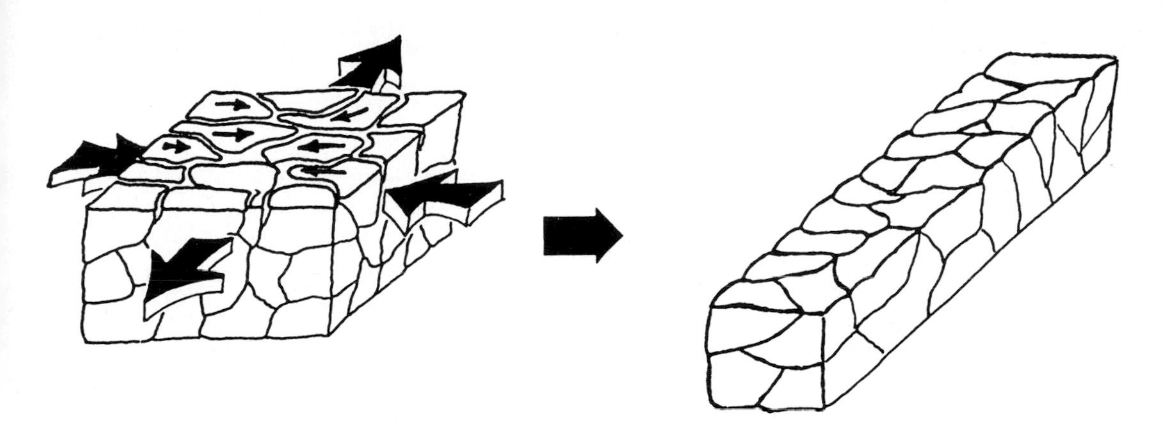

Fig. 1. Narrowing (convergence) and lengthening (extension) of the marginal zone of the early amphibian embryo occurs by active cell rearrangement. The deep cells of the marginal zone actively move between one another (small arrows) to produce a longer, narrower array (large arrows). (From Gerhart & Keller (1986).)

Ambystoma, involves rearrangement of cells to form a longer, narrower array (Poole & Steinberg, 1981).

CELL BEHAVIOUR DURING DEEP CELL REARRANGEMENT IN *XENOPUS* GASTRULATION

The function of cell rearrangement in Xenopus *gastrulation*

A major part of *Xenopus* gastrulation involves convergence and extension of both the involuting marginal zone (IMZ) and non-involuting marginal zone (NIMZ) (Keller *et al.* 1985*a*,*b*; Keller & Danilchik, 1987). Blastopore closure and involution are brought about as the IMZ and NIMZ, particularly their dorsal sectors, narrow in the circumblastoporal direction (convergence) and lengthen in the animal–vegetal direction (extension). The involuted part of the IMZ converges circumferentially and extends toward the inside of the blastoporal lip by a process of active intercalation of deep cells to form a longer, narrower array (Fig. 1). Cells from the part of the IMZ not yet involuted are added to the vegetal end of this intercalating array and presumably they join in the process of intercalation as they are added. The overlying NIMZ is stimulated to converge and extend, but only when its basal surface establishes contact with the involuted IMZ; then it extends and converges at a rate faster than the IMZ and thus tends to push the remaining uninvoluted IMZ over the blastopore lip (Keller *et al.* 1985*a*,*b*; Keller & Danilchik, unpublished). The result of the operation of this double convergence and extension machine is the involution of the IMZ and the simultaneous closure of the blastopore. Results to date show that the deep, non-epithelial cells are probably the cells that generate the force for extension and convergence of these regions (Keller & Danilchik, unpublished) and that the superficial cells passively rearrange to accommodate the tissue distortion driven by the deep region (see Keller, 1978, 1986). Here we will only deal with deep cell behaviour in the IMZ; the deep cell behaviour in the NIMZ appears to be different (Keller & Danikchik, unpublished).

Method of analysis of deep cell behaviour during intercalation

The cell behaviour involved in bringing about intercalation of deep cells was analysed by direct time-lapse micrography of sectors of the IMZ-NIMZ explanted into culture in a solution that mimics the blastocoel fluid (Keller *et al.* 1985*a*,*b*). Cell behaviour is recorded with high resolution and contrast by producing a video image with a Dage high-resolution camera (model 81, set for 1300×1050 lines) and monitor (model 2000). This image is then recorded on 16 mm film off the monitor in time-lapse with an Arriflex time-lapse camera, using a 40 mm macro lens. The resulting film has superb resolution and contrast. Under these culture conditions, deep cells of the dorsal sector will not only rearrange to form a longer, narrower array. Later they will segregate into a notochord and somitic mesoderm; the latter forms individual somites, which undergo the usual cellular rotation. Video-films can be made at high (×40) magnification to resolve cellular details and at low (×10) magnification to determine macroscopic patterns of movement.

Kneading motion due to repetitive, asynchronous shape change among deep cells

Deep cells of the animal cap, the IMZ and the NIMZ show repetitive changes in shape. Their deep aspects are constantly changing in shape by the advancing and retraction of their margins, first along one axis and then another (Fig. 2). The area, the length/width ratio and the perimeter of contact with adjacent cells change as each cell undergoes these repetitive extensions and retractions of its margins. Deep cells are intimately connected to one another by multiple filiform protrusions, both in explants and *in situ* (Fig. 3A), such that changes in the shape of one cell produce accommodating changes in the position and shape of adjacent cells (Fig. 4). Thus the behaviour of an individual cell, at any instant, is partly a product of endogenous contractile or protrusive events and partly a result of these same processes being exercised in adjacent cells. But exercise of these processes in adjacent cells is usually out of phase, both in timing and in the axial orientation of the extension–retraction cycles, so that a 'kneading action' results, and individual cells appear to be constantly massaged one way and then another.

The exercise of this kneading action in the dorsal IMZ, a region that shows convergence and extension, results in the cells jostling together towards the dorsal midline, and rearranging to form a longer, narrower array in the process (see Keller *et al.* 1985*a*,*b*). In contrast, in the animal cap region, which shows no convergence and extension, there is no net movement. We do not yet know why jostling of dorsal cells results in mediolateral intercalation instead of jostling in place. The cycles of marginal extension and retraction, and the resulting jostling process may be random and function only to permit cells to sample new cell–cell contacts. Adhesion in the tissue array could be anisotropic in such a way that some cell–cell contacts are more stable and thus are favoured in the course of the jostling. It is not clear what kind of

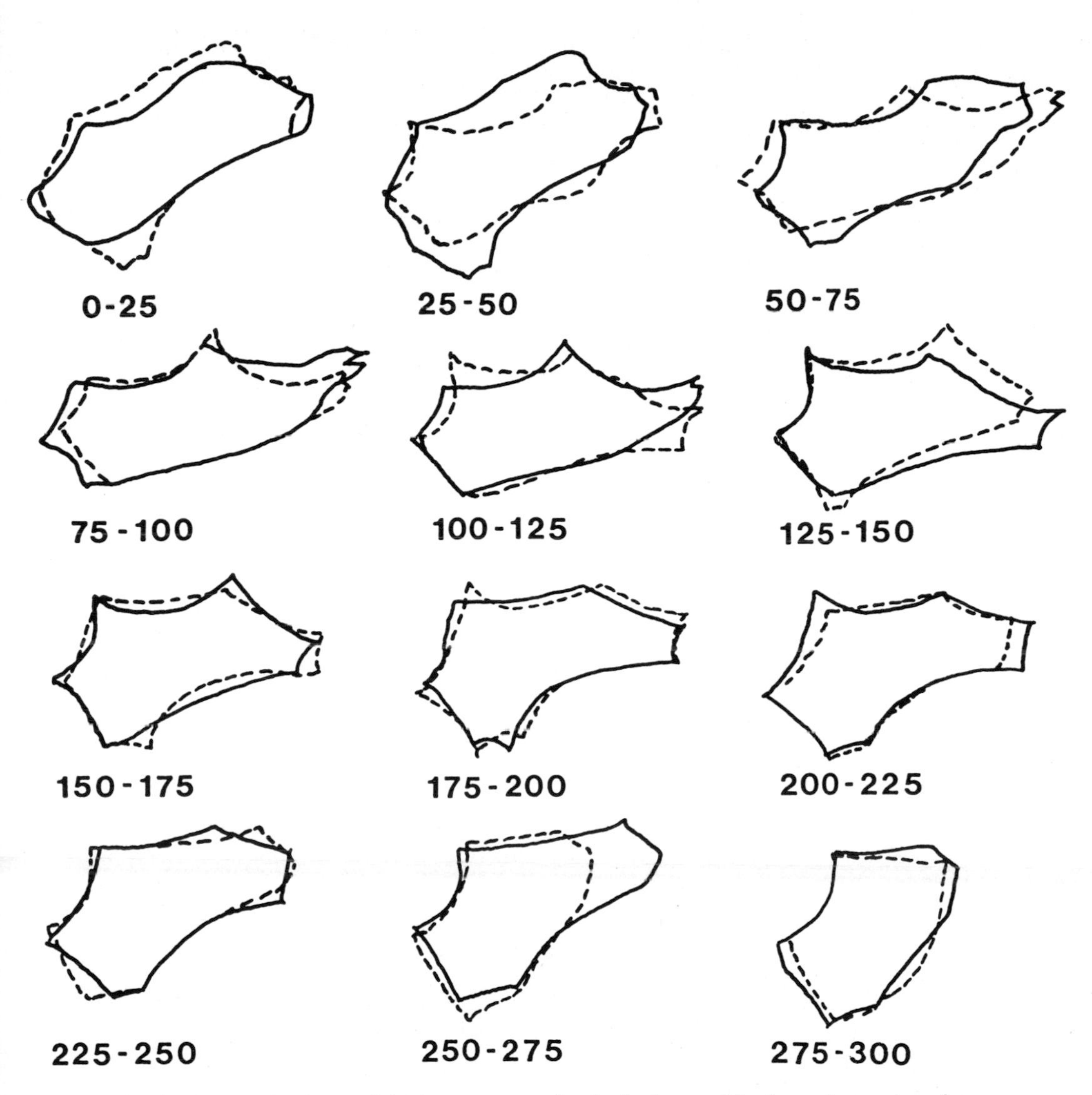

Fig. 2. Change in shape of the inner aspect of a single deep cell is shown by tracings from time-lapse recordings of a cultured explant of the involuting marginal zone of a midgastrula. The continuous line indicates the shape at the first frame number given below each outline and the broken line indicates the shape at the second frame number. The frame interval is 20 s.

pattern of adhesion would result in the mediolateral or circumferential intercalation of cells observed, but some ideas have been presented by Mittenthal & Mazo (1983).

Alternatively, the axial orientation of the cycles of extension–retraction and the resulting boundary relationships between cells may be inherently biased in regions showing directed intercalation of cells. Such is definitely the case after the notochord–somite boundary forms. The extension–retraction cycles of the notochord cells are then oriented mediolaterally or circumferentially (with respect to the

3A

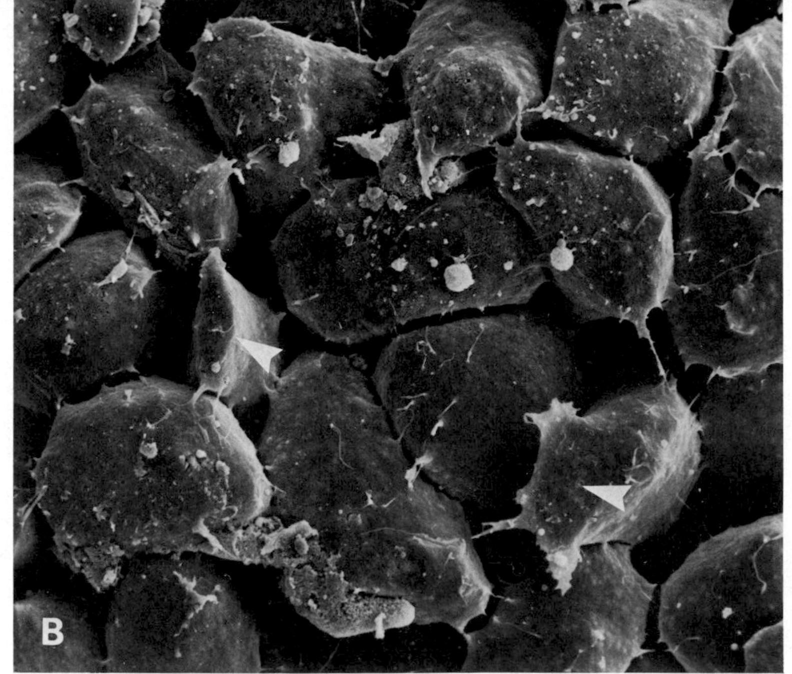
B

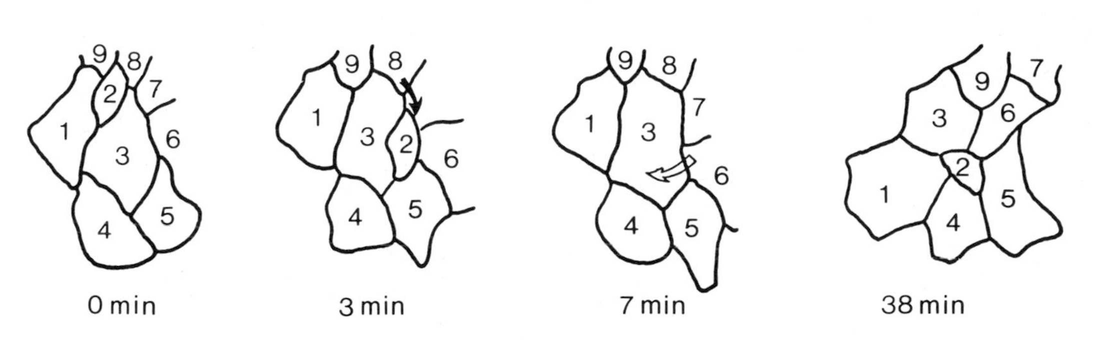

Fig. 4. Outlines of the inner aspects of deep cells of the involuting marginal zone of a late midgastrula traced from time-lapse recordings show the rapid changes in cell position and contact relations during the 'kneading motion' imparted by the exercise of the extension–retraction cycles illustrated in Fig. 2. The less-common rapid movement of individual cells is illustrated by movement of the inner aspect of cell no. 2 around no. 3 (filled arrow), then under 3 (open arrow) to emerge and take up a new position between 3 and the juncture of no. 4 and no. 5. The axis of extension is vertical. Bar, 50 μm.

blastopore) and the cells intercalate transversely with respect to the long axis of the notochord (Keller *et al.* 1985*a*,*b*; also see Miyamoto & Crowther, 1985). We suspect that the same is true at earlier stages of extension and convergence (between stage 10·5 and 11·5), but because of the complexity of the movements in this period we have no proof at present.

Relation of periodic shape change to limnicola movement and intercalation by cytoplasmic flow

Dissociation of gastrula cells by calcium-free media or mechanical means will result in individual, isolated cells showing the 'limnicola' or 'circus' movement described by Holtfreter and others (see Holtfreter, 1947), in which a large bleb forms and rotates around the cell, finally disappearing into the cell body after a good part of a full rotation or more. The rotating bleb is usually clear and inclusion-free, but it may be invaded by yolk platelets and other inclusions. Holtfreter (1947) suggested that the limnicola movement was abnormal behaviour due to loss of cell–cell contact.

However, in the course of the transient extension–retraction events at the margins of deep cells, an extension occasionally results in the formation of a large, blunt protrusion that rotates around part or all of the perimeter of the cell. The protrusion

Fig. 3. The inner aspects of cells of the involuting marginal zone of the late midgastrula are interconnected by filiform protrusions (A). Occasional cells show large, rounded lobopodial structures (central arrowhead) and elongate protrusions extending between adjacent cells (top and bottom arrowheads). The inner aspects of these involuting marginal zone cells may also bear large protrusions that connected these cells to the overlying non-involuting marginal zone or roof of the blastocoel. These are apparent by their flattened morphology and extension out of the plane of the involuting marginal zone (arrowheads in B) in stereo micrographs. ×1000. (Fig. B is from Lundmark *et al.* (1984).)

may extend by the influx of cytoplasm and yolk, probe in several directions, and be abruptly withdrawn by reversal of cytoplasmic flow. In other cases, these protrusions are the initial stage of a rapid translocation of the cell (Fig. 4) in which the protrusion is extended continuously, the cell moves forward rapidly (up to $25\,\mu m\,min^{-1}$) by rapid flow of the cell body into the leading protrusion, and the cell insinuates itself between its neighbours with apparent ease. In some cases this involves simple arcing of the protrusion around an adjacent cell and flow of the cell body into the protrusion to produce intercalation of the cell between its immediate neighbours (see Keller *et al.* 1985*a*,*b*). In other cases, the cell may advance between other cells for a distance of five or six cell diameters and then abruptly resume the more common extension–retraction behaviour pattern. Such behaviour is infrequent and has been seen only in the IMZ to date. These 'sport' cells, so named because of their speed and manoeuvrability, often show putative 'exploratory' behaviour in that they rapidly probe several interstices before abruptly settling on a new position. In the course of this fast mode of movement, the cells appear to be unaffected by contact with their neighbours and move readily between them, often pushing their neighbours apart or even raising an intervening cell up and out of the plane of focus as they pass beneath (Fig. 4).

Because the pulsatile marginal extensions in the extension–retraction cycles lead directly to the fast movements using cytoplasmic flow, we interpret the extension–retraction cycles as reflecting a constant probing of the adjacent cell interstices in which stronger advances, or more favourable external conditions, result in net advance of the cell margin and concomitant change in neighbour relationships. But occasionally, and for reasons not yet understood, the constraints normally limiting the advance to a few micrometres fail, and rapid cytoplasmic flow and rapid, continuous advance of the cell occur until the constraints are reimposed and the cell returns to the extension–retraction cycle.

The rapid movement involving cytoplasmic flow is not likely to be an artifact of culture, but a characteristic though infrequent event in the IMZ of the intact gastrula. The inner surface of the involuted dorsal IMZ consists of cells connected by multiple, filiform and occasionally lamelliform protrusions, but on occasion deep cells will bear large, rounded protrusions (large arrowhead, Fig. 3). Such cells never have the symmetry of form or attachment of dividing deep cells, which are also rotund (see Keller & Schoenwolf, 1977). A continuum of morphologies exists from these short, large diameter protrusions with blunt ends to long, tapered protrusions often ending in filiform attachments to other cells (small arrowheads, Fig. 3). Although we cannot see inside the gastrula, we believe these morphologies to correspond to the transition of a cell *in vivo* from the extension–retraction cycle to the rapid translocation mode seen in time-lapse films of explants.

Coordinated motile phenomena

In general, local cycles of extension–retraction appear, at least in regions other than the dorsal IMZ, to be out of phase with one another, so that the characteristic kneading behaviour arises. However, occasionally contraction of cells and the limnicola movement are coordinated in a transcellular pattern. Local contraction centres occur in which many cells contract together or sequentially, resulting in a displacement of adjacent cells larger than that seen when individual cells retract in extension–retraction cycles. Major contractions of this type will occur from once to a half dozen times, and smaller twitches occur more frequently in the course of extension and convergence of the entire dorsal, axial mesoderm (dorsal IMZ). The cell arrangement before and after these events does not change markedly and these contractions seem to have no obvious function. Similar twitches also occur in films of whole embryos, usually in the marginal zone, and with the same frequency as seen in explants; so it does not appear to be a phenomenon unique to cultured explants.

The second coordinated process is sequential blebbing or limnicola movement in a series of cells. In this situation, limnicola movement will occur in one cell after another in a linear series across the explant. In other cases, a wave of limnicola movement will pass across the tissue as a broad front hundreds of cells across. These types of behaviour appear to be propagated from cell to cell. In the case of a linear series of cells, the event has been observed in all directions for distances of 3–15 cells. In the case of the broad fronts, they pass roughly from the midline laterally and have been observed only in explants that are near or beyond the point of delineating the notochord–somite boundary. The rate of propagation is 40–90 μm min^{-1}. Overall, this phenomenon appears to have no lasting effect on the explant. In response to nudging, *Fundulus* deep cells in culture also propagate blebs from one to another (Tickle & Trinkaus, 1976).

Mesodermal cells of the IMZ are involved in two types of motility: intercalation and migration

In the explant, the circumferential (mediolateral) intercalation of deep cells of the IMZ occurs without benefit of an adhesive external substratum, presumably as a result of forces generated by the protrusions connecting these cells with one another. However, these same cells also have protrusions extending towards and adhering to the overlying NIMZ, which has been removed (see Keller & Schoenwolf, 1977) (arrowheads, Fig. 3). They intercalate between one another but supposedly migrate animal-polewards on the inner NIMZ (Nakatsuji, 1976; Keller & Schoenwolf, 1977). Thus these cells must have specialized behavioural properties, with one set of rules governing their interaction with one another to produce mediolateral intercalation (convergence and extension) and another set of rules governing their interaction with the overlying NIMZ or the animal cap to produce translocation on this surface.

We will now examine the interaction of dorsal IMZ cells with the overlying substrate for migration, the NIMZ or animal cap. If the involuted IMZ of a midgastrula is peeled away from the NIMZ so that individual cells of the IMZ are left attached to the NIMZ (Fig. 5), and cultured in the explant system (Keller *et al.* 1985*a*,*b*), IMZ–IMZ interactions and IMZ–NIMZ interactions can be studied directly by video- or cine microscopy. Individual IMZ cells may or may not move on the inner surface of the NIMZ, depending on circumstances that are not at present understood. If they do move, they can move in any direction (small arrows, Fig. 5).

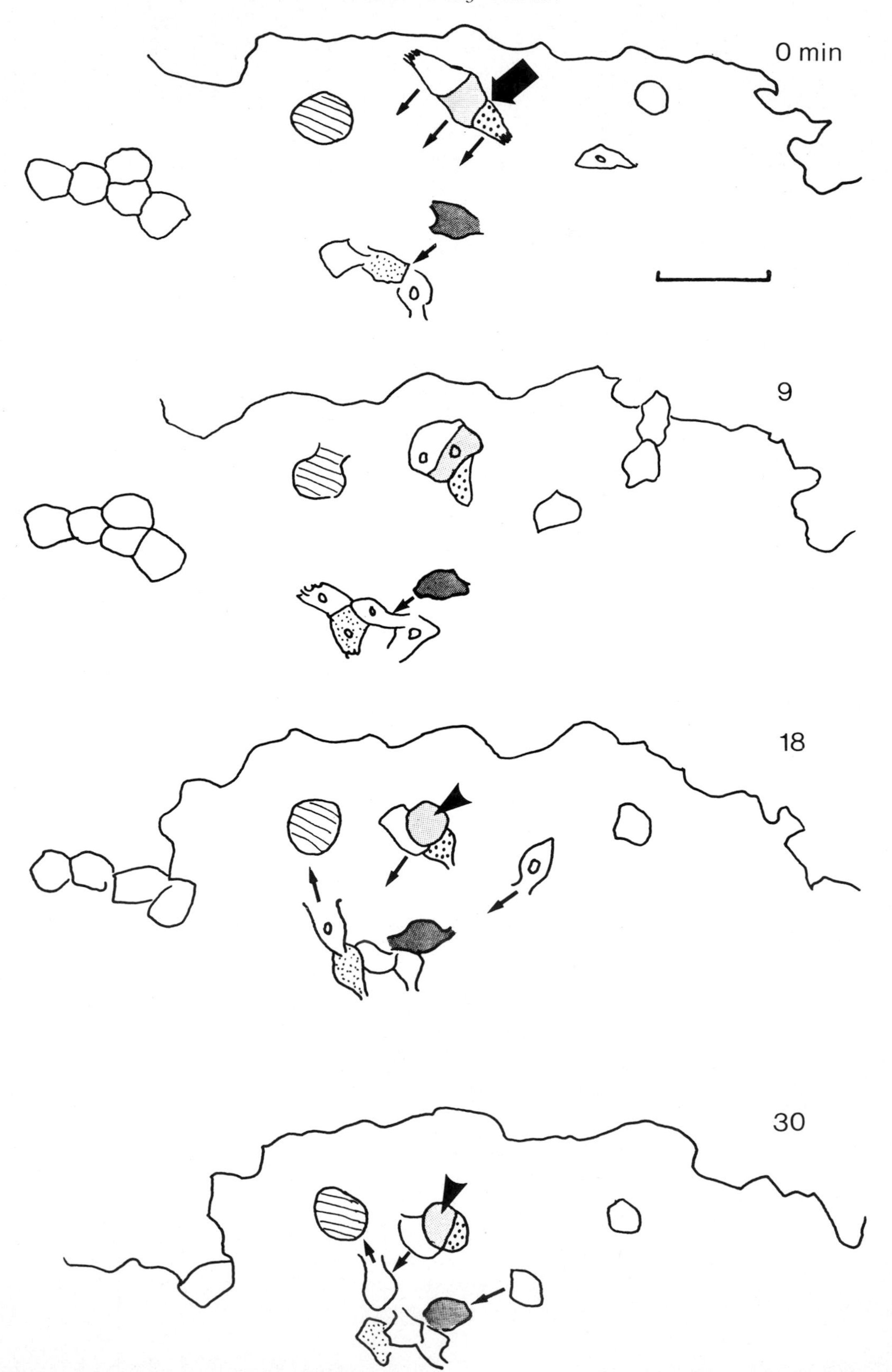
0 min
9
18
30

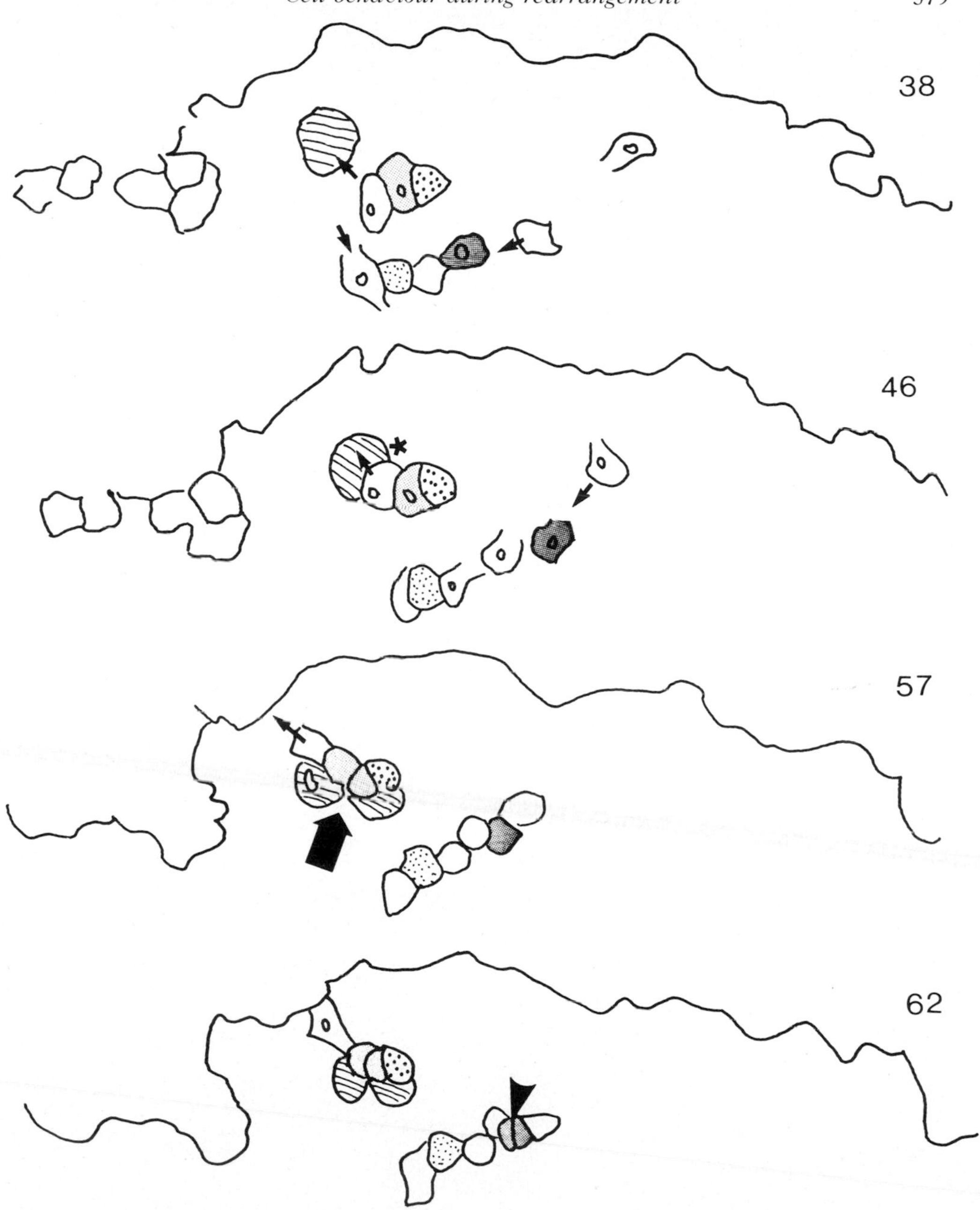

Fig. 5. The migration of individuals and small groups of involuted mesodermal cells on the inner surface of the non-involuting marginal zone of the late midgastrula are illustrated with tracings from time-lapse recordings. The non-involuting marginal zone was stripped off the involuting marginal zone of a stage 11 gastrula in such a way that individual mesodermal cells were left attached at the animal end of the explant (bottom of each figure) and a contiguous mass of involuted mesodermal cells was left attached at the vegetal end of the explant (top of each figure). The line in each figure is the animal-most boundary of the contiguous mass. Identity of individual cells is indicated by symbols and their major movements are indicated by arrows. The arrowheads indicate cells riding on top of cells underneath. Bar, 100 μm.

They may move as groups of several cells, side-by-side (group of three, large arrow, 0 h; Fig. 5), or one may move with another on its back (arrowheads throughout, Fig. 5). When meeting one another or the main mass of IMZ cells, they do not necessarily cease movement or retract as if they were under the influence of contact inhibition of movement (Abercrombie, 1970). They are capable of crawling upon their own kind (asterisk, 46 min, Fig. 5) and crossing over them (large arrow, 57 min, Fig. 5), not only alone but as groups. The migratory behaviour of large populations of mesodermal cells contrasts strongly with the behaviour of individual cells. If an explant retains a large contiguous population of postinvolution mesodermal cells on its inner surface instead of the scattered cells shown in Fig. 5, they move toward the cell-free space at the animal end of the mass as a coordinated unit (data not shown) or cell stream (see pp. 449–450, Trinkaus, 1984*a*). We could find no evidence for the substrate guidance of mesodermal cells seen in culture (see Nakatsuji & Johnson, 1984). In this respect our results are consistent with those of Kubota & Durston (1978) for the axolotl.

Mechanical properties of the involuted IMZ

The dynamic behaviour of the deep IMZ cells with respect to one another during intercalation, and with respect to the overlying NIMZ during migration, should not be taken to suggest that this region is insubstantial in the mechanical sense. The protrusions interconnecting the IMZ cells (Fig. 3) are so substantial that our attempts to break them with microneedles usually lead to dislodgment of the cell or tearing of the cell. The IMZ appears to become stiff and more difficult to bend after its involution, as shown by the fact that if it is transplanted outside the blastopore lip, and expected to involute again, it will not bend over the lip and involute, but instead remains at the lip like a canoe on the edge of a waterfall. Despite this apparent rigidity, the individual cells can move between one another, either slowly by the kneading action of individual pulsatile events or occasionally by the rapid cytoplasmic flow described above.

A WORKING HYPOTHESIS OF HOW CELL MOTILITY GENERATES REARRANGEMENT OF *XENOPUS* DEEP CELLS

We do not know how the motile activities uncovered to date bring about directional cell intercalation to produce convergence and extension. The following is our current, working hypothesis, which we feel incorporates most of what we know.

The kneading action seen among deep cells is a reflection of periodic extension and retraction of the cell margin. At any instant, the bulk of the cell population exercising this kneading action is stabilized by multiple filiform protrusions. As the extension–retraction cycles are repeated, contacts with adjacent cells are modulated at the microscopic level. In regions not showing convergence and extension, these modulations average out, but in regions undergoing convergence and extension, they do not, but are biased in such a way that cells tend to intercalate between those cells that are medial or lateral to themselves. At present we favour a bias in the direction of extension–retraction cycles leading to directional intercalation, because directional bias is displayed by the same cells later, during notochord cell intercalation. The rapidly moving 'sport cells' may reflect abnormal loss of the constraints necessary to prevent all cells from attempting to move rapidly and at the same time.

The extending and converging dorsal, axial mesoderm is a stiff tissue array that may function as a 'skeleton' in the gastrula to close the blastopore and elongate the dorsal side, and it can elongate independently of an external substratum and actually push debris (see Keller *et al.* 1985*b*; Keller, 1986). This mechanical integrity is a necessary part of the function of the extending and converging cell population. Our notion is that to maintain this integrity, many of the cells at any one time must form a rigid tissue array, stabilized by the filiform protrusions connecting them, while a subpopulation of cells, cycling though a motile phase, advance by small increments between their neighbours. Too many cells moving too far at the same time might disrupt the mechanical integrity of the tissue array. In this context, the apparent asynchrony of extension–retraction cycles in a given region may be important. There may be a control system to regulate these cycles, specifically ensuring that adjacent cell populations or adjacent cells are out of synchrony. Alternatively, there may be a pattern in the control of these cells that we do not yet recognize. The coordinated blebbing and contraction that we have observed suggests that there may be a system capable of controlling motility but it is puzzling that these coordinated events are infrequent and have no obvious effects. We are currently analysing temporal and spatial patterns of extension–retraction cycles, contact relations, and fast movements to determine whether such order exists. Our observations on the interaction of involuted mesodermal cells with one another and with the overlying NIMZ or blastocoel roof, raise the possibility that these cells can participate in active intercalation among themselves and simultaneously participate in directional migration on an external substratum. Resolving the rules of interaction of IMZ cells with each other and with the overlying substratum will greatly enhance our knowledge of what constitutes an organized 'stream' of cells in morphogenesis.

CELL BEHAVIOUR AND PROTRUSIVE ACTIVITY DURING REARRANGEMENT OF EPITHELIAL CELLS DURING SEA-URCHIN ARCHENTERON ELONGATION

The role of cell rearrangement in archenteron elongation

The most dramatic change that occurs at the onset of archenteron elongation (secondary invagination) in the sea-urchin embryo is the appearance of long, filopodial protrusions extended by secondary mesenchyme cells at the tip of the gut rudiment. The coincident appearance of these protrusions as the second phase of gastrulation begins provide strong circumstantial evidence that filopodial traction is the dominant mechanism of archenteron elongation (see Gustafson & Wolpert, 1963, for a review). However, mechanical simulations of the effects of filopodial traction suggest that filopodial pulling alone would produce deformations of the gastrula that are not seen in actual embryos (Hardin & Cheng, 1986). More importantly, using Fristrom's (1976) assay for cell rearrangement in a cylindrical epithelium, Ettensohn (1985) was the first to show that cell rearrangement is important during secondary invagination. As in other rearranging epithelia, cell rearrangement occurs despite the presence of typical septate junctions (Spiegel & Howard, 1983; Ettensohn, 1985). Cell rearrangement has been demonstrated in other species as well, and is accompanied by flattening of the cells in the wall of the gut rudiment (Hardin & Cheng, 1986).

Cell rearrangement alone can account for virtually the entire increase in length of the gut rudiment during secondary invagination in *L. pictus* (Hardin & Cheng, 1986). Archenteron elongation does not require cell division or DNA synthesis (Stephens *et al.* 1986), and little or no involution or addition of cellular material occurs during secondary invagination (Hardin, 1986). The extent of cell rearrangement, as judged by the decrease in the number of cells around the circumference of the archenteron, is very closely correlated with archenteron length. At the beginning of secondary invagination, there are approximately 24 cells around the circumference of the archenteron, and this number drops to as low as six to eight in the narrowest portion of the gut rudiment by the end of secondary invagination. The extent of rearrangement is most pronounced in the central region of the archenteron, although all regions participate in the rearrangement to some extent (Ettensohn, 1985; Hardin & Cheng, 1986).

Cell rearrangement also accounts for the closure of the blastopore during secondary invagination (Hardin, 1986). A strong inverse correlation exists between blastopore diameter and archenteron length, and the number of cells around the circumference of the blastopore decreases concomitant with the decrease in the number of cells around the base of the archenteron (Hardin, 1986), in a manner strongly reminiscent of blastopore closure during gastrulation in *Xenopus*. Cell rearrangement thus accounts for most of the tissue distortions that occur during secondary invagination in the sea urchin (Fig. 6).

Cell rearrangement and exogastrulation

The demonstration of cell rearrangement in the archenteron does not provide any information concerning the mechanism(s) by which such rearrangement might be occurring. However, the phenomenon of LiCl-induced exogastrulation can be used as a tool to examine whether cell rearrangement relies solely on filopodial traction, or whether the rearrangement is in some sense intrinsic to the cells of the gut rudiment. Significantly, cell rearrangement can occur without filopodial pulling in the case of LiCl-induced exogastrulation (Hardin & Cheng, 1986), and suggests that autonomous rearrangement of epithelial cells in the wall of the archenteron can cause it to elongate. Furthermore, it is not uncommon for these everted gut rudiments to exhibit a pattern of cell rearrangement similar to that of normal embryos, i.e. cell rearrangement is most pronounced in the central portion of the archenteron (Fig. 7A). Later, the everted gut rudiment differentiates into a typical tripartite gut

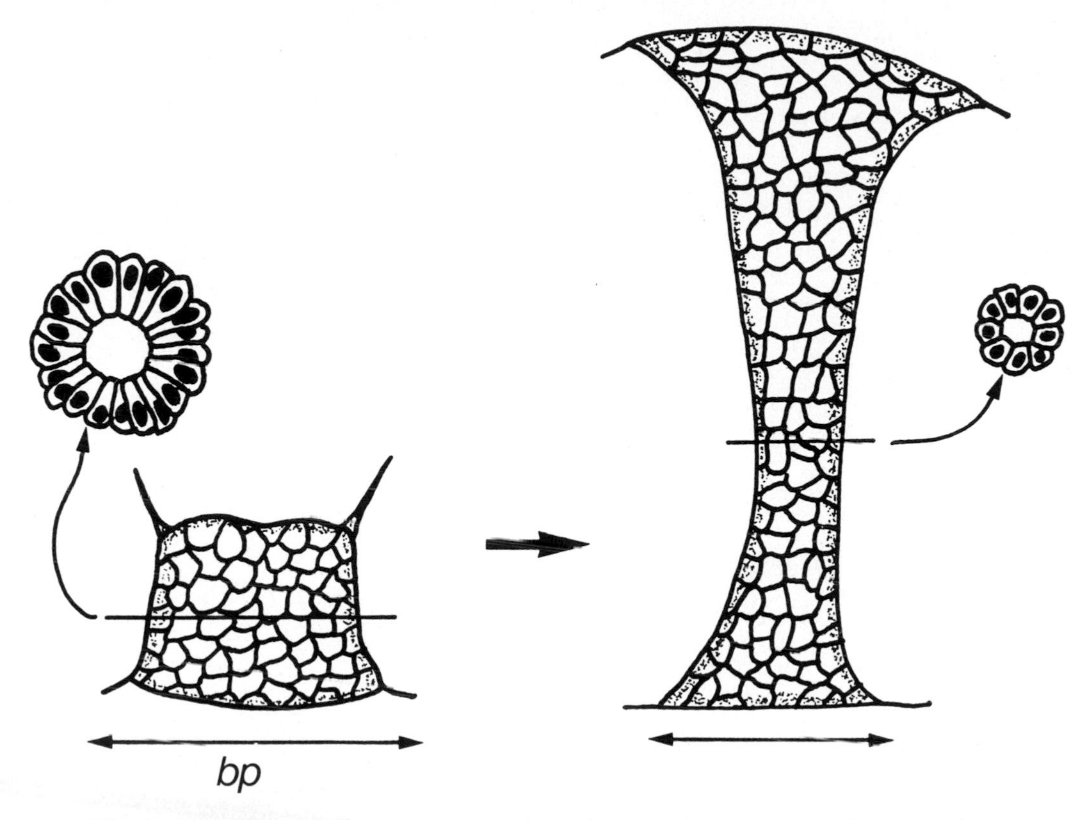

Fig. 6. The role of cell rearrangement in archenteron elongation in the sea-urchin embryo. At the onset of the second phase of gastrulation there are approximately 24 cells around the circumference of the gut rudiment. As the archenteron lengthens, cell rearrangement reduces the number of cells around the circumference, while simultaneously lengthening the cylinder and closing the blastopore (bp).

(Fig. 7B). These facts led to a model of archenteron elongation in which the cells of the archenteron actively rearrange, while the secondary mesenchyme cells at the tip of the gut rudiment serve primarily to guide the archenteron to the correct site to form the mouth primordium (Hardin & Cheng, 1986).

Microtubules and cell rearrangement

The cell rearrangement that occurs in the archenteron as it elongates does not seem to depend on intact cytoplasmic microtubules. Although earlier studies using colchicine had suggested that microtubules were necessary for secondary invagination to occur (Tilney & Gibbins, 1969), subsequent experiments using improved inhibitors combined with immunofluorescent detection of microtubules have demonstrated that microtubules are not crucial for elongation of the archenteron (Hardin, 1987; Fig. 8). Disruption of microtubules with nocodazole does not affect cell rearrangement in the gut rudiment, or spontaneous exogastrulation. On the other hand, treatment of embryos with the colchicine analogue, lumicolchicine, which

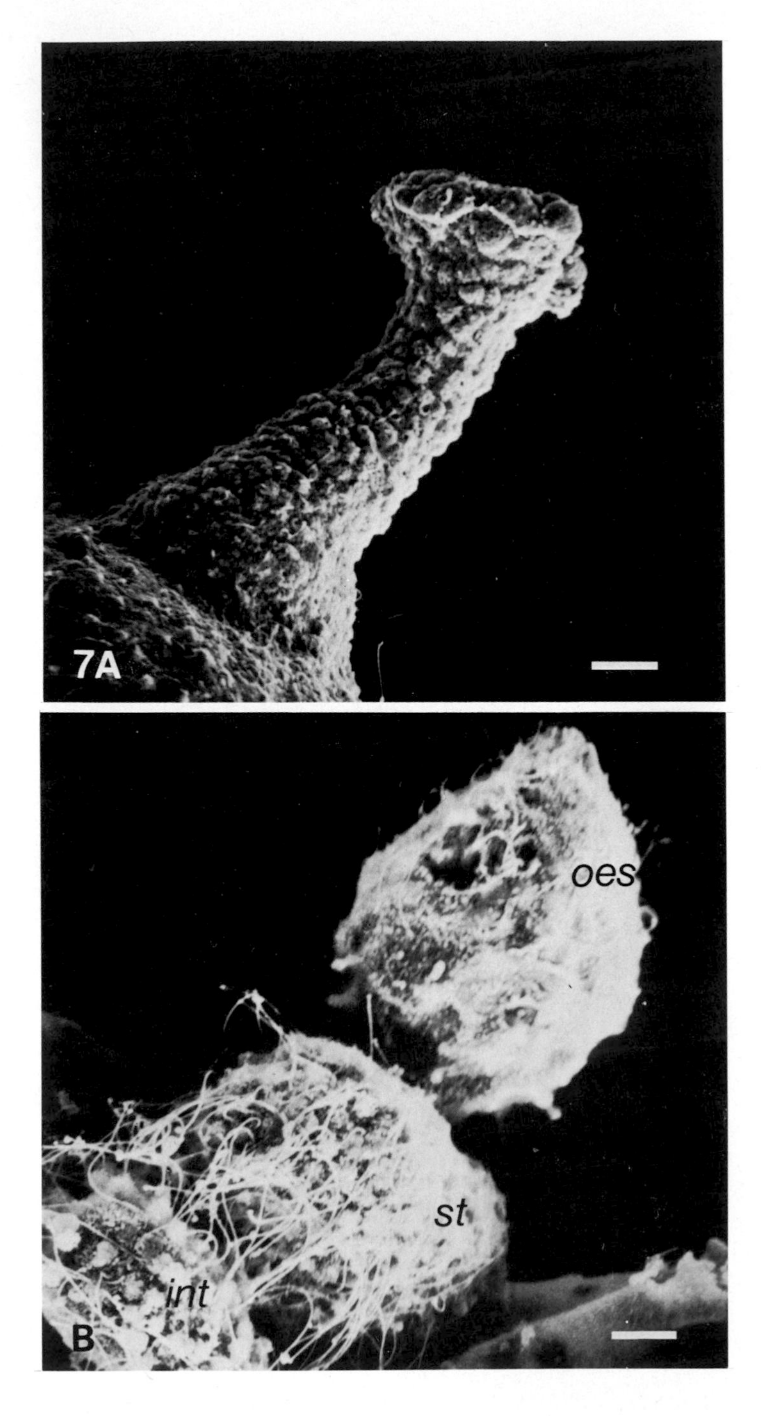

Fig. 7. LiCl-induced exogastrulation in *Lytechinus pictus*. A. SEM of an elongated exogastrula. Note that the central region of the archenteron undergoes more cell rearrangement than the rest of the gut rudiment. Bar, 10 μm. B. Gut rudiment of an exogastrulated pluteus larva. Note the tripartite differentiation of the gut into oesophagus (*oes*), stomach (*st*), and intestine (*int*). Bar, 5 μm.

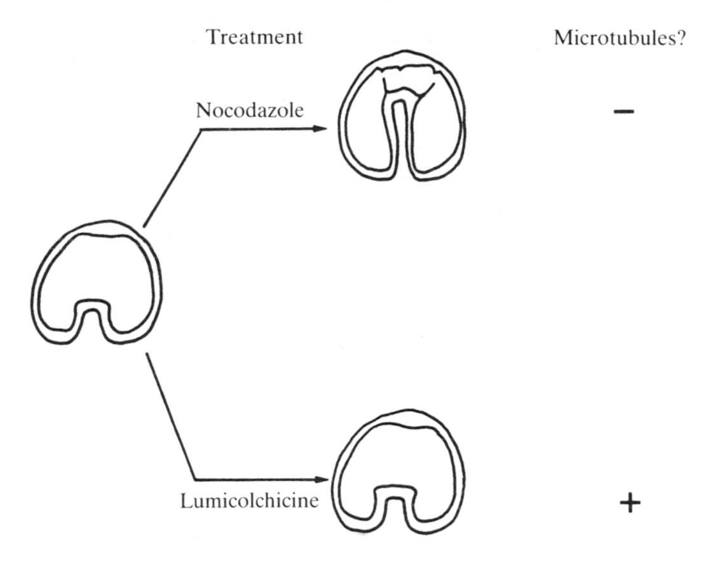

Fig. 8. The role of microtubules in archenteron elongation: 0·1 mM-β-lumicolchicine, an analogue of colchicine that does not bind tubulin, prevents elongation without disrupting microtubules (+); nocodazole (10 μg ml^{-1}) does not prevent elongation, but does disrupt microtubules (−), indicating that microtubules are not crucial for archenteron elongation.

does not bind tubulin, inhibits secondary invagination without disrupting microtubules, indicating that earlier results using colchicine are probably due to side effects of the drug, rather than its effects on microtubules (Hardin, 1987*a*).

Protrusive activity during archenteron elongation

The detailed motile behaviour, which presumably depends on actin microfilaments, of the rearranging epithelial cells in the wall of the archenteron is only beginning to be understood. The elegant use of time-lapse cinemicrography by Gustafson and coworkers (e.g. see Gustafson & Kinnander, 1956; Kinnander & Gustafson, 1960) revealed a general pulsatile behaviour of the basal surfaces of cells in the gut rudiment. As the archenteron elongates, this pulsatile behaviour becomes progressively localized to the tip of the archenteron (Kinnander & Gustafson, 1960). It is not known what relation this pulsatile behaviour has to cell rearrangement, and unfortunately the resolution afforded by the light microscope has to date prevented any further information from being gained using time-lapse techniques.

However, scanning electron microscopy has provided new information on the coordinated motility and shape changes that occur in the archenteron during cell rearrangement (Hardin, 1987*b*). Careful staging of gastrulae at various stages of secondary invagination reveals striking, stage-specific changes in the morphology of the basal surfaces of endoderm cells in the wall of the gut rudiment. At the end of the first phase of invagination, basal surfaces of endoderm cells are bulbous, and occasional lateral processes are seen between neighbouring cells (Morrill & Santos, 1985; Hardin, 1987*b*). When the archenteron begins to elongate, long, highly oriented lamellipodial processes are extended by each cell towards the tip of the archenteron. These lamellipodia overlap one another, giving the archenteron a 'shingled' appearance (Fig. 9A). The broad lamellipodia end in shorter, filopodial processes that extend onto the basal surfaces of cells in overlying tiers, generally at a slight angle to the long axis of the archenteron (Fig. 9B). Similar changes in morphology have been observed by Ettensohn (1984*a*). It is not clear how these protrusions might function in cell rearrangement, but at the least they indicate that all of the cells of the archenteron have inherent directionality; they 'know' which way is 'up' (i.e. towards the animal pole). Furthermore, up no longer corresponds to the inherent apical–basal polarity of the cells of the gut rudiment, but is instead roughly perpendicular to the apical–basal axis.

When the archenteron has lengthened slightly, these oriented protrusions disappear; the basal surfaces of the cells become somewhat rounded, and a dense, overlapping network of cell extensions is visible between cells (Fig. 10A). These extensions make contact with the basal surfaces of neighbouring cells in a criss-crossing fashion. Many of these protrusions are not taut, but instead appear loosely curled (Fig. 10B). The angular distribution of these protrusions is markedly different from the oriented lamellipodia that precede them, and suggests that these smaller protrusions may represent alterations in cell–cell contacts as the cells begin to rearrange (Hardin, 1987*b*).

At the 1/2 to 2/3 gastrula stage, basal surfaces appear rounded, with little evidence of protrusions. By the 2/3 to 3/4 gastrula stage, basal surfaces elongate slightly (Hardin, 1986). The extent of elongation is not uniform; some cells in the thinnest portion of the gut rudiment show marked elongation, while cells in other regions are not nearly as elongated. By the 3/4 gastrula stage, the outer surface of the archenteron becomes covered with a thick layer of extracellular matrix material (Hardin, 1986).

Evidence for protrusive activity on lateral and apical (luminal) surfaces of endoderm cells is considerably more difficult to obtain compared to the basal surfaces, due to the difficulty of fracturing through the archenteron without causing its complete disintegration. However, some generalizations can be made. First, there is little evidence for protrusive activity on lateral cell surfaces during secondary invagination. Small cell processes can occasionally be seen over- or underlapping cells in different tiers at the mid-gastrula stage, but these are relatively infrequent (Hardin, 1987*b*). Second, tenuous apical extensions can sometimes be seen connecting one cell in a given tier with the upper (animal-poleward) region of the apex of a neighbouring cell in the same tier. These extensions may be reasonably (though tentatively) interpreted as domains of decreased contact between cells that are moving past one another as they rearrange.

In addition to any protrusive activity exhibited by the apical surfaces of cells in the archenteron, cell apices probably also modulate their shape and attachment to the hyaline layer during cell rearrangement. The hyaline layer maintains its attachment to the inner surface of the archenteron throughout secondary invagination, requiring not only that it change its shape as the dimensions of the archenteron change, but also

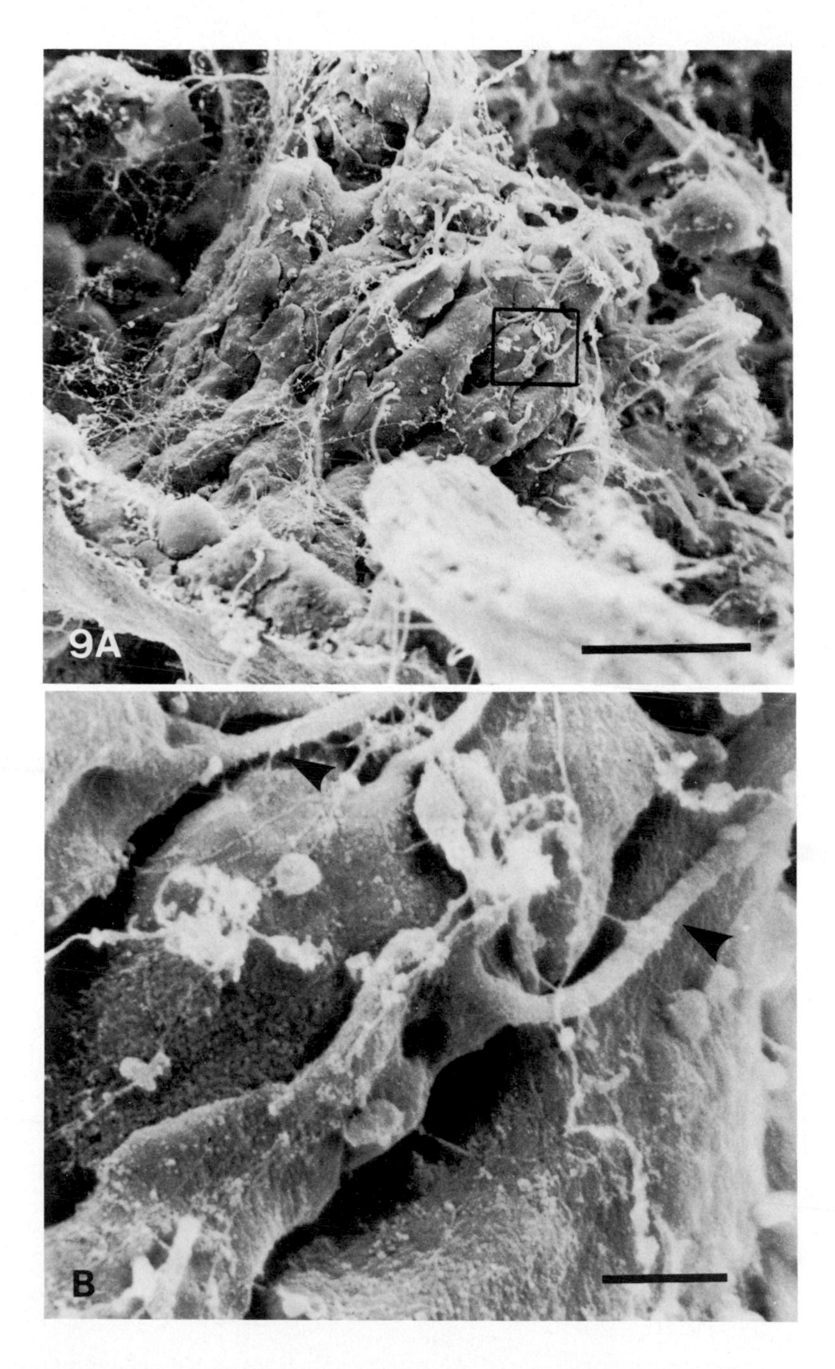

Fig. 9. Lamellar protrusions at the onset of secondary invagination. A. Long, oriented protrusions extend towards the tip of the archenteron. Bar, 10 μm. B. Higher magnification of the enclosed region in A. The lamellipodia end in slender filopodial processes (arrowhead). Bar, 1 μm.

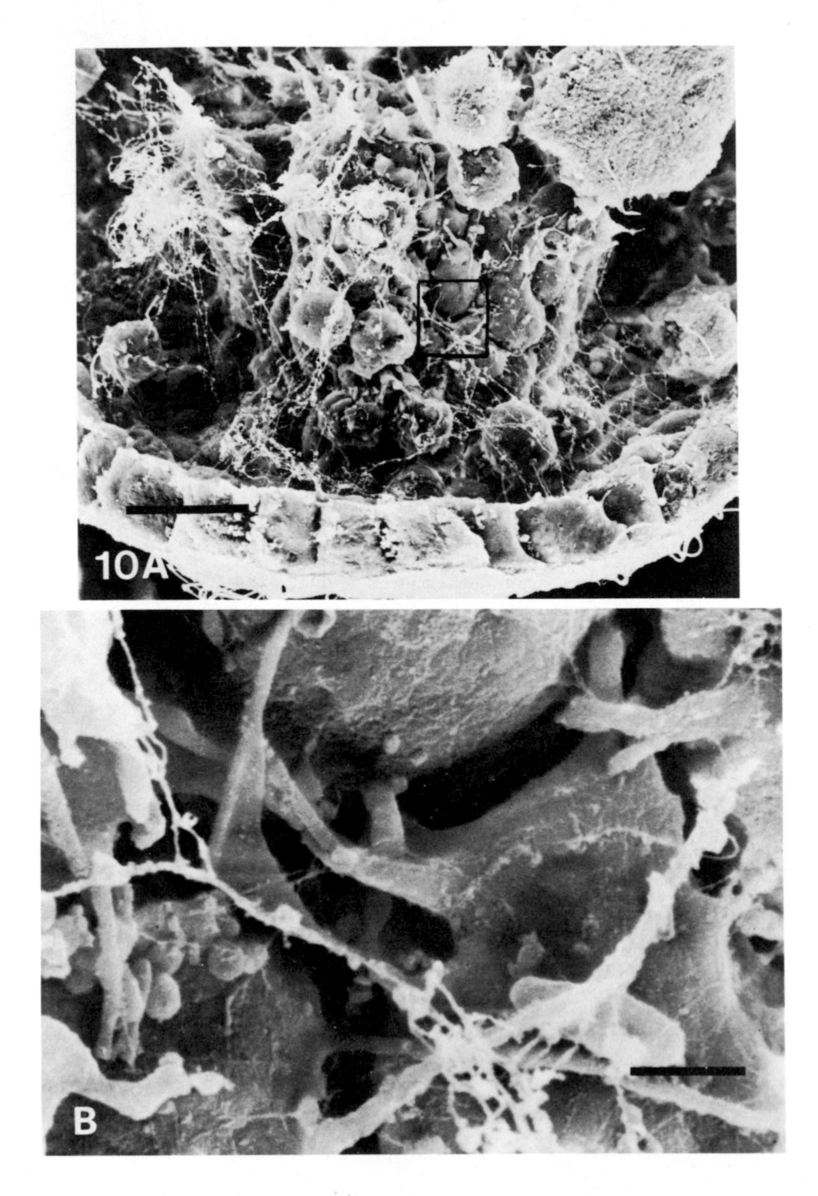

Fig. 10. Slender protrusions at the 1/2 gastrula stage. A. A dense network of overlapping filar processes are extended from the basal surfaces of cells in the archenteron. B. Higher magnification of the enclosed region in A. Cell bodies are rounded, and are studded with overlapping protrusions. Bar, 1 μm.

requiring that the apices of individual endoderm cells change their contacts with it as well. In addition, the apices of all cells in the archenteron and the other epithelial cells of the embryo possess typical apical microfilament bundles, which are clearly revealed both by transmission electron microscopy (TEM) and phallotoxin staining (Ettensohn, 1984*b*; Harris, 1986; J. Hardin, unpublished observations). It is not known what role apical microfilaments might play in archenteron elongation in the sea-urchin embryo, but their modulation is probably necessary during cell rearrangement.

HYPOTHESES CONCERNING HOW CELL MOTILITY GENERATES EPITHELIAL CELL REARRANGEMENT OF SEA-URCHIN ARCHENTERON CELLS

Any epithelium undergoing cell rearrangement is presented with several challenges. First, a functioning epithelium must serve as a barrier separating the internal from the external environment. Thus rearranging epithelial cells must have a means by which they can change their neighbour relations while maintaining the tight or septate junctional seals at their apical surface. That this is possible is dramatically demonstrated by the enveloping layer during epiboly in *Fundulus*, which undergoes extensive cell rearrangement while maintaining its integrity as a high-resistance permeability barrier (Keller & Trinkaus, 1987). In the case of septate junctions, Fristrom (1982) has proposed a model by which septate junctional domains may be modulated as cells progressively lose their contact with one another, resulting in the appearance of 'tricellular plugs' as the contact domain between cells shrinks to a vertex. The sea-urchin gastrula also possesses such tricellular junctions (Spiegel & Howard, 1983), and it is tempting to suppose that they have a similar function during cell rearrangement in the archenteron. In addition, the apical extensions seen in fractured archenterons (Hardin, 1987*b*) lend credence to the notion of gradually reduced zones of contact between rearranging epithelial cells in the archenteron.

A second issue that must be faced by a rearranging epithelium is the relationship between the apical and basal surfaces of the epithelium. It is generally believed that the basal surfaces of embryonic epithelial cells are the only surfaces that display significant protrusive activity and that if protrusive activity helps to generate cell rearrangement, then it must arise (Kolega, 1986). These notions have led Jacobson *et al.* (1986) to propose the 'cortical tractor' model of epithelial cell rearrangement in the urodele notoplate. In this model, new apical contacts are made by rotation of basal protrusions laterally and finally apically, so that new apical surface is produced by wedging of basolateral membrane onto the apical surface *via* cortical cytoplasmic flow. It is thought that the 'tractoring' of the cortex sweeps junctional components continually up to the apex, maintaining the circumapical junctional arrangement in a state of dynamic equilibrium. Such cortical or amoeboid protrusive activity clearly seems to be important in the case of deep cells (see above). However, in the case of epithelial cells, models that imply a plasticity of the apical–basal boundary of the cell do not seem to be in accord with current thinking in epithelial cell biology, which views the apical–basal boundary as stable, and encompassing not only junctional specializations but sharp differences in membrane proteins, secretory protein traffic and cytoskeletal specializations as well (reviewed by Kolega, 1986).

Alternatively, basal protrusive activity could still be invoked as the driving force for epithelial cell rearrangement, but without altering the apical–basal polarity of the epithelium. In this case, force production would occur on the basal surface of the epithelium, and apical surfaces of epithelial cells would rearrange in response to forces exerted by their basal ends. A likely candidate for such a mechanism is the cell rearrangement that occurs during insect pupal morphogenesis. The contraction of basal 'feet' probably causes the shape transformations and cell rearrangement associated with insect pupal segment morphogenesis (Locke, 1985).

In the case of rearranging epithelial cells in contact with deep cells, cell rearrangement may simply be a response to extrinsic forces. This suggestion has been made in the case of epiboly of the enveloping layer in *Fundulus* (Trinkaus, 1984*b*), and the superficial layer in *Xenopus* (Keller, 1980). Although the epithelial cells in these cases may not be responsible for force production, it may be misleading to refer to them as strictly 'passive', since they must accommodate massive distortions at the tissue and cellular levels. In the case of *Fundulus* epiboly, 'flowering' of apical membrane occurs as submarginal cells separate from one another, suggesting that the cells of the marginal zone themselves may actually show 'responsive', rather than 'passive', rearrangement.

In addition to the complications introduced by junctional complexes and apical–basal polarity, rearranging epithelial cells also possess a circumapical band of actin filaments. During cell rearrangement or shape change, these microfilament bands must be modulated. It is not clear what role such actin bundles play in force production in epithelia. Tension exerted by apical microfilaments has been suggested as a sufficient mechanism to generate the forces necessary for cell rearrangement in epithelial wound healing (Honda *et al.* 1982), and is presumed to produce invaginations in other epithelia (reviewed by Hilfer & Searles, 1986). The possibility that one function of actin bundles may be to maintain a steady-state tension in an epithelial sheet (Owaribe *et al.* 1981) has led to the 'boundary shortening' model of cell rearrangement (Honda, 1983). In this model, when the shape of cell apices is perturbed in some way (e.g. by wounding the epithelium), the tension generated by the circumapical actin bundles causes the cells to reassume a hexagonal arrangement, accompanied by changes in neighbour relations of the cells. Although not expressly mentioned by Honda, it seems possible that any perturbation introduced at the apical surface, including shape changes initiated at the basal surface, could be accounted for by the boundary shortening model.

None of the foregoing considerations can account for the directionality of cell rearrangement along a preferred axis. Some asymmetry must exist to bias extension in a particular direction. For example, such a bias could manifest itself as an asymmetric distribution of protrusions or cell shape changes, or an anisotropic mechanical response to otherwise isotropic protrusive activity (cf. the discussion of deep cell behaviour above).

The above considerations regarding rearranging epithelia must be brought to bear on the problem of archenteron elongation during sea-urchin gastrulation. The archenteron is a typical monolayered epithelium, with circumapical actin bundles (see above). At least at the outset of secondary invagination, basal surfaces exhibit general pulsatile behaviour (Kinnander & Gustafson, 1960), a feature they share with basal surfaces of *Drosophila* imaginal disc cells (Fristrom, 1976; D. Fristrom, personal communication). It is not known what function, if any, such surface activity has in cell rearrangement, although this behaviour is similar to that of deep cells in *Xenopus* (see above).

Later, basal surfaces of the archenteron clearly undergo dramatic, coordinated changes in morphology and protrusive activity as the gut rudiment elongates. The oriented lamellipodia that appear at the outset of secondary invagination are particularly intriguing. Their orientation suggests that they are not involved in force production by direct contraction. However, it is possible to imagine that they may be involved in altering the shape of the apical ends of the cells. If the apical surfaces change their shape, then a 'relaxation' phase, perhaps involving some sort of boundary shortening step, could produce the required axial extension. Perhaps the rounded morphology exhibited by the basal surfaces following the extension phase represents the onset of such relaxation during cell rearrangement. While this model is speculative at best, it is at least a step in beginning to unravel the complex processes at work during epithelial cell rearrangement in the archenteron.

REFERENCES

ABERCROMBIE, M. (1970). Contact inhibition in tissue culture. *In Vitro* **6**, 128–142.

BODE, P. M. & BODE, H. R. (1984). Formation of pattern in regenerating tissue pieces of *Hydra attenuata*. III. The shaping of the body column. *Devl Biol.* **106**, 315–325.

CLONEY, R. (1964). Development of the ascidian notochord. *Acta embryol. morph. exp.* **7**, 111–130.

ETTENSOHN, C. A. (1984*a*). An analysis of invagination during sea urchin gastrulation. Ph.D. dissertation, Yale University.

ETTENSOHN, C. A. (1984*b*). Primary invagination of the vegetal plate during sea urchin gastrulation. *Am. Zool.* **24**, 571–588.

ETTENSOHN, C. A. (1985). Gastrulation in the sea urchin embryo is accompanied by the rearrangement of invaginating epithelial cells. *Devl Biol.* **112**, 383–390.

FRISTROM, D. (1976). The mechanism of evagination of imaginal disks of *Drosophila*. III. Evidence for cell rearrangement. *Devl Biol.* **54**, 163–171.

FRISTROM, D. K. (1982). Septate junctions in imaginal disks of *Drosophila*: A model for the redistribution of septa during cell rearrangement. *J. Cell Biol.* **94**, 77–87.

GERHART, J. & KELLER, R. (1986). Region specific cell activities in amphibian gastrulation. *A. Rev. Cell Biol.* **2**, 201–229.

GUSTAFSON, T. & KINNANDER, H. (1956). Microaquaria for time-lapse cinematographic studies of morphogenesis in swimming larvae and observations on gastrulation. *Expl Cell Res.* **11**, 36–57.

GUSTAFSON, T. & WOLPERT, L. (1963). The cellular basis of morphogenesis and sea urchin development. *Int. Rev. Cyt.* **15**, 139–214.

HARDIN, J. D. (1986). Active cell rearrangement in the archenteron: A new mechanism for driving sea urchin gastrulation. *J. Cell Biol.* **103**, 3a.

HARDIN, J. D. (1987*a*). Archenteron elongation in the sea urchin is a microtubule-independent process. *Devl Biol.* **121**, 253–262.

HARDIN, J. (1987*b*). The cellular mechanisms and mechanics of archenteron elongation in the sea urchin embryo. Ph D thesis, University of California at Berkeley.

HARDIN, J. D. & CHENG, L. Y. (1986). The mechanisms and mechanics of archenteron elongation during sea urchin gastrulation. *Devl Biol.* **115**, 490–501.

HARRIS, P. K. (1986). Cytology and immunocytochemistry. *Meth. Cell Biol.* **27**, 243–262.

HILFER, S. R. & SEARLES, R. L. (1986). Cytoskeletal dynamics in animal morphogenesis. In *Developmental Biology: A Comprehensive Synthesis*, vol. 2, *The Cellular Basis of Morphogenesis* (ed. L. Browder), pp. 3–29. New York: Plenum Press.

HOLTFRETER, J. (1947). Structure, motility, and locomotion in isolated embryonic amphibian cells. *J. Morph.* **79**, 27–62.

HONDA, H., OGITA, Y., HIGUCHI, S. & KANI, K. (1982). Cell movements in a living mammalian tissue: Long-term observation of individual cells in wounded corneal endothelia of cats. *J. Morph.* **174**, 25–39.

HONDA, H. (1983). Geometrical models for cells in tissues. *Int. Rev. Cyt.* **81**, 191–248.

JACOBSON, A. G. (1982). Morphogenesis of the neural plate and tube. In *Morphogenesis and Pattern Formation* (ed. T. G. Connelly, L. Brinkley & B. Carson), pp. 223–263. New York: Raven Press.

JACOBSON, A. & GORDON, R. (1976). Changes in shape of the developing nervous system analyzed experimentally, mathematically, and by computer simulation. *J. exp. Zool.* **197**, 191–246.

JACOBSON, A. G., OSTER, G. F., ODELL, G. M. & CHENG, L. Y. (1986). Neurulation and the cortical tractor model for epithelial folding. *J. Embryol. exp. Morph.* **96**, 19–49.

KAGEYAMA, T. (1982). Cellular basis of epiboly of the enveloping layer in the embryo of the medaka, *Oryzias latipes*. II. Evidence for cell rearrangement. *J. exp. Zool.* **219**, 241–256.

KELLER, R. E. (1975). Vital dye mapping of the gastrula and neurula of *Xenopus laevis*. I. Prospective areas and morphogenetic movements of the superficial layer. *Devl Biol.* **42**, 222–241.

KELLER, R. E. (1976). Vital dye mapping of the gastrula and neurula of *Xenopus laevis*. II. Prospective areas and morphogenetic movements of the deep region. *Devl Biol.* **51**, 118–137.

KELLER, R. E. (1978). Time-lapse cinematographic analysis of superficial cell behavior during and prior to gastrulation in *Xenopus laevis*. *J. Morph.* **157**, 223–248.

KELLER, R. E. (1980). The cellular basis of epiboly: An SEM study of deep cell rearrangement during gastrulation in *Xenopus laevis*. *J. Embryol. exp. Morph.* **60**, 201–234.

KELLER, R. E. (1984). The cellular basis of gastrulation in *Xenopus laevis*: Active, postinvolution convergence and extension by mediolateral interdigitation. *Am. Zool.* **24**, 589–603.

KELLER, R. E. (1986). The cellular basis of amphibian gastrulation. In *Developmental Biology: A Comprehensive Synthesis*, vol. 2, *The Cellular Basis of Morphogenesis*, pp. 241–327. New York: Plenum Press.

KELLER, R., DANILCHIK, M., GIMLICH, R. & SHIH, J. (1985*a*). The function of convergent extension during gastrulation of *Xenopus laevis*. *J. Embryol. exp. Morph.* **89 Supplement**, 185–209.

KELLER, R., DANILCHIK, M., GIMLICH, R. & SHIH, J. (1985*b*). Convergent extension by cell intercalation during gastrulation of *Xenopos laevis*. In *Molecular Determinants of Animal Form* (ed. G. M. Edelman), *UCLA Symp. Molec. Cell. Biol.*, vol. 31. New York: Alan Liss.

KELLER, R. E. & SCHOENWOLF, G. C. (1977). An SEM study of cellular morphology, contact, and arrangement, as related to gastrulation in *Xenopus laevis*. *Wilhelm Roux Arch. EntwMech. Org.* **182**, 165–186.

KELLER, R. E. & TRINKAUS, J. P. (1982). Cell rearrangement in a tightly joined epithelial layer during *Fundulus* epiboly. *J. Cell Biol.* **95**, 325a.

KELLER, R. E. & TRINKAUS, J. P. (1987). Rearrangement of enveloping layer cells without disruption of the epithelial permeability barrier as a factor in *Fundulus* epiboly. *Devl Biol.* **120**, 12–24.

KINNANDER, H. & GUSTAFSON, T. (1960). Further studies on the cellular basis of gastrulation in the sea urchin larva. *Expl. Cell Res.* **19**, 276–290.

KOLEGA, J. (1986). The cellular basis of epithelial morphogenesis. In *Developmental Biology: A Comprehensive Synthesis*, vol. 2, *The Cellular Basis of Morphogenesis* (ed. L. Browder), pp. 103–143. New York: Plenum Press.

KUBOTA, H. & DURSTON, A. J. (1978). Cinematographical study of cell migration in the opened gastrula of *Ambystoma mexicanum*. *J. Embryol. exp. Morph.* **44**, 71–80.

LOCKE, M. (1985). The structure of epidermal feet during their development. *Tissue & Cell* **17**, 901–921.

LUNDMARK, C., SHIH, J., TIBBETTS, P. & KELLER, R. (1984). Amphibian gastrulation as seen by scanning electron microscopy. *SEM* **III**, 1289–1300.

MITTENTHAL, J. & MAZO, R. (1983). A model for shape generation by strain and cell–cell adhesion in the epithelium of an arthropod leg segment. *J. theor. Biol.* **100**, 443–483.

MIYAMOTO, D. & CROWTHER, R. (1985). Formation of the notochord in living ascidian embryos. *J. Embryol. exp. Morph.* **86**, 1–17.

Morrill, J. B. & Santos, L. L. (1985). A scanning electron microscopical overview of cellular and extracellular patterns during blastulation and gastrulation in the sea urchin, *Lytechinus variegatus*. In *The Cellular and Molecular Biology of Invertebrate Development* (ed. R. H. Sawyer & R. M. Showman), pp. 3–33. Columbia, S.C.: University of South Carolina Press.

Nakatsuji, N. (1976). Studies on the gastrulation of amphibian embryos: Ultrastructure of the migrating cells of anurans. *Wilhelm Roux Arch. EntwMech. Org.* **180**, 229–240.

Nakatsuji, N. & Johnson, K. (1984). Experimental manipulation of a contact guidance system in amphibian gastrulation by mechanical tension. *Nature, Lond.* **307**, 453–455.

Nardi, J. & MaGee-Adams, S. M. (1986). Formation of scale spacing patterns in a moth wing. I. Epithelial feet may mediate cell rearrangement. *Devl Biol.* **116**, 278–290.

Owaribe, K., Kodama, R. & Eguchi, G. (1981). Demonstration of contractility of circumferential actin bundles and its morphogenetic significance in pigmented epithelium *in vitro* and *in vivo*. *J. Cell Biol.* **90**, 507–514.

Poole, T. & Steinberg, M. (1981). Amphibian pronephric duct morphogenesis: Segregation, cell rearrangement and directed migration of the *Ambystoma* duct rudiment. *J. Embryol. exp. Morph.* **63**, 1–16.

Spiegel, E. & Howard, L. (1983). Development of cell junctions in sea urchin embryos. *J. Cell Sci.* **62**, 27–48.

Stephens, L., Hardin, J., Keller, R. & Wilt, F. (1986). The effects of aphidicolin on morphogenesis and differentiation in the sea urchin embryo. *Devl Biol.* **118**, 64–69.

Tickle, C. & Trinkaus, J. P. (1976). Observations on nudging cells in culture. *Nature, Lond.* **261**, 413.

Tilney, L. G. & Gibbins, J. R. (1969). Microtubules and filaments in the filopodia of the secondary mesenchyme cells of *Arbacia punctulata* and *Echinarachnius parma*. *J. Cell Sci.* **5**, 195–210.

Trinkaus, J. P. (1984*a*). *Cell into Organs: The Forces that Shape the Embryo*, 2nd edn. Englewood Cliffs: Prentice-Hall.

Trinkaus, J. P. (1984*b*). Mechanisms of *Fundulus* epiboly – A current view. *Am. Zool.* **24**, 673–688.

Vogt, W. (1929). Gesaltungsanalyse am Amphibienkeim mit örtlicher Vitalfärbung. II. Teil. Gastrulation and Mesodermbildung bei Urodelen and Anuren. *Wilhelm Roux Arch. EntwMech. Org.* **120**, 384–706.

Waddington, C. H. (1940). *Organizers and Genes*. Cambridge University Press.

J. Cell Sci. Suppl. 8, 395–413 (1987)
Printed in Great Britain © *The Company of Biologists Limited 1987*

ANALYSIS OF *IN VIVO* CELL MOVEMENT USING TRANSPARENT TISSUE SYSTEMS

PETER THOROGOOD* AND ANDREW WOOD

Department of Biology, Medical and Biological Sciences Building, Bassett Crescent East, Southampton SO9 3TU, UK

SUMMARY

The embryos of certain teleost species are transparent and cell behaviour within the intact embryo can be observed and recorded using Nomarski microscopy coupled with time-lapse video recording or time-lapse cine filming. In this report we review some of our recent analyses of cell behaviour patterns underlying key morphogenetic events. (1) Contact-guided cell migration through a structurally ordered extracellular matrix during fin development; (2) movement of tissue layers during epibolic overgrowth; and (3) cell 'social' behaviour during the establishment of the body axis (i.e. notochord formation and somitogenesis).

These results, on cell behaviour correlated with *normal* morphogenesis, provide a baseline for further work in which hypotheses concerning subcellular and molecular controls of cell behaviour can be tested by experimental perturbation *in vivo*.

INTRODUCTION

Cell 'behaviour', which we may define as changes in the parameters of cell shape, volume, adhesiveness, motility and contact relationship in response to intrinsic or extrinsic signals, is one of the chief driving forces of morphogenesis during embryonic development. Deviation from the normal spectrum of cell behaviour will, on the one hand, generate dysmorphogenesis and, on the other, phenotypic novelties at the organismic level, which may have phylogenetic, that is to say evolutionary, significance (Wessells, 1982). Thus, if we are to understand fully how an embryo is assembled and, furthermore, use such knowledge of the mechanisms of embryogenesis as a predictive tool in analysing evolutionary (morphological) change, then we must: (1) have a description of the phenomenology of cell behaviour; and (2) understand the molecular events generating and controlling that behaviour.

Ideally, one would study cells *in situ*, that is in their normal *in vivo* microenvironment (see Keller & Hardin, this volume). However, attaining that objective is usually thwarted by the natural opacity of many living tissues and the inability of current imaging techniques to overcome that obstacle with sufficient resolution. As a consequence, studies of cell behaviour have typically used cultured cells, mostly on artificial substrata but, more recently, as our knowledge of the composition of extracellular matrices (ECM) has increased, on either isolated/purified matrix components or on naturally deposited ECMs (e.g. see Nakatsuji & Johnson, 1983;

* Author for correspondence.

Yallup *et al.* unpublished). Other cell populations may be incorporated and the 'social' behaviour of cells assessed during homotypic and heterotypic cell encounters (e.g. see Abercrombie & Heaysman, 1976). Such *in vitro* approaches have enormous scope and from them a great deal has been learnt about the fundamental aspects of cell surface character, the composition and deployment of the cytoskeleton, and the social behaviour of cells. However, attempts to reconstruct *in vitro*, the normal *in vivo* conditions of the cells, will necessarily be inadequate until we have a complete characterization of the cell environment and possess an ability to reconstruct it with fidelity.

An alternative strategy has been to explore and exploit those *in vivo* systems that have an inherent transparency. As a result the ideal of studying cells in their normal environment *has* been achieved for a limited range of tissue systems (reviewed by Trinkaus, 1984). However, many of the published studies, whilst of great value, are purely descriptive, lack quantitative assessment and thus remain anecdotal. In addition, we contend that a properly quantified analysis of *in vivo* cell behaviour is a necessary prerequisite in seeking to explain the mechanisms of morphogenesis at the cellular or molecular level. It is in this context that we will discuss some of our recent work on teleost embryos which, in some species, are transparent or semi-transparent.

Using Nomarski differential interference contrast (DIC) microscopy, cells within the interior of the teleost embryo can be visualized and their behaviour monitored using time-lapse video recording (TLV) or cine filming (TLC). Three aspects of development have been studied: namely, cell migration during fin formation, cell translocation during epiboly, and cell social behaviour during the formation of notochord and somites. One assumption running throughout this work is that it is necessary to know what cell behaviour patterns correlate with key morphogenetic events *before* experimentally perturbing the system with, for example, monovalent antibody fragments or catabolic enzymes to either inactivate or degrade ECM components. Consequently, much of what follows is an account of *normal* development.

THE FIN: AN *IN VIVO* CONTACT GUIDANCE SYSTEM

The pedigree of the embryonic teleost fin as an appropriate system for the study of *in vivo* cell movement was established many years ago by the early work of Ross Harrison, who provided one of the first, and still one of the best, morphological accounts of fin development at the light-microscopic level (Harrison, 1895). From that early work and from any contemporary account we can see that the paired fins of fish develop initially very like their tetrapod homologues, the limb buds. The fin bud grows out from the flank of the embryo as a mass of mesenchyme covered with an ectodermal layer that, around the distal margin of the bud, is thickened to form an 'apical ectodermal ridge'. However, development then diverges from the tetrapod limb bud, in that the ridge develops a prominent basal cleft along its anterio–posterior axis, which transforms the ridge into a fin 'fold' (Fig. 1; and see Wood, 1982).

Internally, within the fin fold, lie two planar arrays of large diameter collagen fibrils or 'actinotrichia', deposited by the epithelium in a parallel arrangement and aligned proximo–distally (Fig. 2); the actinotrichia support the growing embryonic fin paddle (Fig. 1). Into the space enclosed by the epithelial fin fold, and *between* the arrays of actinotrichia, migrate mesenchymal cells. These are of mixed origin, in that some are derived from somatopleure and others from somitic outgrowths (as in tetrapods); subsequently these cells will give rise to the connective tissues of the functional fin (fin rays, tendons, blood vessels, etc.). Clearly the manner in which this migration takes place is important because it positions the mesenchyme cells appropriately for the normal pattern of connective tissue differentiation.

Several years ago we discovered that the fin bud and the early fin paddle of a killifish, *Aphyosemion scheeli*, are transparent and that migration of the mesenchymal cells can be monitored, as it happens, within the intact fin. The developing fin can be excised together with the adjacent flank and maintained in a perfusion chamber on a microscope stage. Nomarski DIC microscopy enables one to focus through the overlying ectoderm and onto the migrating cells themselves (Fig. 3). Using a coupled TLV system, we have analysed migratory behaviour at three significant developmental stages: before, at the start of, and during migration (Wood & Thorogood, 1984). During this period of time, cell morphology changes dramatically, from a stationary, rounded phenotype with one or two processes that have an equal likelihood of being aligned or non-aligned with respect to the proximo–distally oriented actinotrichia, to a motile phenotype with a large number (up to seven or eight) of filopodia, the majority of which are extended distalwards and aligned parallel to the actinotrichia (Fig. 3). A number of behavioural parameters were analysed quantitatively and have been presented elsewhere; the chief conclusions are: (1) the majority of *aligned* processes were less than $2\,\mu m$ in diameter whereas the majority of *non-aligned* processes were greater than $2\,\mu m$ in diameter. (2) Aligned processes move faster ($18\,\mu m\,h^{-1}$) than non-aligned processes ($5\,\mu m\,h^{-1}$) and the appearance of large numbers of aligned cell processes per cell is associated with the onset of cell migration. (3) Contact inhibition events occur both between cell processes (laterally) and with other cells (proximally).

Clearly, what we have described is a contact-guided migration 'driven' distalwards by proximal cell population density and consequent contact-inhibition events. But that simple conclusion leaves a number of issues unresolved. For example, are the oriented cell processes aligned on the actinotrichia or along the inter-actinotrichial areas? (that is to say, along the ridges or along the grooves?); in this respect the Nomarski image is equivocal because of limited resolution and the fact that one can only focus on one array of actinotrichia at any one time. Furthermore, whatever surface is used as a migration substratum, what is the nature of the contact sites whereby the cell gains tractional purchase?

In order to answer these points, an ultrastructural analysis has been carried out examining fin buds in longitudinal (i.e. vertically along the proximo–distal axis) and transverse (i.e. vertically but along the anterio–posterior axis) planes, at a range of sectioning levels and at the same three 'significant' developmental stages (i.e. before,

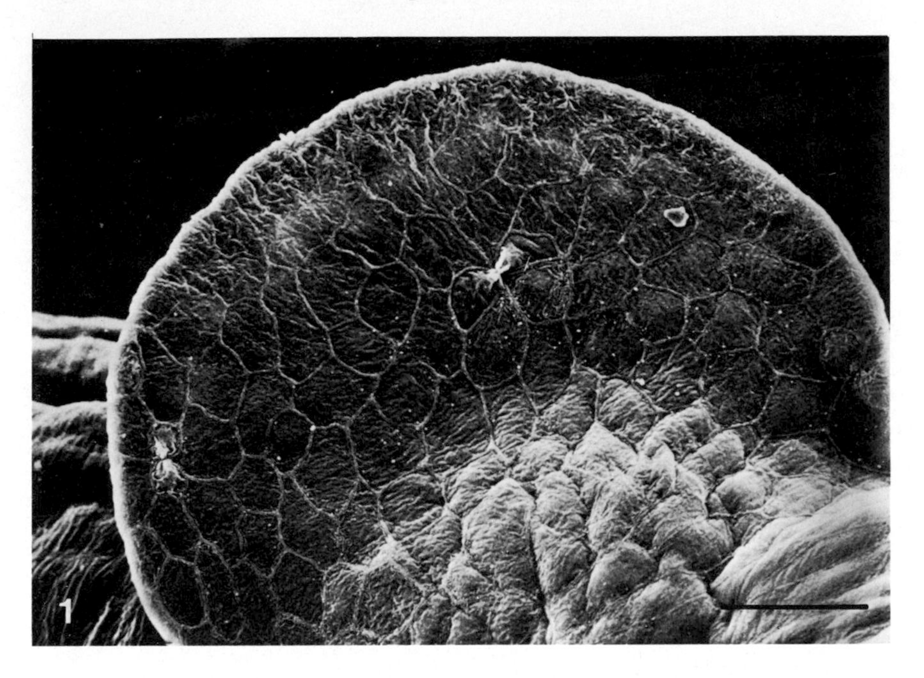

Fig. 1. Scanning electron micrograph of developing pectoral fin paddle of *A. scheeli*. The bulk of the mesenchyme at this stage is proximal and adjacent to the flank: two dividing cells can be seen in the flattened peridermal covering. Bar, 50 μm. (From Wood (1982)).

at the start of and during migration) (Wood & Thorogood, unpublished). The ultrastructural relationship between the migrating cell and its environment is seen most clearly in transverse section at the proximo–distal level of distally extended filopodia of the marginal mesenchyme cells (Fig. 4). Three clear-cut conclusions emerge: (1) aligned cell processes use actinotrichia as a migration substratum and the inter-actinotrichial/basal lamina is not used in this way. (2) No mesenchymal cell surface specializations were detectable at points of contact with actinotrichia. (3) No high-order cytoskeletal organization was detectable in the migrating mesenchyme cells (determined from longitudinal sections and not illustrated here).

Thus, in this contact guidance system, it is the actinotrichia (the collagen fibrils) that are used almost exclusively as the preferred substratum for movement. But in spite of this unequivocal observation, identification of the actual mechanism of guidance is problematical because several possibilities exist. First, the cells may simply be responding to topological cues; i.e. *physical topology* might constrain either the orientation of the cytoskeleton (Dunn & Heath, 1976) or the orientation of focal/tractional contacts with the substratum (Ohara & Buck, 1979). Second, the cells may be displaying a preferred adhesion to the collagenous actinotrichia; i.e. *differential adhesiveness* of the substratum may determine cell shape and the orientation of the cells. Third, rather than actively seeking the actinotrichia as a migration substratum, the cells may simply be excluded from the inter-actinotrichial areas. Any one, or a combination, of these mechanisms might be operative.

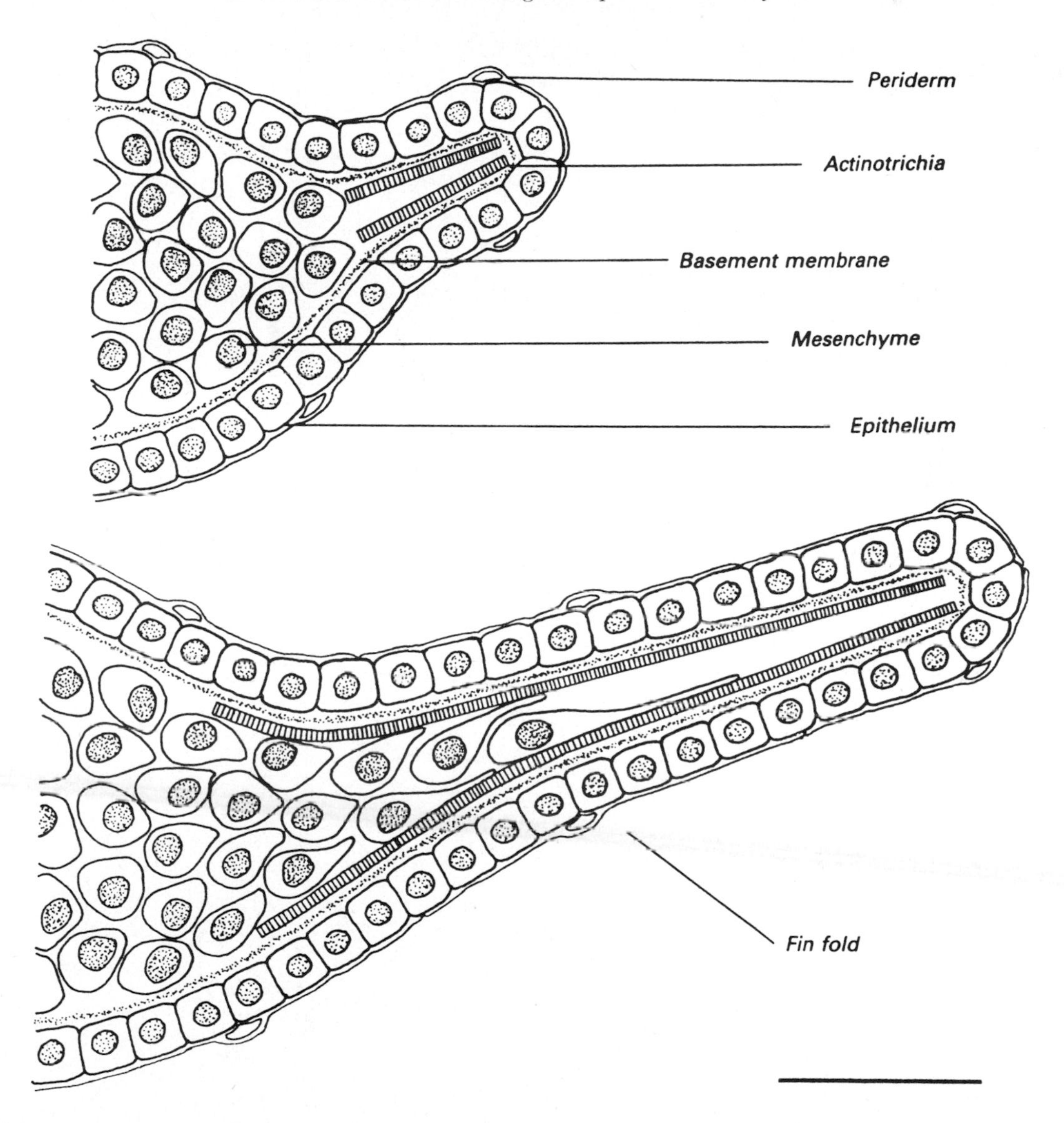

Fig. 2. Diagram illustrating the early development of the pectoral fin fold: the plane of section is vertical and along the proximo–distal axis of the fin. As the fold develops, from what was originally a basal cleft in the ectoderm of the ridge, mesenchymal cells proceed to migrate into the space enclosed by the fin fold, in close association with the collagenous actinotrichia. Bar, 20 μm. (From Wood & Thorogood (1984).)

Before proceeding further and in order to place this analysis firmly on a quantitative basis, a morphometric survey was made applying computer-based image analysis techniques (Wood & Thorogood, unpublished). Using the Kontron IBAS 2 Image Analysis System, and transversely sectioned material from the same three 'significant' developmental stages, we have evaluated changes in four parameters (Fig. 5). They are: (1) actinotrichial diameter ('DCRCL'); (2) width of the inter-actinotrichial spaces/grooves ('INTERSPACE'); (3) distance between the two basal laminae of the dorsal and ventral ectoderms ('INTERFOLD'); and (4) distance between the actinotrichia of the dorsal and ventral arrays ('OPP-ACT'). Full details of this analysis and the data generated can be found elsewhere (Wood & Thorogood, unpublished) and here we will consider only the major conclusions emerging from analysis of two of these parameters: DCRCL and INTERSPACE: (1) A progressive

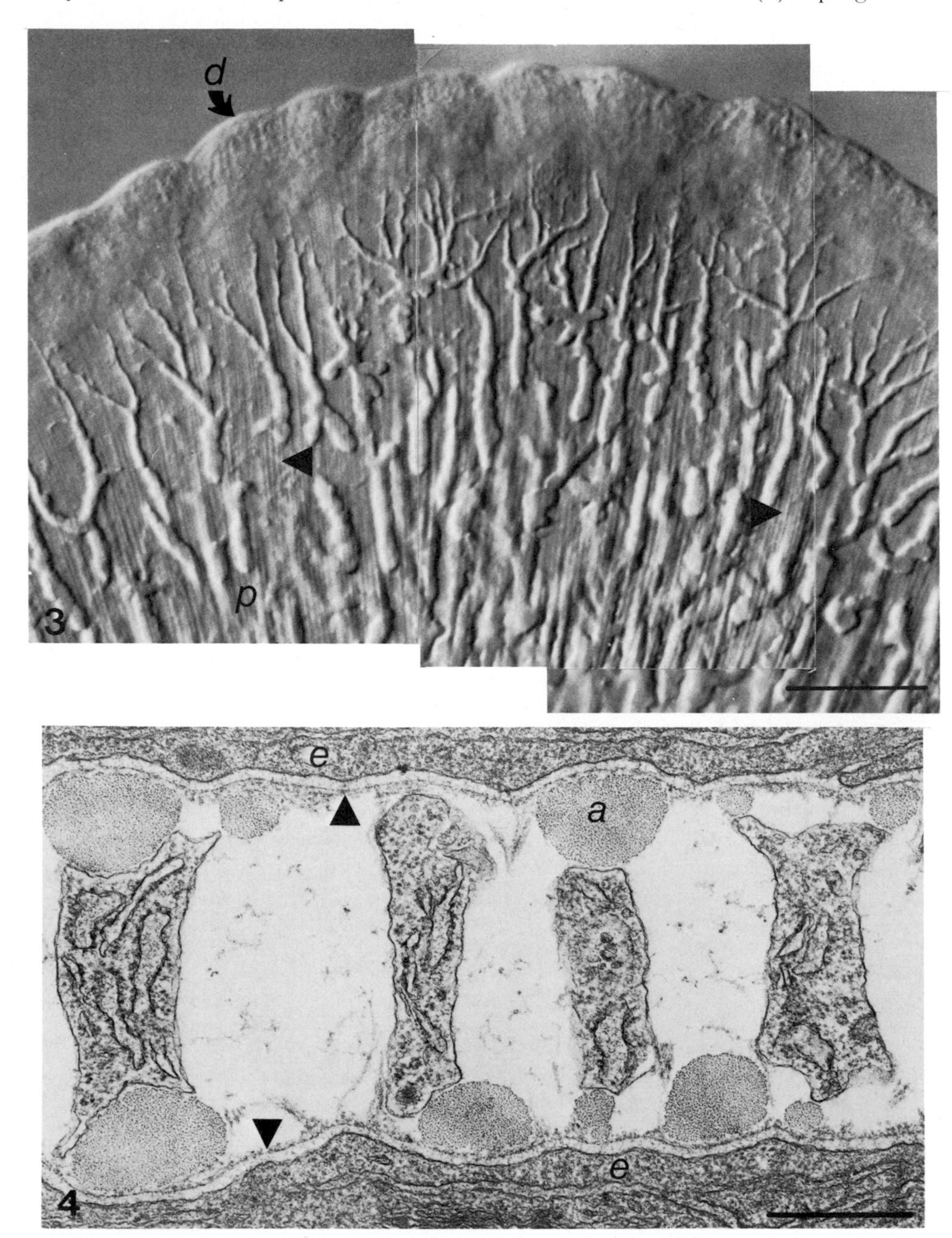

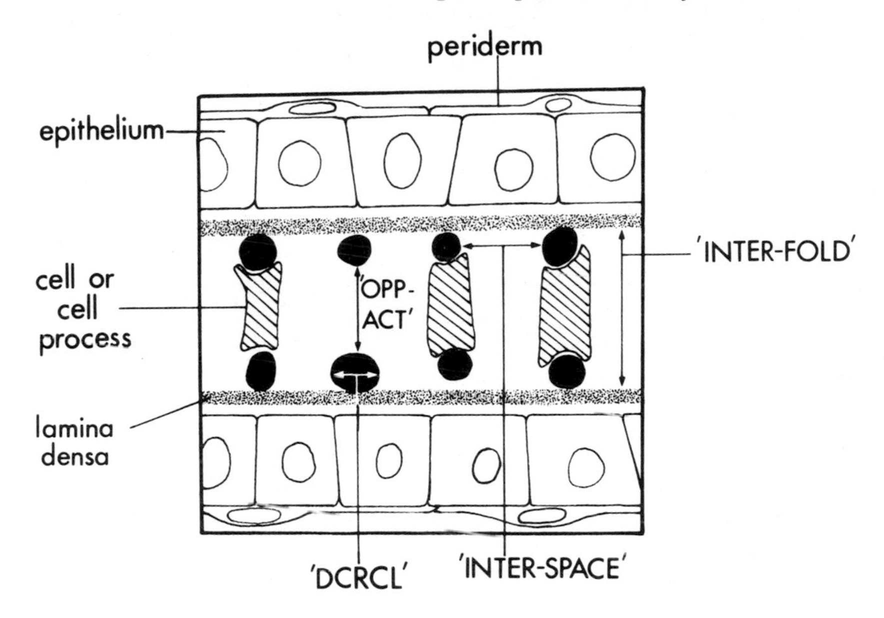

Fig. 5. Diagram of field similar to that shown in Fig. 4, to illustrate the parameters that have been monitored at different proximo–distal levels and at different developmental stages, using image analysis techniques. For definitions of OPP-ACT, INTERFOLD, DCRCL, and INTER-SPACE, see the text. (From Wood & Thorogood (1987).)

increase in actinotrichial diameter with time correlates with increasing numbers of aligned filopodia along the actinotrichia themselves and with the onset of migration. (2) The constancy of inter-actinotrichial space width with time indicates that spacing between actinotrichia is not significant in eliciting changes in mesenchymal cell phenotype and behaviour. (3) Very high radius of curvature in the substratum is avoided by the cells; 87 % of the actinotrichia *without* filopodial associations were distributed at the lower end of the size range.

Assuming that smaller actinotrichia have an identical composition to larger ones, then this last point suggests that there is at least a topological component in the system: smaller diameter fibrils will have a higher radius of curvature, which cell processes will be unable to use, for reasons given earlier. In order to pursue this further, we have cultured the cells *in vitro* on microfabricated ridged and grooved substrata of periodicities down to 1 μm width and depth, but of uniform adhesiveness (created by ion etching and photolithography of quartz discs). The cells, whilst not necessarily displaying the arborized phenotype with multiple filopodia as seen *in vivo*

Fig. 3. Nomarski DIC micrograph of living caudal fin of *A. scheeli*, selected to show clearly the morphology of individual migrating cells within a developing fin (*D*, distal margin of fin; *p*, proximal; arrowheads indicate actinotrichia). Bar, 8 μm.

Fig. 4. Transmission electron micrograph of transverse section through filopodia and actinotrichia within the fold of a developing *A. scheeli* pectoral fin (*e*, ectoderm; *a*, actinotrichia; arrowheads indicate the basal lamina subjacent to each ectoderm). The almost exclusive use of actinotrichia by filopodia of migrating cells is clearly shown. Bar, 0·5 μm. (From Wood & Thorogood, unpublished.)

(Fig. 3), nevertheless become aligned and display contact-guided movement in the absence of any chemical heterogeneity in the substratum (Wood, unpublished observations).

Thus, the developing teleost fin provides a clear example of an *in vivo* unidirectional cell taxis. The guidance of the cells, eliciting a highly aligned phenotype and oriented movement, clearly arises from the ordered matrix through

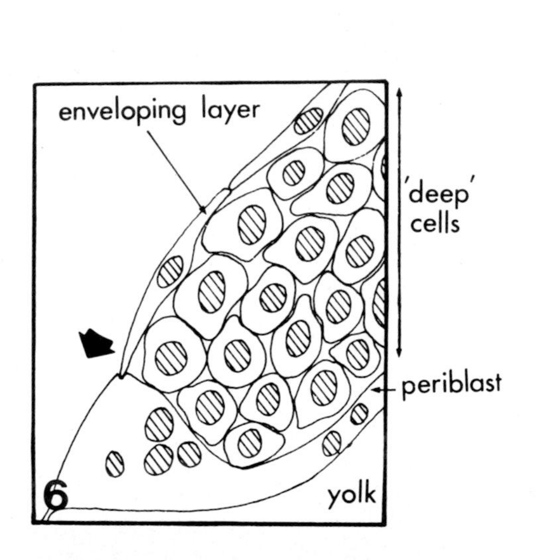

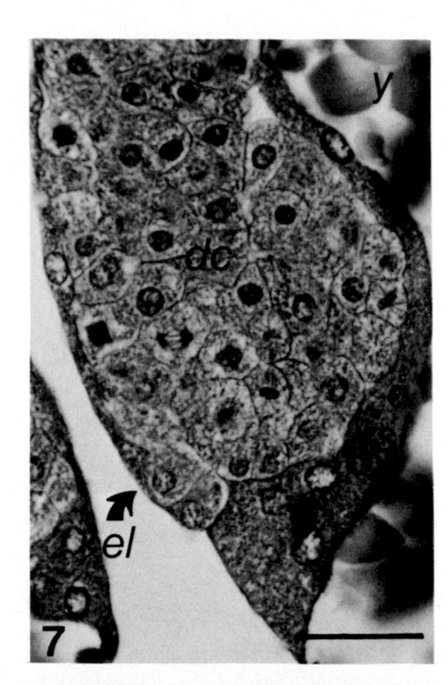

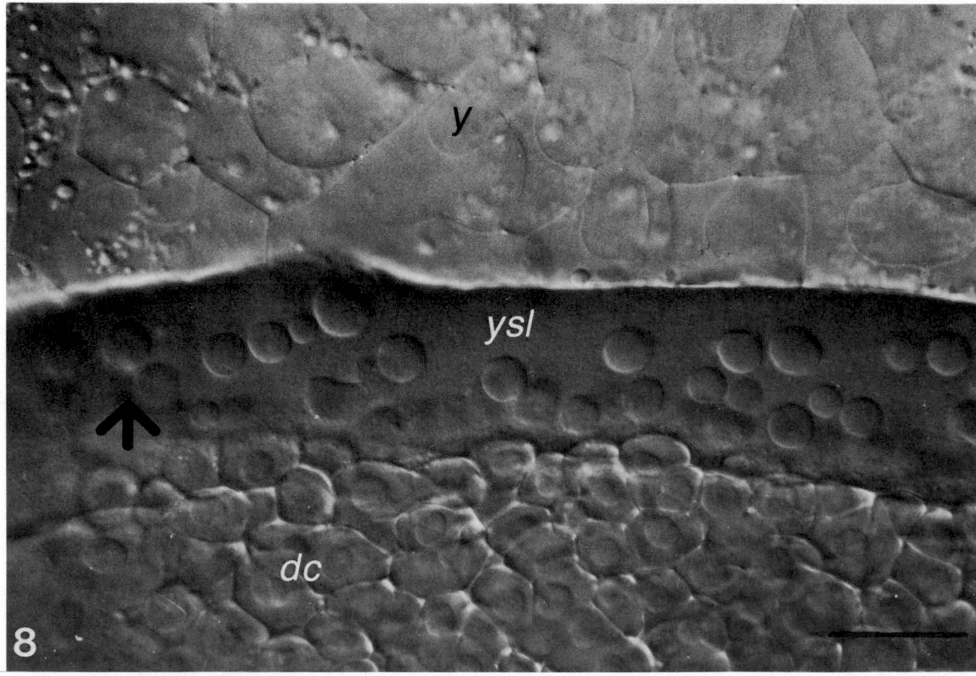

which the cells migrate. Although the cells can be shown to be capable of responding *in vitro* to substratum topology alone, the precise roles of topology, differential adhesiveness and possible exclusion by matrix heterogeneity, remain to be clarified. An immunocytochemical analysis of matrix composition, currently in progress, offers the greatest potential for resolving this issue.

EPIBOLY: A REASSESSMENT OF CELL MOVEMENTS

Most teleost fish display what embryologists refer to as 'meroblastic' cleavage, i.e. the cleavage divisions are confined to a relatively yolk-free cytoplasm at the (animal) pole of the yolk-filled egg. The resultant cellular mass proceeds to grow out over that inert yolk mass from animal to vegetal pole, to produce a cellular blastoderm covering its entire surface. This phenomenon of overgrowth is termed 'epiboly' and it is within the blastoderm that morphogenesis of the embryo and the yolk sac takes place.

Upon closer examination of the blastoderm we find that it consists of three distinct cell layers. Innermost, against the yolk itself, is the yolk syncytial layer (YSL), a multinucleate layer, which is continuous at points with the yolk as a result of incomplete cleavage division. Outermost is a thin squamous epithelium, the enveloping layer (EL), which around its margin forms a very strong adhesion to the outer aspect of the margin of the YSL. Sandwiched between the two is a third cell population, the 'deep cells'. These constitute a layer several cells thick and the cells are characteristically large, rounded and mitotically very active. It is from the deep cells that the embryo proper and the yolk sac are derived.

The behaviour of individual deep cells has been the subject of intense scrutiny by Trinkaus and colleagues; the cells are known to move quickly at speeds of up to 10–15 $\mu m\,min^{-1}$, and to display a variety of locomotory structures ranging from blebs and lobopodia to filopodia and lamellipodia (Trinkaus & Erickson, 1983). However, in this discussion we are not addressing the question of individual deep cell movement but rather examining the coordinated movements of the deep cell population as a whole.

To understand the mechanism of epiboly we must focus our attention on the prominent, growing margin of the blastoderm, the so-called 'germ ring' (Figs 6, 7).

Fig. 6. Diagram of a germ ring (i.e. the epibolizing margin of the blastoderm) in vertical section illustrating the various cell layers. See the text for a full explanation (arrow indicates direction of epibolic overgrowth).

Fig. 7. Light micrograph of a vertically sectioned germ ring of *B. conchonius* at mid-epiboly; an identical field to that shown in Fig. 6 but rotated to the right (*y*, yolk; *dc*, deep cells; *ysl*, yolk syncytial layer; *el*, enveloping layer). Part of a second embryo is seen lower left. Haematoxylin and eosin. Bar, 20 μm.

Fig. 8. Nomarski DIC micrograph illustrating the *en face* view of the germ ring; top edge of frame is vegetal, bottom edge, animal. The plane of optical section is focussed on the deep cells (*dc*) within the germ ring, and through the enveloping layer, which consequently cannot be seen. In the exposed edge of the multinucleate yolk syncytial layer (*ysl*) can be seen numerous large nuclei. The yolk (*y*), seen in the upper part of the field has a pseudo-cellular appearance due to the packing of the fat droplets contained within it. Bar, 45 μm.

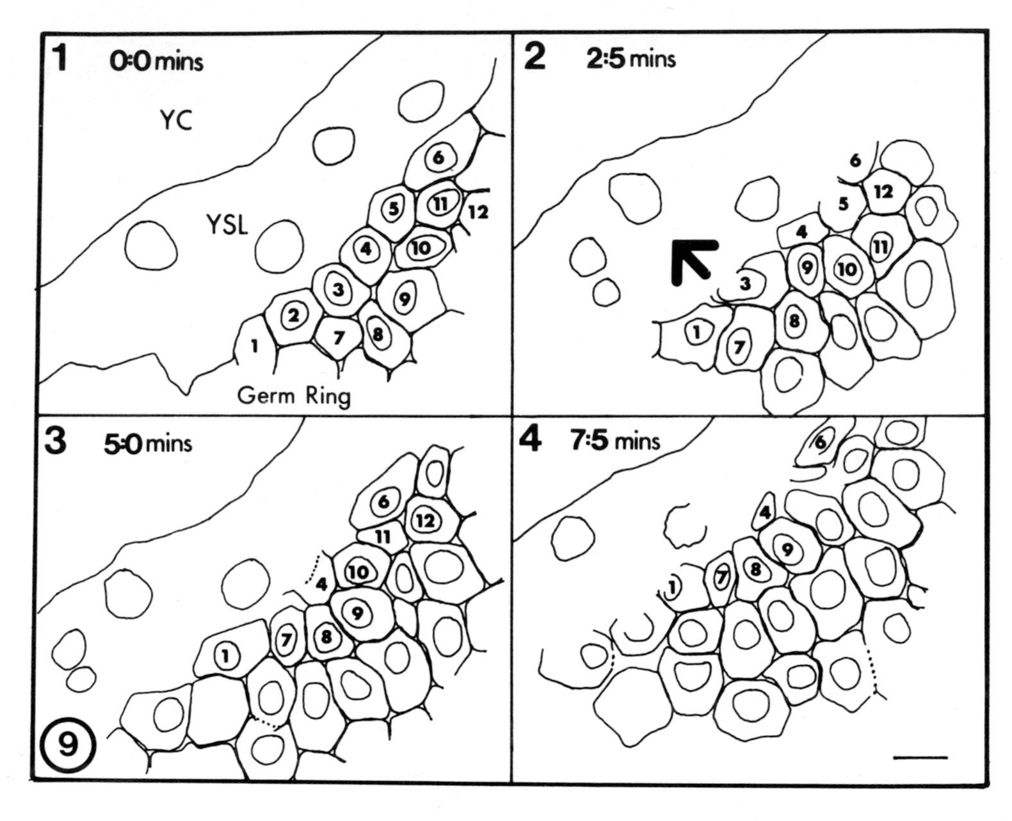
1 0:0 mins
YC
YSL
Germ Ring
2 2:5 mins
3 5:0 mins
4 7:5 mins
9

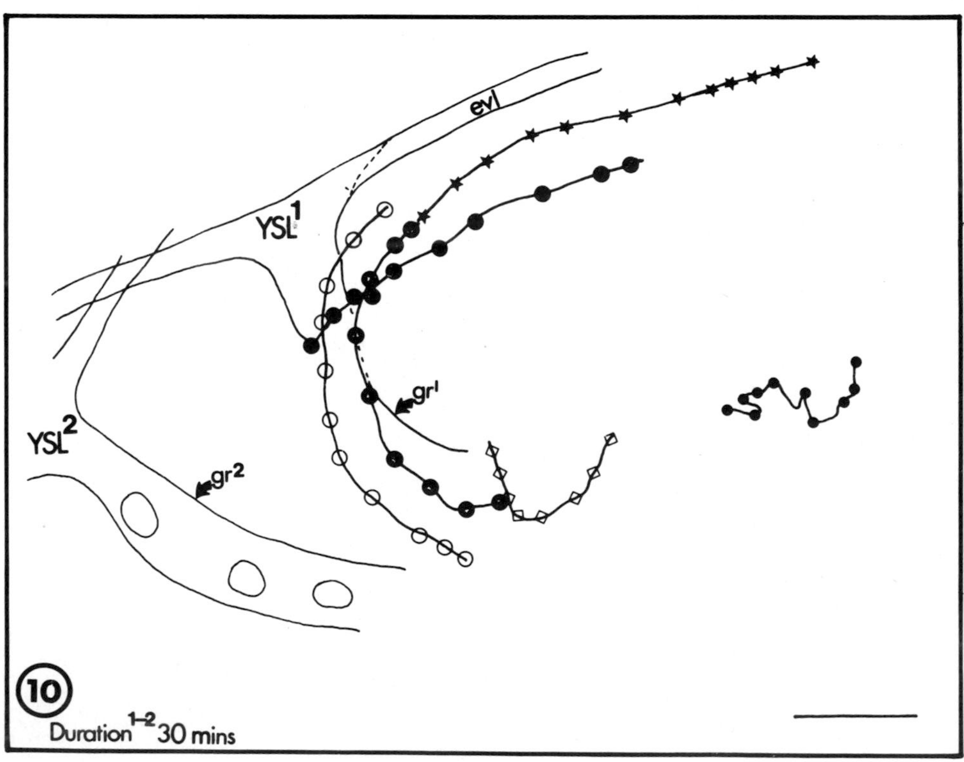
evl
YSL1
YSL2
gr1
gr2
10
Duration 1–2 30 mins

In a classic paper, Trinkaus (1951) demonstrated that the principal motive force arises from the YSL, which contracts around the yolk mass, pulling the EL passively around with it; hence the strong adhesion of the latter to the former. Interestingly, the cells of the EL display considerable lateral movement, changing neighbours within the plane of the epithelium yet still maintaining epithelial integrity and a high resistance barrier to ion movement between the embryo and its environment (Keller & Trinkaus, 1987). Although the deep cells are known to be highly motile, they appear not to provide any driving force underlying epiboly but, instead, simply move (vegetally) to occupy the increased space made available as the YSL and EL epibolize (for a full account see Trinkaus, 1984).

Regarding precise movements of the deep cells within the germ ring there seems to be a tacit agreement that *no* involution or internalization of the deep cell layer takes place (Ballard, 1966, 1973; Trinkaus, 1984). Thus, although this phase is usually regarded as a homologue of gastrulation, there is thought to be no global re-arrangement of deep cells to establish the germ layers, as typifies gastrulation in virtually all 'higher' vertebrates. Indeed, Ballard (1982) has claimed that the absence of involution within the germ ring of modern teleosts makes their embryonic morphogenesis qualitatively different from that of all other vertebrates. Here, therefore, we have an example of a morphogenetic movement with a pivotal position in an evolutionary discussion and assessment of phylogenetic relationships. It should be pointed out that this conclusion, regarding lack of cell internalization, was reached very largely as a result of vital staining of deep cells or marking their surface with fine chalk particles (Ballard, 1966, 1973). Given the inherent transparency of the system it seemed appropriate to use Nomarski DIC and time-lapse techniques and we have now analysed deep cell behaviour within the germ ring, viewing the structure both '*en face*' and in 'profile', using embryos of the Rosy Barb, *Barbus conchonius* (Wood & Timmermans, unpublished).

The *en face* view is that obtained by observing the embryo along an axis perpendicular to its surface at any selected point around the germ ring, and focusing through the EL onto the deep cells (Fig. 8). TLC reveals several important points. First, advance of the germ ring is very rapid; during the first half of epiboly it moves towards the vegetal pole at speeds in excess of $200\,\mu m\,h^{-1}$ and the whole of epiboly, around an egg of about 1·0 mm diameter, is completed within 4 h. Second, and of great importance, tracking of individual cells on an analytical projector demonstrates

Fig. 9. Diagram made from TLC, of field similar to that shown in Fig. 8, over a period of 7·5 min (YC, yolk; YSL, yolk syncytial layer; the arrow in frame 2 indicates the direction of epiboly throughout the sequence. Note the gradual disappearance by a sinking inwards of cells, e.g. cell 3, which begins to sink by frame 2 and has completely sunk from view by frame 3. Meanwhile, the margin of overgrowth has continued to move from lower right to upper left. Bar, 15 μm. (From Wood & Timmermans, unpublished.)

Fig. 10. Diagram made from TLC, of paths of nuclear (and thus, cell) displacement during epiboly obtained by viewing the germ ring in profile (YSL, yolk syncytial layer; evl, enveloping layer; gr, distal edge of germ ring). The tracks of six nuclei from different regions of the deep cell layer are plotted over a 30-min period. Note the reduction in track length and directionality following involution of superficial deep cells. Bar, 45 μm. (From Wood & Timmermans, unpublished.)

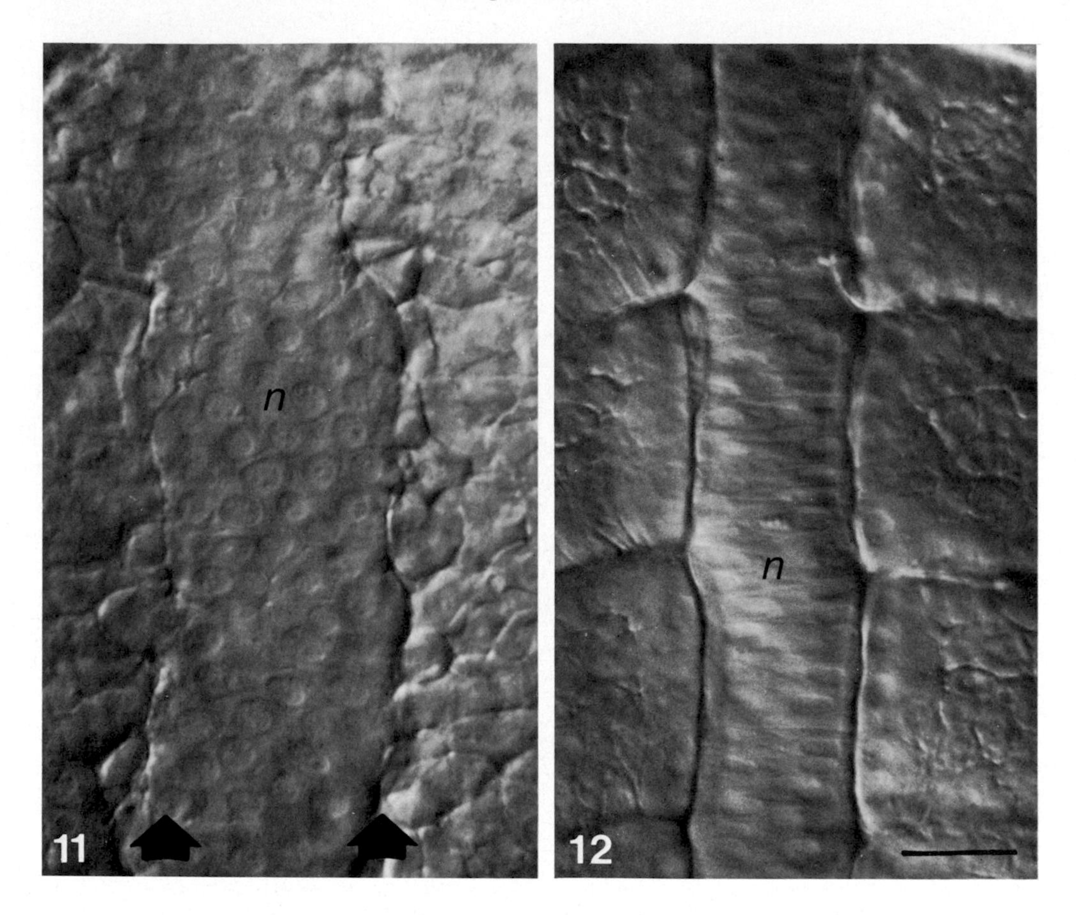

Fig. 11. Nomarski DIC micrograph of the anterior portion of the notochordal primordium prior to the start of somitogenesis, in *B. conchonius* (*n*, notochord; arrows indicate interface between the forming notochord and paraxial mesenchyme, seen in optical section as two longitudinal clefts). Bar, 20 μm.

Fig. 12. Nomarski DIC micrograph of newly formed vagal somites and notochord in *B. conchonius* (*n*, notochord). Note the emerging stack of coins appearance of the notochord, which precedes vacuolation of the individual cells. Bar, 20 μm.

that a proportion of the cells at the margin of the deep cell layer itself progressively disappear or, rather, sink out of view as epiboly progresses. This occurs at a remarkably fast rate and in the sequence shown in Fig. 9, during a period of 7·5 min, the cells comprising the advancing 'edge' are replaced by more proximal neighbours several times. Whether or not *all* cells at the advancing edge are displaced in the same way throughout epiboly has not be ascertained, but the first half of this morphogenetic stage is characterized by a significantly high proportion of deep cells moving inwards and out of the plane of focus.

The critical question is what happens to the deep cells and this can be answered by viewing the living cells in profile, again by DIC. By focussing along a latitudinal line coincident with the germ ring itself, one can observe the germ ring in optical section

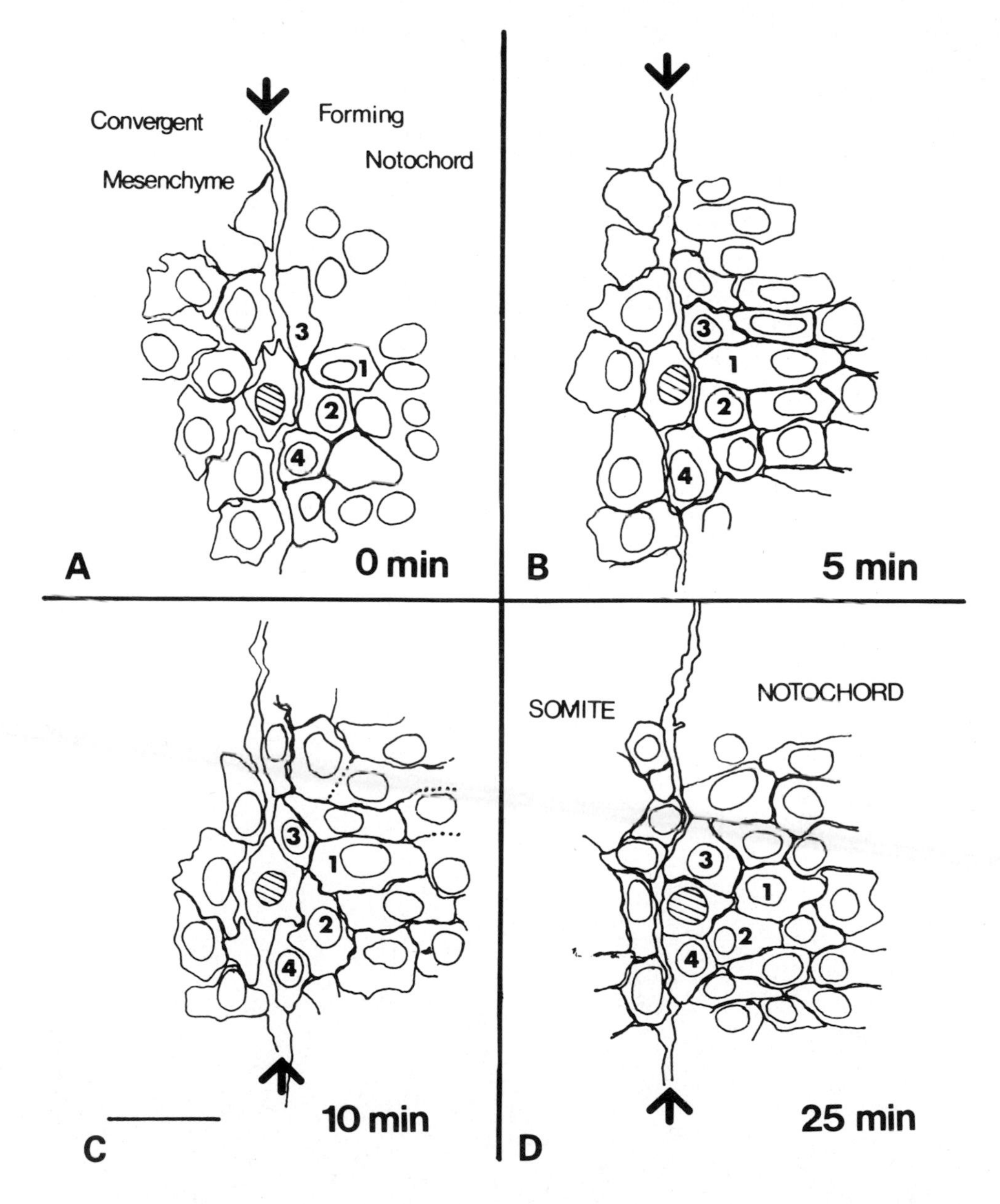

Fig. 13. Diagram made from TLC, of a field containing notochord/paraxial mesenchyme interface, as in Fig. 11 (arrowheads indicate the emerging clefts between the two tissues). Note how, over a 25-min period, the cell with a hatched nucleus, which initially lies in the cleft, intercalates between cells 3 and 4 and becomes a part of the notochord. Bar, 20 μm.

and view the structure in profile (not illustrated but identical in aspect to the histological section shown in Fig. 8). The degree of resolution is not as fine as that obtained viewing *en face*, when focussing only through the EL, because in this

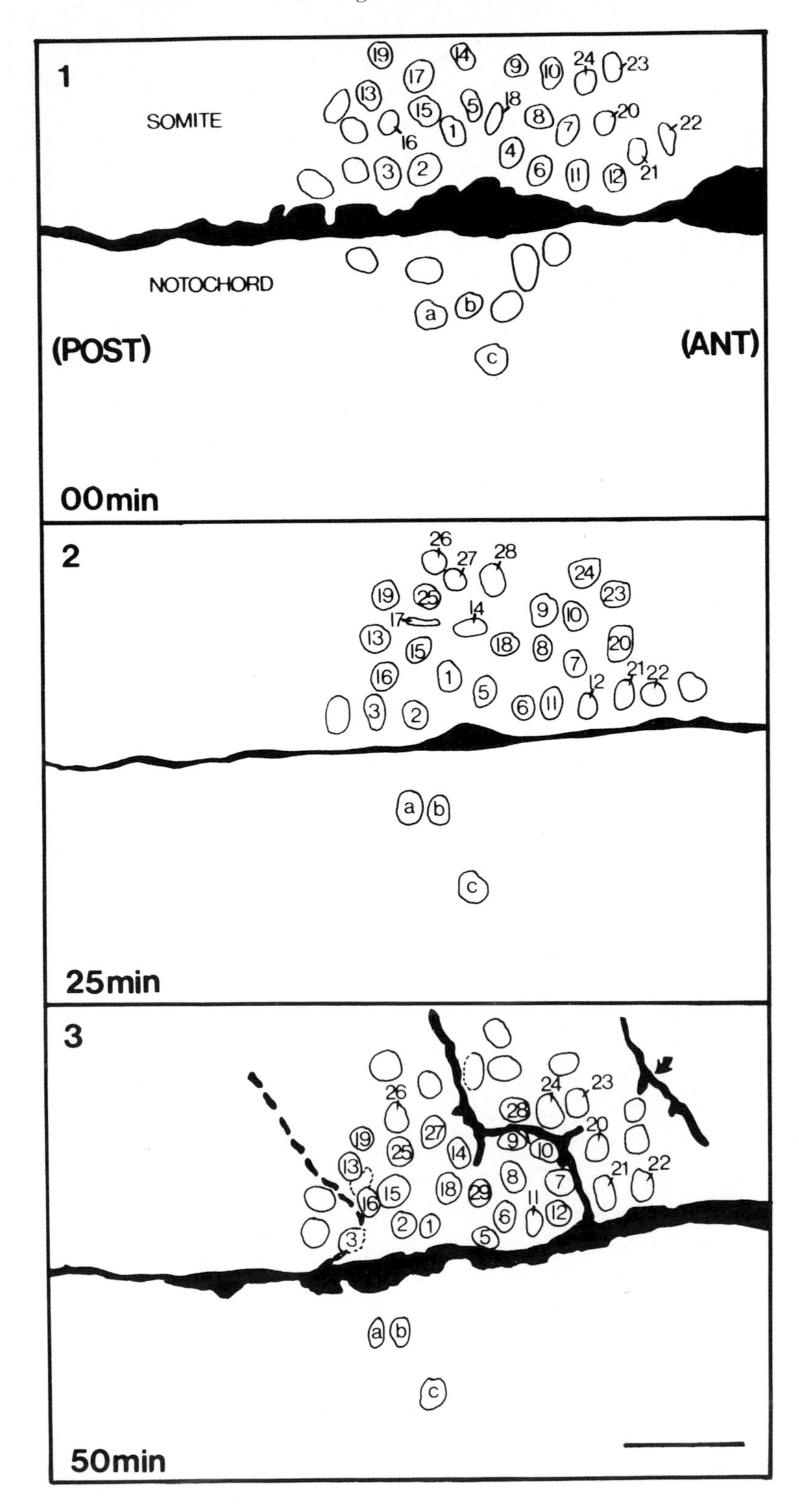
1
SOMITE
NOTOCHORD
(POST)
(ANT)
00min
2
25min
3
50min

instance one is focussing through a number of cells lying along that particular line of latitude, but nevertheless sufficient detail can be obtained, enabling one to follow individual deep cells by tracing paths of nuclear displacement.

Viewing of TLC or TLV reveals an apparent 'rolling in' motion of the superficial deep cells at the germ ring as epiboly takes place. It is difficult to follow a single cell continuously over a long period from this aspect but, by collating the movement of a number of individual cells from different points in the field, an unambiguous behavioural pattern emerges. Fig. 10 illustrates a typical field filmed over a period of 30 min. At the more superficial loci, deep cells translocate towards the vegetal pole at a rate of approximately $350\,\mu m\,h^{-1}$ and these cells are the counterparts of those displayed in Figs 8 and 9, i.e. that disappear or sink out of *en face* view as epiboly progresses.

At the distal margin of the deep cell layer, subjacent to the point of attachment of the EL to the YSL, the cells roll under their more proximal neighbours and are displaced below the superficial deep cells, i.e. against the YSL. Once displaced in this way, the movement or translocation of individual cells is considerably reduced and may, in some cases, be temporarily arrested. Deep cells that have been 'internalized' in this way are continuously replaced at the margin of the deep cell layer by other superficial deep cells, as seen in the *en face* analysis earlier. The behaviour of the deep cell layer within the germ ring is rather like the motion of an escalator, continuously rolling in at its margin. As it does so cells are deposited on the YSL as epiboly progresses; meanwhile, the margin itself, although its cellular composition is constantly turning over, moves globally towards the vegetal pole.

Three further features should be mentioned. First, the 'rolling in' motion, or involution, of the deep cell margin is at its most dramatic during early to mid epiboly and less apparent during the later stages. Second, it occurs around the entire circumference of the germ ring and is *not* confined to any one point, which might presage the point of embryonic axis formation; whether or not the process varies significantly in rate around the germ ring circumference has not yet been ascertained but no major difference in rate has been detected to date. Third, this analysis does not address the nature of the motive force behind deep cell involution; the respective roles of active cell migration, passive cell displacement or even 'trapping' on the YSL, can only be the subject of speculation at this stage.

The unambiguous conclusion emerging from this analysis is that, contrary to previous reports, involution *does* occur at the germ ring during epiboly of teleost embryos (Wood & Timmermans, unpublished). Therefore, modern teleosts, like other vertebrates, do display a phase of cell internalization during early development.

Fig. 14. Diagram made from TLC, of a field containing notochord/paraxial mesenchyme interface, and covering the formation of the first three somites. A group of nuclei are labelled to indicate relative cell position and extracellular spaces blocked in (ANT, anterior; POST, posterior; a,b,c, three notochordal cells arbitrarily selected as reference points). During somitogenesis there is a net medial movement (note how the interface moves in successive frames). Most cells display little, if any, re-arrangement and retain their neighbours during the net medial movement and formation of intersomitic clefts (two of which are well formed and the third beginning to appear). Bar, $30\,\mu m$.

Apart from leading to a re-appraisal of events during epiboly, this conclusion illustrates clearly the limitations that are inherent in using traditional means of cell marking, and which, in transparent systems, can be overcome using DIC coupled with time-lapse techniques.

NOTOCHORD FORMATION AND SOMITOGENESIS: CELL BEHAVIOUR CAN BE MONITORED DURING THE ESTABLISHMENT OF THE VERTEBRATE BODY PLAN

Shortly after epiboly is completed embryonic axis formation starts. The notochord can be recognized first and is distinguished initially by the two longitudinal clefts indicating the interface between presumptive notochord and paraxial mesenchyme (Fig. 11). Shortly afterwards the first, i.e. most anterior, somite pairs are formed and thereafter somite pairs are added sequentially in an anterio–posterior direction. The rate of somitogenesis is temperature dependent and, at 25°C, one somite pair is added every 20–25 min. Thus, quite rapidly the embryo displays multiple somite pairs and other aspects of organogenesis, such as neural tube formation and craniofacial morphogenesis, begin. By focussing down through overlying tissue, Nomarski DIC images such as those shown in Figs 11 and 12 can be obtained and a particular dorsi–ventral plane of optical section selected; using time-lapse techniques it is possible to follow individual cells during notochord formation and somitogenesis. Thus, we have been able for the first time, to monitor and analyse individual cell behaviour during establishment of the axial and segmental pattern in an intact embryo (Wood & Thorogood, unpublished).

Given the current interest in these events there are many questions to be studied; however, we shall focus on just two aspects. First, what kind of cell behaviour underlies the formation of the notochord? How is it formed initially and how does it subsequently transform from the organization shown in Fig. 11 to the characteristic 'stack of coins' (Keller *et al.* 1985) appearance shown in Fig. 12? From work on tissue explants of amphibian chordamesoderm, Keller has defined two possibilities. On the one hand, cells may actively insert or *intercalate* between neighbours with a net movement at right angles to the longitudinal axis of the notochord. On the other hand, cells may (less 'aggressively') move into extracellular spaces previously opened up by neighbouring cells moving apart along the anterio–posterior axis, i.e. presumptive notochord cells *converge* towards the midline moving into extracellular domains opened up by *extension* of the anterio–posterior axis (see fig. 9 of Keller *et al.* 1985). Whichever strategy the cells adopt, the end point is the same: cells aligned parallel to one another and at right angles to the anterio–posterior axis.

Frame-by-frame analysis of TLC has enabled us to resolve these questions. Fig. 13 shows four frames from a typical sequence of an embryo at a slightly earlier stage to that shown in Fig. 11. The notochord/paraxial mesenchyme interface is only just becoming apparent as the clefts around the notochord coalesce. During the 25 min of the sequence, the cell identified with the hatched nucleus moves from an indeterminate position at the interface to deep within the notochord itself. Whereas the interface clefts appear to open up by de-adhesion between notochordal and paraxial mesenchyme cells, no comparable de-adhesion can be identified between notochordal cells. Thus, no pre-existing spaces can be identified between cells 3 and 4 and, in fact, the identified cell intercalates between them by an active insertion (the dynamic nature of which is best conveyed by viewing the films). Our conclusion to the first question is, therefore, that during the formation of the early notochord within an intact embryo, cells do intercalate to establish the notochordal primordium. The stack of coins morphology arises subsequently, due to a continued intercalation supplemented by cell elongation and aligned cells sliding past one another (Wood & Thorogood, unpublished).

The second question concerns somitogenesis and the extent of cell re-arrangements during somite formation. This is of interest because the mechanisms by which segments are specified and segmental patterns are established are unknown; for instance, in what manner do intersomitic clefts form? Since Remak's (1855) observation that the sclerotome re-segments during the formation of the vertebral bodies, there have been a number of reports of apparent differences between the rostral and caudal halves of individual somites. Recently it has been shown that, in the avian embryo, neural crest cells and motor axons migrate through rostral but not caudal portions of somites and that only caudal but not rostral portions stain with peanut agglutinin (Stern *et al.* 1986). Furthermore, by transplantation of half-somites to orthotopic and heterotopic sites to produce compound somites along the axis, it can be shown that sclerotome cells from like somite halves will mix, but when unlike somite halves are juxtaposed no cell mixing is seen (Stern & Keynes, 1987). It has been suggested by these authors that rostrocaudal differences within intact somites have a role in the establishment and maintenance of tissue organization during sclerotome re-segmentation and the concomitant patterning of vertebrate, axonal outgrowth, ganglion formation and vasculature.

Such observations have fuelled speculation that the subdivision of somites may reflect compartmentalization of somites and that segmentation in vertebrates might parallel segmentation in other metamerically patterned organisms, such as *Drosophila* (Stern & Keynes, 1986). Is there any justification for the proposal that there might be a compartment boundary between rostral and caudal halves of somites, or at least within the sclerotomes? Such a compartment boundary, if it exists and if it is comparable with possible counterparts in *Drosophila*, will form because cells in adjacent compartments are unable to mix freely ('adjacent compartments' in this sense means the rostral and caudal halves of each sclerotome). Using DIC, we can observe not only somites as they form but also, using frame-by-frame analysis, monitor cell rearrangements using nuclei as reference points. Fig. 14 illustrates one typical sequence during the formation of the three most anterior somites and at the plane at which the sclerotome will form.

One of the most striking results to emerge from our analysis to date is that relative cell position within the paraxial mesenchyme remains remarkably constant during formation of somites and inter-somitic clefts. In other words, there is virtually *no* cell mixing. During the net medial movement of paraxial tissues as the notochord differentiates, a very small minority of cells do move, or are displaced relative to their neighbours (note for example cells 5 and 28 in Fig. 14), but whether this rare event has any significance or is just developmental 'noise' is not clear at present. Intersomitic clefts, like those formed earlier between presumptive notochord and paraxial mesenchyme, appear as lines of apparent de-adhesion between cells, initially quite irregular in form but gradually becoming more precisely defined. Within the future sclerotome region, these clefts form in a latero–medial fashion. Two further points emerge from such analysis. First, soon after their formation, somites are displaced anteriorly relative to the notochord, to the extent of approximately half a somite. Second, the most anterior pair of somites is a transient structure, disappearing at approximately the 8–10 somite stage.

The lack of detectable cell mixing across any putative compartment boundary between rostral and caudal halves of individual somites could be interpreted as supporting evidence for compartmentalization; however, it more probably reflects the *general* absence of cell re-arrangements during somitogenesis in the teleost embryo (Wood & Thorogood, unpublished). Whether this is a general feature of vertebrate somitogenesis is not clear, but it may be a consequence of the relatively small number of cells comprising a newly formed somite in the teleost embryo (when compared with somites in higher vertebrates).

CONCLUSION

Within the constraints of space we have chosen to review, briefly and with barest of experimental detail, the range of morphogenetic systems that can be studied directly *in vivo* in teleost embryos. The results described are phenomenological, correlating cell behaviour with key morphogenetic events. It is our contention that such 'baseline' information is a necessary prerequisite to the formulation of hypotheses (and their experimental testing) regarding the nature of the underlying molecular mechanisms.

We thank Barry Lockyer for photographic assistance, the Department of Teaching Media, Southampton University, for providing access to an analytical projector, and Professor L. Timmermans of Wageningen University, the Netherlands, for allowing us to refer to unpublished results arising from collaborative work.

REFERENCES

ABERCROMBIE, M. & HEAYSMAN, J. E. M. (1976). Invasive behaviour between sarcoma and fibroblast populations in cell culture. *J. natn. Cancer Inst.* **56**, 561–569.

BALLARD, W. (1966). The role of the cellular envelope in the morphogenetic movements of the teleost embryo. *J. exp. Zool.* **161**, 193–200.

BALLARD, W. (1973). Morphogenetic movements in *Salmo gairdneri*. *J. exp. Zool.* **184**, 27–48.

BALLARD, W. (1982). Morphogenetic movements and fate maps of vertebrates. *Am. Zool.* **21**, 391–399.

DUNN, G. A. & HEATH, J. P. (1976). A new hypothesis of contact guidance in tissue cells. *Expl Cell Res.* **101**, 1–14.

HARRISON, R. G. (1985). Die Entwickelung der unpaaren und paarigen Flossen der Teleostier. *Arch. mikrosc. Anat. EntwMech.* **46**, 500–578.

KELLER, R. E., DANILCHIK, K. M., GIMLICH, R. & SHIH, J. (1985). The function and mechanisms of convergent extension during gastrulation of *Xenopus laevis*. *J. Embryol. exp. Morph.* **89 Supplement**, 185–209.

KELLER, R. & HARDIN, J. (1987). Cell behaviour during active cell rearrangement: evidence and speculations. *J. Cell Sci. Suppl.* **8**, 369–393.

KELLER, R. E. & TRINKAUS, J. P. (1987). Rearrangement of enveloping layer cells without disruption of the epithelial permeability barrier as a factor in *Fundulus* epiboly. *Devl Biol.* **120**, 12–24.

NAKATSUJI, N. & JOHNSON, K. E. (1983). Conditioning of a culture substratum by the ectodermal layer promotes attachment and oriented locomotion by amphibian gastrula mesoderm cells. *J. Cell Sci.* **59**, 43–60.

O'HARA, P. T. & BUCK, R. C. (1979). Contact guidance *in vitro*. A light, transmission and scanning electron microscope study. *Expl Cell Res.* **121**, 235–249.

REMAK, R. (1855). *Untersuchungen uber die Entwicklung der Wirbelthiere*. Reimer: Berlin.

STERN, C. D. & KEYNES, R. J. (1986). Cell lineage and the formation and maintenance of half somites. In *Somites in Developing Embryos* (ed. R. Bellairs, D. A. Ede & J. W. Lash), pp. 147–159. New York: Plenum.

STERN, C. D. & KEYNES, R. J. (1987). Interactions between somite cells: the formation and maintenance of segment boundaries in the chick embryo. *Development* **99**, 261–272.

STERN, C. D., SISODIYA, S. M. & KEYNES, R. J. (1986). Interactions between neurites and somite cells: inhibition and stimulation of nerve growth in the chick embryo. *J. Embryol. exp. Morph.* **91**, 209–226.

TRINKAUS, J. P. (1951). A study of the mechanism of epiboly in the egg of *Fundulus heteroclitus*. *J. exp. Zool.* **118**, 269–320.

TRINKAUS, J. P. (1984). *Cells into Organs: The Forces that Shape the Embryo*, 2nd edn. New York: Prentice-Hall Inc.

TRINKAUS, J. P. & ERICKSON, C. A. (1983). Protrusive activity, mode and rate of locomotion, and pattern of adhesion of *Fundulus* deep cells during gastrulation. *J. exp. Zool.* **228**, 41–70.

WESSELLS, N. K. (1982). A catalogue of processes responsible for metazoan morphogenesis. In *Evolution and Development* (ed. J. T. Bonner), pp. 115–154. Dahlen Konferenzen: Springer-Verlag.

WOOD, A. T. (1982). Early pectoral fin development and morphogenesis of the apical ectodermal ridge in the killifish, *Aphyosemion scheeli*. *Anat. Rec.* **204**, 349–356.

WOOD, A. T. & THOROGOOD, P. (1984). An analysis of *in vivo* cell migration during teleost fin morphogenesis. *J. Cell Sci.* **66**, 205–222.

J. Cell Sci. Suppl. 8, 415–431 (1987)
Printed in Great Britain © The Company of Biologists Limited 1987

EARLY FUNCTIONAL DIFFERENTIATION IN THE CHICK EMBRYONIC DISC: INTERACTION BETWEEN MECHANICAL ACTIVITY AND EXTRACELLULAR MATRIX

PAVEL KUČERA* AND FLORIANNE MONNET-TSCHUDI
Institute of Physiology, Medical Faculty, University of Lausanne, Switzerland

SUMMARY

The mechanical behaviour of ectodermal cells in the area opaca and the supracellular organization of fibronectin in the adjacent extracellular matrix were studied in whole chick blastoderms developing *in vitro*. The pattern of spontaneous mechanical activity and its modification by immunoglobulins against fibronectin were determined using a real-time image-analysis system. The pattern of fibronectin was studied using immunocytochemical techniques.

It was found that the ectodermal cells in the area opaca actively develop a radially oriented contraction, which leads to a distension of the area pellucida from which the embryo develops. Abnormally increased tension resulted in perturbations of gastrulation and neurulation. An optimized mechanical equilibrium within the blastoderm seems to be necessary for normal development. Anti-fibronectin antibodies applied to the basal side of the blastoderm led rapidly and reversibly to an increase of tension in the contracted cells. This observation indicates that modifications of the extracellular matrix can be transmitted to cytoskeletal elements within adjacent cells.

The extracellular matrix of the area opaca contains fibronectin arranged in radially oriented fibrils. This orientation corresponds to the direction of migration of the mesodermal cells. Interestingly, the radial pattern of fibronectin is found in the regions where the ectodermal cells are contracted and develop radially oriented forces. This observation suggests that the supracellular assembly of the extracellular materials could be influenced by the mechanical activity of adjacent cells. Possible modulations of the supracellular organization of extracellular matrix by other factors, e.g. diffusible metabolites, is also discussed.

The presence of characteristically organized extracellular matrix components, of spatially differentiated cell activities and of reciprocal interactions between them makes the young chick blastoderm an excellent system for physiological studies of the coordinated cellular activities that lead to changes in form, complexity and function.

INTRODUCTION

The mechanical activity of cells is of fundamental importance in all morphogenetic processes. Embryogenesis, organogenesis, regeneration and malignant transformation are characterized by cell proliferation, shaping and migration, which are expressions of the mechanical work of cells. These phenomena, remarkably organized in space and in time, lead to the development of the complexity and order seen in all metazoan organisms.

* Author for correspondence at Institut de Physiologie, Rue du Bugnon 7, CH-1005 Lausanne, Switzerland.

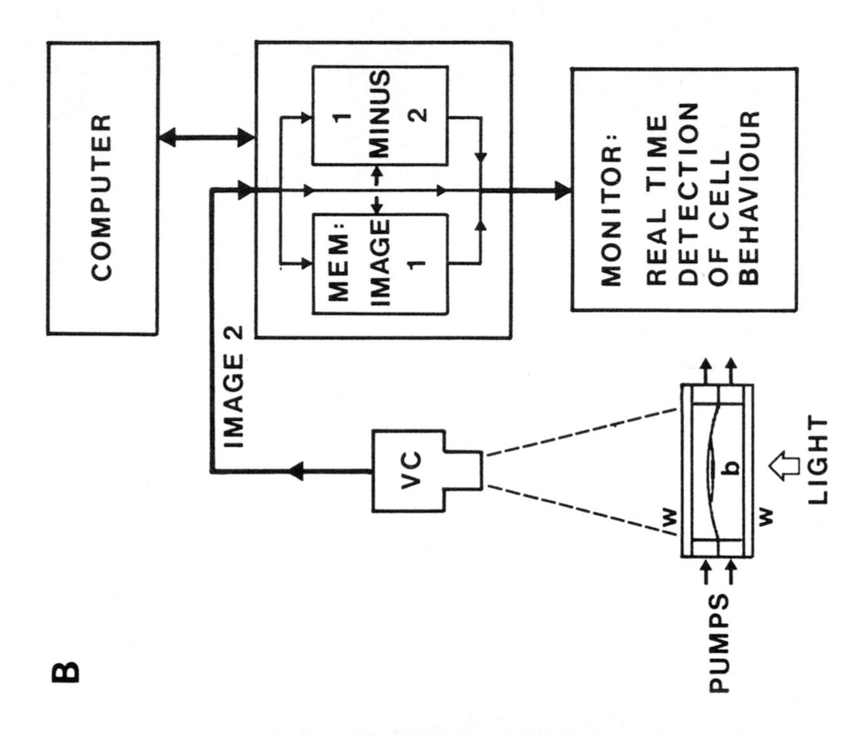
B
COMPUTER
MEM:
IMAGE
1
1
MINUS
2
MONITOR:
REAL TIME
DETECTION
OF CELL
BEHAVIOUR
IMAGE 2
VC
w
b
w
PUMPS
LIGHT

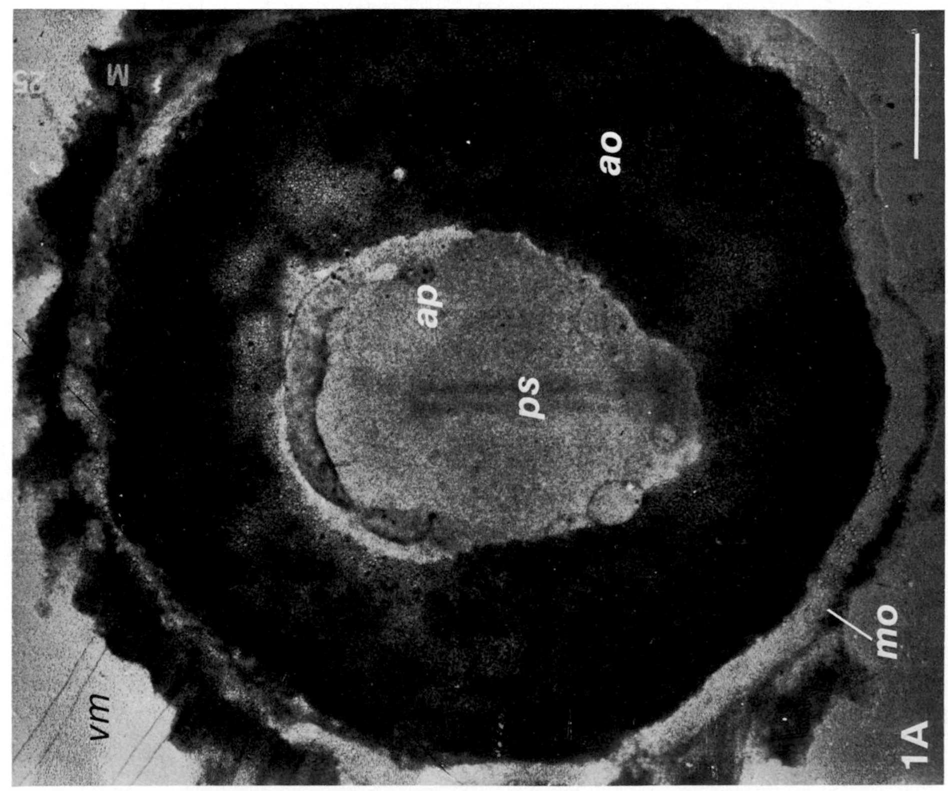
1A
vm
mo
ps
ap
ao

One of the most interesting problems in developmental biology is the way in which these phenomena are controlled. In particular, the factors controlling the migrations of embryonic cells have been extensively analysed. Mechanical and electrochemical conditions surrounding the migrating cell have been considered, and the role of the extracellular matrix (ECM) as a physical and chemical support for cell migration has been stressed (see e.g. Sanders, 1986, for a recent review). Among the ECM components, fibronectin has been extensively studied. In the chick embryo, fibronectin appears shortly before gastrulation in the ectodermal ECM (Mitrani & Farberov, 1982; Duband & Thiery, 1982). At gastrulation and neurulation, the distribution of fibronectin in the area pellucida (Critchley *et al.* 1979) and in the area opaca (Monnet-Tschudi *et al.* 1985) is similar to the organization of ECM as described by scanning electron microscopy (England & Wakely, 1977), and is compatible with at least some of the migrations observed in the embryo. In addition to these morphological data, results of *in vitro* and *in vivo* studies using antibodies to fibronectin (Rovasio *et al.* 1983; Boucaut *et al.* 1984) and oriented deposits of fibronectin (Turner *et al.* 1983) support the idea that the migration of embryonic cells is guided by the spatially organized ECM.

This hypothesis of guidance raises the question of the mechanisms responsible for the generation of the spatial organization of ECM. The intracellular synthesis and assembly of ECM precursors and their molecular forms have been studied in some detail (Engel *et al.* 1981; Gross & Bruns, 1984). However, the mechanisms of supracellular assembly of ECM are still very poorly understood (Trelstad & Birk, 1984). A reductionist approach, e.g. cell culture, has yielded only partial answers. The formation of the ECM must be studied *in situ* in a physiological cellular and extracellular environment where local constraints and interactions are operating. Under such conditions, the activities of the cell preceding or concomitant with the formation of ECM are of primary importance.

In this paper, we present experiments done in whole chick embryonic blastoderms cultured under controlled conditions. Our results suggest that the supracellular organization of ECM is controlled by mechanical forces developed in the blastoderm and that modifications of the ECM in turn influence the mechanical activities of the cells.

THE CHICK BLASTODERM IN 'AN ARTIFICIAL EGG'

After 18 h of incubation, the chick blastoderm (Fig. 1) is a discoidal structure that consists of a central region (area pellucida), which develops into the embryo, and a

Fig. 1. Recording the development of the chick blastoderm. A. Chick blastoderm at stage 4 HH excised from an egg preincubated for 18 h. *ap*, area pellucida; *ao*, area opaca; *mo*, margin of overgrowth; *ps*, primitive streak; *vm*, vitelline membrane. Bar, 1 mm. B. The blastoderm (b) is mounted in a chamber closed by two plan-parallel windows (w) and superfused with defined media. The temperature of the chamber is controlled. The image of the blastoderm is continuously recorded and digitized by a video camera (VC) and can be temporarily memorized and algebraically transformed by a video processor. This permits the detection and monitoring in real time, of any changes in the preparation. Off-line operations and storage are done by a host computer.

peripheral region (area opaca), which develops into the extraembryonic membranes. The peripheral cells of the area opaca attach to and migrate centrifugally on the vitelline membrane. This phenomenon is known as the expansion of the blastoderm (Bellairs, 1963). In a blastoderm excised from the egg, the area opaca can be carefully cleaned from the adhering yolk and becomes an almost transparent sheet of epithelial cells. Such blastoderms, still attached to the vitelline membrane, have been extensively used in our laboratory for physiological and toxicological studies. Our standardized technique and the *in vitro* development of the embryos have been described in detail (Kucera & Burnand, 1987*a*). The blastoderms are mounted in transparent incubation chambers, perfused with chemically defined media and maintained at 37·5 °C (see Fig. 1). Under such conditions the blastoderms develop normally, although at a slightly slower rate, for at least 3 additional days (reaching stage 17–18 HH).

The great advantage of these preparations is that development takes place mainly in the plane of the disc. Thus, morphogenesis, growth, metabolism, mechanical and electrical activity can be studied in different regions of the disc using sensitive and, if possible, non-invasive techniques (Kucera & Raddatz, 1980; Kucera & de Ribaupierre, 1982; Kucera & Burnand, 1987*b*; Raddatz *et al.* 1987). After physiological experiments the preparation can be fixed in its natural configuration for subsequent morphological evaluation.

MECHANICAL ACTIVITY WITHIN THE BLASTODERM

The mechanical forces generated by the cells in the blastoderm produce, on the one hand, active and passive tensions leading to changes in cell number, form and position (convection displacements). On the other hand, these forces lead to individual cell translocations (migrations). These phenomena are conveniently analysed by using real-time video processing (Fig. 1), which permits the detection of small, low-contrast and slow changes in the blastoderm. This is achieved by continuously comparing the past images (stored in live video-memories) with the present image. A powerful approach is to subtract the present image from the reference image and to monitor, for instance in a colour code, only those changes that happened in the corresponding time interval. This approach reveals those regions showing the greatest changes. In addition, the present and reference images can be alternatively flickered on the screen. This approach helps us to discriminate between tension (displacement of identified image points with conserved local topology) and movement (displacements with changes in local topology) (Kucera & Burnand, 1987*b*).

The first mechanical phenomenon observed upon incubation is the appearance within the blastoderm of radially oriented tension. This is illustrated in Fig. 2. The images represented in Fig. 2A–C were recorded, respectively, at the beginning of incubation (22 °C), after 15 min of incubation (32 °C) and after 40 min of incubation (37 °C). Although some changes in the preparation can be detected from these original images, a precise and rapid analysis is easily performed using the differential images shown in Fig. 2E,F. These differences are displayed using shades of grey: no difference is expressed in an intermediate grey, positive differences (increase in opacity) in lighter tones and negative differences (decrease in opacity) in darker tones. The interpretation of these differences (e.g. displacement of thickening) at a given frame-line, can be facilitated by evaluation of transmission profiles and their differences. Such profiles are shown in Figs 2D and 6.

Fig. 2E shows that, upon warming, the area pellucida with the adjacent yolk ring became larger (white contour) and more transparent while, in contrast, the diameter of the blastoderm decreased slightly (black contour). As the margin of the blastoderm was attached to the vitelline membrane, which was itself fixed to the chamber, the decrease in diameter of the blastoderm must mean that the membrane had been stretched. Thus tension had been established in the system. This tension was generated in the area opaca. Fig. 2E shows that, at constant temperature (37·5 °C), the periphery of the blastodisc had already started to expand (white narrow contour). The enlargement of the area pellucida and the retraction of the area opaca continued to develop and were of greater amplitude than the expansion (large white band). Upon further incubation the margin of the blastoderm expanded at about 1–3 μm min^{-1} and the blastoderm remained under tension, at least until stage 8, the oldest stage studied.

Thus the activation of cellular metabolism by warming results in the development of mechanical tension radially oriented in the plane of the blastoderm and corresponding to at least 1×10^4 to 4×10^4 dyne cm^2, which is a value about 100 times lower than the maximal isometric tension developed by differentiated muscle cells (Kucera & Burnand, 1987*b*). It has been shown that this tension originates in the cells located in the area opaca. These cells actively contract and thereby stretch the inner region of the area opaca and the area pellucida, and also the vitelline membrane. Irreversible relaxation was observed in experiments using colchicine and cytochalasin, which suggests that the contraction is dependent on both microtubules and microfilaments. Reversible relaxation resulted from cooling and from anoxia, which suggests that the contraction is dependent on aerobic energy metabolism (Kucera & Burnand, 1987*b*). The energy spent on the contraction seems to be high, since blastodiscs that were detached from the vitelline membrane and maintained at 37·5 °C decreased their glucose uptake by about 50 % (Kucera *et al.* 1984; Baroffio, 1985).

Tension was observed in all (more than 100) the blastoderms studied so far. At stage 4, maximal contraction of the cells was observed in the intermediate zone of the area opaca. At stages 5 and 6, the contracting cells formed a band about 1–2 mm wide at the periphery of area opaca. The edge cells, which attach the blastoderm to the vitelline membrane, did not contract.

In blastoderms submitted to additional passive tension (prestretching of the vitelline membrane), the expansion of the blastoderm was either much slower or inhibited and morphogenetic movements in the area pellucida were impaired: the edges of the primitive streak became separated, formation of the notochord was delayed and neurulation was incomplete (Kucera & Burnand, 1987*b*). In some cases,

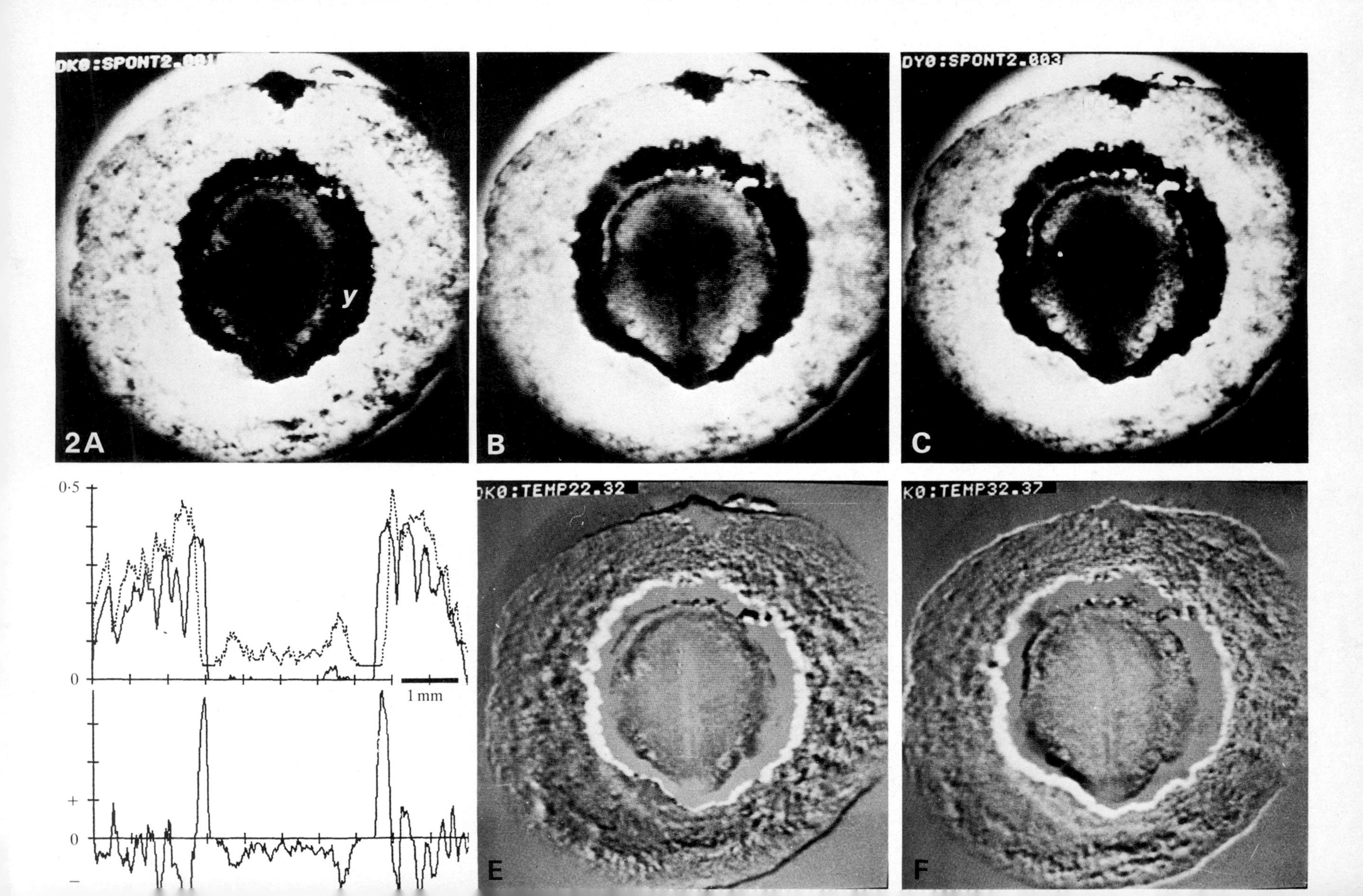
DK0:SPONT2.0
2A
y
B
DY0:SPONT2.003
C
0·5
0
1 mm
+
0
–
DK0:TEMP22.32
E
K0:TEMP32.37
F

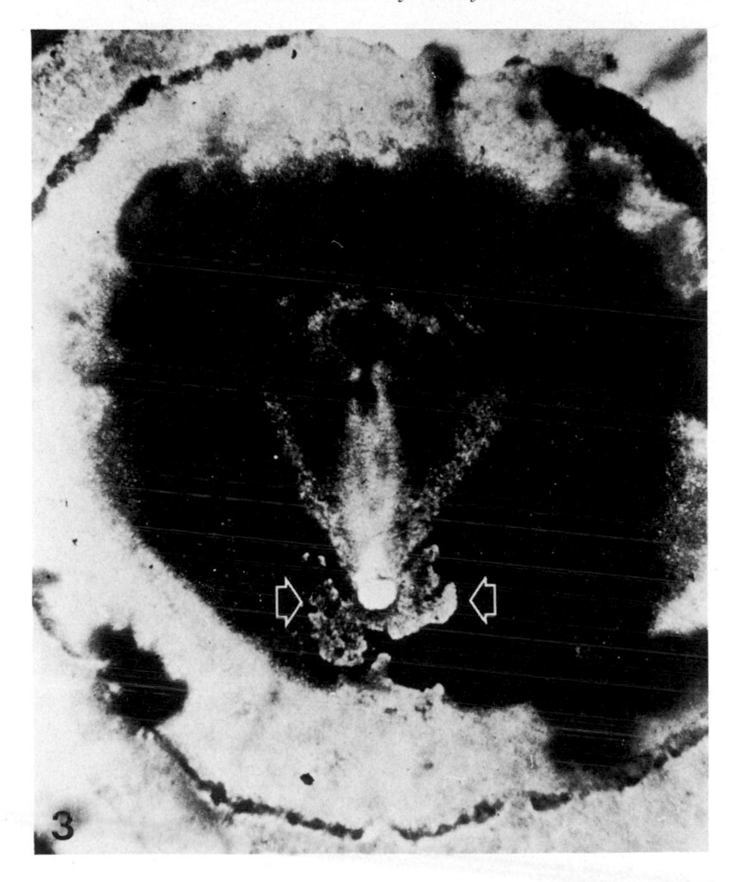

Fig. 3. Effects of increased tension on development. The vitelline membrane of this blastoderm, explanted at stage 4, was overstretched in the chamber. The increased tension in the blastoderm resulted in decreased expansion rate, separation of the edges of the primitive streak, delayed gastrulation and incomplete neurulation. Fenestrations (arrows) appeared in the posterior part of area pellucida. Compare with Fig. 5.

mesodermal and endodermal layers became extremely thin and even fenestrated. This was consistently observed only around the posterior half of the primitive streak (Fig. 3). The anterior half of the area pellucida seemed to be protected against the

---

Fig. 2. Tension generated in the blastoderm upon metabolic activation as evaluated by real-time image analysis. A–C. Images of the blastoderm taken before incubation (22°C), after 15 min (32°C) and after 40 min (37°C) of incubation, respectively. *y*, yolk ring surrounding the area pellucida. D. Top: transmission profiles at the central frame-line of image A (continuous line) and B (dotted line, shown shifted by 0·05); bottom: the difference between these profiles. Positive and negative differences result from increases and decreases in opacity. The sharp peaks correspond to displacements of high contrast components. E. Difference between images A and B. Increase and decrease in opacity are displayed in lighter and darker shades of grey, respectively. The white zone results from a centrifugal displacement of the yolk ring surrounding area pellucida. The black contour at the periphery corresponds to a shrinkage of the blastoderm. These changes are due to tension generated in the area opaca. F. Difference between images B and C. The outer white contour indicates the expansion of blastoderm, the inner white zone a further stretching of the ara pellucida.

stretching. This is shown schematically in Fig. 5: in the anterior half, passive tension is distributed along the border of the area pellucida, in the posterior half, the distension also includes the cells within the area pellucida. Fig. 5 also shows schematically that myosin was found only in the cells of the inner zone of area opaca, i.e. the zone that withstands the tension generated at the periphery (Monnet-Tschudi & Kucera, unpublished data).

SUPRACELLULAR ORGANIZATION OF THE EXTRACELLULAR MATRIX

The distribution of fibronectin-like immunoreactivity in the area opaca of the blastoderms from stage 4 to stage 6 was studied using techniques of immunofluorescence and protein A coupled to colloidal gold (Monnet-Tschudi *et al.* 1985). Fibronectin was found to be associated with the ectodermal basement membrane and formed a fibrillar network, which showed characteristic changes between the central area and the peripheral border of the area opaca. The fluorescence decreased from the centre to the periphery, suggesting a concentric gradient of fibronectin density in the basement membrane. In all stages studied, radially oriented and densely packed fibrils were observed. As shown in Fig. 4 these fibrils spanned many cell diameters and sometimes were up to 1 mm long. This radial pattern of fibronectin was constantly found at the peripheral zone of the area opaca as is schematically depicted in Fig. 5. In addition to its presence in the ectodermal basement membrane, fibronectin was also found all around actively moving cells, i.e. the edge cells and the mesoblastic cells crawling on the basement membrane (Monnet-Tschudi *et al.* 1985).

In order to test the possible interactions between fibronectin and the ectodermal cells that secrete it, we used specific antibodies against chicken fibronectin (Calbiochem) and $F(ab')_2$ fragments prepared from them: 1 mg of the original antibody was dialysed overnight against sodium acetate buffer (20 mM, pH 4·5) and then exposed to pepsin immobilized on agarose beads (Pierce Chemicals Company, 2250 units) for 2 h at 37 °C. Beads were removed by centrifugation and the supernatant was deposited on a protein A–agarose column (Pierce Chemical Company). Elution was carried out in Tris · HCl buffer (10 mM, pH 7·5) and two fractions were collected. The first fraction contained the digested $F(ab')_2$ fragment, and the second probably the Fc fragments and non-digested immunoglobulins. The final dilution of these fractions was 1:20 corresponding to that used with the intact immunoglobulins. In addition, 3 ml of the first fraction was absorbed with 1 mg of bovine fibronectin (Calbiochem) at 37 °C for 1 h. This solution was transferred into a Costar culture flask and incubated at 37 °C for 3 h to remove the unbound fibronectin. The supernatant was concentrated in Centricon 10 (Amicon) to recover the initial dilution (1:20). The absorption of $F(ab')_2$ fragments, as checked by polyacrylamide gel electrophoresis, was about 98 %.

These solutions, pre-warmed to 37·5 °C were applied by perfusion to the ventral side of blastoderms already expanding in the chamber and the effects were studied by real-time image analysis. Eighteen blastoderms were evaluated in this study.

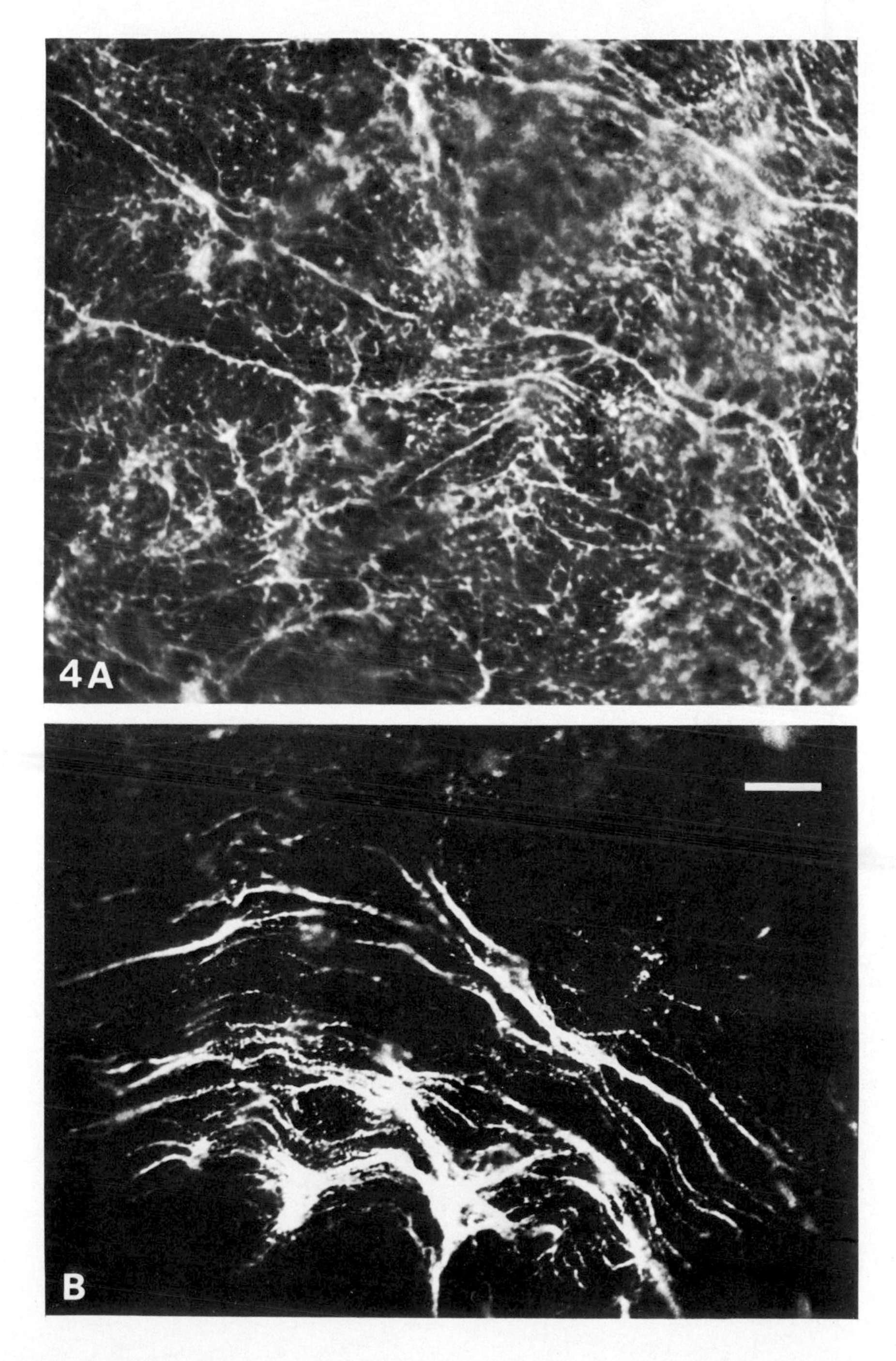

Fig. 4. Pattern of fibronectin-containing fibrils in the area opaca. A. Fibronectin-like immunoreactivity (immunofluorescence) associated with finely woven radially oriented fibrils. This arrangement was characteristic of the basement membrane at the outer zone of the area opaca (see Fig. 5). B. Fibronectin-containing arcuate fibrils from the anterior border of the area pellucida (see Fig. 5). Bar, 25 μm.

The anti-fibronectin and its $F(ab')_2$ fraction produced a reaction that was maximal within 5–10 min, and very similar to that observed upon warming. The area pellucida became enlarged, the area opaca became narrower and the diameter of the blastodisc remained the same or was slightly decreased (see Fig. 6). Thus the reaction between the antibodies and the fibronectin in the blastoderm induced an additional contraction of the cells in the area opaca and distension in the area pellucida. The amplitude of this response started to decrease after about 20 min. Upon washing, the development of the blastoderm resumed at a normal rate. The

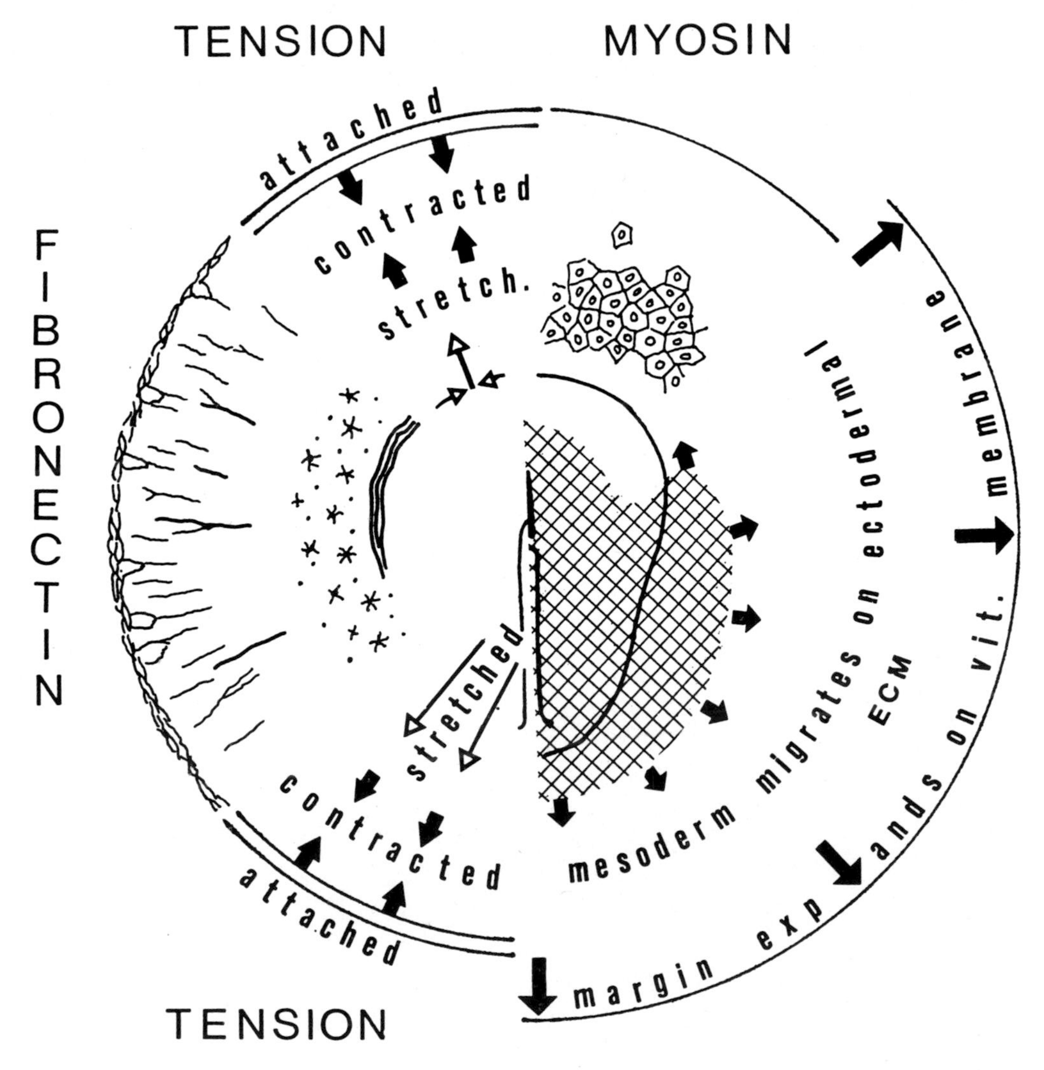

Fig. 5. Schematic comparison of patterns of mechanical activity and organization of extracellular matrix in the area opaca of the chick blastoderm. The left-hand side of the figure depicts the organization of the ECM and the mechanical equilibrium between active (black arrows) and passive (white arrows) forces generated in the ectoderm. The right-hand side depicts active cell migrations. The cross-hatched area represents the mesoderm.

response to the anti-fibronectin $F(ab')_2$ fragments seems to be specific as it was not obtained with the second fraction or with the absorbed first fraction.

DISCUSSION

The following observations are of particular interest: (1) The period of gastrulation and neurulation is characterized by development within the blastoderm of mechanical tension.

The existence of tension in the blastoderm has previously been inferred from the fact that blastoderms that have been detached from the vitelline membrane shrink. The origin of tension in the blastoderm has been discussed by Bellairs, (1963). She proposed that the edge cells of the blastoderm, while migrating on the internal surface of vitelline membrane, also pull the cells within the blastoderm. This idea was adopted also by Downie, who suggested that the tension in the blastoderm results from an imbalance between the migration rate of the edge of the blastoderm and the proliferation rate within it (Downie, 1976). However, the tension has not previously been measured and analysed *in vivo*.

Our results do not support the previous explanations. We have demonstrated that tension is generated actively by the contraction of cells situated in the intermediate and/or peripheral zone of the area opaca. As a result of this contraction the area pellucida, with the adjacent border tightly adhering to the germ wall, is under passive tensile stress. The maximally strained region is the posterior part of the primitive streak (see Figs 3, 5). Tension appears as soon as the cell metabolism is activated by increasing the temperature of incubation 20–30 min before the margin starts to migrate. Furthermore, in strongly contracting blastoderms the edge cells may initially recede and only later resume expansion (Kucera & Burnand, 1987*b*). Finally, we have never observed a contraction within the zone of attachment itself. As far as the role of tension is concerned, Bellairs *et al.* (1967) found that a decrease in tension (due to slacking of the vitelline membrane) did not influence the rate of cell proliferation but led to an increased number of dead cells in the blastoderm and to poor differentiation of the embryo. We have found that experimentally increased tension leads to abnormal gastrulation and neurulation.

Thus it seems that normal development of the embryo depends on an optimized mechanical equilibrium between the regions that generate the tension and those that are subjected to it. § (2) The characteristic organization of extracellular matrix, regularly found in the area opaca, could arise as a result of several mechanisms.

We propose that the mechanical activity of the cells secreting ECM materials might be an important factor modulating the *in situ* supracellular assembly of ECM components. This idea is based on the fact that a radial pattern of fibronectin fibrils (Fig. 4) is found in those regions that also contract in a radial direction (see Fig. 5). Also, the arcuate fibronectin fibrils (Fig. 4) described by Critchley *et al.* (1979) are oriented along the lines of the mechanical forces that prevent the distension of the anterior part of area pellucida (see Fig. 5). Our hypothesis, based on observations made in a whole developing organism, is strongly supported by the data obtained

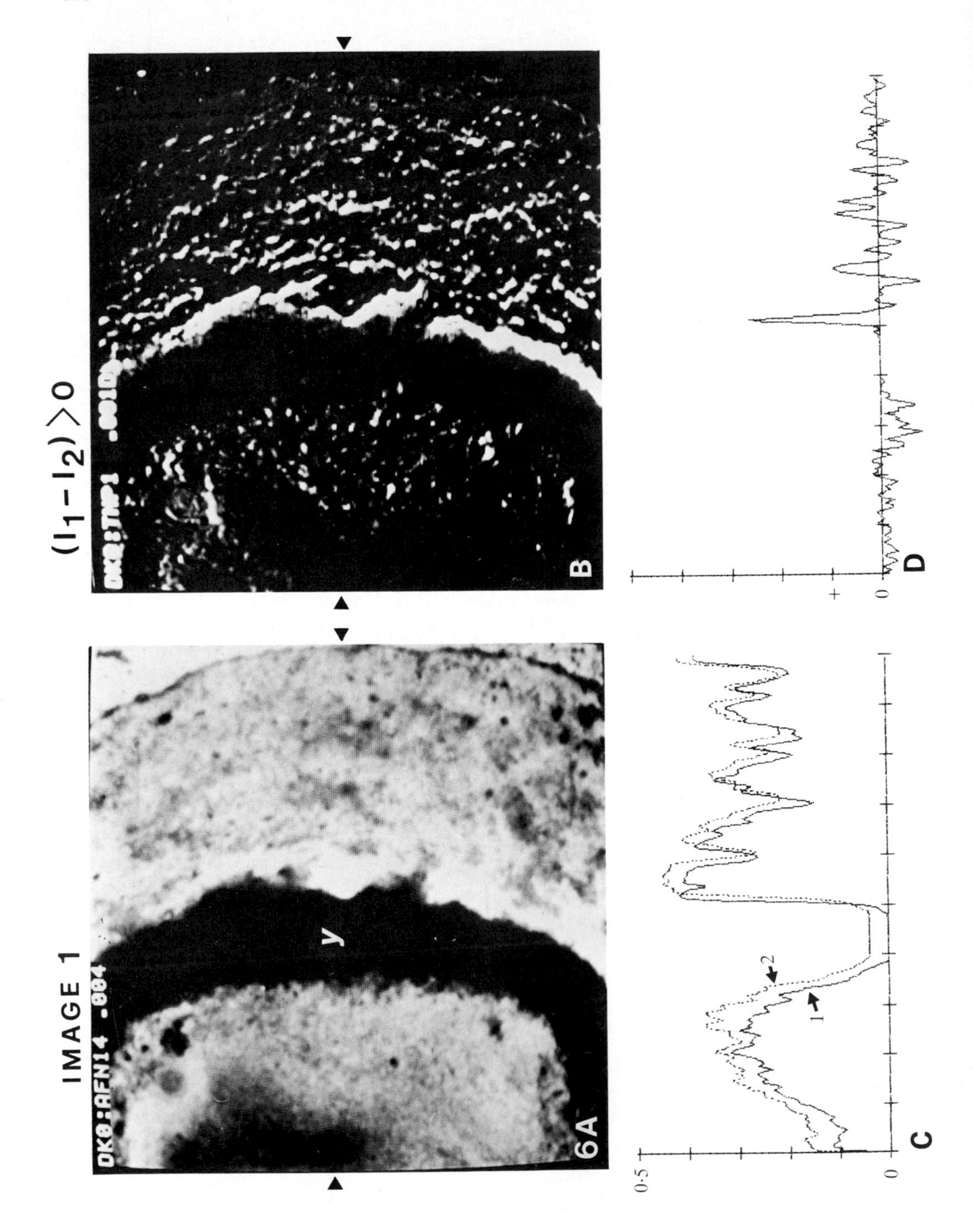
IMAGE 1
$(I_1 - I_2) > 0$
6A
y
B
C
D
0.5
0
+
0
1
2

from experiments *in vitro*. Thus, it has been shown that fibronectin-containing fibres, found around fibroblasts cultured *in vitro*, are oriented in line with bundles of intracellular microfilaments (Singer, 1979). Moreover, Harris and collaborators have elegantly demonstrated that collagen fibrils, at first randomly dispersed in culture media, can be aligned by mechanical forces produced by fibroblasts adhering to them (Harris *et al.* 1981; Harris, 1986).

Another parameter controlling the *in situ* modelling of ECM could be a non-uniform distribution of factors known to modulate the conformation and interaction of proteins, e.g. pH and ionic strength. We have found that the area pellucida depends more on aerobic glycolysis (lactate production in presence of oxygen) whilst the area opaca depends more on respiration (Kucera *et al.* 1984; Baroffio, 1985). We have also shown (Raddatz *et al.* 1987) that the area pellucida and the adjacent posterolateral border produce much more CO_2 than the area opaca. An example of such a CO_2 production pattern is illustrated in Fig. 7.

These results suggest that catabolites of glucose (e.g. protons, lactate, CO_2) accumulate in the narrow sub-blastodermal space. Concentration gradients of these metabolites could modulate not only the supramolecular assembly of the ECM precursors but also the activity of cells. It is unlikely that such gradients would be equilibrated by diffusion of these molecules across (CO_2) and under (lactate) the blastoderm, because the metabolism during this period continues to increase rapidly (Kucera & Raddatz, 1980; Raddatz & Kucera, 1983) and the rate of exchange due to convection has not been established. We do not know the values of pH under the area opaca but in the embryos during somitogenesis, the pH of the intraembryonic interstitial space differs by up to 0·5 pH unit with respect to the site of measurement (Gillespie & McHanwell, 1987).

Finally, the spatial organization of fibronectin could also be modulated by a differential distribution of cell surface receptor for fibronectin as suggested by Lee *et al.* (1984). § (3) The migrations of mesoblastic cells and, later, of the edge of area vasculosa have the same orientation as that of fibronectin fibrils in the same area.

This suggests that the migrating cells use these fibrils as support. The arguments in favour of this idea come from observations of the presence of fibronectin in the expanding edge of the area vasculosa (Mayer *et al.* 1981) and from our own immunoelectron microscopic study showing individual migrating mesoblastic cells attached to the fibronectin-containing fibrils in the basement membrane (Monnet-

Fig. 6. Response of the blastoderm to anti-fibronectin as evaluated by real-time video processor. A. Image of a portion of a stage 5 blastodisc recorded before application of the antibody. Arrowheads locate frame-line 121. *y*, yolk ring surrounding the area pellucida. B. Transmission profiles at line 121 obtained from image 1 (continuous line) and image 2 (not shown) recorded 20 min after application of anti-fibronectin $F(ab')_2$ fraction (dotted line, shown shifted by 0·05). C. Positive differences (increases in opacity) between images 1 and 2. The white zones correspond to centrifugal displacements of high-contrast components in the preparation (e.g. the periphery of the yolk ring). The amplitude of these displacements decreases from the centre to the periphery of the area opaca. The anti-fibronectin thus produced a shrinkage of the area opaca and an enlargement of the area pellucida. D. Difference between the profiles at line 121 from images 1 and 2. The sharp peaks correspond to displacements of high-contrast components.

Tschudi *et al.* 1985). Fibrillar supports are known to be able to align cells that attach to them (Dunn & Heath, 1976) and to modify their motility (Kolega, 1986) but they do not control the direction of subsequent movements. In the area opaca, at least three factors could provide directional information to the migrating cells: (a) the gradients of metabolites (e.g. lactate and CO_2) discussed above; (b) the concentration of fibronectin in the ECM, which probably decreases from the centre to the periphery of the area opaca as indicated by the decreasing density of immunofluorescence staining (Monnet-Tschudi *et al.* 1985); (c) the gradient of cell population density; the density of mesodermal cells decreases from the centre to the periphery of the area opaca. This latter mechanism has been shown to operate during the migration of neural crest cells (Rovasio *et al.* 1983). § (4) The reaction of antifibronectin with the blastoderm (presumably with the fibronectin in the ECM) enhances the contraction of cells in the area opaca and therefore leads to modifications in the shape of the cells.

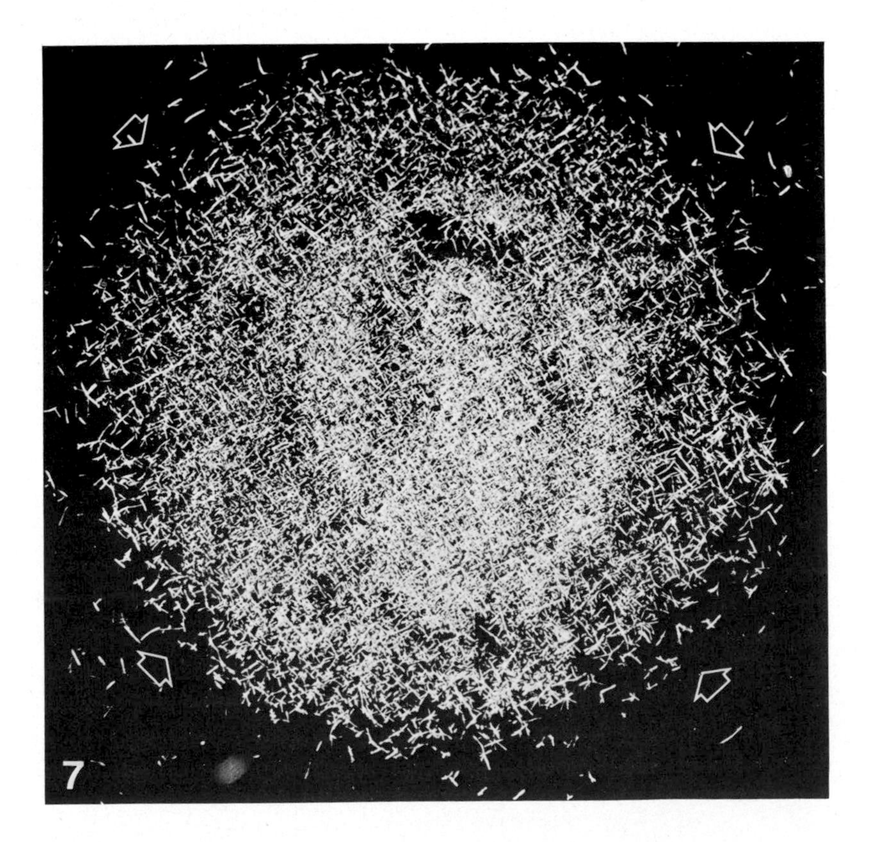

Fig. 7. Pattern of CO_2 production in the blastoderm. The vitelline membrane with the blastoderm was covered by a thin transparent silicone membrane permitting perfusion of the chamber by $Ba(OH)_2$. The CO_2 produced during a 3-h incubation precipitated onto the silicone membrane as $BaCO_3$. The blastoderm was removed and the crystals photographed in polarized light. The limits of the blastoderm are indicated by arrows. To a first approximation, the CO_2 pattern corresponds to the distribution of mesoderm in the blastoderm (cf. Fig. 5). The margin of blastoderm does not seem to produce CO_2.

This observation is consistent with that of Grinnell *et al.* (1982), who described a correlation between cell shape and the pattern of fibronectin distribution. Similarly, Nagata *et al.* (1985) have shown that inhibiting cell interactions with fibronectin prevents changes in cell shape occurring in control conditions.

The effect of anti-fibronectin could be due to passive or active mechanisms. The molecules of ECM have particular shapes and flexibility (see e.g. Engel *et al.* 1981). Binding of the antibody to fibronectin could result in a conformational change in the fibronectin and consequently of the ECM. However, the mechanical forces directly resulting from such a conformational change would probably be insufficient to produce the observed changes in the mechanical equilibrium, i.e. elongations and shortenings amounting to 16% (Kucera & Burnand, 1987*b*). Moreover, the basement membrane of the area opaca is very thin (about 10–100 nm) when compared with the thickness of the adjacent cells (about 10–15 μm). On the other hand, it is known that extracellular fibronectin is coupled by means of a membrane receptor or a transmembrane protein to intracellular actin filaments (Hynes & Yamada, 1982; Pierschbacher *et al.* 1981; Chen *et al.* 1985; Rogalski & Singer, 1985). Therefore, we think that the response to anti-fibronectin is due to transmembrane activation of cytoskeletal elements. If this conclusion is confirmed, the area opaca becomes a very suitable subject for studies of the transmission of signals between extracellular matrix and cells.

CONCLUSION

The young chick blastoderm, in particular the area opaca, represents a society of embryonic cells undergoing structural and functional differentiation. This is illustrated by the remarkable spatial organization of metabolic activity, mechanical activity and formation of extracellular matrix.

These activities are probably closely interrelated: the pattern of the mechanical behaviour of the cells seems to condition the supracellular arrangement of the extracellular matrix. In turn, the physicochemical state of the extracellular matrix seems to modulate the cytoskeleton and thereby the shape and probably also the movement of the cells. The interactions between the cells and the matrix might also be dependent on gradients of diffusible metabolites produced by the cells themselves.

In such a dynamic and unsteady system, the intimate interactions of cells with their environment would constantly determine the local physical and chemical conditions. These conditions would provide the information for the ordered cell migrations necessary for the generation of new cell combinations and the expression of new characters.

We believe that the gastrulating chick blastoderm is an excellent system for experimental studies of the cascade of events that leads to modifications in structural complexity and to functional diversification.

We thank Mrs M. B. Burnand, Miss D. Bays and Miss M. Capt for expert technical help. This work was supported by grant 3.418–0.86 from the Swiss National Science Foundation.

REFERENCES

Baroffio, A. (1985). Etude de métabolisme du glucose pendant le développement précoce de l'embryon de poulet a l'aide d'une adaptation de la méthode du 2-désoxyglucose. Thesis, University of Lausanne.

Bellairs, R. (1963). Differentiation of the yolk sac of the chick studied by electron microscopy. *J. Embryol. exp. Morph.* **11**, 201–225.

Bellairs, R., Bromham, D. R. & Wylie, C. C. (1967). The influence of the area opaca on the development of the young chick embryo. *J. Embryol. exp. Morph.* **17**, 197–212.

Boucat, J. C., Darribere, T., Boulekbach, H. & Thiery, J. P. (1984). Prevention of gastrulation but not neurulation by antibodies to fibronectin in amphibian embryos. *Nature, Lond.* **307**, 364–367.

Chen, W.-T., Hasegawa, E., Hasegawa, T., Weinstock, C. & Yamada, K. (1985). Development of cell surface linkage complexes in cultured fibroblasts. *J. Cell Biol.* **100**, 1103–1114.

Critchley, D. R., England, M. A., Wakely, J. & Hynes, R O. (1979). Distribution of fibronectin in the ectoderm of gastrulating chick embryo. *Nature, Lond.* **280**, 498–500.

Downie, J. R. (1976). The mechanism of chick blastoderm expansion. *J. Embryol. exp. Morph.* **35**, 559–575.

Duband, J. L. & Thiery, J. P. (1982). Appearance and distribution of fibronectin during chick embryo gastrulation and neurulation. *Devl Biol.* **94**, 337–350.

Dunn, G. A. & Heath, J. P. (1976). A new hypothesis of contact guidance in tissue cells. *Expl Cell Res.* **101**, 1–14.

Engel, J., Odermatt, E., Engel, A., Madri, J., Furthmayr, H., Rohde, H. & Timpl, R. (1981). Shapes, domain organizations and flexibility of laminin and fibronectin, two multifunctional proteins of the extracellular matrix. *J. molec. Biol.* **150**, 97–120.

England, M. & Wakely, J. (1977). Scanning electron microscopy of the development of the mesoderm layers in chick embryos. *Anat. Embryol.* **150**, 291–300.

Gillespie, J. I. & McHanwell, S. (1987). Measurements of intraembryonic pH during the early stages of development in the chick embryo. *Cell Tiss. Res.* **247**, 445–451.

Grinnell, F., Head, J. & Hoffpanir, J. (1982). Fibronectin and cell shape *in vivo*: studies on the endometrium during pregnancy. *J. Cell Biol.* **94**, 597–606.

Gross, J. & Bruns, R. (1984). Another look at fibrillogenesis. In *The Role of Extracellular Matrix in Development* (ed. R. L. Trelstad), pp. 479–512. New York: A. R. Liss.

Harris, A. K. (1986). Cell traction in relationship to morphogenesis and malignancy. In *The Cell Surface in Development and Cancer* (ed. M. S. Steinberg), pp. 339–357, New York: Plenum.

Harris, A. K., Stopak, D. & Wild, P. (1981). Fibroblast tension as a mechanism for collagen morphogenesis. *Nature, Lond.* **290**, 249–251.

Hynes, R. O. & Yamada, K. M. (1982). Fibronectins: multifunctional modular glycoproteins. *J. Cell Biol.* **95**, 369–377.

Kolega, J. (1986). Effects of mechanical tension on protrusive activity and microfilament and intermediate filament organization in an epithelium moving in culture. *J. Cell Biol.* **102**, 1400–1411.

Kucera, P. & Burnand, M. B. (1987*a*). A routine teratogenicity test that uses chick embryos *in vitro*. *Teratogen, Carcinogen, Mutagen* (in press).

Kucera, P. & Burnand, M. B. (1987*b*). Mechanical tension and movement in the chick blastoderm as studied by real time image analysis. *J. exp. Zool. Suppl. 1*, 329–339.

Kucera, P. & de Ribaupierre, Y. (1982). *In situ* recording of mechanical behaviour of cells in the chick embryo. In *Embryonic Development,* part B, *Cellular Aspects* (ed. M. M. Burger & R. Weber), pp. 33–444.

Kucera, P. & Raddatz, E. (1980). Spatiotemporal measurements of the oxygen uptake in the developing chick embryo. *Resp. Physiol.* **39**, 199–215.

Kucera, P., Raddatz, E. & Baroffio, A. (1984). Oxygen and glucose uptakes in the early chick embryo. In *Respiration and Metabolism of Embryonic Vertebrates* (ed. R. S. Seymour), pp. 299–309. Dordrecht, Boston, London: Dr W. Jung.

Lee, G., Hynes, R. & Kirschner, M. (1984). Temporal and spatial regulation of fibronectin in early *Xenopus* development. *Cell* **36**, 729–740.

MAYER, B., HAY, E. D. & HYNES, R. O. (1981). Immunocytochemical localization of fibronectin in embryonic chick trunk and area vasculosa. *Devl Biol.* **82**, 267–286.

MITRANI, E. & FARBEROV, A. (1982). Fibronectin expression during the processes leading to axis formation in the chick embryo. *Devl Biol.* **91**, 197–201.

MONNET-TSCHUDI, F., FAVROD, P., BURNAND, M. B., VERDAN, C. & KUCERA, P. (1985). Fibronectin in the area opaca of the young chick embryo. *Cell Tiss. Res.* **241**, 85–92.

NAGATA, K., HUMPHRIES, M., OLDEN, K. & YAMADA, K. (1985). Collagen can modulate cell interactions with fibronectin. *J. Cell Biol.* **101**, 386–394.

PIERSCHBACHER, M., HAYMAN, E. & RUOSLAHTI, E. (1981). Location of the cell-attachment site in fibronectin with monoclonal antibodies and proteolytic fragments of the molecule. *Cell* **26**, 259–267.

RADDATZ, E. & KUCERA, P. (1983). Mapping of the oxidative activity in the gastrulating chick embryo. *Resp. Physiol.* **51**, 153–166.

RADDATZ, E., KUCERA, P. & DE RIBAUPIERRE, Y. (1987). Micromeasurements of total and regional CO_2 productions in the one-day-old chick embryo. *Resp. Physiol.* (in press).

ROGALSKI, A. & SINGER, S. J. (1985). An integral glycoprotein associated with membrane attachment sites of actin microfilaments. *J. Cell Biol.* **101**, 785–801.

ROVASIO, R. A., DELOUVEE, A., YAMADA, K. M., TIMPL, R. & THIERY, J. P. (1983). Neural crest cell migrations: requirements for exogeneous fibronectin and high cell density. *J. Cell Biol.* **96**, 463–473.

SANDERS, E. J. (1986). Cytochemistry of the cell surface and extracellular matrix during early embryonic development. *Progr. Histochem. Cytochem.* **16**, 1–57.

SINGER, I. I. (1979). The fibronexus: A transmembrane association of fibronectin-containing fibres and bundles of 5 nm microfilaments in hamster and human fibroblasts. *Cell* **16**, 675–685.

TRELSTAD, R. L. & BIRK, D. E. (1984). Collagen fibril assembly at the surface of polarized cells. In *The Role of Extracellular Matrix in Development* (ed. R. L. Trelstad), pp. 513–543. New York: A. R. Liss.

TURNER, D.C., LAWTON, J., DOLLENMEIER, P. & CHIQUET, M. (1983). Guidance of myogenic cell migration by oriented deposits of fibronectin. *Devl Biol.* **95**, 497–504.

J. Cell Sci. Suppl. 8, 433–449 (1987)
Printed in Great Britain © The Company of Biologists Limited 1987

FLUIDITY OF THE NEURAL EPITHELIUM DURING FOREBRAIN FORMATION IN RAT EMBRYOS

GILLIAN MORRISS-KAY AND FIONA TUCKETT
Department of Human Anatomy, South Parks Road, Oxford OX1 3QX, UK

SUMMARY

During neurulation in rat embryos, the forebrain grows more rapidly than can be accounted for by intrinsic cell division alone, while the adjacent midbrain/rostral hindbrain maintains a constant cell number despite a high mitotic index (the cell cycle time is 6 h throughout the neural epithelium). We have proposed that neuroepithelial cells flow in a rostral direction within the midbrain/rostral hindbrain region, towards and into the rapidly expanding forebrain. Evidence in support of this hypothesis is provided by cell-labelling studies: labelled neuroepithelial cells were injected into specific sites in the midbrain or rostral hindbrain neuroepithelium of unlabelled embryos; after culture of these embryos for 24 h, the labelled cells were found in positions rostral to the injection sites.

In the midbrain/rostral hindbrain region, mitotic spindles were found to be predominantly orientated parallel with the long axis of the embryo; transversely orientated spindles were more frequently observed close to the lateral edges than more medially. Neural crest cells emigrate from the lateral edges during neurulation. These observations suggest that mitotic spindle orientation reflects the direction of cell movement: in the lateral region movement towards the lateral edge would maintain cell number in the transverse plane as neural crest cells emigrate; elsewhere, cells are moving mainly in the longitudinal plane, towards the forebrain. The possible causal relationship between cell movement and mitotic spindle orientation is discussed.

Cell flow within the intact neural epithelium is compared with cell flow in the intestinal villus epithelium. Other types of epithelial cell movement observed in the cranial neural epithelium during neurulation include expansion and shrinkage of the epithelial surface associated with change of cell shape and microfilament-mediated curvature. Cell rearrangement involving exchange of neighbours and cell movement towards and into a site of epithelio–mesenchymal conversion are also implicated.

INTRODUCTION

Epithelial morphogenesis is an important feature of development in all multicellular organisms. For some years now we have been studying the morphogenesis of the cranial neural epithelium of rodent embryos, particularly during the period of neural tube formation and neural crest cell emigration. Scanning electron micrographs of the neural epithelium during neurulation are shown in Fig. 1. Like the embryo as a whole, the neural epithelium differentiates in a cranio–caudal sequence; this directional developmental sequence is also observed in formation of the neural tube in the spinal region, though not in the head. The cranial neural epithelium differs from the spinal part in its pattern of growth and morphogenesis, presaging the differences in size and complexity between the brain and spinal cord of the adult

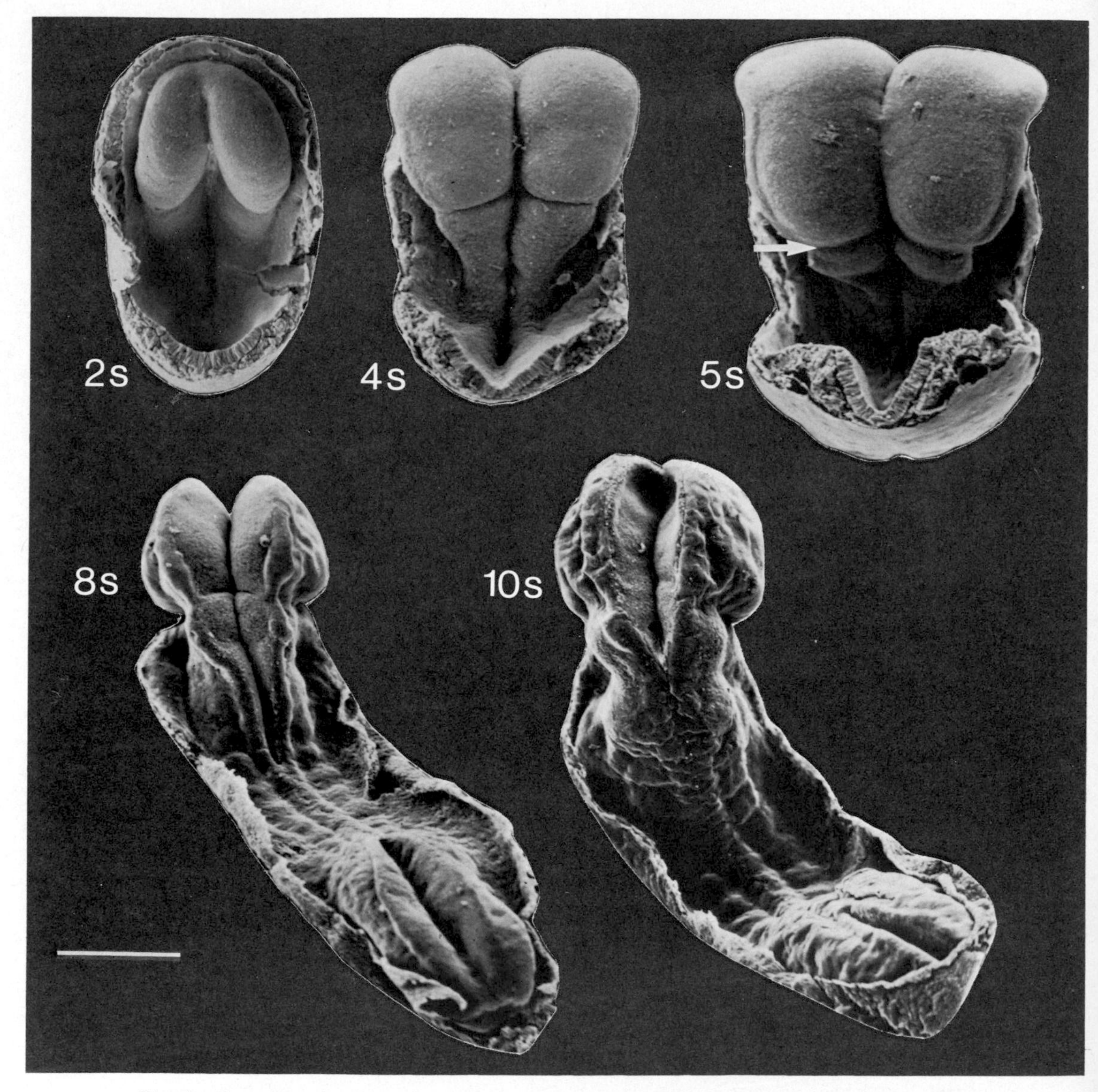

Fig. 1. Scanning electron micrographs of rat embryos during neurulation. Somite stages (s) as indicated. Arrow, preotic sulcus. Bar, 200 μm. Further explanation in the text.

animal. To begin with, the cranial neural plate is broader than that of the spinal region. Then, during neurulation, the spinal region forms V-shaped neural folds (seen in section in Fig. 1, 5-somite stage), whereas the cranial neural plate first develops neural folds that are convex in profile (Fig. 1, somite stages 2–5). As neural tube closure progresses down the spinal region, the convex cranial neural folds are converted to a V-shaped profile, becoming concave as the lateral edges approach each other in the dorsal midline to form the brain part of the neural tube (Fig. 1, somite stages 8, 10).

The sequence of changes in shape involves a variety of cell behaviour patterns. In this article we concentrate on one type of behaviour: cell flow within the epithelium. However, since this phenomenon occurs concomitantly with several other patterns of epithelial behaviour, we present first a simple classification of epithelial cell movement.

PATTERNS OF EPITHELIAL CELL MOVEMENT

Expansion or shrinkage of the epithelial surface associated with change of cell shape

Increase in cell height is often the first sign of specialization of a specific part of a larger epithelium. It results from an inductive tissue interaction, and is often followed by microfilament-mediated curvature of the thickened area. Examples from vertebrate embryos include formation of the otic and lens placodes, and differentiation of the amphibian neural plate (e.g. see Spemann, 1938; Burnside, 1971; Meier, 1978; Spooner, 1974).

Decrease in cell height, bringing about expansion and thinning of the epithelium, occurs during formation of the filtration membrane of the vertebrate kidney (Aoki, 1966), and during chick blastoderm expansion, where it is microtubule-mediated (Downie, 1975). It is also seen in the presumptive surface ectoderm of mammalian embryos during neurulation; this epithelium is pseudostratified or columnar at the start of neurulation, thinning progressively to a squamous form as it expands to accommodate the increasing height of the attached neural folds (illustrated by Morriss-Kay, 1981, figs 2a, 5).

Changes in cell shape also occur at the free edge of spreading cell sheets, e.g. during epiboly in *Fundulus* embryos where narrowing of the margin of the enveloping layer is accomplished through a combination of cell narrowing and cell rearrangement (Keller & Trinkaus, 1987; see below, and Keller & Hardin, 1987).

Microfilament-mediated curvature

Active changes in epithelial shape, such as bending, invagination and cleft formation, have been correlated with the appearance of microfilament bundles close to the contracting side of the epithelium. Examples include neurulation, vesicle formation (e.g. otocyst, lens vesicle), diverticulum formation (e.g. thyroid rudiment), and branching morphogenesis (e.g. pancreas, lung, salivary gland and mammary gland). In many of these examples, the epithelium thickens before deformation, suggesting that synthesis of microtubules and an increase in cell adhesiveness precede microfilament contraction (Spooner, 1974; Ettensohn, 1985*a*).

Ettensohn (1985*a*) has surveyed many examples of epithelial curvature, and states that only in cleft formation during glandular morphogenesis is mitosis an active component of the morphogenetic mechanism. More recently, however, Nakanishi *et al.* (1987) have demonstrated that neither cell division nor DNA synthesis is required for cleft formation in the developing salivary gland. It is therefore probably safe to assume that mitosis does not play a role in microfilament-mediated epithelial morphogenesis even when the cell division rate is high.

Cell rearrangement involving exchange of neighbours

Following induction of the neural plate in amphibian embryos, the whole plate elongates. Boerema (1929) reported that elongation was greatest in the midline. More recently, the application of vital dyes to the neural plate surface, time-lapse cinematography and computer analysis have revealed that the differential elongation of the supranotochordal and more lateral parts of the plate involve cells exchanging neighbours rather than cell distortion or cell division (Jacobson, 1962; Jacobson & Gordon, 1976). The epithelium appears to behave as a liquid within which cells flow past one another.

Cell rearrangement in the teleost blastoderm during epiboly enables the initially disc-shaped sheet to cover the spherical egg, a process involving first increase and then, after a half-way stage, decrease in the circumference of the advancing margin (Keller & Trinkaus, 1987). A similar phenomenon has been described where blind-ended tubular structures elongate. Evagination of the imaginal discs of *Drosophila* larvae to form the adult appendage takes place over a period of 6 h after treatment with B-ecdysone, and can be accelerated to an amazing 10 min by mild trypsinization (Fristrom, 1976). This remarkable event involves considerable reorganization of cell position, but no change in cell shape and no mitosis. Similar cell rearrangements have been observed during pronephric duct elongation in amphibian embryos (Poole & Steinberg, 1981) and elongation of the sea-urchin gut rudiment during gastrulation (Ettensohn, 1985*b*). Change in shape of the epithelium is accomplished through cells changing their neighbours while maintaining specialized junctional contacts (Ettensohn, 1985*b*; Keller & Trinkaus, 1987).

Spreading of epithelial sheets with a free edge

This category of epithelial cell behaviour includes the mutual approach of the free edges during wound healing, a phenomenon that has been observed both *in vivo* and *in vitro*, for instance in chick corneal epithelium (Takeuchi, 1976, 1979) and amphibian epidermis (Radice, 1980*a*,*b*). Developmental examples include spreading of the blastoderm of chick (Downie, 1975) and teleost (see above) embryos, and the migration of chick corneal epithelial cells (Dipasquale, 1975*a*,*b*).

A common feature of these examples is that behaviour of the cells along the free edge of the migrating epithelium differs from that of cells enclosed within the sheet: they have leading lamellae showing ruffling activity similar to that of fibroblasts, they form focal contacts like those of fibroblasts, and are in general more strongly adherent to the substratum than the cells behind their line of advance (Heath, 1982). Spreading also involves changes in marginal cell number, necessitating cell re-arrangement to maintain shape or accommodate specific changes in shape. This has been observed during wound healing (Honda *et al*. 1982) as well as during blastoderm spreading.

Movement of epithelial cells associated with epithelio–mesenchymal interconversion

Cell movement of this type occurs during gastrulation in amniote embryos, as epiblast (primitive ectoderm) cells move towards and into the primitive streak. There they detach basally from the epithelium and migrate away as mesenchymal cells. The continuing flow of more lateral cells towards and into the midline streak is limited in extent by the continuous caudal regression of the streak as the embryo elongates. Cell-labelling studies in chick embryos have demonstrated, as one would expect, that there is a general epithelial movement towards the midline at the level of the primitive streak (Pasteels, 1937). Other examples of epithelio–mesenchymal interconversion include neural crest cell emigration from the neural epithelium and from placodes, and sclerotome formation from somites. All of these must be associated with some degree of epithelial cell movement. This category of cell movement is relevant to the study of mammalian cranial neurulation, since neural crest cells migrate from the open neural folds (see below).

Epithelial flow within an intact sheet

Perhaps the clearest example of epithelial cell flow in a normal tissue lacking a free edge is the movement of cells in the small intestine from crypt to villus tip. Cairnie *et al.* (1965) measured cell proliferation and cell movement in the upper jejunum of young adult male rats: the cell cycle time was 14 h in the bottom of the crypts and 10 h at the top of the proliferation zone; cells left the mitotic cycle somewhere between 10 and 18 cell positions from the bottom of the crypt and continued their movement to the top of the villus (25–51 cells total height) at a rate of $1{\cdot}27 \pm 0{\cdot}21$ cell diameters per hour. Their final fate was to be ejected as pyknotic cells from the villus tip into the intestinal lumen. The system was considered to be a 'steady state', i.e. for each cell produced, one is lost.

This example has many similarities to the previous category, since the epithelial flow ends with cell loss at the villus tip just as cells are lost from an epithelium by conversion to mesenchyme. Similarly, cell movement in the early amphibian gastrula, discussed by Trinkaus (1984) in this context, shows a discontinuity as the cells convert to bottle cells while passing through the blastopore lip.

An example of an epithelium showing mitosis-related expansion without concomitant cell loss is provided by formation of the amnion and chorion in most amniotes (not including higher primates: Hamilton & Mossman, 1972). This is a double epithelium composed of a layer of ectoderm and a layer of mesoderm attached by their basal surfaces. Like all morphogenetic phenomena, expansion is a controlled event and therefore presumably involves cell movement, though this has not been studied. The trophectoderm of the mouse blastocyst does not fulfil all the criteria of an epithelium, but may be mentioned in this context. Cell proliferation is greatest in the polar trophectoderm, the area in contact with the inner cell mass; cells move radially outward from this region, gradually losing their ability to divide (Copp,

1978). In this article we will present evidence for cell flow within the cranial neural epithelium of rat embryos during neurulation.

THE RELATIONSHIP BETWEEN EPITHELIAL CELL MOVEMENT AND MITOSIS

Mitosis is not an essential feature of epithelial curvature and does not occur during the active cell rearrangement that brings about *Drosophila* imaginal disc evagination (see above). There is no evidence that it plays any role in change of epithelial thickness. The relationship between mitosis and the types of epithelial cell movements described in categories 4–6 above is less clear. Spreading of epithelial sheets involves an element of mitosis; however, the most active movement occurs at the free edge, and there is no reason to assign any movement-associated role to mitosis here.

When epithelial cells are lost into the primitive streak or shed from the tip of an intestinal villus, mitosis is clearly required to maintain (or increase) the cell population of the epithelium. This is not to imply that mitosis plays any active role in 'driving' the epithelial cell movement, but there must be some interdependence between the two phenomena. This relationship was discussed by Abercrombie (1980), who suggested that in addition to the active cell crawling movements observed during healing: "the crawling machinery comes into play . . . when rapid growth within an *undamaged* tissue occurs (Abercrombie, 1957), such as happens in the hyperplasias, familiar in the vertebrates, for instance in kidney, thyroid and liver, when some stimulus, usually blood-borne, sets going a sudden generation of new functional tissue. Rapid growth of differentiated tissue happens, generally, of course, in all tissues, in the postembryonic phase of development. In all these instances, the active mitosis responsible for the growth seems to be accompanied by an increased ability to undertake crawling locomotion".

The relationship between mitosis and cell flow in the cranial neural epithelium of rat embryos will be discussed in the concluding section.

COMBINATIONS OF EPITHELIAL BEHAVIOUR PATTERNS ARE CHARACTERISTIC OF DEVELOPING SYSTEMS

Epithelial movements during development and regeneration frequently combine two or more types of cell behaviour. We have already seen an illustration of this in the *Fundulus* blastoderm, which during epiboly combines spreading with a free edge, change of cell shape and exchange of neighbours. Similarly, the amphibian neural plate deploys three of the above categories: differentiation involves increase in cell height and concomitant decrease in surface area, elongation involves exchange of cell neighbours, and neurulation is the consequence of a combination of elongation and microfilament-mediated curvature (Jacobson, 1962; Baker & Schroeder, 1967; Burnside, 1971, 1973; Jacobson & Gordon, 1976).

Mammalian embryos show a different pattern of neurulation from that of amphibians, so it is not surprising that the pattern of epithelial cell behaviour also differs. The cranial neural epithelium shows four, possibly five, of the categories of movement described above. Thus although the experimental work to be described here provides evidence for cell flow within the intact epithelium, it is not appropriate to describe this phenomenon in isolation from the other aspects of cell behaviour that occur during cranial neurulation.

CRANIAL NEURULATION IN RAT EMBRYOS

As illustrated in Fig. 1, cranial neurulation differs from spinal neurulation in lacking an antero–posterior sequence of development, in showing a greater complexity of morphogenetic change, and in being a slower process. The neural epithelium is a single cell layer throughout neurulation, but its thickness and cellular organization are not constant. Fig. 2 shows a series of scanning electron micrographs (SEM) of the cut surface of embryos transsected midway between the preotic sulcus and the forebrain/midbrain junction (these landmarks are illustrated in Figs 1, 3). Up to the 5-somite stage, while the neural folds are convex, the neural epithelium expands and thins (i.e. the cellular organization changes from pseudostratified to columnar to cuboidal) without any change in cell number in the transverse plane. It then gradually thickens by regaining a pseudo-stratified organization, with a consequential decrease in apical surface area, until neurulation is completed at the 14-somite stage. Cell number in the transverse plane, and surface area of the transverse sections of neural epithelium, remain constant throughout neurulation (Morriss-Kay, 1981).

Where the apical neuroepithelial surface is concave in profile, transmission electron microscopy (TEM) shows subapical, junction-associated microfilament bundles (Morriss & New, 1979). The complexes of microfilament bundles and junctions can also be seen in light micrographs as a more or less continuous line parallel with and close to the apical surface. Evidence that microfilament bundle contraction is instrumental in generating the concave curvature has been provided by culturing embryos at different stages of neurulation for one hour in medium containing cytochalasin D, followed by a period of recovery in normal culture medium (Morriss-Kay & Tuckett, 1985).

Neural crest cell emigration from this region begins at the 4-somite stage and continues throughout neurulation (Nichols, 1981; Tan & Morriss-Kay, 1985). There is no crest cell production from the forebrain region (Tan & Morriss-Kay, 1986). A small amount of physiological cell death occurs within the cranial neural epithelium during neurulation (Morriss & New, 1979). Hence there is a small amount of cell loss from the neural epithelium in the transverse plane while the cell number remains constant. This is more than compensated for by a rapid mitotic rate: the cell cycle time is 6 h (Tuckett & Morriss-Kay, 1985).

The pattern of growth in the longitudinal plane is illustrated in Fig. 3. There is no clear indication of the midbrain/hindbrain junction until the neuromeres are well established late in neurulation, so we have used the preotic sulcus as a posterior landmark. Anteriorly, the clearest landmark is the tip of the notochord. The

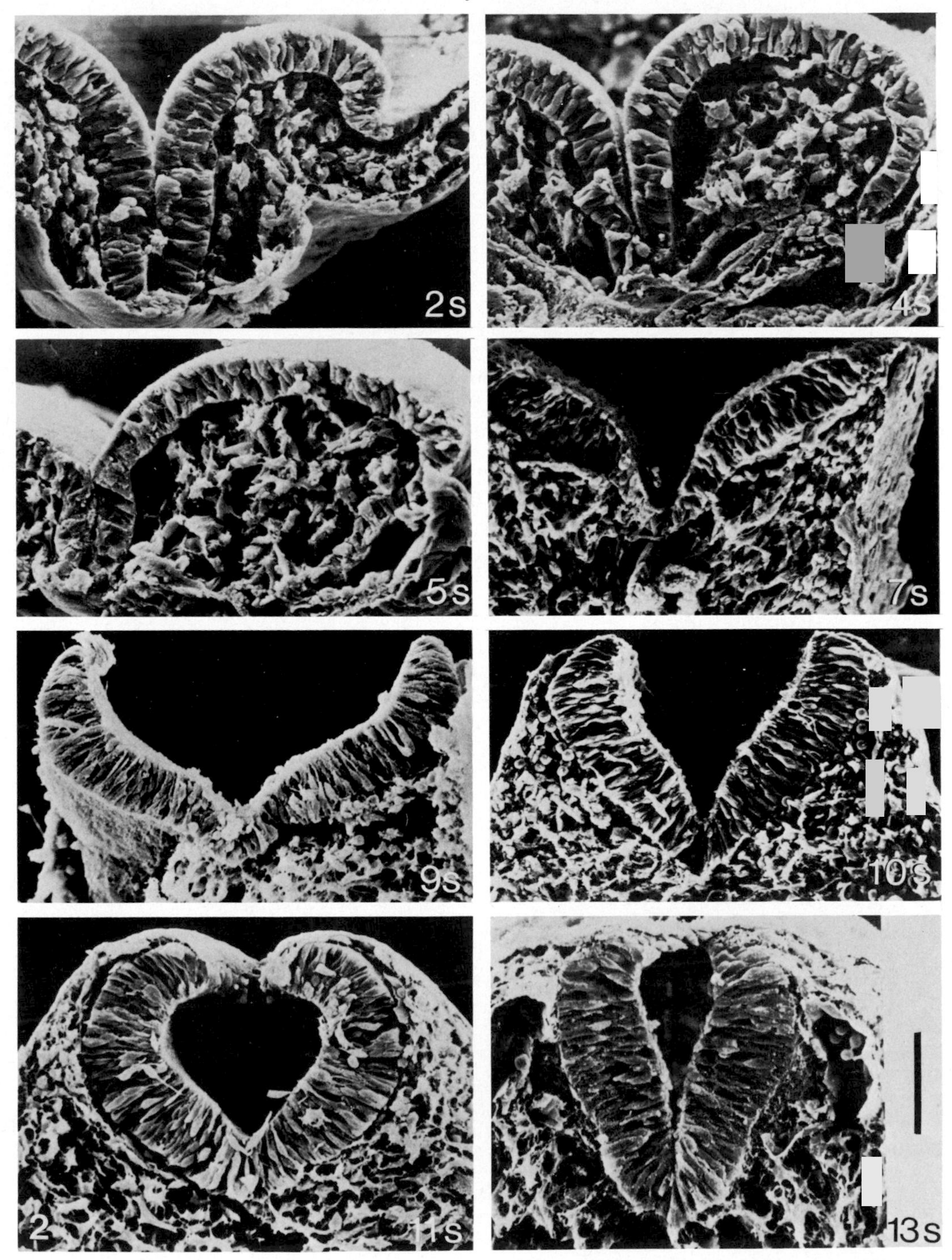

Fig. 2. Scanning electron micrographs of the fractured surface of rat embryos transversely cut across the midbrain/upper hindbrain region. Somite numbers (s) as indicated. Cell number in the transverse plane of the neural epithelium at this level remains constant throughout neurulation. Bar, 50 μm. (Reprinted from Morriss-Kay (1981).)

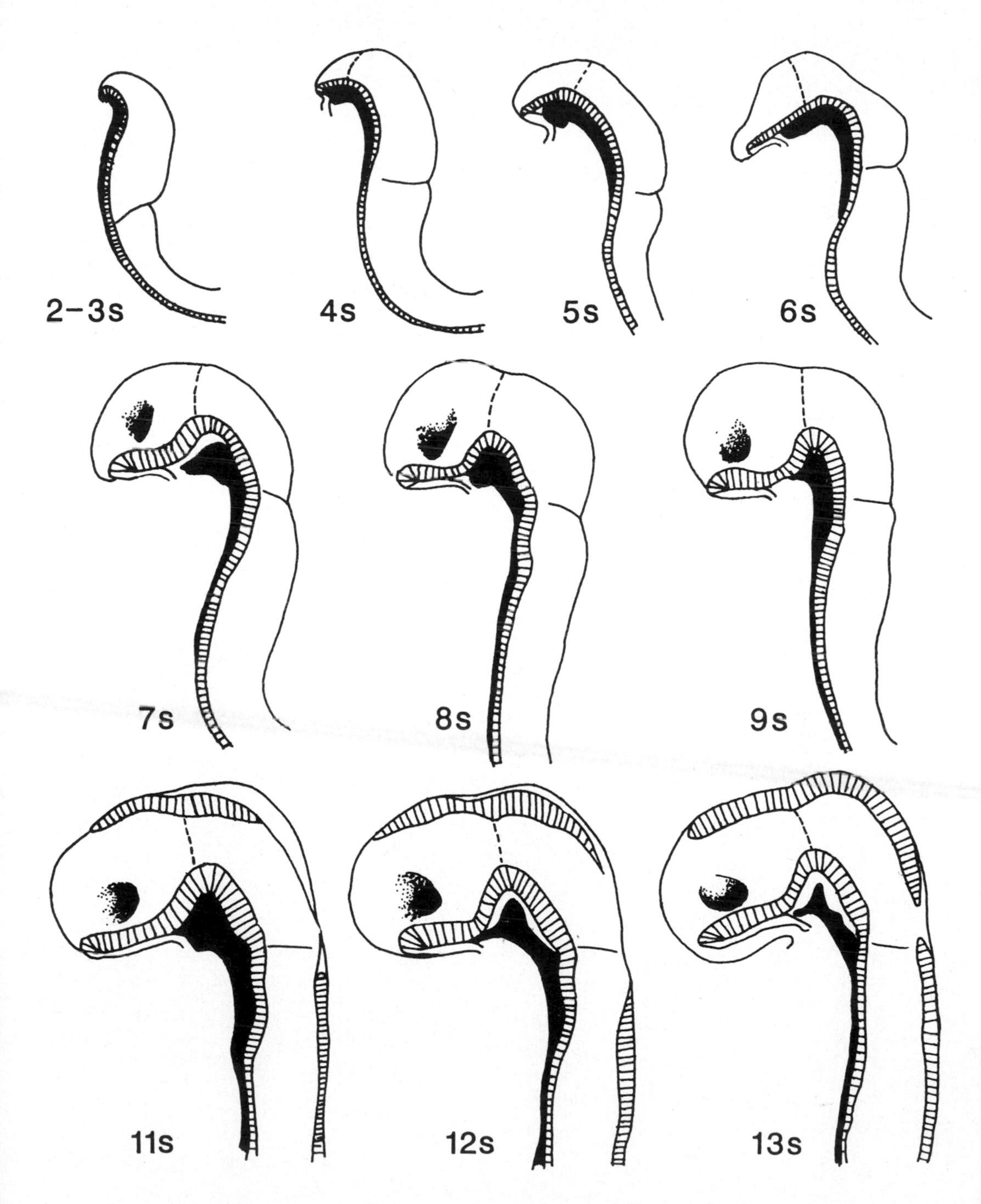

Fig. 3. The pattern of longitudinal growth of the neural epithelium during cranial neurulation is shown here in tracings from scanning electron micrographs of embryos cut in the sagittal plane. Somite stages as indicated. Notochord, black; cut neuroepithelial surfaces, striped; optic sulcus, stippled; forebrain/midbrain junction, broken line; preotic sulcus, continuous line.

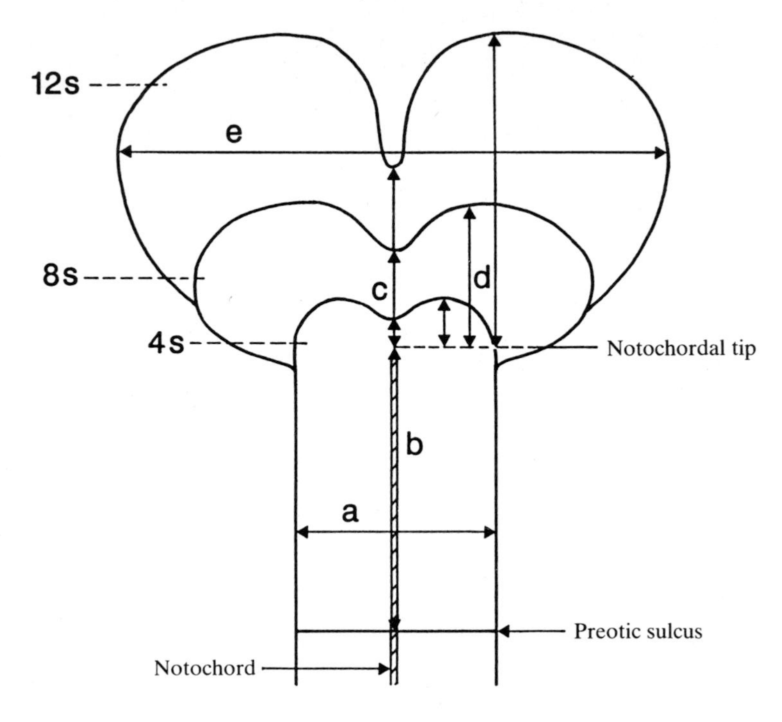

Fig. 4. The dimensions of this diagrammatic representation of the cranial neural epithelium are based on cell number counts at the 4-somite, 8-somite and 12-somite stages of development. a. Cell number in the transverse plane, midbrain/rostral hindbrain region (125 cells); b, cells overlying the notochord from the preotic sulcus to the notochordal tip (175 cells); c, cells in the midline, rostral to the notochordal tip (16 cells (4s), 57 cells (8s), 98 cells (12s)); d, dimension based on size comparison with c on SEMs, giving an estimate of cell number from the level of the notochordal tip to the rostral tip of the forebrain; e, cells across the greatest width of the forebrain (125 cells (4s), 260 cells (8s), 330 cells (12s)).

forebrain/midbrain junction lies a short distance behind this, and can be clearly identified as a decreasing angle in the neural epithelium in the sagittal plane from the 4/5-somite stage onwards. Throughout cranial neurulation, the length of the neural epithelium from the tip of the notochord to the preotic sulcus, and the number of cells within it, remain constant (see Fig. 4). Taken together with the cell-number data from the transverse plane, it appears that the neural folds lying over and alongside this stretch of notochord maintain a constant cell number despite some cell loss and a rapid mitotic rate. The increases in size and cell number are in the forebrain, which initially does not project beyond the tip of the notochord, but forms a very large structure by the end of neurulation. The cell cycle time is the same (6 h) throughout the cranial neural epithelium. Measurements on human embryos indicate that here, too, midbrain size remains constant during neurulation, whereas the forebrain grows at first rapidly and then more slowly (Müller & O'Rahilly, 1986).

This pattern of growth (in rat embryos) is illustrated in Fig. 4, in which the epithelium is represented as a two-dimensional structure with its dimensions based on cell number in the planes indicated. The diagram thus illustrates regional cell

Table 1. *Percentage of dividing cells within the cranial neural epithelium having the spindle axis orientated in the transverse plane of the embryo*

Embryo stage	Lateral region	Intermediate region	Basal region	Mean
A. *Midbrain/upper hindbrain region* (means from five embryos per stage)				
4-somite	13	3	3	6
8-somite	14	3	2	6
12-somite (open region)	9	7	3	6
12-somite (closed region)	15	16	22	18
16-somite	23	23	19	22
B. *Forebrain region* (means)				
4 somite stage ($n = 2$)		26·2		
8-somite stage ($n = 5$)		47·6		
12-somite stage ($n = 5$)		63·0		

numbers at three stages of development without any indication of change in shape related to histological organization or microfilament contraction. While the cell number remains constant in the midbrain/upper hindbrain region, the increase in the forebrain is too great to be accounted for by intrinsic cell division alone. In order to explain these data, we have suggested that neuroepithelial cells are flowing from the region of constant cell number into the rapidly expanding forebrain (Tuckett & Morriss-Kay, 1985).

Our studies imply that the neural epithelium is a fluid structure within which cells are moving forward in/a strictly controlled manner at the same time as the morphogenetic movements of neurulation take place in both transverse and longitudinal planes. A small degree of lateral movement must also take place close to the lateral edges during neural crest cell emigration, since crest cell loss does not result in a decrease in cell number in the transverse plane. This pattern of maintenance and change of cell number could be brought about by cell rearrangement, as in the examples discussed earlier, and/or by appropriate orientation of mitotic spindles.

We have examined mitotic spindle orientation in sectioned embryos and have summarized our observations in Table 1. In the open neural epithelium, the great majority of cell divisions were in the longitudinal plane. Of the small number of transversely oriented spindles, most were close to the lateral edge; these mitoses are most likely to be related to maintenance of cell number in the transverse plane as neural crest cells emigrate, together with a small contribution to compensate for cell death.

CELL-LABELLING STUDIES

In order to obtain direct evidence of epithelial flow, we injected labelled cells into specific sites in the neural epithelium of 4/5 somite-stage embryos. Fig. 5 illustrates the injection technique. Cells were labelled intracellularly with wheat-germ agglutinin and subsequently identified in histological sections by an immunocytochemical technique as described by Tan & Morriss-Kay (1986). The cells were injected into three sites, which could be clearly seen during the injection procedure: just rostral to the preotic sulcus, just caudal to or on the forebrain/midbrain flexure, and midway between these two landmarks. The embryos were then cultured for 24 h (to approximately the 20-somite stage), fixed in dilute Bouin's fluid, processed for immunocytochemistry, then conventionally dehydrated, embedded in paraffin, sectioned in the longitudinal plane and counterstained with light green. Four embryos showing labelled cells (i.e. cells having brown intracellular vesicles) well integrated within the neural epithelium are illustrated in Fig. 6. In the first specimen (A,B), the labelled cells are close to the dorsal midline, i.e. the region of neural-fold

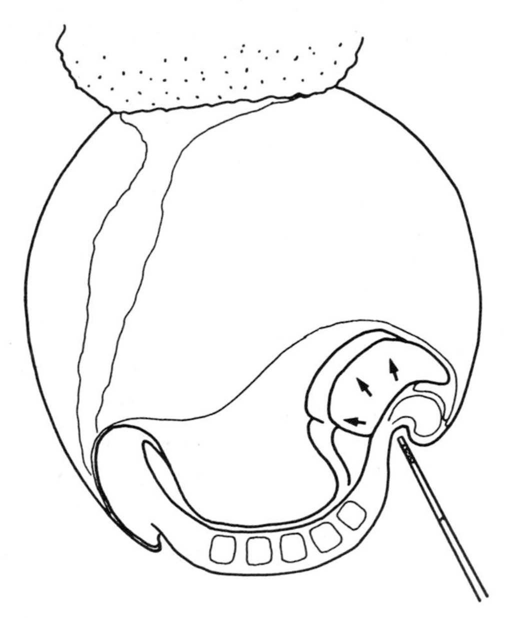

Fig. 5. Injection technique for the cell-labelling study. The embryo is held by mild suction of the holding pipette (not shown) on the yolk sac. The injection pipette contains labelled cells. Access to the neural folds was gained by piercing the foregut endoderm and overlying mesenchyme before entering the neural epithelium and releasing the cells into one of the positions indicated by arrows (right, just caudal to the angle formed by the forebrain/midbrain junction; middle, midway between this angle and the preotic sulcus; left, just rostral to the preotic sulcus).

Fig. 6. Longitudinal sections of embryos cultured for 24 h after injection of labelled cells. Left side, head region; right side, the area of labelled cells at higher magnification. In A, the labelled cells lie in the midline, so the section is near-sagittal. Cells were injected into the neural epithelium just caudal to the forebrain/midbrain junction (A,C); midway between the forebrain/midbrain junction and the preotic sulcus (E); just rostral to the preotic sulcus (G). In E there are labelled cells in the mesenchyme as well as in the neural epithelium. Broken lines indicate the forebrain–midbrain and midbrain–hindbrain junctions; *d*, labelled dead cells; *n*, notochord; *p*, preotic sulcus. Bars: A,C,E,G, 10 μm; B,D,F,H, 100 μm.

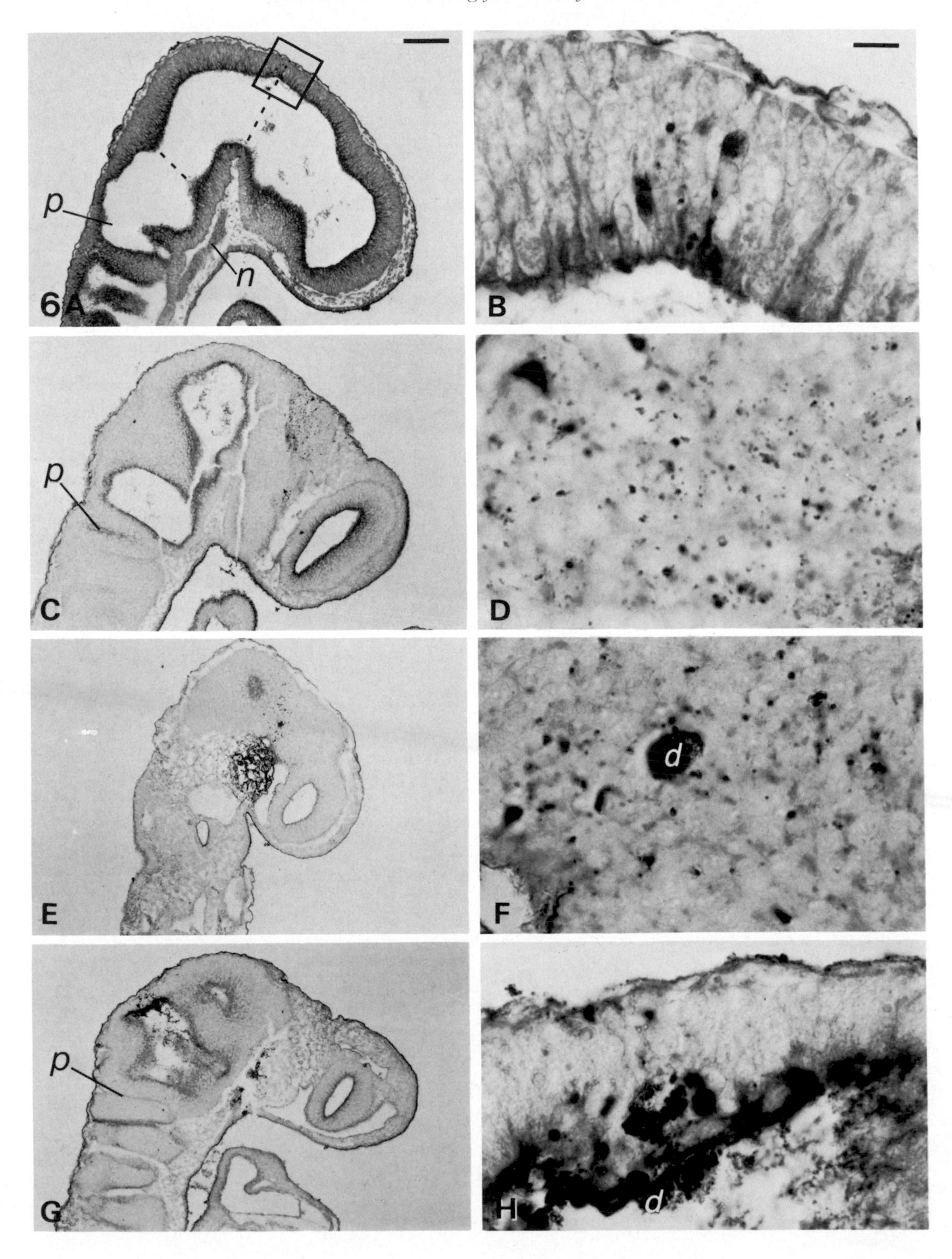
p
n
6A
B
p
C
D
E
d
F
p
G
H
d

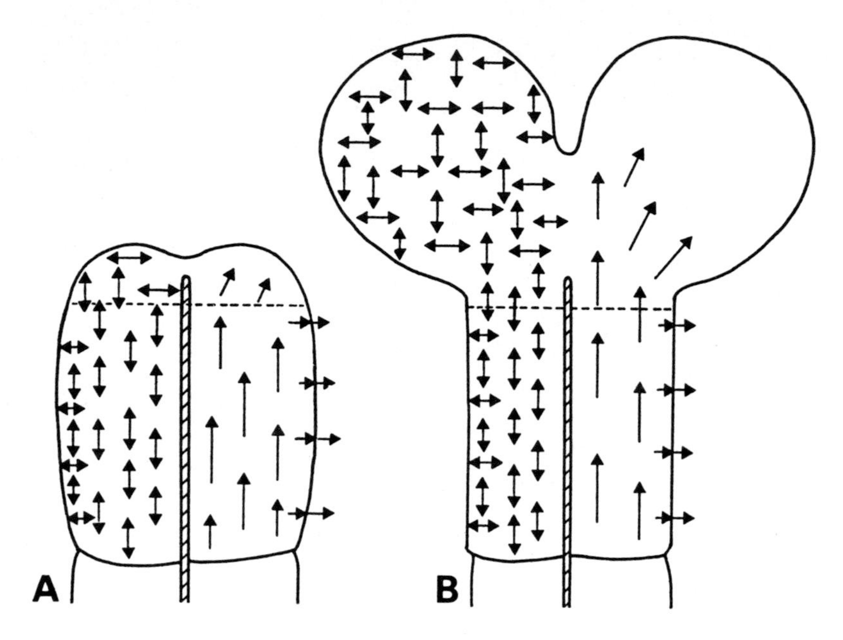

Fig. 7. Summary diagram of the cranial neural epithelium at early (A) and late (B) stages of forebrain development. The epithelium is represented as a flat sheet, as in Fig. 4. Diagonal hatching, notochord; broken line, forebrain/midbrain junction; continuous line, preotic sulcus. Mitotic spindle orientation is indicated on the left side of each diagram, and cell flow on the right. Arrows directed away from the epithelium represent emigrating neural crest cells (from 6-somite stage onwards, simplified).

fusion, suggesting that they were injected into a very lateral position. The longitudinal injection position was just behind the forebrain/midbrain junction, and the final position was precisely on this junction, indicating very little movement from their original position. This result might be expected of cells close to the lateral border of the epithelium, in which the proportion of cells dividing in the transverse plane is higher than elsewhere, and where cell loss due to neural crest cell emigration may be compensated for by less forward (rostrad) movement than elsewhere.

The other three specimens (Fig. 6C–H) show labelled cells well away from the dorsal midline, having been injected closer to the midline of the embryo. In the second specimen (C,D) cells were injected in the same longitudinal position as in the first, i.e. just caudal to the forebrain/midbrain junction. The labelled cells have moved over the junction to lie fully within the forebrain. Similarly, in the third specimen (E,F), cells were injected midway between the preotic sulcus and the forebrain/midbrain junction, and after 24 h show a broad spread across the junction from rostral midbrain to caudal forebrain. The fourth specimen (G,H) was injected just rostral to the preotic sulcus, and shows labelled cells close to the hindbrain/midbrain junction (with some attached dead cells in the ventricular lumen).

Thus these three specimens all have labelled cells within the neural epithelium in positions significantly more rostral than the original site of the injection 24 h before.

The results are preliminary, but they do support our original hypothesis that the neural epithelium rostral to the preotic sulcus is flowing forward in a highly controlled manner. The positional relationship between the forebrain/midbrain junction and the rostral tip of the notochord is maintained during this epithelial flow.

TYPES OF EPITHELIAL CELL MOVEMENT IN THE NEURAL EPITHELIUM DURING NEURULATION

In terms of the classification of epithelial cell movement set out at the beginning of this article, studies in the rat cranial neural epithelium have provided evidence for all classes of movement for epithelia lacking a free edge: (a) change of cell shape involving both expansion and shrinkage of the epithelium is illustrated in Fig. 3; (b) evidence for microfilament-mediated curvature comes from electron microscopy and studies using cytochalasin D (Morriss & New, 1979; Morriss-Kay & Tuckett, 1986); (c) cell rearrangement involving exchange of neighbours is implicated by the cell-labelling study combined with mitotic spindle orientation observations, suggesting a lesser tendency for rostrad movement at the lateral edge than more medially; (d) epithelio–mesenchymal interconversion, as lateral edge cells emigrate as neural crest, may involve some associated lateral movement towards and into the conversion site; (e) as suggested by our previous kinetic study (Tuckett & Morriss-Kay, 1985) and by the cell-labelling study described here, expansion of the forebrain depends on movement of cells within the intact epithelium.

Movement classified as categories (c), (d) and (e) above is correlated with mitotic spindle orientation. The relationship between these three types of cell movement, spindle orientation, and the pattern of growth is illustrated in Fig. 7. One of the most remarkable aspects of this complex pattern of epithelial behaviour is the constancy of cell number in the area lying between the preotic sulcus and the forebrain/midbrain junction. This situation is a highly dynamic steady state, reminiscent of the intestinal villus cell turnover described earlier, but of much shorter duration.

What is the nature of the relationship between mitotic spindle orientation and cell movement? So far we have only shown an interesting correlation between the distribution of transversely and longitudinally orientated spindles and the pattern of cell distribution. One possible explanation is that the orientation of cell movement is the direct result of the orientation of cell division. But it is equally plausible that the observed mitotic spindle orientations simply reflect forces generated within the cells as they move in a lateral direction close to the lateral edge and in a rostral direction elsewhere. The neuroepithelial cells clearly have an inherent ability to move during cranial neurulation; the epithelium behaves as a fluid, not just as a deforming sheet. We now need to discover how this fluid behaviour is controlled in relation to regional cell number, cell movement, and the orientation of mitosis.

We thank Martin Barker for technical assistance, Glenys Davies for typing the manuscript, Professor J. P. Trinkaus for a useful discussion on the relationship between cell movement and mitosis, and the MRC for financial support.

REFERENCES

Abercrombie, M. (1957). Localized formation of new tissue in an adult mammal. In *The Biological Action of Growth Substances, SEB Symp.* 2, pp. 235–254. Cambridge University Press.

Abercrombie, M. (1980). The crawling movement of metazoan cells. *Proc. R. Soc.* B **207**, 129–147.

Aoki, A. (1966). Development of the human renal glomerulus. I. Differentiation of the filtering membrane. *Anat. Rec.* **155**, 339–352.

Baker, P. C. & Schroeder, T. E. (1967). Cytoplasmic filaments and morphogenetic movement in the amphibian neural tube. *Devl Biol.* **15**, 432–450.

Boerema, I. (1929). Die Dynamik der Medullarrohrschlusses. *Wilhelm Roux Arch. EntwMech. Org.* **115**, 601–615.

Burnside, B. (1971). Microtubules and microfilaments in newt neurulation. *Devl Biol.* **26**, 416–441.

Burnside, B. (1973). Microtubules and microfilaments in amphibian neurulation. *Am. Zool.* **13**, 989–1006.

Cairnie, A. B., Lamerton, L. F. & Steel, G. C. (1965). Cell proliferation studies in the intestinal epithelium of the rat. I. Determination of the kinetic parameters. II. Theoretical aspects. *Expl Cell Res.* **39**, 528–538, 539–553.

Copp, A. J. (1978). Interaction between inner cell mass and trophectoderm of the mouse blastocyst. I. A study of cellular proliferation. *J. Embryol. exp. Morph.* **48**, 109–125.

DiPasquale, A. (1975*a*). Locomotory activity of epithelial cells in culture. *Expl Cell Res.* **94**, 191–215.

DiPasquale, A. (1975*b*). Locomotion of epithelial cells. Factors involved in extension of the leading edge. *Expl Cell Res.* **95**, 425–439.

Downie, J. R. (1975). The role of microtubules in chick blastoderm expansion – a quantitative study using colchicine. *J. Embryol. exp. Morph.* **34**, 265–277.

Ettensohn, C. A. (1985*a*). Mechanism of epithelial invagination. *Q. Rev. Biol.* **60**, 289–307.

Ettensohn, C. A. (1985*b*). Gastrulation in the sea urchin embryo is accompanied by the rearrangement of invaginating epithelial cells. *Devl Biol.* **112**, 383–390.

Fristrom, D. (1976). The mechanism of evagination of imaginal discs of *Drosophila melanogaster*. III. Evidence for cell rearrangement. *Devl Biol.* **54**, 163–171.

Hamilton, W. J. & Mossman, H. W. (1972). *Human Embryology*. Cambridge: Heffer.

Heath, J. P. (1982). Adhesions to substratum and locomotory behaviour of fibroblastic and epithelial cells in culture. In *Cell Behaviour* (ed. R. Bellairs, A. Curtis & G. Dunn), pp. 77–108. Cambridge University Press.

Honda, H., Ogita, Y., Higuchi, S. & Kani, K. (1982). Cell movements in a living mammalian tissue: Long-term observation of individual cells in wounded corneal endothelia of cats. *J. Morph.* **174**, 25–39.

Jacobson, A. G. & Gordon, R. (1976). Changes in the shape of the developing vertebrate nervous system analysed experimentally, mathematically and by computer simulation. *J. exp. Zool.* **197**, 191–246.

Jacobson, C. O. (1962). Cell migration in the neural plate and the process of neurulation in the axolotl larva. *Zool. Bidr. Upps.* **35**, 433–449

Keller, R. E. & Hardin, J. (1987). Cell behaviour during active cell rearrangement: evidence and speculations. *J. Cell Sci. Suppl. 8*, 369–393.

Keller, R. E. & Trinkaus, J. P. (1987). Rearrangement of enveloping layer cells without disruption of the epithelial permeability barrier as a factor in *Fundulus* epiboly. *Devl Biol.* **120**, 12–24.

Meier, S. (1978). Development of the embryonic chick otic placode. II. Electron microscopic analysis. *Anat. Rec.* **191**, 459–477.

Morriss, G. M. & New, D. A. T. (1979). Effect of oxygen concentration on morphogenesis of cranial neural folds and neural crest in cultured rat embryos. *J. Embryol. exp. Morph.* **54**, 17–35.

Morriss-Kay, G. M. (1981). Growth and development of pattern in the cranial neural epithelium of rat embryos during neurulation. *J. Embryol. exp. Morph.* **65 Supplement**, 225–241.

Morriss-Kay, G. M. & Tuckett, F. (1985). The role of microfilaments in cranial neurulation in rat embryos: effects of short-term exposure to cytochalasin D. *J. Embryol. exp. Morph.* **88**, 333–348.

MÜLLER, G. & O'RAHILLY, R. (1986). The development of the human brain and the closure of the rostral neuropore at stage 11. *Anat. Embryol.* **175**, 205–222.

NAKANISHI, Y., MORITA, T. & NOGAWA, M. (1987). Cell proliferation is not required for the initiation of early cleft formation in mouse embryonic submandibular epithelium *in vitro*. *Development* **99**, 429–437.

NICHOLS, D. H. (1981). Neural crest formation in the head of the mouse embryo as observed using a new histological technique. *J. Embryol. exp. Morph.* **64**, 105–120.

PASTEELS, J. J. (1937). Etudes sur la gastrulation des vertebrées méroblastiques. III. Oiseaux. IV. Conclusions générales. *Archs Biol., Paris* **48**, 381–448.

POOLE, T. J. & STEINBERG, M. S. (1981). Amphibian pronephric duct morphogenesis: segregation, cell rearrangement and directed migration of the *Ambystoma* duct rudiment. *J. Embryol. exp. Morph.* **63**, 1–16.

RADICE, G. P. (1980*a*). The spreading of epithelial cells during wound closure in *Xenopus* larvae. *Devl Biol.* **76**, 26–46.

RADICE, G. P. (1980*b*). Locomotion and cell–substratum contacts of *Xenopus* epidermal cells *in vitro* and *in vivo*. *J. Cell Sci.* **44**, 201–223.

SPEMANN, H. (1938). *Embryonic Development and Induction*. Yale University Press.

SPOONER, B. S. (1974). Morphogenesis of vertebrate organs. In *Concepts of Development* (ed. J. Lash & J. R. Whittaker). Stamford: Sinauer Associates, Inc.

TAKEUCHI, S. (1976). Wound healing in the cornea of the chick embryo. III. The influence of pore size of millipore filters on the migration of isolated sheets in culture. *Devl Biol.* **51**, 49–62.

TAKEUCHI, S. (1979). Wound healing in the cornea of the chick embryo. IV. Promotion of the migratory activity of isolated corneal epithelium in culture by the application of tension. *Devl Biol.* **70**, 232–240.

TAN, S. S. & MORRISS-KAY, G. M. (1985). The development and distribution of the cranial neural crest in the rat embryo. *Cell Tiss. Res.* **240**, 403–416.

TAN, S. S. & MORRISS-KAY, G. M. (1986). Analysis of cranial neural crest cell migration and early fates in postimplantation rat chimaeras. *J. Embryol. exp. Morph.* **98**, 21–58.

TRINKAUS, J. P. (1984). *Cells Into Organs*, 2nd edn. New Jersey: Prentice Hall.

TUCKETT, F. & MORRISS-KAY, G. M. (1985). The kinetic behaviour of the cranial neural epithelium during neurulation in the rat embryo. *J. Embryol. exp. Morph.* **85**, 111–119

British Society for Cell Biology
(conjointly with the British Society for Developmental Biology)

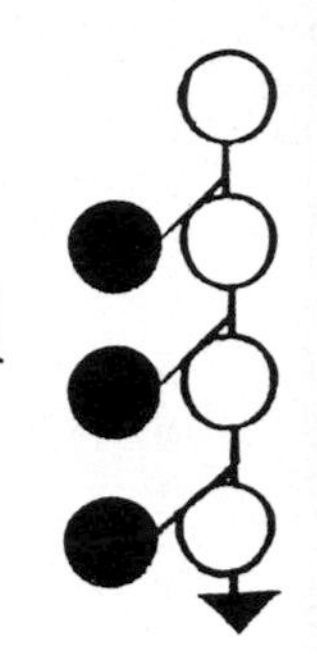

Spring Meeting, University of Bristol

12–14 April 1988

STEM CELL SYMPOSIUM

Sponsor: The Company of Biologists Limited
Organizer: Professor T. M. Dexter (Manchester)

Sessions and Main Speakers:

I *Stem cells in development:* Wolpert (London), Gardner (Oxford), Le Douarin (France), de Rooij (Netherlands)

II *Stem cell signals and stem cell genes:* Harrison (Glasgow), Verma (USA), Marshall (London), Klein (Sweden)

III *Stem cells in differentiating systems:* Johnson (Australia), Potten (Manchester), Owen (Oxford), Ferguson (Manchester)

IV *Differentiation in stem cells:* Raff (London), Watt (London), Rudland (Liverpool), Bayreuther (Germany)

V *Tumour stem cells:* Lord (Manchester), Heath (Oxford), Steel (London), McCulloch (Canada)

Further information from Professor T. M. Dexter and Dr Brian I. Lord (Paterson Laboratories, Christie Hospital and Radium Institute, Wilmslow Road, Manchester M20 9BX, UK; Tel.: 061-445 8123)

The Local Organizer is Dr Beverly Randle, Department of Obstetrics and Gynaecology, Bristol Maternity Hospital, Southwell Street, Bristol BS2 8EJ, UK; Tel.: 0272-215411 ext. 267

Deadline for Registration: 28 February 1988

British Society for Cell Biology/British Society for Developmental Biology

Announcement of Spring Meeting and AGMs, 1988

The Spring conjoint meeting of the two societies will be held at the University of Bristol on 12–15 April 1988. The main BSCB symposium sponsored by The Company of Biologists Limited will be on "STEM CELLS", organized by Professor T. M. Dexter (Manchester; see separate panel). In addition there will be three main BSCB sessions on:

I *Retroviruses:* (organized by Chris Marshall, London); speakers include Pirie (London), Land (London), Collins (London), Evans (Cambridge), Wagner (Heidelberg)

II *Gene amplification:* (organized by George Stark, London); speakers include Wahl (San Diego), Debatisse (Paris), Rolfe (London)

III *Second messengers:* (organized by Robin Irvine, Babraham); speakers include Downes (Welwyn), Houslay (Glasgow), Siddle (Cambridge), England (Welwyn)

Plenary Lectures will be given by Ling (Toronto), Johnson (Melbourne) and Pierce (Colorado).

The BSDB main symposium is on segmentation and includes sessions on "Regulation of Sperm Function and Fertilization" and "Teratomas".

Workshops will be held on the evening of Tuesday 12 April on "*In situ* hybridization" (organized by Mike Akam, Cambridge) and "Retroviral cell lineage markers" (organized by Jack Price, London).

□ □ □

The AGMs of the two societies will take place consecutively in the early afternoon of 13 April 1988.

□ □ □

Original communications in the form of posters are called for. The deadline for abstracts of posters, registration, etc. is 28 February 1988. The local organizer is Dr Beverly Randle (Department of Obstetrics and Gynaecology, Bristol Maternity Hospital, Southwell Street, Bristol BS2 8EJ) (0272-215411 ext. 267), to whom abstracts and booking forms should be sent.